PRINCIPLES OF GEOLOGY

A SERIES OF GEOLOGY BOOKS

EDITORS: James Gilluly and A. O. Woodford

Howel Williams, Francis J. Turner, and Charles M. Gilbert

PETROGRAPHY: AN INTRODUCTION TO THE STUDY OF ROCKS IN THIN SECTIONS

Paul Niggli

ROCKS AND MINERAL DEPOSITS

A. I. Levorsen

GEOLOGY OF PETROLEUM

Maurice Gignoux

STRATIGRAPHIC GEOLOGY

Charles F. Richter

ELEMENTARY SEISMOLOGY

W. F. de Jong

GENERAL CRYSTALLOGRAPHY
A BRIEF COMPENDIUM

L. G. Berry and Brian Mason

MINERALOGY: CONCEPTS, DESCRIPTIONS, DETERMINATIONS

A. I. Levorsen

PALEOGEOLOGIC MAPS

Bernhard Kummel

HISTORY OF THE EARTH: AN INTRODUCTION TO HISTORICAL GEOLOGY

Jean Goguel

TECTONICS

James C. Brice; John P. Miller and Robert Scholten

LABORATORY STUDIES IN GEOLOGY (201–208; 213–227)

LABORATORY STUDIES IN GEOLOGY (213–227)

James Gilluly, A. C. Waters, and A. O. Woodford

PRINCIPLES OF GEOLOGY

Second Edition

A. A. Beus

BERYLLIUM: EVALUATION OF DEPOSITS DURING PROSPECTING AND EXPLORATORY WORK

PRINCIPLES OF
GEOLOGY Second Edition

BY

JAMES GILLULY U. S. Geological Survey

A. C. WATERS The Johns Hopkins University

A. O. WOODFORD Pomona College

Drawings by ROBERT R. COMPTON and EVAN L. GILLESPIE

W. H. FREEMAN AND COMPANY
SAN FRANCISCO and LONDON

PREFACE TO SECOND EDITION

THE KIND RECEPTION accorded our attempt to provide a textbook that emphasizes geologic processes instead of geologic terms, and that gives the student some background for evaluating the basis (and also the intrinsic uncertainties) of geologic methods, is the reason for this Second Edition of "Principles of Geology." In this revision we attempt to incorporate many of the significant advances in geologic science made in the last seven years, and also to integrate the material into a more closely knit and hence more teachable arrangement. All chapters have been rewritten and reorganized to take account of new developments. The advances in knowledge of sedimentary rocks and of their environments of deposition seemed to demand inclusion of an entirely new chapter (Chapter 17) on these subjects, and the expansion of the material on Strata, Fossils, and Time into a full chapter instead of a half chapter. We have also reorganized and expanded the sections dealing with metamorphic rocks and metamorphic processes.

This second edition is properly dedicated to the great number of teachers who have written to us or to the publishers in sympathy with our approach, and who also offered valuable suggestions for improvement in arrangement or in choice of subject matter. Our cordial thanks go to each who were so kind. More specifically, we wish to thank Dr. Frank C. Calkins, who read the first edition carefully and supplied us with a fully annotated copy. Dr. Charles G. Higgins critically reviewed Chapters 1 to 10 of the present manuscript, and Dr. Olcott Gates reviewed Chapters 11 to 21. The excellent suggestions of these three geologists helped immeasurably in condensing the material, and in rearranging it into a better order. Mr. Charles B. Hunt helped with the material in Chapter 4, Dr. M. G. Wolman with Chapters 5 and 12 and Dr. Francis J. Pettijohn with Chapter 17.

For a selection of new illustrative material we are indebted to Dr. P. D. Snavely, to Dr. Vincent Kelley, and to Dr. W. B. Hamilton.

Finally, our special thanks are due Mrs. Mary Gill who typed most of the manuscript and relieved us of many other bothersome details.

August 18, 1958

JAMES GILLULY

A. C. WATERS

A. O. WOODFORD

PREFACE TO FIRST EDITION

THIS book attempts to summarize some of the knowledge that geologists have won from the study of the earth. A subject so large must be treated very briefly if it is to be presented between the covers of a single book; we have chosen to concentrate on the analysis of processes that are at work upon and within the earth, rather than to present a catalog of descriptive facts and terms. We have felt, too, that the student is entitled to know something of the kind of evidence on which geologic conclusions are based, even though its presentation takes valuable pages that might be used to put forth more facts.

Some teachers will regret our brief treatment of many of the standard topics usually found in textbooks of physical geology. We can only hope that the loss will be balanced by the new material included covering many phases of the science in which rapid advances have been made in recent years, and more particularly by the emphasis on leading the student through approximately the same sequence of reasoning that was used in the historical development of the subject. We believe that the student may retain more of the basic principles on which geology is based if he knows how a geologic map is made, and if he is introduced to Werner's and Desmarest's divergent views on the origin of basalt, than if he is instructed too minutely on the purely technical terminology of landscape morphology or rock classification. It is our hope, too, that such a presentation carries with it an understanding of the intrinsic uncertainties of indirect evidence, upon which so much of geology depends.

Geology, as we know it, could hardly exist without the foundation of stratigraphy, which gave the dimension of time to the science. Accordingly, we have outlined a little of the development of stratigraphy instead of leaving it entirely for a later course in historical geology.

We are indebted for assistance in the preparation of this book to many persons, only a few of whom can be mentioned here. The contribution of Robert R. Compton goes far beyond that indicated on the title page; in addition to preparing the illustrations, he wrote one chapter of the book and acted as critic on all the others.

The staff of W. H. Freeman and Company gave its unfailing help and encouragement and relieved us of many bothersome details.

Special thanks are due our colleagues S. E. Clabaugh, John Shelton, George A. Thompson, Roger Revelle, Walter Munk, John C. Crowell, Arthur D. Howard, C. Melvin Swinney, Robert Sharp, D. I. Axelrod, W. C. Putnam, Cordell Durrell, George Tunell, M. N. Bramlette, and George Bellemin, who have read certain chapters and have generously aided us with constructive criticism and new ideas.

Specific credit for illustrative material is given in the captions for individual figures. More generally, we wish to acknowledge here the kindness of the U. S. Geological Survey, the Geological Survey of Canada, and the

U. S. Air Force for opening photographic files to us. Individuals who also allowed us to make selections from large photographic collections include Eliot Blackwelder, Robert C. Frampton, Howard A. Coombs, John Shelton, and Arch Addington.

Miss Margaret Ellis and Mrs. Priscilla Feigan typed the manuscript and helped in other ways.

Finally, the three of us are greatly indebted to our families who patiently served as "guinea pigs" for our ideas and as good-humored critics of our literary eccentricities.

December 23, 1950

JAMES GILLULY

A. C. WATERS

A. O. WOODFORD

CONTENTS

INTRODUCTION

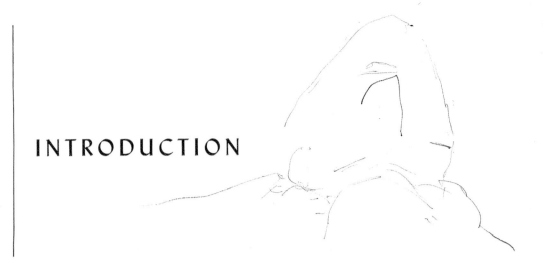

The Earth's Riddles

SINCE THE DAWN of civilization, men have been filled with curiosity about the earth on which they live. Why does a volcano erupt? What causes an earthquake? What is the source of the water that bubbles up in a spring?

As man's curiosity led him to seek answers to such questions, he often found that he was faced with new riddles even more baffling. How did sea shells become entombed in the rocks of high mountain ranges? Why do some streams have quicksand on one bank and solid rock on the other? What controls the beautiful geometric forms of snowflakes and other crystals? Why does one well yield water in abundance, whereas another of the same depth is dry?

It would be interesting to know how early man attempted to solve such riddles, but the first roots of man's knowledge of the earth are lost in antiquity. By comparison, we of today have signposts along the way, for reasoning man has built up the method of investigation and the compilation of knowledge that is known as **geology**—the science of the earth.

To some of earth's riddles, geologists have found solutions. To others, the answers are still tentative; and to still others, only the faintest glimmering of light that may ultimately illuminate the way to solutions has, so far,

been discovered. Progress in geology has not been at a uniform rate. There have been periods, usually following fundamental discoveries, when outbursts of fruitful activity quickly revolutionized some of geology's theories and methods. During other periods there was little advance. At times geologists even followed the wrong trail, and progress in some branches of the science came to a dead end. Then more information and new skills were acquired, until, finally, the accumulated dogmas were overthrown and a new start made.

The early Greeks and peoples of other early civilizations made some progress in geologic study, but their ideas were based largely on untested speculations, and little has survived. The modern science of geology is of comparatively recent origin—the word itself is less than 200 years old. Despite its youth, however, geology has already done much to stimulate and unshackle the thinking of mankind. The demonstration that seashells and other fossils* entombed in the rocks are the remains of animals and plants that lived in the geologic past routed dogmas that had warped men's thinking for centuries. From the detailed study of the biological relationships of living and fossil organisms, coupled with geologic investigations of the sequence and

---

* Fossils are the remains or imprints of animals and plants of the geologic past, naturally preserved by burial under sediments.

changes of fossil assemblages with time, the doctrine of evolution emerged. This doctrine profoundly influenced modern philosophical and scientific thought.

Evidence, well documented, that the landscapes about us are not static but slowly change through time has not failed to stimulate the imagination of thinking men. The wheat farmer tilling the cold, wind-swept plains of Alberta is curious about the shells turned up by his plow; his interest increases when told that scientific comparison of these shells with living marine organisms shows that his farm was once the bottom of a warm, shallow sea.

Who can deny the thrill that comes with the realization that less than 20,000 years ago the site of Chicago lay under a sheet of ice such as enshrouds Antarctica today? Or that the green, well-watered hills of Scotland's Midland Valley were once the site of shifting sand dunes similar to those of the modern Sahara? Yet, preserved in the rocks and soils along Lake Michigan's shore and in sandstone quarries near Glasgow are the proofs—as clearly recorded in the rocks as the deliberations of the Roman Senate are preserved in the writings of Cicero.

The science of geology has brought to mankind new conceptions of time, just as astronomy has revolutionized ideas of space. The rocks record events, some dating back at least two and a half billion years, and throw into sharp perspective the short period of human history, as compared with that of the earth as a whole. There is fascination in reading records in the rocks from which we can reconstruct events in the drama of earth history that happened millions of years ago. This is the fascination that has led men to develop the science of geology, and that, together with economic benefits, will cause them to continue to explore earth's riddles.

Minerals, Wealth, and Politics

Man's interest in the minerals and rocks of the earth's crust ceased long ago to be that of mere curiosity. There are sound practical reasons for his investigations. Our modern civilization makes many uses of the minerals and rocks that compose the earth's crust. Industry is almost wholly dependent on them. From minerals we obtain the iron, copper, aluminum, and other metals that make an industrial civilization possible. Our chief sources of power are the mineral fuels, coal and petroleum. Recently we have learned how to release stupendous amounts of energy from radioactive minerals.

Even many of our individual desires and needs are fulfilled by the mineral industries. The bricks in our houses, the salt that seasons our food, the material that paves our highways, the gold and silver ornaments and precious stones with which we adorn ourselves —all have been won from mineral deposits in the earth's crust. Man's avid search for the gold and silver, the copper and gem stones, that pleased his vanity and brought him security and wealth began early in the annals of civilization. Once he possessed the minerals, he sought to refine and improve them and to discover new uses for them. As a result, the arts and crafts in metal and stone were born; and these, in turn, expanded into the vast industries we know today.

On the international scene, the power and wealth of a nation is largely determined by its supplies of useful minerals, its authority over the areas that contain them, and its skill in discovering and utilizing them. In this age of political readjustment, we know that the vast accumulation of petroleum in Iran, Arabia, and Kuwait is a potent force in world politics. We shall be wiser in world affairs if we know how petroleum occurs, how it is discovered, and how its quantity may be estimated.

Without the economic urge to find and exploit the mineral wealth hidden in the earth, many of the great forward steps in geology would never have been made; for geology is the science of the mine and the quarry, of the oil field and the placer.

The Study of Geology

Although geology is a complex and varied subject, it is also a stimulating and interesting one. Few of its problems are so simple that they can be solved directly by one method of approach. Many require supplementary investigations using techniques borrowed from other sciences. Geologists are constantly taking over from chemistry, biology, physics, and engineering new methods, data, and theories that can be applied to earth problems. Geologists, in turn, have contributed to these bordering sciences. Progress in one science advances all the others.

Because of the complexity of its problems, and the size of the phenomena with which it deals, geology has not advanced so rapidly as physics or mathematics. The geologist cannot move a volcano to the laboratory to observe the growth of its cone, nor can he spread a bed of peat on the laboratory table to watch for millions of years its development into coal. Yet these are among the simpler phenomena of geology. Factors of size and time make experimental study of many geologic processes difficult and often impossible. Faced with these apparently insurmountable difficulties, geologists have had to devise ingenious, indirect methods for getting the answers to many of their questions. Despite the difficulties inherent in their subject matter, however, geologists have been outstandingly successful in predicting where to drill for oil or other mineral deposits, and in arriving at verifiable solutions of complex scientific problems.

To succeed, geologists must develop resourcefulness and imagination. They must be able to make sound decisions on the basis of data that are incomplete and ofttimes apparently conflicting. In deciding where to drill an oil well or where to develop a gold placer, the geologist must frequently evaluate and coordinate several kinds of evidence. His fundamental guides, of course, are the data derived from geologic mapping and other geologic techniques. He may also need to consider the results of geophysical exploration, data regarding production of other wells or placers, and miscellaneous additional evidence drawn from engineering, economics, chemistry, physics, and many other sources.

These very factors of complexity and diversity, together with the newness of the science, combine to make geology a vigorous, rapidly expanding field. A student who selects geology as his profession has a wide choice of what he shall learn and do. For his first two years of training, he may study more chemistry, physics, and mathematics than geology, because a sound elementary knowledge of these basic sciences is essential for many advanced geology courses. He will learn something of ordinary laboratory techniques, but will soon find that his main laboratory is not a building lined with bottle-filled shelves and machinery. Instead, he works out-of-doors; the bold cliffs of mountain peaks, the walls of deep canyons, and the slopes of desert ranges are the geologist's laboratory. A part of his education will be spent in strenuous hiking and climbing in mountainous areas, perhaps far from civilization, where he will map rocks and their structures and collect other geological data. Such "field work" is essential to geological training.

Upon completion of his training, the geologist will find many opportunities open to him. He may work for an oil company and travel all over the world in search of new oil fields. He may direct exploration to find new bodies of ore in a mine. He may have the responsibility of estimating accurately the reserves of ore in the ground beneath a mining property or the amount of oil that can be recovered from a partly developed oil field. He may be called upon to decide which of several small mines or quarries offers the best opportunities for development and investment.

As an employee of a federal or state geological survey, the geologist may map rocks and mineral deposits, investigate the occurrence and supplies of underground water, study conservation problems such as soil erosion and mineral depletion, or classify public lands according to their minerals, soils, water, and other natural resources.

Or the geologist may teach at a college or university training future geologists, and at the same time engage in basic research with the aim of discovering new principles or of unifying and correlating old ones. Similar opportunities for research are also open in the United States Geological Survey and other federal and state agencies, in various research institutes, and in industrial laboratories.

In time of war, the geologist can serve by giving authentic information on problems of terrain, by discovering new sources of critically short mineral supplies and assisting in their development, and by selecting targets in enemy territory which, when demolished, will cripple some vital industry of the enemy nation. He may sit at peace conferences and advise on the mineral resources of various nations and their resulting industrial potential.

There are also opportunities in commerce for the geologist. His geological knowledge can be used to good purpose in the development of a cement plant, or in the operation of a stone quarry, a brick yard, or a sand-and-gravel pit, and in all engineering construction projects that involve moving earth and rock.

Whatever path the geologist takes, it is likely to lead to widespread travel, for the whole earth is the field for his investigations.

2 | MINERALS AND MATTER

THE EARTH'S CRUST is not homogeneous. During a walk in the country, we seldom fail to find a wide variety of rocks and soils that differ in color, coherence, density, and other characteristics. If we pick up a fragment of rock or a handful of soil and examine it closely, we find that it, too, is a mixture of different substances (Fig. 2-1). The individual grains, however, that make up the rocks and soils are not mixtures. Each is a distinct, homogeneous substance with definite chemical and physical characteristics. Some may be hard, transparent particles that resemble bits of broken glass; some may be dull, earthy grains; some may be tiny, elastic flakes that flash brilliantly in the sun. Each of these distinct, homogeneous substances is a mineral. *Rocks and soils are aggregates of minerals.* Hence, if we are to understand the origin and classification of rocks, we must learn something about the various minerals that compose them.

Figure 2-1. *The mineral constituents of the common rock granite. Note that the mineral magnetite is visible only when the rock is greatly magnified* (right).

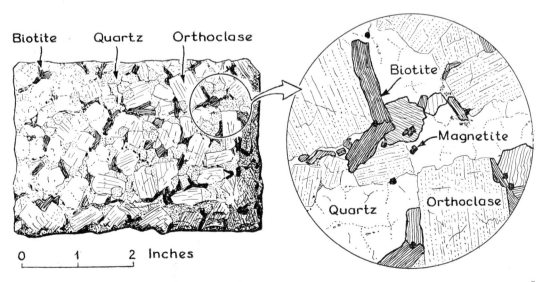

Definition of Mineral

If we are to learn to recognize different minerals, and to discriminate one from another, we must define their real nature precisely. Stated formally: A **mineral** is a naturally occurring substance with a characteristic internal structure determined by a regular arrangement of the atoms or ions within it, and with a chemical composition and physical properties that are either fixed or that vary within a definite range.

Minerals, then, are natural substances, found ready-made out-of-doors. Synthetic products made in a laboratory are not minerals. A druggist who tells you that a certain pharmaceutical preparation is "rich in vitamins and minerals" is using the term mineral in an entirely different way than it is used by a geologist. He is not prescribing a diet of mud and rocks; nor is a geologist professionally interested in vitamin pills.

To say that minerals have definite chemical and physical properties, or properties that vary within certain definitely fixed limits, is merely to point out that all particles of a single kind of mineral are alike in their physical and chemical characters, whether one particle comes from Brazil and another from the United States, or whether one may have crystallized in the shell of a snail and another in the overflow from a hillside spring.

The most definitive characteristic of a mineral is its internal structure: this is the core of our definition. Air, natural gas, and water are naturally occurring substances and each has fairly definite chemical and physical properties, but they are not minerals—the arrangement of the atoms and ions within such fluids is more or less haphazard. Wood and coal are not minerals; the regular pattern of the "grain" in wood, or of the layering in a bed of coal, is not at all comparable to the precise geometrical packing together of atoms and ions which produces the characteristic internal structure of minerals. To understand what we mean by internal structure, and hence the true nature of minerals, it is necessary first to recount what has been learned about the external form of crystals, and then to digress into a brief summary of some of the things chemists and physicists have learned about the fundamental structure and properties of matter itself.

Form and Structure of Crystals

Geometrical Form

Everyone is familiar with the crystals of certain minerals, for example, those of garnet, quartz (also called rock crystal), and ice, for, strange as it may seem, ice is a mineral. Some crystals occur in strikingly regular geometric forms with surfaces bounded by smooth planes called **crystal faces** (Fig. 2-2), but such well-formed crystals are rare. Most snowflakes fall as beautiful, six-sided, perfect crystals (Fig. 13-2), but frost on a windowpane shows much less perfect ones, and the granules of ice that form on the surface of a freezing pond may show few, if any, crystal faces. Relatively few minerals have crystals completely bounded by plane faces and some show none at all. Nevertheless, study of the common imperfect crystals, together with the relatively rare perfect ones, permitted **mineralogists** (as geologists who specialize in minerals are called) to make sound deductions about the internal structure of minerals long before physicists and chemists had proved that all matter is made up of atoms.

Constancy of Interfacial Angles

The first important step in the analysis of minerals by their crystal faces was made by Nicolaus Steno (1631-1687), a Danish physician who lived in Florence, Italy. Steno, one of the outstanding figures in the history of geology, showed, with the crude instruments at his disposal, that the characteristic crystal faces found on different specimens of quartz always meet at the same angle, regardless of the size and shape of the crystals. An Italian student, Guglielmini, showed in 1688 and 1705 that this was also true of other minerals. He also noted that the angles characteristic

Figure 2-2.

Common minerals showing good crystal form: (a) epidote; (b) potassium feld-spar; (c) garnet; (d) pyrite. (Photos by Alexander Tihonravov.)

of one species of mineral differed from those of another. In halite (Fig. 2-6), for example, the angle between adjacent surfaces is always a right angle; this means the crystal is a cube, or else a rectangular boxlike figure. In quartz, as Steno had found, the angles between the long crystal faces that form the sides of the crystal are always 120°.

Steno's and Guglielmini's methods were refined and extended by later workers. From an analysis of the thousands of measurements eventually made on many kinds of crystals, mineralogists long ago concluded that the internal structure of each kind of mineral is unique. They reasoned that the constancy of the interfacial angles in different specimens of the same mineral, regardless of the size and shape of the crystals, could only mean that each mineral is built up of minute particles regularly packed together in a definite geometric pattern. The pattern of packing determines the angles between faces and is identical in all specimens of a particular mineral. The size of the specimen depends merely on the number of such particles it contains.

Optical Properties

Other studies of minerals from a different viewpoint fortified this conclusion. Among the most important were the studies of the

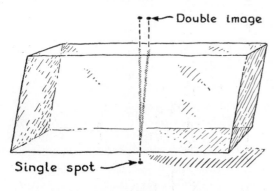

Figure 2-3. A fragment of clear calcite showing double refraction.

effects that crystals produce on light transmitted through them. The Dutch physicist Christian Huygens (1629-1695) discovered the phenomenon of "double refraction" (Fig. 2-3) while studying the mineral calcite. One can easily observe this phenomenon by placing a fragment of transparent calcite above a dot on a sheet of paper. Instead of one dot, two are seen. If the calcite is revolved slowly, one dot traces a circle about the other. More than a hundred years later physicists showed that this effect could be explained in terms of a theory of light. According to this theory, the light ray which penetrates the crystal is broken into two rays which deviate slightly from one another as they travel through the crystal.

This discovery opened the way for an important new technique in studying and identifying minerals. William Nicol, who taught natural philosophy (today, we call it physics) at Edinburgh, showed in 1829 that transparent fragments of calcite could be cut and glued together in such a way as to eliminate one of the two rays. Others adapted these Nicol prisms to microscopes, making it possible to study the effects that crystals produce on light as it passes through them. Discussion of these effects is beyond the scope of this book, but it should be emphasized that the optical properties of minerals, determined by means of the petrographic microscope (a microscope equipped with two Nicol prisms), are precise and diagnostic. By them most minerals can be quickly identified. The petro

graphic microscope is the geologist's most useful instrument for mineral and rock study.

But more important to our present discussion is the fact that the petrographic microscope also gave clues to the fundamental nature of matter and light. The behavior of light in minerals is systematically related to the angles between the crystal faces. This suggests that light is influenced by very minute, systematically arranged particles within the crystal, and strengthens the conclusion drawn from the constancy of interfacial angles that minerals are made up of submicroscopic particles systematically packed together.

The Atomic Theory

In 1805, the English chemist, John Dalton, advanced the hypothesis that all matter is composed of tiny individual particles which he called **atoms.** Dalton conceived this idea to explain certain previously observed relations about the weights of substances participating in chemical reactions with one another—an approach entirely different from the studies of external form and optical properties which had led mineralogists to the same conclusion. Further work in chemistry, physics and mineralogy has verified the atomic hypothesis completely. Among the most significant and interesting proofs of the theory are those that came from X-ray studies of minerals, but before we discuss these, we must first briefly review some of the things chemists and physicists have learned about atoms.

Atoms are extremely minute particles. If a piece of crystal the size of a walnut were enlarged until it became the size of the earth, the atoms that compose it would average about the size of baseballs. One hundred million atoms placed side by side make a row only an inch long. Yet by ingenious experimental and theoretical work chemists and physicists have been able to show that the atom, small as it is, is composed of particles still smaller. Only three of the several subatomic particles that have been discovered are important in discussing the chemical behavior of minerals: the proton, the neutron, and the electron.

Subatomic Particles

These subatomic particles differ in important respects: for example, each has electrical properties different from those of the others. The electron carries a definite charge of negative electricity—a charge whose amount has been chosen as the unit of electrical measurement. The proton has a positive charge of exactly the same amount. The neutron, as the name implies, is electrically neutral. Despite these differences, all are about the same size, about one millionth of one millionth of an inch in diameter. They differ in weight, however: the proton weighs 1,845 times as much as the electron and the neutron weighs slightly less than the combined weight of an electron and a proton. Each of these particles is identical with all its namesakes, no matter whether they form parts of atoms of oxygen, of iron, or of sulfur. In any atom, the various subatomic particles composing it are always present in amounts that add up to electrical neutrality—that is, there are always the same number of protons as of electrons.

Structure of the Atom

Every atom has a small, dense nucleus that contains one or more protons, and, except in the simplest atom, that of hydrogen, one or more neutrons. The nucleus holds over 99.9 per cent of the mass of an atom but only about one-billionth of its volume, so the outer parts of atoms are mostly empty space. An **element** is a substance that consists of atoms of only one kind, which is just another way of saying that the nucleus of each of the atoms in any particular element must have exactly the same electrical charge. Atoms behave chemically as though their electrons circle about the nucleus in concentric shells. Hydrogen, the simplest element, consists of one proton around which an electron revolves. Helium, the next simplest element, has a nucleus composed of two protons and two neutrons: two electrons revolve about this nucleus (Fig. 2-4). More complex atoms with larger nuclei retain this inner electron shell, but additional electrons lie in one or more shells farther out. The chemical characteristics of an element seem to depend entirely on the number of positive electric charges—and thus on the number of protons—in its nucleus. This num-

Figure 2-4.   *Schematic drawing of hydrogen and helium atoms.*

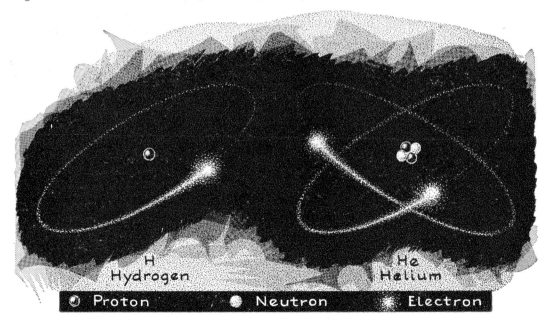

H
Hydrogen

He
Helium

Proton   Neutron   Electron

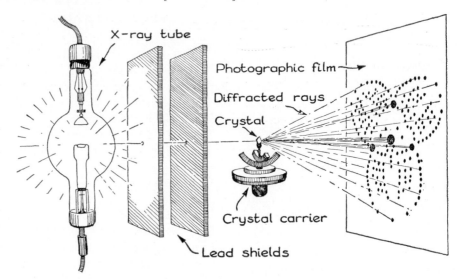

Figure 2-5.

Sketch of apparatus used in obtaining a diffraction pattern. The crystal is calcite.

ber is the **atomic number** of the element. About ninety different elements have been found in nature, and scientists have made a few others artificially.

Each element has been assigned a definite symbol, such as H for Hydrogen and Pb (from *plumbum,* its Latin name) for Lead. This is merely a convenient shorthand that scientists use in writing chemical formulas and equations. The elements, together with their symbols, atomic numbers, and atomic weights are listed in Appendix IV, Table 1.

For some reason, *those elements are chemically the most stable whose outermost electron shell contains eight electrons.* Such elements —for example, argon, neon and xenon— never combine with each other or with any other elements and hence are called the **inert gases.** (Helium, with only two electrons, is also an inert gas.)

Atoms having fewer than eight electrons in the outer shell do combine with others. The most chemically active seem to be those whose outermost shells contain either one or seven electrons. For example, sodium (Na) has eight electrons in its next-to-outer shell, but only one electron in the outermost shell. Chlorine (Cl) has seven electrons in its outer shell. Sodium has only to lose, and chlorine to gain, a single electron for each to attain the stable number of eight. This is exactly what happens when sodium and chlorine combine to form the **chemical compound** sodium chloride (NaCl), common table salt: an electron is transferred from the sodium atom to the chlorine atom. But the loss of an electron leaves the sodium atom no longer electrically neutral; it now has one more positively charged proton in the nucleus than it has negatively charged electrons in its electron shells. Hence the atom has one unbalanced positive charge. Similarly, the chlorine atom, by gaining an electron, acquires one unbalanced negative charge; there is one more electron in its electron shells than there are protons in its nucleus. Such a charged atom, in which the number of protons is either more or less than the number of electrons, is called an **ion.** Because unlike charges of electricity attract and like charges repel, the positively charged sodium ion, if it is free to move, as in a solution or a gas, is drawn to the negatively charged chlorine ion, and the two may join to form a molecule of sodium chloride, which has properties very different from those of either of its component atoms. **Molecules** are distinct groups of two or more atoms tightly bound together.

X-ray Study of Crystals

Conclusive proof of Dalton's atomic theory, and simultaneous proof that crystals are composed of atoms arranged in a geometrical latticework, came in 1912. In that year Max von Laue, a specialist in the physics of light, proposed the theory that X-rays behave like waves. When a series of closely spaced parallel lines are scratched on the surface of a mirror, the light reflected from the mirror is broken into the colors of the spectrum. Laue reasoned that if X-rays are like light but with a much shorter wave length, and if crystals are really composed of atoms geometrically packed in parallel planes, the surface of a crystal might act on X-rays much as the ruled mirror surface does on light.

In order to test this idea, two young Munich students, W. Friedrich and P. Knipping, placed a crystal of copper sulfate in an apparatus much like that illustrated in Figure 2-5, bombarded it with X-rays, and developed the first "Laue X-radiogram." Repetition of the experiment and additional tests with other minerals gave conclusive proof of definite patterns of crystal structure, confirming Laue's reasoning about the wave properties of X-rays. The experiments also proved beyond debate the inference already made by mineralogists that the internal structure of crystals can be explained only in terms of a regular packing of submicroscopic particles. A versatile new tool also had been discovered for the study of minerals, for by X-ray methods the geometrical arrangement of the atoms within a crystal, its **internal structure,** could be worked out. This developed into one of the most useful diagnostic techniques for recognizing different minerals, for it can even be applied to grains so small that they can hardly be seen microscopically.

Internal Structure of Crystals

X-ray studies show, for example, that crystals of halite (NaCl) have the structure illustrated in Figure 2-6. We have already seen that by the transfer of the one lone electron in the outer shell of a sodium atom to the almost-filled outer shell of a chlorine atom, each atom can achieve the stable arrangement of eight electrons in its outer shell. In acquiring this stable arrangement, each atom sacrifices its electrical neutrality and acquires a charge—in short it becomes an ion. In a liquid or gas, the sodium and chlorine ions might be drawn together to form a molecule, but in a crystal, the close packing of the particles necessitates a fixed geometrical arrangement of the ions. In such an arrangement, however, the electrical forces set up by the attraction of ions of unlike sign and the repulsion of those with the same sign must be balanced somewhat differently. Figure 2-6 shows how this is accom-

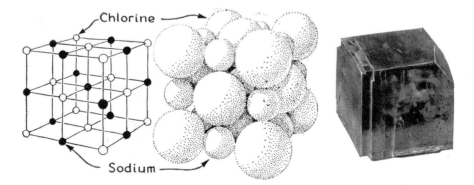

Figure 2-6.

The cubic form (right) *and internal structure of halite. The lattice diagram* (left) *shows the relative position of Na and Cl nuclei. The packing arrangement of the ions is depicted in the* center. (*Photo from the Smithsonian Institution.*)

plished in halite. Each positively charged sodium ion is equidistant from, and at the center of, six symmetrically placed chlorine ions. Each negatively charged chlorine ion is similarly surrounded by six symmetrically placed sodium ions. Most minerals are held together by similar ionic bonds, although in general the internal structure is far more complex and not so easily visualized as in halite.

Some minerals—diamond, for example—are held together through "sharing" of electrons by the atoms that compose them. Diamond is composed entirely of carbon; it is one of the crystalline forms of this element. Carbon atoms have four electrons in the outer shell. In crystals of diamond (Fig. 2-7), each carbon atom is linked with four others. This linking allows each of the four outer electrons in each carbon atom to be shared with an adjacent carbon atom. Thus the carbon atoms in

diamond achieve stability; each may be considered to have a complete outer shell of eight electrons, though every electron in this shell is actually shared with a neighboring carbon atom. In terms of atomic structure, each electron may be thought of as a part of the outer shell of two neighboring carbon nuclei.

This close bonding of the atoms in diamond is very strong; hence diamond is the hardest natural substance known. In this type of crystal, there are no ions—the atoms retain electrical neutrality by sharing electrons.

Diamond and graphite (Fig. 2-7) strikingly illustrate that the fundamental difference between minerals is not their chemical composition, but their internal structure. Both are pure carbon; their chemical composition is identical; but they occur in crystals with different internal structures (Fig. 2-7). Diamond is the hardest natural substance; graphite is soft and greasy. Most diamonds are trans-

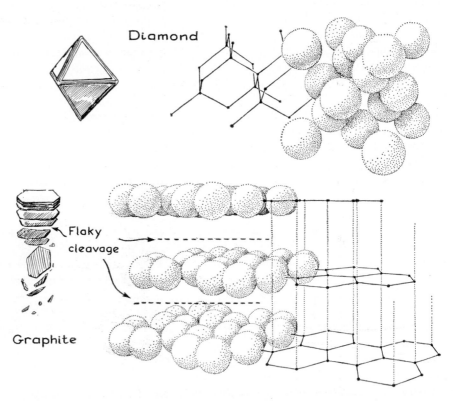

Figure 2-7.

The crystal forms and internal structures of diamond and graphite. Note how the packing of the atoms into layers gives graphite its excellent cleavage.

parent; graphite is opaque. Diamond is used as an abrasive and cutting tool; graphite is used as a lubricant because it cleaves into fine flakes that glide smoothly over one another.

Even this brief discussion of the internal structure of minerals shows that the chemist's concept of molecules, though applicable to gases and liquids, fails to apply to most minerals. Both in crystals bound together by electron exchange, such as halite, and in crystals with shared electrons, such as diamond, there is no particular part of the crystal that can be considered a molecule. Instead the ions and atoms behave as if they were solid spheres of different size packed together to form a geometric pattern, just as we might pack a mixture of grapefruit, oranges, and tangerines together to form a fruit display.

Ionic Radii

Each ion in a crystal surrounds itself with ions of opposite electrical charge, as we saw in halite. The number of such oppositely charged ions that can be packed around it is determined partly by the charges on the various ions but a more important limitation is the *size* of the ions involved.

In the most general way, the size of an atom depends upon the number of electron shells surrounding its nucleus, and upon the amount of charge on the nucleus. When electrons are added or lost by transforming an atom into an ion, the electrical balance is upset and there is a corresponding change in the radius of the ion. If the atom loses an electron and becomes a positive ion, for example, the excess positive charge on the nucleus pulls the remaining electrons a little closer; if an electron is gained, the electron shells are less closely held, and the radius expands. Changes in size may also occur during ionization because of a change in the number of electron shells. For example, the sodium atom has three electron shells, but there is only one electron in the outermost shell. If this electron is lost, the resulting sodium ion is left with only two electron shells, of which the outer-

most has the stable configuration of eight electrons. But the sodium ion thus formed is nevertheless somewhat smaller than the closely similar atom of neon, which has exactly the same number of electrons distributed in the same shells. The excess positive charge on the nucleus of the sodium ion shrinks its electron shells to slightly smaller dimensions than those around the electrically neutral neon atom.

Table 2-1 gives the atomic and ionic radii of the nine most abundant elements in the earth's crust in Ångstrom units. An **Ångstrom** is one hundred-millionth of a centimeter (0.00000001 cm., or 10^{-8} cm.). Sizes of atoms and ions are measured by determining the distances between successive rows of atoms or ions in crystals by X-ray and similar methods. Note that negatively charged ions are consistently larger, and positively charged ions smaller, than the corresponding atoms. The abundance of the elements given in the table has been determined indirectly as follows: Thousands of chemical analyses have been made of the different rock groups that compose the earth's crust. From geologic maps (Chapter 6), we can also determine the areas they occupy, and hence their relative abundance. From these data, the percentages of the different elements that compose the crust of the earth have been calculated. Table 2-1 makes it clear that investigation of the chemical relations between oxygen and silicon is of the greatest importance in our study of minerals because these two elements comprise about 75 per cent (by weight) of the crust. Nearly all the most common minerals of the crust are **silicates** formed by the combination of oxygen and silicon with one or more of the abundant metals, aluminum, iron, calcium, sodium, potassium, and magnesium.

The volume relations are even more striking; so large is the oxygen ion (O^{2-}, 1.40 Ångstroms) that, although oxygen forms only 47 per cent by weight of the rocks of the crust, it accounts for 92 per cent of their volume. Thus, by far the largest part of the earth's solid crust is composed of the same

Abundant Elements in the Earth's Crust

TABLE 2-1

ATOMIC NUMBER	ELEMENT	ATOMIC AND IONIC RADII (Size in Ångstroms)		ABUNDANCE IN EARTH'S CRUST	
		ATOM	ION	WEIGHT (Per cent)	VOLUME (Per cent)
8	Oxygen	O 0.60	O^{2-} 1.40	46.60	91.97
14	Silicon	Si 1.17	Si^{4+} 0.42	27.72	0.80
13	Aluminum	Al 1.43	Al^{3+} 0.51	8.13	0.77
26	Iron	Fe 1.24	Fe^{2+} 0.74	5.00	0.68
			Fe^{3+} 0.64		
20	Calcium	Ca 1.96	Ca^{2+} 0.99	3.63	1.48
11	Sodium	Na 1.86	Na^{+} 0.97	2.83	1.60
19	Potassium	K 2.31	K^{+} 1.35	2.59	2.14
12	Magnesium	Mg 1.60	Mg^{2+} 0.66	2.09	0.56
22	Titanium	Ti 1.46	Ti^{3+} 0.76	0.44	0.03
			Ti^{4+} 0.68		

SOURCE: Data on abundance from Brian Mason, *Principles of Geochemistry*, New York, John Wiley and Sons, 1952, p. 42. Data on atomic and ionic radii from Jack Green, "Geochemical Table of the Elements for 1953," *Geological Society of America Bull.*, Vol. 64 (1953), pp. 1001-1012.

element that we are accustomed to think of only as a gas in the atmosphere!

Although more than two thousand different minerals are known, most are rare. Twenty common ones compose almost all of the visible rocks, and of these nearly all are silicates.

The Silica Tetrahedron

The silicon ion (Si^{4+}) has a radius of 0.42 Ångstroms; that of the oxygen ion (O^{2-}) is 1.40 Ångstroms. In silicates four oxygen ions and one silicon ion pack together readily into a compact pyramidal figure called the **silica tetrahedron** (Fig. 2-8). In the lattice diagram (A of Fig. 2-8), the nucleus of the silicon ion is shown at the center of the tetrahedron, and the nucleus of each of the four oxygen ions is located at a corner; in B of Figure 2-8 the ions are drawn to scale. Note that the oxygen ion is much the larger. The silica tetrahedron is itself a complex ion (not

Figure 2-8.   The silica tetrahedron. (A) lattice diagram; (B) packing arrangement of the atoms; (C) the mathematical figures called tetrahedra.

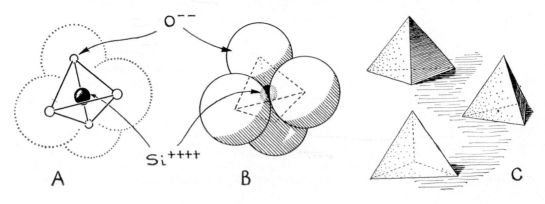

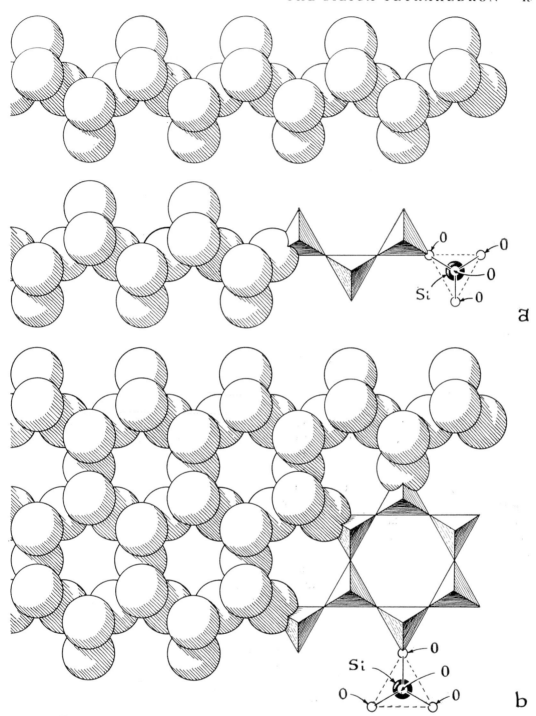

Figure 2-9.   *Structural diagrams showing how the silica tetrahedra may be strung out in chains (a) as in pyroxene, or grouped into layers (b) as in many minerals with a micaceous cleavage. In mica the tetrahedra are grouped into double plates of which the sketch (b) shows only one layer within such a double plate.*

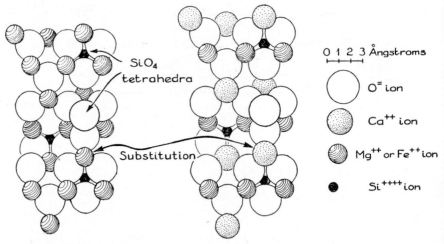

0 1 2 3 Ångstroms

$O^=$ ion

Ca^{++} ion

Mg^{++} or Fe^{++} ion

Si^{++++} ion

Figure 2-10.   Olivine — $(Mg,Fe)_2SiO_4$ Monticellite — $MgCaSiO_4$

Olivine and monticellite, showing how substitution of the larger calcium ion for ferrous or magnesium ion requires an expansion of the crystal structure. (After W. L. Bragg, 1928.)

a crystal or a molecule) because the packing of four oxygen ions, each with two negative charges, and of one silicon ion with four positive charges leaves the resultant tetrahedral ion with four unsatisfied negative charges. To form an electrically neutral unit within a crystal this tetrahedral ion must be bonded with additional positive ions, for example, with ions of magnesium (Mg^{2+}) or iron (Fe^{2+}) as in the mineral olivine (Fig. 2-10), or else the oxygen ions at the corners of the tetrahedra must be shared as in quartz (see Appendix, Fig. II-2).

Because nearly all the common minerals are silicates, and because silicates are formed by combinations of this fundamental tetrahedral ion $(SiO_4)^{4-}$ with one or more additional elements, *the silica tetrahedron is the most important "building block" in the architecture of the earth's crust.* In different minerals, silica tetrahedra are linked with one another and with various positive ions in characteristic geometrical patterns. One classification of silicate minerals is based on the kind of linkage. In the common mineral pyroxene, the tetrahedra are strung together in long chains (Fig. 2-9, *a*); in micas they form

double sheets (Fig. 2-9, *b*); and in the olivine and monticellite crystals sketched in Figure 2-10 they form a framework tied together by magnesium, iron, and calcium atoms.

Variation in Chemical Composition of Minerals

Some minerals, including diamond (C), sulfur (S), copper (Cu), and gold (Au) are elements. Others, such as ice (H_2O), quartz (SiO_2), calcite ($CaCO_3$), and kaolinite ($H_4Al_2Si_2O_9$), are compounds whose composition can be expressed by simple chemical formulas. Nevertheless, as is indicated in the definition of a mineral, many minerals vary within definite limits in the percentage of the various elements they contain, so that their composition cannot be expressed by a simple formula. One cause of such variation is that certain elements may replace one another within a crystal, resulting in a marked variation of chemical composition within a single mineral species. Such replacement is called **solid solution.** One of the simplest examples of solid solution is the olivine group of minerals. The formula of this group is written

$(Mg,Fe)_2SiO_4$, meaning that different specimens of olivine may have chemical compositions intermediate between the two "end members"; that is, they range from pure Mg_2SiO_4 (called forsterite) to pure Fe_2SiO_4 (called fayalite). It is only the proportions of iron (Fe) and magnesium (Mg) that vary; the proportions of silicon and oxygen remain constant. The intermediate members of the olivine series are regarded as solid solutions of the two end members: it should be noted that these intermediate members are homogeneous crystals and not merely mixed aggregates of two different crystals.

Solid solution series cannot be explained by the molecular concept applicable to gases and liquids, but only in terms of an ionic structure, as we shall now show.

Mechanism of Substitution in Solid Solution

The application of X-ray and similar studies to minerals has revealed much of the mechanism by which one element substitutes for another in crystals. The major controlling factor in solid solution is not the number of electrons in the outer shell of the atoms of the two elements concerned, as might be thought, but their ionic radii. In olivine, Fe and Mg can readily substitute for one another, not just because each contains two electrons in its outer shell, but more important, because their ionic radii are very nearly the same.

In many mineral groups, sodium (one electron in the outer shell) readily substitutes for calcium (two electrons in the outer shell) because their ionic radii are almost identical (0.97 and 0.99 Ångstroms). But sodium cannot substitute to nearly the same extent for potassium, although each has one electron in its outer shell, because the potassium ion is so much larger (1.33 Ångstroms) than the sodium ion. The importance of ionic radius in controlling substitution is particularly striking in this example because sodium and potassium are so very similar in chemical properties. In plagioclase feldspar crystals, a little potassium may indeed substitute for sodium— the internal structure is warped to take care of the difference in ionic diameters —but when the substitution exceeds a certain amount, the warping is evidently too great to allow the structure to remain stable, and it breaks up into interlocking crystals of two distinct minerals, potassium feldspar and plagioclase feldspar. Such warping of the internal structure of a mineral during substitution is illustrated in Figure 2-10, which shows the result of substituting calcium ions for about half of the iron and magnesium ions in the internal structure of olivine, giving the slightly different structure of monticellite, a mineral of closely related chemical composition.

Clearly, an element that has only one electron in its outer shell cannot be substituted for another that has two without destroying the electrical neutrality of the structure; a second, concurrent substitution is required to maintain neutrality. For example, in the plagioclase series of solid solutions, the change from pure albite ($NaAlSi_3O_8$) to pure anorthite ($CaAl_2Si_2O_8$) takes place by the simultaneous substitution of Ca (2 electrons in outer shell) and Al (3 electrons) for Na (1 electron) and Si (4 electrons). Chemical neutrality is thus retained, since $3 + 2 = 4 + 1$. The ionic diameter of sodium is almost the same as that of calcium; the ionic diameter of aluminum is so near that of silicon (Table 2-1) that the internal change by substitution does not warp the structure enough to cause it to break up. These slight changes in structure and composition, however, are large enough to produce measurable variations in the optical properties of plagioclase crystals of different compositions.

Mineraloids

Some natural substances that do not fulfill all the conditions given in the definition of a mineral are nevertheless commonly grouped with them as **mineraloids.** Perhaps the commonest of these is opal—a common constituent of rocks but one that is **amorphous,** that is, noncrystalline and without orderly internal structure.

Identification of Minerals

Of the more than two thousand minerals that have been recognized and described, only about twenty are abundant constituents of the earth's crust. Most of these can readily be identified at sight by anyone who will make a careful study of their ordinary physical properties. Appendix II, which should be studied in conjunction with this chapter, describes the methods used in identifying minerals, and lists the properties of twenty-five common minerals, and of twelve others worthy of study because of their economic importance.

FACTS, CONCEPTS, TERMS

MINERAL, ROCK, SOIL
THE ATOMIC THEORY
ATOM, MOLECULE
PROTON, NEUTRON, ELECTRON
IONS, COMPLEX IONS, SILICA TETRAHEDRON
ELEMENTS, ISOTOPES, COMPOUNDS, AGGREGATES
INTERNAL STRUCTURE OF MINERALS
    Crystal form
    Constancy of interfacial angles
    X-ray studies
    Exchange and sharing of electrons

Relation to cleavage and other physical properties
SOLID SOLUTION
    Role of ionic radii
(*Based on Appendix II*)
METHODS OF IDENTIFYING MINERALS
PHYSICAL PROPERTIES
    Cleavage and fracture; crystal form
    Color and streak; luster
    Hardness; scale of hardness
    Specific gravity
    Other properties

QUESTIONS (Based in part on Appendix II)

1. What is the essential difference between a mineral and an animal? Between a mineral and a rock? Between a mineral and a chemical element?

2. What controls the external geometrical form of crystals? Explain how we know this to be true.

3. Why is the petrographic microscope more useful in mineral identification than the methods of analysis used by the chemist?

4. Name three subatomic particles and outline briefly their chief characteristics.

5. State the characteristics that distinguish the following forms of matter: elements, isotopes, ions, atoms.

6. What is the basic difference between a crystal and a molecule? Why does the idea of molecules fail to apply to most minerals?

7. What factors control the substitution of one element for another in a solid-solution mineral series?

8. Explain how the difference in internal structure of diamond and graphite accounts for their differences in such physical properties as cleavage, hardness, and specific gravity.

9. Why is the specific gravity of quartz definite (2.65), whereas that of pyroxene is variable (3.2 to 3.6)?

10. Suggest a reason why the streak of a mineral is often more characteristic than the color of a large piece of the mineral.

SUGGESTED READINGS

Bragg, W. L. *The Atomic Structure of Minerals.* Ithaca, N. Y., Cornell University Press, 1937.

English, G. L. *Getting Acquainted with Minerals.* New York, McGraw-Hill, 1934.

Mason, Brian. *Principles of Geochemistry.* New York, John Wiley and Sons, 1952.

Tutton, A. E. H. *The Natural History of Crystals.* New York, N. Y., E. P. Dutton, 1924.

3 | THE RECORD
OF THE ROCKS

ROCKS are all about us—on mountain peaks, in the walls of cliffs, on the banks of rushing streams. Even where soil completely covers the surface, deep roadcuts and well borings reveal solid rocks beneath. Rocks are aggregates of minerals. The wide variations in appearance and physical properties that they show depend upon the amounts and kinds of different minerals they contain, and upon how the grains of these minerals are held together. But we can learn far more from rocks than the names of the minerals that compose them. So far our study of minerals has been focused upon their chemical composition and physical properties. Were this all we wished to know, **mineralogy** (the science of minerals) and **petrology** (the science of rocks) would consist of little more than studies of the chemistry and physics of earth materials. But to a geologist the chief interest of rocks is the record they reveal about the physical conditions, or the environment, at the time when the minerals aggregated into rock. Imprinted upon most rocks are tell-tale records of the conditions under which they formed. Often, too, because many later physical events have also left their traces, the reading of the rock record becomes a fascinating exploration into the history of the earth. The geologist is concerned not only with physical and chemical measurements; he becomes a detective who ferrets out clues, and pieces together seemingly unrelated evidence to form a logical picture of events of the past.

This chapter outlines some of the methods geologists use in reconstructing the geologic past from the record of the rocks. To go back to statements made in Chapter 1: What is the evidence that the site of the city of Glasgow did not always have a dour wet climate, but once glittered under a brilliant desert sun? Or that the cold Alberta plains were once covered by a shallow tropical sea such as bathes northeastern Australia today? To lay the groundwork for answers to these questions we introduce one of the great geological generalizations—the Uniformitarian Principle—which first began to unlock the dimension of time in our investigation of the earth.

"The Present Is the Key to the Past"

Geology, like all sciences, systematizes the data collected by observation and experiment into certain broad generalizations. The inquiring student should look critically into the validity of each of these generalizations.

The **Uniformitarian Principle** was proposed by James Hutton of Edinburgh in 1785, and popularized in a textbook by the English geologist Charles Lyell in 1830. This principle of "uniformity in the order of nature" may be stated as follows: *"The present is the key to the past,"* or, applied more specifically to our present subject: *Rocks formed long ago at the earth's surface may be understood and explained in accordance with processes now in operation.*

The Uniformitarian Principle assumes that physical laws now operating have always operated throughout the geologic past. It assumes, for example, that in the geologic past, just as today, water collected into streams and carried loads of mud and silt to the sea. Presumably, too, organisms lived and died in ancient seas, and their shells were buried in the sands and mud accumulating on the sea floor. A record of these past events can be found in the solid rocks, many of which have features identical to those we now see forming.

The Uniformitarian Principle, like any other scientific "law," is considered valid because all known facts conform to it. Geologic study extending over many generations has failed to find evidence of ancient conditions totally unlike those existing today. Yet, like most scientific laws, this one must be interpreted carefully and rather broadly. In applying the principle that "the present is the key to the past," we must keep in mind that although there is good evidence to believe geologic processes have always operated in the same way, they may not always have operated at their present rate or intensity. From evidence that will be developed in Chapter 13, we know that the climate was colder and glaciers more widespread some 15,000 years ago than now; but there is every reason to believe that the glaciers of that time formed, moved, eroded, and deposited precisely as they do today.

It is not easy to judge the rate of a process that operated in the geologic past. To early geologic observers the enormous thickness of rocks composed of hardened sand and mud that had been deposited by ancient streams and seas seemed to demand agencies of deposition far more powerful than those we see at work today. But a slow process can achieve in millions of years what a rapid operation could do more quickly. Now that several independent kinds of investigations show that more than two billion years is available in the geologic record (see Chapter 7), the great thickness of the sediments does not have to be explained in terms of catastrophic floods but is the inevitable result of long continued operation of the slow processes we observe today.

In the following discussion, some problems of rock origin are considered in the light of the Uniformitarian Principle.

Sedimentary Rocks

Everyone has observed how rills that form on a hillside during a downpour of rain spread sheets of mud, sand, and gravel at the base of steep slopes. Every stream, whether a tiny rill or a great river, sweeps debris downstream. Most of the rock waste forms temporary sand and gravel bars or is dropped in beds of silt and mud in the slack-water parts of the stream's course, but floods carry it farther, and most of it eventually reaches the ocean.

So commonplace are these features that more than two thousand years ago the Greeks learned to recognize water-borne deposits. Some of them reasoned that beds of gravel and sand high above the reach of present-day floods must be deposits of former streams, and they saw in the clam and oyster shells protruding from soft sandstone ledges far above high tide the evidence of former higher-standing seas.

It was a more difficult step—and one probably not made by the ancients—to conclude that a hard, well-consolidated sandstone containing only a few scattered fossil shells, and exposed on the peaks of a mountain range far from the ocean, is actually the cemented, shell-strewn sand of an ancient sea floor. Yet rocks containing fossil shells are so common that even in the early stages of Western Civilization they became the subject of much philosophical and theological controversy. Medieval churchmen ruled that fossils were not organic remains but "sports of nature," perhaps put in the rocks by the devil to confuse mankind. Even so careful an observer as Georgius Agricola (1494-1555), the German scholar in whose words and woodcuts the late medieval Saxon mines and miners are still preserved for us, described only the leaves, wood, bones, and fish skeletons embedded in the rocks as organic remains. To him the fossil shells were "solidified accumulations from water" (whatever that may mean).

The restraints of tradition and authority were not thrown off until the geological pioneers of the late seventeenth and eighteenth centuries repeatedly collected and compared the shells in hard rocks with those in unconsolidated sands along the seashore. They found that the same varieties of shells that are strewn along a modern beach may also occur as fossils in hard sandstones, although much more commonly the consolidated rocks contain shells not closely similar to those of living animals. Then, between 1790 and 1815, the early geologists made maps showing the distribution of strata of sandstone, limestone, and other rocks. Their mapping demonstrated that layers of soft sand may change gradually into firm rock when traced over some distance.

Today, with such modern tools as the petrographic microscope, it is only the work of minutes to trace the stages whereby loose sand like that on a beach has been transformed to **sandstone,** a hard rock made of cemented sand grains (Fig. 3-1). It is easy to see that the individual grains of fossiliferous sandstone (Fig. 3-1, c), when magnified by the microscope, are of the same shapes and are composed of essentially the same minerals as the sand grains of a modern beach (Fig. 3-1, a). Fossil shells in the sandstone, even though different from shells of living animals, show microscopic structures so similar as to compel belief that they are remains of former living things. The loose beach sand and the

Figure 3-1.   *Cementation of sand, as seen under the microscope:* (a) *loose sand from an Oregon beach;* (b) *partly cemented sandstone from a Brazilian coral reef; and* (c) *completely cemented sandstone from Ohio.*

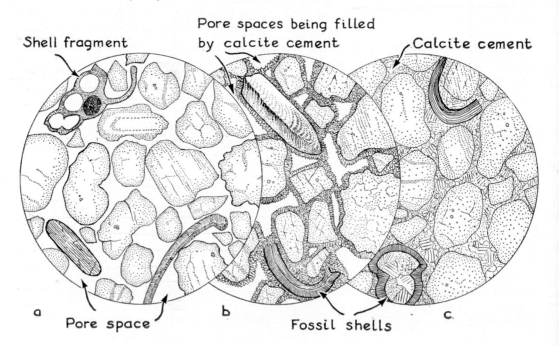

firm sandstone differ only in **cementation:** the voids or pores between the grains of the fossiliferous sandstone have been almost completely filled with mineral matter. By the filling of these voids, unconsolidated sand has been made into sandstone.

The sandstone just described is representative of the great group of rocks that geologists call **sedimentary rocks:** rocks that were formed at the surface of the earth, either by accumulation and cementation of fragments of rocks, minerals, and organisms, or as precipitates from sea water and other surface solutions. As we shall see, there are many varieties of sedimentary rocks besides sandstone, and there are also many rocks whose characteristics are inconsistent with a sedimentary origin.

Characteristic Features of Sedimentary Rocks

SORTING. We have mentioned only sediments that were transported and deposited by water. Glaciers and wind also move rock and mineral particles that may ultimately accumulate and be cemented into rock. Each of these agents of deposition leaves a characteristic stamp upon the sediments it forms.

Wind winnows the dust cleanly from sand, but it does not have power enough to move coarse boulders. Hence, the grains of wind-blown sand in a group of shifting dunes are all of about the same size. Such a sediment is called *well sorted,* which means that it shows little variation in grain size. Water currents also remove mud and fine sand from coarser material, but not as effectively as the wind. In general, deposits formed by the action of ocean waves are better sorted than river deposits, but neither are as well sorted as windblown sands. By contrast, glaciers dump *unsorted* coarse boulders, sand, and fine mud all together in heterogeneous heaps.

ROUNDING. The rushing water of a swiftly flowing stream tumbles loose fragments of rock over and over, grinding them against one another and against the stream bed. This slowly wears off their sharp corners and rounds

them into smooth-surfaced pebbles. The rounded pebbles thus formed accumulate in bars on the bed of any swiftly flowing river. Sand grains also lose their corners by scraping against other particles as they are carried along by wind or water. The degree of rounding of pebbles and sand grains depends on their original shape, on their resistance to abrasion, on the medium in which they are transported, and on the distance they have been rolled. Hence it may give some indication of the kind of agent that shaped the particles of sedimentary rock.

STRATIFICATION. Most sedimentary rocks show distinct layers, or **strata.** This layering, called **stratification** or **bedding,** generally results from variations in the supply of sedimentary detritus during deposition, or from changes in the velocity of the currents that are laying down the material, or from still other causes.

Visits to an ocean beach before, during, and after a storm reveal changes in the coarseness of the beach material that reflect differences in the power of the currents and waves during periods of calm and storm. A pit dug by a child in the sand nearly always shows distinct layers of varying coarseness. The strong waves and currents of a great storm may completely remove a layer of sand and mud on the sea floor or sweep a sheet of coarse gravel over it, as has been proved by samples dredged from the same spot before and after storms. In the southwest Pacific the accumulation of shells and coral in an offshore reef is sometimes interrupted by ash and pumice falling from a nearby volcano, or by mud swept far out to sea during unusually heavy floods in the rivers of the nearby land. Such deposits form distinct sedimentary strata, and because the interruptions vary in intensity and frequency, some strata are thin and others many feet thick.

The stratification of a sedimentary rock usually gives clues to the conditions of deposition. Mud that accumulates slowly on the bottom of a large fresh-water lake is generally bedded into closely parallel, paper-thin strata. This leads us to suspect that many "paper shales" such as the one shown in Figure 17-2 *b* may have been laid down under similar environmental conditions. Artificial cuts through sand dunes reveal that the stratification of windblown sand is quite complex and not at all like that of a lake sediment. It runs in long sweeping curves that are more or less parallel to the surface of the dune. The upper strata commonly cut across the edges of older sets of curving beds which formed when the wind was blowing in a different direction or when the surface of the dune had a different shape. These older sets may, in turn, lie across the edges of still older sets of strata. Exactly the same complex intersecting patterns of **cross-bedding** are found in many hard, consolidated sandstones (Fig. 15-16).

Interpretations

Many of the buildings of Glasgow are constructed from blocks of cross-bedded sandstone that have been quarried from the nearby rocky hills. The cross-bedding is one of the many pieces of evidence that Scotland once had a desert climate. Not only does the sandstone show dune cross-bedding, but the individual sand grains in it are well rounded and evenly and cleanly sorted, as is typical of windblown sand. Still more significant, many grains are "frosted," like the sandblasted

grains in modern desert dunes. Here and there in the sandstone are scattered pebbles like those shown in Figure 15-6 whose surfaces have been carved and faceted by the impact of wind-driven grains.

Associated with these strata are other layers of sandstone that contain pancake-like patches, or more commonly tongues and streaks of rounded gravel like that left along channel bottoms by the sudden flash floods that occur after the infrequent heavy rains in the desert. At times the lifting of a huge slab of sandstone by the quarry machinery reveals a beautifully rippled surface preserved in the stone below. These ripples, complete in every detail, are identical with those forming today on the sandy beds of desert streams in the arid southwestern United States (Fig. 3-2). Moreover, some of the sandstone shows a cross-bedding that differs in detail from that in windblown dunes, but is identical with that formed in the sandbars of intermittent desert streams. Such cross-bedded sandbars can be seen forming on the floors of sandy washes in southern Utah and many other desert regions.

The few shales interbedded with these sandstones give additional evidence of the existence of an ancient desert. Their distribution and character suggest that they were originally deposits of mud in shallow pools which dried up periodically under the desert

Stream ripples on the flat sandy channel of the San Juan River near Mexican Hat, Utah. (Photo by A. C. Waters.)

Figure 3-2.

sun. They show typical six-sided shrinkage cracks, like the mud cracks that form on drying mudflats today. At times quarrymen uncover perfectly preserved fish skeletons, or the shells and skeletons of other organisms that lived in these shallow pools.

Thus the rocks of the Glasgow region record their story. The evidence is circumstantial; it rests upon a close comparison of all the features of the Glasgow rocks with the sands and associated deposits in modern deserts. But, taken together, the many different bits of evidence point unequivocally to the conclusion that millions of years ago this area had a climate like that of the Mohave Desert or of southern Arizona today.

How different, though, is the record of these Glasgow rocks from that revealed by certain **limestones** found in part of the Alberta plains: rocks composed mostly of cemented marine shells and deposits of coral. In every detail of composition and structure (except that most of the organisms are of species and genera different from their modern analogs) these rocks closely resemble the great reefs of white coralline rock, many miles long, off the shores of northern Australia and Indonesia today. There the shells of clams, oysters, and many other marine organisms are accumulating along with the limy deposits made by coral animals. In these reefs even the shells of living creatures are being cemented together by lime-depositing algae, and the interstices between them filled with limy (calcite-rich) mud to form solid rock upon which new shells will grow. The close similarity of the rocks in Alberta with these modern reefs compels the belief that this part of Canada was not always a cold semiarid steppe, but once lay beneath a warm tropical sea. "The present is the key to the past."

Laws of Sedimentary Sequence

Observations of strata now accumulating make possible the following generalizations, which, though rather obvious, are nevertheless useful in interpreting ancient sedimentary rocks. The first is the **Law of Original Horizontality:** *Water-laid sediments are deposited in strata that are almost horizontal, and parallel or nearly parallel to the surface on which they are accumulating.*

This law was first clearly stated in 1669 by the same Nicolaus Steno whose measurements of quartz crystals led to important discoveries in mineralogy. It applies to all sediments deposited in water except certain small accumulations, such as sandbars, in which, as in dunes of windblown sand, some strata may be laid down at a marked angle to the other strata within the same deposit. This is cross-bedding, already discussed.

Steno also first stated the **Law of Superposition:** *In any pile of sedimentary strata that has not been disturbed by folding or overturning since accumulation, the youngest stratum is at the top and the oldest at the base.* In other words, the order of deposition is from the bottom upward.

Many applications of these generalizations appear in subsequent chapters. That they are not insignificant truisms may be realized from the fact that in most mountain ranges the strata of sedimentary rocks are no longer horizontal, but are steeply tilted or even overturned. Because we recognize that these rocks were once sheets of sand, shells, and gravel deposited in horizontal layers and then cemented together, their present inclined position shows that great forces must have buckled and folded the rocks of the region. A simple structure like the stratification of a sediment thus helps us to read the record of great changes in the earth's crust—changes that have bent and broken once horizontal sheets of rock into fantastically complex patterns.

Classification of Sedimentary Rocks

Sedimentary rocks are named and classified mainly on the basis of their **texture** (size and shape of the constituent particles) and **composition** (kinds of materials that compose the particles and cements). We have already found that cemented sand is called sandstone; similarly, rocks composed of cemented pebbles are called conglomerate, and very fine-grained rocks composed mainly of compacted mud and silt are called shale. All these belong to a class of sedimentary rocks called **clastic**—from the Greek word for "broken" (see Appendix III)—because they are composed mainly of broken and worn fragments of pre-existing minerals, rock particles, or shells that were carried to the site of deposition by moving agencies such as streams, wind, waves, or glaciers, and there cemented.

The most important aspects of *clastic texture* are grain size and grain shape. The fragments may be large or small, rounded or angular. Although all kinds of mineral and rock fragments may appear, the coarser clastics such as conglomerate and sandstone generally contain much quartz because this hard and chemically resistant mineral does not rot even after long exposure to air and water, and also resists the grinding process of transportation better than other common minerals. The cements that bind clastic rocks together are most commonly calcite, clay, quartz, and limonite, but many other minerals may also cement the sedimentary grains.

There is a second broad subdivision of the sedimentary rocks which geologists generally call the **organic and chemical** sedimentary rocks. These consist of sedimentary materials formed by organisms, and of sediments deposited as chemical precipitates from sea water or other solutions on the earth's surface; they are grouped together because most of them show a *crystalline texture*. They have little or no cement; the grains are interlocked by mutual interpenetration during growth. Such rocks accumulate in place, without mechanical transport, and so their grains generally do not show the rounding and other effects of mechanical wear that characterize clastic sediments, although in places the shells and other fragments of organic origin they contain may be broken or worn by waves and currents. Moreover most organic and chemical sedimentary rocks contain at least some clastic fragments of minerals washed in from the land.

Many organisms are rock builders, like those that create the coralline limestone forming off the shores of northern Australia and Indonesia. In such accumulations the structure and shape of each shell or other bit of organic debris is generally well preserved, and these organic features dominate the texture of the rock; such rocks are said to have *organic texture*. Most coal also shows organic texture; the well-preserved cell structures and other plant characteristics visible under the microscope prove that it is made from accumulated plant remains.

Most shells are composed of calcium carbonate ($CaCO_3$), but some organisms, especially diatoms, radiolaria, and some sponges, have hard parts composed of silica. Bones and the shells of a few marine molluscs are largely calcium phosphate. The woody tissues of plants are the parent materials of coal.

The most common chemical sedimentary rocks consist of intergrown crystals precipitated from sea water or other natural solutions on the surface of the earth. Some limestones (in contrast to the organically accumulated limestone reefs, or to the clastic limestones made of worn fragments of shells and of older carbonate rocks) are chemical sediments. They show features indicating they were formed by precipitation of calcium carbonate from the sea, from desert lakes, or from hot springs. Rarer, but perhaps more typical chemical sediments are the evaporites such as the salt deposits (chiefly halite) on the Bonneville Salt Flats west of Salt Lake City, Utah. These crystallized during the evaporation of a large saline lake of which the present Great Salt Lake is only a remnant—identical beds are now precipitating in parts of Great Salt Lake. Other evaporites have crystallized from masses of sea water cut off from the open ocean by a reef or other obstruction. They generally contain large amounts of gypsum and anhydrite as well as halite. In chemical sediments the minerals precipitated from solution are generally tightly intergrown with one another, giving the rock its characteristic crystalline texture.

COMMON VARIETIES OF SEDIMENTARY
ROCKS. Hundreds of different kinds of sedimentary rocks have been described and named, but most are comparatively rare. For an elementary knowledge of geology, learning to recognize the common ones listed in Table III-1 of Appendix III will suffice. This appendix contains fairly full descriptions of each of the major groups of rock. The student should turn to the appendix at this point and read the descriptions of sandstone, shale, and limestone—three rocks that have been given more than passing mention in the preceding pages. The descriptions should be studied with a specimen of the rock at hand, so that one can note and compare its properties with those listed in the description. In making such a comparison, do not expect specimen and description to correspond exactly, for rocks vary widely and grade into one another. Nearly all sedimentary rocks are really mixtures—organic, chemical, and clastic debris are present in varying proportions in practically all of them. Hence our classifications can do little more than call attention to the dominant constituent or process of formation. The aim of rock study is not merely to fit rock specimens into the pigeonholes of a man-made classification. Far more important is the observation of compositional, textural, and other variations that give clues to the origin of the rock and to events that happened during its deposition and subsequent history.

Igneous Rocks

In January, 1938, a white-hot stream of molten lava issued from a fissure near the base of Nyamlagira volcano, in Africa, and poured quietly downward into a forested plain below. For two years and four months the lava continued to escape, until the molten rock had devastated an area of more than twenty-five square miles. Finally the flow ceased and the lava congealed into the black slaggy rock that we call basalt. Similar lava flows have been observed in many other parts of the world.

Other volcanoes, among them Vesuvius in Italy, Bandai-San in Japan, and Mont Pelée in the West Indies, have been observed to erupt explosively, blowing vast quantities of volcanic ash (fine bits of volcanic glass and pumice, see Appendix III) and broken rock fragments high into the air. Such hot ash has been known to consolidate into firm, coherent rock within a generation. It was this kind of eruption from Vesuvius that overwhelmed Herculaneum and Pompeii in 79 A.D., preserving in minute detail the buildings, household objects, and even some of the people and animals that lived in these flourishing ancient cities. That rocks were created by volcanic action was well known to early civilizations because of the many active volcanoes in the Mediterranean countries.

But the ancients did not recognize that volcanic rocks are common in regions far from any active volcanoes. It is one thing to watch liquid lava emerge from a fissure, flow down a slope, and congeal into a mass of basalt, and quite another to recognize a basalt flow that was extruded millions of years ago. This is especially true if the flow has since been detached from its parent cone or fissure by erosion, or buried under later sedimentary rocks. Because of their manner of formation, it is common for volcanic and sedimentary rocks to be interlayered. In the Samoan Islands basalt has been seen to flow into the sea and to spread over reefs in which limestone was forming; today deposits of coral and shells are collecting on the upper surface of the congealed lava. The great flow at the base of Nyamlagira covers older volcanic material, but earlier flows in the same region spread over a plain underlain by lake and river deposits, and were in turn partly buried beneath later sediments. Scarcely any thick pile of sedimentary rocks is completely free from volcanic interlayers.

It is not surprising that flows of lava and beds of volcanic ash interstratified with sedimentary rocks were regarded by the early geologists as hardened sediments, just as they often are by the uninitiated today. Indeed, fifty years of violent controversy took place before the volcanic origin of basalt was definitely established.

The Controversy over the Origin of Basalt

The interpretation of scientific phenomena is often influenced by the philosophy and background of the worker. The history of geology, like that of other sciences is replete with examples of unsuccessful attempts to fit the features seen in the field into the preconceived notions of the observer, or into the results of incomplete or inappropriate laboratory experiments. One of the classical examples of the conflict between theoretical and field interpretations was the controversy concerning the origin of basalt, a controversy that raged from about 1775 to 1822.

Some of the hills of Saxony near the famous mining academy of Freiberg are composed chiefly of sedimentary rocks, but interstratified with them are a few layers of hard, dark-colored basalt. The basalt is more resistant to erosion than the sedimentary rocks with which it is associated, and forms picturesque colonnaded cliffs at or near the summits of many of the hills.

In 1775 the Stolpen, one of these basalt-capped hills, was visited by Abraham Gottlob Werner, professor of mining and mineralogy at Freiberg, a scientist who was destined to wield great influence on the development of geology ("geognosy," as he called it). From his observations on this and later visits, Werner wrote, in 1787, that the hill showed ". . . not a trace of volcanic action, nor the smallest proof of volcanic origin . . . After further more matured research and consideration, I hold that no basalt is volcanic but that all these rocks . . . are of aqueous origin."

Following up his idea that all basalts were precipitated from the ocean, Werner proceeded to divide the crust of the earth into a series of "Universal Formations." These, he taught, were all precipitated from a primeval ocean, and could be definitely recognized all over the world, each formation having the same char-

acter and occurring in the same order no matter in what country it might be found. Thus he attempted to apply to the whole earth the same kind of precise system he had used in organizing and classifying the minerals in the laboratory collections at Freiberg.*

Werner's personal charm was great, and he attracted large numbers of able students whom he fired with great zeal. They came to believe that the "Universal System" of the great teacher would unlock the geologic history of every country. But other workers were reaching different conclusions. Even before Werner first visited Stolpen, Nicholas Desmarest, a French government official who published several excellent papers on geology during his spare time, had studied in careful detail some basalt flows that he found in the Auvergne region of central France. The Auvergne has had no eruptions within historic times but it contains well preserved craters, lava flows, and other volcanic phenomena. How different was the approach of this clear-eyed observer from that of the dogmatic Werner to essentially the same problem!

In his first journey into the Auvergne in 1763, Desmarest found a cliff of basalt. Searching at the base of the cliff, he noticed that the soil beneath the flow had apparently been burned and hardened. He also noticed that the basalt grades upward into masses of scoria, a coarsely frothy basaltic rock filled with small, spherical holes. Scoria is common along the base, and much more abundant in the upper part, of basalt flows. It has been observed to form in moving lava when rising bubbles of steam are caught by congealing of the sticky lava around them. When he visited the Auvergne, Desmarest had never seen lava flowing from an active volcano, but by care-

---

* Because of the errors he promulgated about the structure of the earth's crust and the origin of basalt, the remarkably effective work that Werner did in mineralogy is often neglected or forgotten. The science of mineralogy in his day was a chaos of jumbled terminology and haphazard descriptions; he reduced some of this to order, and provided the original impetus that has led Germany to excel in this branch of geology.

ful observation and by reasoning he established two of the criteria now universally used in the recognition of ancient basalt flows—the baking of the ground beneath a lava flow, and the presence of scoria formed by the congealing of bubble-filled lava. Desmarest, however, did not consider that even these observations were proof of volcanic origin. He wrote that his curiosity was aroused, but that he drew no certain conclusions. He decided to examine and map the outlines of the entire flow. This work disclosed similar features at many points along the base of the flow. He also traced the flow to its source in a round, steep-sided hill which, despite some modification by erosion, still retains the characteristic form of a volcanic cone.

Still not entirely satisfied, Desmarest decided to plot on a map the distribution of all the different kinds of rocks of the Auvergne. By carefully following the boundaries between the lavas and other kinds of rocks, and by plotting these boundaries on a map, he proved that the volcanic history of the Auvergne was very long. Some eruptions had been followed by quiet periods during which streams cut valleys into the flows and removed much of the ash from the cones. These newly cut valleys were then filled and obliterated by renewed volcanic activity. Eventually he traced out three main cycles in the volcanic history. His map, one of the first geologic maps ever made, is a monument to his good judgment and his ability to interpret field relations.

Ironically, although most of Desmarest's reports were published before Werner tried to formulate his "Universal System," they remained almost unnoticed for many years. While Werner's teachings and ideas were sweeping over Europe, Desmarest took no part in the controversy. When asked for his opinion on the origin of basalt, he would reply: "Go to the Auvergne and see." Eventually, two of Werner's own students, D'Aubuisson and von Buch, eager to establish the "Universal System" of their teacher in other countries, did visit the Auvergne. How great was their disillusionment as they fol-

lowed, step by step, the evidence and lines of reasoning that Desmarest had so carefully recorded! Here in the Auvergne, D'Aubuisson and von Buch saw the burned and hardened ground on which the lava had flowed. They saw the scoriaceous tops and bottoms of the flows where bubbles of steam had been trapped in the congealing lava. All these features could also be seen at Stolpen, but Werner and his students, eager to establish the sequence of the "Universal System," and interested in the basalt chiefly as something to study in the laboratory, had missed the critical details in the field.

The straightforward reports of D'Aubuisson and von Buch did much to overthrow the theory that basalt was a precipitate from a "Universal Ocean," although some disciples of the great teacher, content to work in the laboratory instead of examining rocks in the field, continued for a time to promulgate the Wernerian doctrines. Yet, more than a hundred and fifty years ago, this failure of Werner's speculations to withstand the rigorous test of careful field observations showed geologists that the ultimate worth of geologic theories can be proved only in the field.

Nevertheless, the controversy over the origin of basalt stimulated great interest in geology. The study of ancient volcanoes spread wide and far and bore abundant fruit, particularly in the British Isles, an area rich in varied and spectacular volcanic phenomena, despite the fact that none of the British volcanoes has been active in historic time.

Plutonic Rocks

The rocks described above obviously differ, both in nature and origin, from sedimentary rocks. They are called **igneous rocks** (from the Latin word for "fire"), and they are formed by the congealing of **magma**—the name for melted rock, formed deep within the earth. If magma is erupted to the surface as lava flows or in explosions of ash it forms **volcanic** igneous rocks, but if it crystallizes slowly in deep underground chambers it forms **plutonic** igneous rocks, to which we now turn.

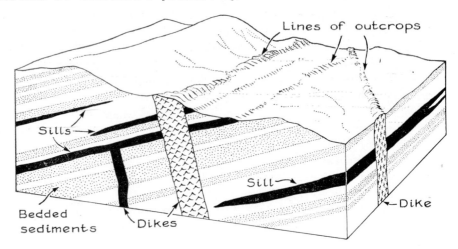

Figure 3-3.

Sills are concordant, dikes are discordant tabular intrusions.

As the details of lava streams and deposits of volcanic ash became better understood, British geologists began to study the conduits through which the magma had reached the surface. In the Midland Valley of Scotland and in parts of the Hebrides, just as in northwestern New Mexico and parts of central Oregon, erosion has swept away most of the lava flows and bitten deeply into the foundation beneath. A few of the old flows, however, pass downward without a break into pipe-like masses (**volcanic necks**) or filled fissures (**dikes**) that cut through the basement rocks on which the lava rests. These cross-cutting masses fill the conduits through which magma rose to form the volcanic rocks. A few volcanic feeders have been observed to pass at still greater depths into much larger and more complex igneous bodies. Masses of plutonic igneous rock formed by consolidation of magma beneath the surface are called **intrusive bodies.**

Although a few intrusive bodies can be traced continuously into recognizable lava flows, many may never have had any direct outlet to the earth's surface. That these masses were likewise formed by crystallization from a magma is proved by several lines of evidence: the rocks along their contacts are commonly hardened, or even completely recrystallized by the heat from the magma;

tongues and stringers from them penetrate into cracks in the adjacent rock in the manner of a liquid; they show chilled borders of fine-textured rock.

The rocks formed by magma that has congealed underground generally have coarser mineral grains than lava flows. Such coarsely crystalline igneous rocks have never been seen in process of formation, but laboratory investigations prove that heat is transmitted by solid rock much less rapidly than it is carried off by rising air (convection currents) above a molten lava flow, and that the more slowly silicates cool the coarser the crystals they form. Thus it is evident that the rock lying above an intrusive body acts as a blanket that permits only slow cooling of the magma, enabling the crystals to grow to larger size than those in lava, which cools in the open air.

Rounded gas bubbles are absent or at least very rare in plutonic rocks because the pressure of the roof rocks keeps the gas in solution in the magma. Gas separates into bubbles only when the pressure is released, as when magma suddenly rises from the depths and is extruded on the surface.

The different forms assumed by intrusive bodies are systematically described in Chapter 18, but one form, called a **sill,** is worthy of special comment here. Most intrusive bodies cut across the bedding of the enclosing sedimentary rocks and are called **discordant,** but a sill is a rock mass congealed from magma forced **concordantly** between sedimentary strata. The magma spreads between the strata like the grease squirted between metal surfaces by a grease gun (Fig. 3-3). A sill might thus occur low in a sedimentary sequence and yet be much younger than strata hundreds of feet above it. Here, then, is a possible source of error in applying our generalization about the Law of Superposition—for how can we tell an intrusive sill from a lava flow that had been buried under a later accumulation of sedimentary rocks?

Contacts of Rock Masses

The key to this question, as to many others in geology, lies in the interpretation of the boundary surfaces between rock bodies. A mass of a single kind of rock, whether sandstone, basalt, or any other, does not extend indefinitely; somewhere it must come in con-

tact with another. These common boundary surfaces of adjacent rock masses are called their **contacts.** There are two general kinds: **sharp,** with a definite surface of junction; and **gradational** (especially common in sedimentary rocks), in which there is no sharp boundary but an intermediate zone—in some places thick, in others thin—in which the transition from one rock mass to the other takes place.

In interpreting the relative age of two rock masses in contact, the following generalizations are useful. They apply not only to problems of sequence among igneous rocks, but to all kinds of rock bodies.

Of two rock masses in contact, that one is younger which contains within it fragments or inclusions of the other. Thus, a sill might be expected to enclose, at some places near its upper surface, fragments torn from the overlying stratum at the time of intrusion (Fig. 3-4). On the other hand, fragments of a buried lava flow are likely to be found as in-

Figure 3-4.   Criteria for distinguishing between a sill and a buried lava flow.

Sill:

Baked contacts

Small dikes

Inclusions of wall rocks

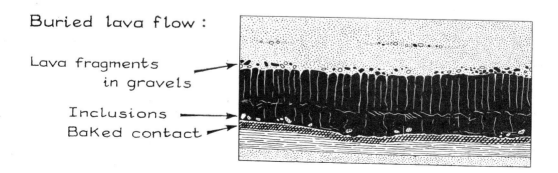

Buried lava flow:

Lava fragments in gravels

Inclusions

Baked contact

clusions in an immediately overlying sedimentary stratum, since loose pieces of lava and scoria would probably be picked up and mixed with overlying detritus by the moving agent that deposited the sediment (Fig. 3-4).

If a rock sends tongues and branches into another, it is younger than the rock it penetrates. The sedimentary strata above most sills, or for that matter the older rocks in contact with any igneous intrusion, commonly contain tongues or dikes of igneous rock formed when the magma penetrated fissures or other openings in the older rock and solidified there.

Although this rule applies mostly to igneous rocks, some sediments may also, in places, penetrate adjacent rocks. Thus, cracks and openings in the upper part of a lava flow may be filled with debris from the immediately overlying sediment that had filtered into the cracks during deposition (Fig. 3-5, *left*).

The generalization must be used with care, however, when applied to sedimentary rocks. Rarely one sees examples where an underlying and hence older bed of poorly consolidated sand has sent **sandstone dikes** upward into younger overlying shale (Fig. 3-5, *right*). This seems an exception to the rule stated above, though of course the actual rise of the sand into dikes did occur after the formation of the overlying shale and hence the dikes are younger than the rocks that contain them. What apparently happened was that the underlying water-logged sand was forced upward into cracks opened in the overlying rock. Presumably cementation of the sandstone had been delayed until after the shale was laid down and consolidated.

If an igneous rock bakes or alters another rock with which it is in contact, it is younger than the rock it bakes. So stated, this is a truism, but recognition of baked contacts is not always easy. Some rock masses are impregnated and discolored by mineral matter deposited along their contacts by percolating waters. Careful observations or even microscopic study is generally needed to distinguish such features from baked contacts.

The criterion of alteration by a hot magma can in general be more readily applied to intrusive rocks than to lava flows. We have already seen how Desmarest recognized the baked rock beneath the Auvergne lavas, but it is not always possible to do this. The interior of a lava flow commonly remains molten long after a thick rind of lava has congealed on its upper and lower surfaces. Many flows have been seen to creep forward beneath this rind, and owing to this motion the solidified crust on the top of the flow breaks up into blocks that are rolled under the advancing front. Such blocks are generally so cool that they fail to bake the material beneath. Intrusive masses, on the contrary, invariably alter the walls that surround them, at least to some degree.

Figure 3-5.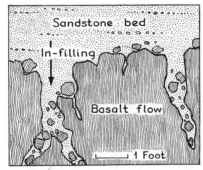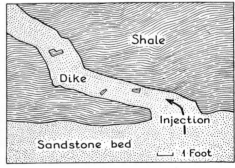

Sandstone dikes. Left: *Near Stanford University, California.* Right: *Santa Monica Mountains, California.*

Classification of Igneous Rocks

With the petrographic microscope, much information can be obtained about the minerals in an igneous rock, including their kinds, shapes, sizes, patterns of arrangement, order of crystallization, and the alterations brought about in them either by hot gases from the magma or by outside agencies such as air and atmospheric moisture. The possible variations in so many different features yields infinite possibilities for classification, and hundreds of kinds of igneous rocks have been discriminated and given separate names. However, most (approximately 95 per cent) of the igneous rocks can be lumped into about 15 major groups. The simplified list given in Appendix III, Table III-2, suffices for our purpose; we shall not need names for the numerous varieties within each group, or for the rare groups not included. This simplified classification of the igneous rocks is based on the minerals and textures visible to the eye, thus dispensing completely with the microscope. It is widely used in field work where laboratory equipment is not immediately available.

Comparison of mineral composition and the bulk chemical composition of thousands of igneous rocks shows that the *kinds and amounts of different minerals depend, in general, on the chemical composition of the original magma. Magmas rich in silica yield,* on cooling, large amounts of feldspar and quartz; *magmas low in silica form rocks rich in the ferromagnesian minerals* such as pyroxene and olivine.

Differences in the amount of glass and crystalline material and in the size and arrangement of the crystals determine the texture of an igneous rock. Texture is an important element in classification. *The size of the mineral grains depends chiefly on the rate of cooling,* although the chemical composition of the magma plays a part. It has been inferred from field observations, and confirmed by laboratory experiment, that a high content of water and other volatile substances also promotes the growth of larger crystals. Field observations of large intrusive masses reveal

that the crystals generally grow large enough so that the minerals can be readily identified with the eye. If the magma forms a lava flow, however, rapid cooling by the air prevents the growth of large crystals after extrusion, although a few large ones may already have formed underground. Such mixtures of large crystals enclosed in a groundmass of much smaller crystals forms the **porphyritic** texture common in many lava flows, and more fully described in Appendix III. Lava erupted to the surface chills quickly to mixtures of microscopic mineral grains and glass. If cooling is extremely rapid, it may congeal to a glass containing hardly any crystals.

The Enigmatic Rock Called Granite

As careful geologic mapping in many areas of volcanic and shallow plutonic rocks disclosed more and more about the contact relations of intrusive igneous rocks, a spirited discussion arose over the origin of **granite,** a common coarse-grained rock composed chiefly of feldspar and quartz. The origin of granite is still a lively topic, indeed it seems clear that this enigmatic rock can be formed in more than one way.

Geologic mapping in many different countries shows that granite and the similar rock granodiorite are among the most abundant rocks in the accessible part of the earth. They form great uniform bodies hundreds of square miles in extent. At many places granites are covered with sedimentary rocks that contain pebbles of the underlying granite: the sediments are therefore younger than the granite. This relation persuaded some early geologists that granite was the earth's "original crust." Werner considered granite to be the first precipitate out of his "Universal Ocean," but others thought it might have formed when the earth first solidified from a molten state.

But the idea that all granites are old did not remain unchallenged. James Hutton, the Edinburgh physician who proposed the principle of Uniformitarianism, was one of the first to become dissatisfied with the prevailing Wernerian view on the origin of granite. Hutton was familiar with old volcanic conduits that penetrate the sandstones near Edinburgh, and he noted that their rocks resemble granite in crystallinity and in generally uniform character, although their color and minerals are different. As he studied more and more samples of granite, Hutton became convinced that the prevailing belief it was precipitated from a primitive ocean could not be correct. He made the bold suggestion that granite must have cooled from great subterranean masses of molten rock. But how was he to test this hypothesis? Hutton reasoned that if granite had welled up in a molten or even in a semi-liquid condition it would surely have forced its way into cracks in any rock with which it came in contact. He decided to search for such "veins" (dikes, in our terminology). A likely place to look was in the Grampians, a chain of granite mountains southwest of Aberdeen, along whose lower slopes the granite must somewhere come in contact with the prevailing dark colored schists that form the lowlands and hills in this part of Scotland.

The project was discussed at scientific meetings, and the Duke of Athol, who owned a hunting lodge on the River Tilt in the foothills of the Grampians, invited Hutton to visit him and test the hypothesis. Soon after arrival the party started up the deep precipitous glen of the river. They were hardly underway when a resounding shout came from Hutton as he pointed to a large dike of pink granite that broke upward through the dark schist on the wall of the glen. In the space of a mile five more "veins" were seen to branch from the underlying granite into the dark stone above.

On a later expedition to the seaside at Galloway, Hutton found place after place where granite had broken into older rock, distorting and pushing the walls aside, and forcing its way into every fissure and cranny. His predictions that granite would be found to behave as though it had once been a molten subterranean mass had been amply confirmed, yet it brought him only scathing attacks from the followers of Werner. But as more and more geologists studied granite in the field they noted that granitic dikes, tongues, and complicated offshoots of considerable size penetrate the overlying rocks in locality after locality. Only in the scale of the injection features—thousands of feet rather than feet or inches—were the contacts notably different from those of small intrusive masses. Moreover, the invaded rocks at such contacts are altered, and so thoroughly recrystallized that their origin as sedimentary or volcanic rocks is difficult to establish. Such changes in the wall rocks suggest the effect of high temperatures. Detailed field studies also showed that most of the great expanses of granite, far from being as uniform as had been supposed, actually embrace several distinct intrusions, the younger penetrating the older. Abundant fragments of adjacent older rock are also strewn through the granite along many contacts, as though pried off by the intruding granite magma. (Fig. 3-6.)

Thus many granites have been shown to be igneous rocks, congealed at considerable depth. Diked contacts and flow structures also indicate that some masses are not single intrusions but have been formed by successive invasions separated by intervals of inaction. This recalls the Auvergne, where Desmarest demonstrated three distinct effusive periods separated by long interludes of quiet. Apparently the emplacement of large bodies of igneous rock, whether at the surface or far beneath it, is a slow and intermittent process.

If we left the subject of the origin of granite here, however, we should be greatly oversimplifying a complex problem. By no means are all granite contacts either clearly erosional or clearly intrusive. Many are gradational, the granite fading gradually into rocks that are altered and recrystallized but that nevertheless show clear relics of undoubted sedimentary or volcanic structure. Moreover, some rocks that are definitely granites in composition and texture contain faint nebulous patterns that resemble stratification, outlines of pebbles, or other sedimentary structures. Still

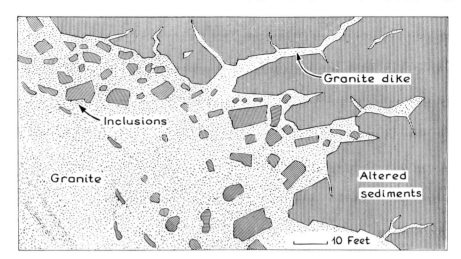

Figure 3-6.

Intrusive relations at a granite contact.

other granites are in places penetrated by frail layers of recrystallized limestone and sandstone only a foot or two thick which project from the wall rock for tens or even hundreds of feet into the granite. It is inconceivable that magma could break up and engulf wall rocks in the manner shown in Figure 3-6 and yet leave such frail unbroken layers behind. More likely former sedimentary rocks were transformed into granite by a process of slow recrystallization and replacement in the solid state. Certain beds, less susceptible to replacement than others, have been left as relics. Thus some granites appear to be the products of **metamorphic** (from the Greek word for "change of form") transformations. The problem of telling a granite of metamorphic origin from one of igneous origin is decidedly difficult. We will return to the controversial subject of the origin of granite in Chapter 18, but first let us consider other and less perplexing rocks that we know belong to our third great group of rocks.

Metamorphic Rocks

We have seen that the sedimentary origin of many rocks can be confidently inferred from their stratification, water-worn pebbles, and fossils. Other rocks have textures and mineral compositions that, by analogy with volcanic rocks permit us to classify them just as confidently as igneous rocks.

There remains a third great group, the **metamorphic rocks,** in which diagnostic features of igneous or sedimentary origin are absent or have been so obscured by the growth of new minerals that they are scarcely recognizable. For example, we find rocks containing pebbles, and with a stratification much like that of conglomerate, but the pebbles are stretched and flattened into spindles and the matrix between these deformed pebbles consists not of sand and clay, but of glassy quartz interlocked with lustrous flakes of mica. Long delicate needles of tourmaline may also cut through two or more adjacent pebbles and the intervening matrix (Fig. 3-7). It is inferred that such rock was once a conglomerate but that the tourmaline and mica could not have been present when the conglomerate was deposited; they grew in the solid rock long after deposition. Apparently the original round pebbles have been squeezed and stretched, and the sand and clay which formed the matrix of the original conglomerate have been metamorphosed to mica and quartz. Original features such as the flattened pebbles must mean that the rock did not melt in attaining its present condition. The metamorphism appears

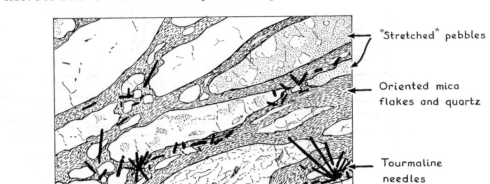

"Stretched" pebbles

Oriented mica
flakes and quartz

Tourmaline
needles

Figure 3-7.

Metamorphosed conglomerate with tourmaline needles cutting the other constituents. (Enlarged about four times).

to have been accomplished by recrystallization of some of the minerals while the rock remained solid.

From such relations—and there are many rocks with relic igneous textures as well as sedimentary—we infer that the *metamorphic rocks must have been formed deep beneath the surface of the earth by the transformation of other rocks, while in the solid state, by the heat, pressure, and chemically active fluids to which they were subjected after burial in the earth.* From the nature of their origin it is clear that there can be an infinite number of gradations between metamorphic rocks and the igneous or sedimentary rocks from which they were formed.

Foliation, and the Origin of Slate

Most metamorphic rocks have a banded or layered structure called **foliation.** The layers may be relatively coarse bands 1/24 inch or more thick, as in **gneiss,** or layers thinner than a sheet of paper, as in **slate,** or of intermediate thickness, as in **schist** (see App. III for rock names). Most foliated metamorphic rocks split readily along these layers. The foliation appears to record slow pervasive movement within the rock mass, during which most of the original minerals were broken,

streaked out, and recrystallized into new minerals.

When geology was first emerging as a science, coarse-grained, faintly foliated metamorphic rocks such as gneiss were generally classified with the granites and assumed to be igneous rocks, whereas the fine-grained, well-foliated ones like slate were thought to be sedimentary. For example, the metamorphic foliation in slate, a rock much used for roofing, flagstones, and other building purposes, was erroneously considered to be stratification. Geologic study of European and American slate quarries disclosed, however, that many slates have two distinct layered structures. The older of these, the true sedimentary stratification, is parallel with alternations in grain size, color, and composition, and with bedding in neighboring rocks like limestone or quartzite. The other structure, the foliation, often crosses the stratification, commonly breaking it and displacing it a small (usually microscopic) distance (Fig. 3-8), thus proving that the foliation is younger than the bedding. The slate does not split along the stratification planes like a normal sedimentary rock except where the younger structure, the metamorphic foliation, happens to coincide with the older stratification. When foliation and stratification do coincide, recognizable but dis-

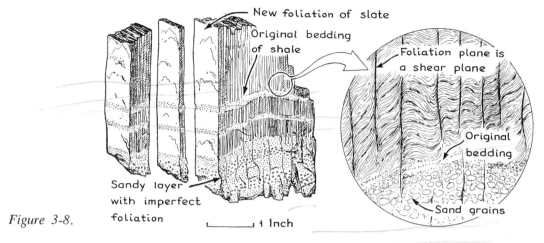

Figure 3-8.

Fragments of slate (left) *showing relics of original bedding. The enlargement shows small offsets along the cleavage surface.*

torted fossils are occasionally found along the foliation surfaces. If these fossils are compared with fossils of the same species from little-changed sedimentary rocks, they are seen to have been greatly thinned in the direction across the foliation and to be stretched out parallel to it (Fig. 3-9). If the foliation cuts the stratification at a high angle, however, it is almost useless to look for fossils, because the rock will rarely split along the stratification where the fossils lie. Furthermore, a fossil may be broken and displaced by so many microscopic slips along foliation planes as to be unrecognizable.

From the vestiges of stratification and the occasional distorted fossils, it is clear that most slates were derived from fine-grained sedimentary rocks, such as shale. This is confirmed by chemical analyses, which in general show no essential difference between shale and many slates. Field and laboratory studies show, however, that not every slate is derived from shale; some were formed from other fine-grained rocks such as volcanic tuff.

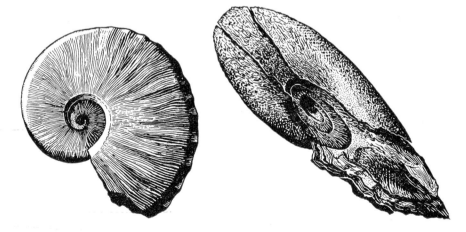

Figure 3-9.

The fossil at the left was collected from unaltered limestone in Idaho; that at the right, the identical species, occurred in slates in the Inyo Mountains, California.

Only by the use of the petrographic microscope and by X-rays can we determine the true nature of the foliation. Slates are exceedingly fine-grained—in fact, most of the mineral particles in slate are ultramicroscopic. X-ray studies show, however, that slate is made up largely of tiny flakes of white mica, all of which are aligned nearly parallel with one another. Since mica has only one direction of cleavage, the cleavage plane of nearly all the mica flakes within the slate must lie nearly parallel. That is why slate splits so readily into thin sheets. Evidently slate is merely shale that has been sheared and heated sufficiently to cause the original clay minerals composing it to recrystallize into tiny flakes of mica, nearly all of which lie parallel with the foliation.

Deep-Seated Origin of Metamorphic Rocks

So far our interpretations have followed the Uniformitarian Principle rather closely. Slate is considered to have originally been a sedimentary rock because of its stratification and fossils—features we can see developing on the sea floor. But in slate the fossils are rare and distorted; even the stratification is being obliterated by the growth of new minerals and by slippage along foliation planes. These changes clearly took place after the sediment was consolidated, and we have reason to assume they occurred deep within the earth. Furthermore, in some areas, slate passes by imperceptible gradation into more coarsely crystalline metamorphic rocks in which every trace of the original stratification and of fossils has disappeared. Although these rocks contain minerals different from those in slate, the new minerals grew from the micaceous minerals of the slate, gradually replacing and obliterating them just as the micas in slate replaced the minerals of the shale. We consequently conclude that even these rocks were derived from sedimentary rocks but that they are more thoroughly metamorphosed. Moreover, the common association of metamorphic rocks with plutonic rocks that surely congealed below the surface under conditions of high temperature and pressure leads us to infer that metamorphic rocks must have been formed deep below the surface.

How can we interpret rocks in which recrystallization has obliterated all the original sedimentary features, leaving just a puzzling mixture of new minerals from which to reconstruct the history of past events? It is impossible to observe processes taking place at the depths at which these rocks are formed, for even our deepest oil wells penetrate not quite four miles—a mere pin prick in the earth's skin. Do certain subtle features of the minerals of metamorphic rocks record the changes they have gone through? If so, how can we learn to read this record?

In part we gain insight into metamorphic processes by studying transitions. We noted that slates may grade into coarsely crystalline metamorphic rocks. We find that detailed mapping of the foliation in areas of metamorphic rocks commonly reveals fantastically complex patterns of streaks and contortions, indicating that the rock has flowed like putty. But how can it flow? The same rock is now brittle and hard; if put in a press it will fracture instead of flow. Then we remember the complicated flow patterns that develop in glaciers (Fig. 13-5). Ice, too, is a brittle substance; strike a piece of it with a hammer and it shatters into hundreds of fragments. Yet crevasses in glaciers extend little more than two hundred feet below the surface because below this depth they are closed by plastic flow induced by the weight of the overlying load of ice and snow. Will microscopic comparison of glacier ice and of silicate minerals from metamorphic rocks reveal textures in common? Does rock at great depth flow like a glacier, and is its foliation a record of such flow? Petrographic comparisons of rock and glacier ice are beyond the scope of this book but they give affirmative answers to this question; further details of the causes of rock flow will be given in Chapters 8 and 10. Yet many questions remain unanswered. For example, at what depths, and under what conditions of temperature and pressure do rocks behave as puttylike masses? How can we attack such a problem?

Experimental Study of Metamorphic Processes

One way to gain insight into these problems is to attempt to duplicate in the laboratory the conditions that might be expected at depths where metamorphism is believed to take place, and where magmas might form. Ingenious presses have been devised to squeeze minerals under confining pressures equivalent to a load of rock more than fifty miles thick. In other experiments rock is sealed in "bombs" and subjected to high temperatures and pressures in the presence of water vapor. Under such conditions many minerals become unstable and recrystallize, either by reacting with other minerals or by rearrangement of their crystal structure. In such presses man has even made artificial diamonds.

From these experiments we are slowly learning about the chemical reactions that occur during metamorphism. In such studies the physical chemist comes to the aid of the geologist. Minerals, however, are highly complex chemically, and so, despite epochal pioneering work in a few laboratories, knowledge of the chemistry of solids, and particularly of solid silicates while they are being deformed, still lags far behind what is known about reactions in solution. Only in the last few years has mica been successfully synthesized from clay minerals—the major reaction in the transformation of shale to slate. Much effort is now being directed toward determining the **stability ranges** of various minerals, that is, the ranges of temperature and pressure under which a given mineral will remain stable and not break down or react with other minerals to form some new substance. If we knew these constants for many minerals we might have a golden key that would enable us to translate the enigmatic crystal assemblages in a metamorphic rock into a readable account of the changing physical conditions that brought about the present crystalline state of the rock.

RECRYSTALLIZATION OF THE STASSFURT SALTS. Such physical-chemical investigations must be constantly guided and tested by field work on the rocks themselves. Without "checking the laboratory against nature," sterile leads may be followed and erroneous conclusions reached. The relative roles of the physical chemist and field geologist in checking one another's conclusions are well illustrated by one of the first such studies ever made—that of the origin of the salt beds at Stassfurt, Germany.

The salt deposits at Stassfurt are valuable not only because they contain sodium chloride, but also salts of magnesium and potassium. Since the salts are associated with sedimentary rocks it was believed that they were typical **evaporites**, the residue of a former body of sea water isolated from the open ocean by a reef or other obstruction, and slowly evaporated in the desert climate of Permian time, more than two hundred million years ago. Van't Hoff, a famous Dutch chemist who studied the salt deposits intensively from 1900 to 1905, accepted this theory, but was puzzled by one feature of the salts. Although their chemical composition is consistent with their being evaporites, the actual minerals of the deposit are not the same as those formed when sea water evaporates slowly. Patiently van't Hoff worked out in the laboratory the temperature stability ranges for many of the sodium, potassium, and magnesium chlorides and sulphates that occur in the deposits. He found that one association of minerals, a rock which the miners call *Hartsalz,* cannot be formed below 72°C (157°F), far above the temperature of the most tropic sea. One possible explanation was that perhaps in Permian time, when the salt beds were deposited, the climate might have been much warmer than now, and that the oceans of that time could have been near boiling. This was pure deduction, based only on van't Hoff's proof that *Hartsalz* crystallized above 72°C. Geologists could not accept this deduction because fossil shells of various kinds are found in sandstone and shale closely associated with the salt, and it was inconceivable that these animals had lived in a near-boiling sea. Clearly, re-examination of the geologic and chemical evidence was needed.

Arrhenius, a Swedish chemist, recognized that van't Hoff had not eliminated the possibility that mineral changes might have occurred in the salts because of a rise in temperature after burial. Investigation of the geologic setting of the salt deposits gave a more complete picture. It was found that after the salt was deposited by evaporation of a part of the ancient sea the newly formed evaporites were warped down and covered by thousands of feet of younger sedimentary strata. Measurements in deep wells show that the temperature in the outer crust of the earth increases, on the average, about 1°C for every 100 feet of depth; presumably it also did so in Permian time. The heating of the salt beds beneath the surface could therefore have caused the original salt minerals to recrystallize into *Hartsalz*. Confirming this, the textures of the salt beds, as seen under the petrographic microscope, show abundant evidence of postdepositional recrystallization. Van't Hoff's conclusion as to the temperature of mineral formation was correct, but the search for exceptionally high climatic temperatures was not needed. Perhaps the most interesting point of all is that clues to all these events are recorded in the composition and textures of the *Hartsalz* itself, but it took much geologic and physical-chemical detective work before they could be read correctly.

Thermal Metamorphism

Salt beds are particularly susceptible to temperature changes. Salts recrystallize completely at temperatures so low that the silicate rocks associated with them are not metamorphosed. Thus fossil shells are still found in the sandstones associated with the Stassfurt *Hartsalz*. But where a pure quartz sandstone containing marine shells has been heated to very high temperatures (as at the contact with a plutonic igneous rock) no shells can be found near the contact. Sheaves of the min-

eral wollastonite take their place. These field relations suggest, and laboratory experiments support the idea, that wollastonite has been formed according to the following reaction:

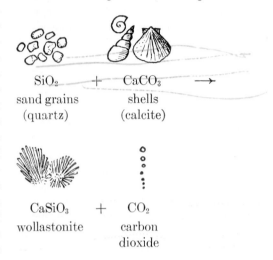

$$SiO_2 + CaCO_3 \longrightarrow$$
sand grains   shells
(quartz)   (calcite)

$$CaSiO_3 + CO_2$$
wollastonite   carbon
                dioxide

The new mineral resembles neither the quartz grains nor the shells that have combined to make it. Under laboratory conditions it requires temperatures of over 500°C to bring about the change. Most fossiliferous sandstones also contain many other substances besides quartz—usually a little clay, some limonite or ferromagnesian minerals, and various other impurities. If the rock is metamorphosed at high temperature these also join in the reaction, yielding not a simple mineral like wollastonite, but a more complex solid solution such as amphibole, garnet, or pyroxene.

The Significance of Metamorphic Rocks in Geologic History

Even these brief descriptions—and scores of additional examples could be given—show that many minerals are stable only within a limited range of pressure and temperature. If brought into a part of the earth's crust where the temperature is high, or where crushing and shearing are taking place, or where hot fluids permeate them, many minerals break down and form other minerals. Metamorphic rocks result from such transformations. Alteration may transform only part of the minerals of the original rock, yielding a metamorphic rock whose surviving unchanged minerals and textures still give clear evidence of its former origin, but commonly transformation is complete.

From relations revealed mainly by geologic maps but also in part from physical-chemical deductions, we know that nearly all metamorphism takes place deep within the crust of the earth—far below the depths we can reach in mines and wells. We can, therefore, make the following generalization about areas of the earth's surface where metamorphic rocks are widespread.

Where large areas of metamorphic rocks— particularly the foliated rocks called crystalline schists—are found at the surface, deep erosion has taken place. This conclusion applies equally well to plutonic rocks such as granite. Indeed granite and crystalline schists are common associates. The ways in which the rocks overlying plutonic and metamorphic rocks have been broken up and eroded away to expose these deep-seated rocks will be discussed in the next two chapters.

Classification of Metamorphic Rocks

Since any rock may be metamorphosed in one of several different ways, there are many different kinds of metamorphic rocks. For example, there are at least five different metamorphic rocks with the chemical composition of basalt and all are, in fact, derived from basalt, yet each differs from the others in texture, mineral composition, and general appearance. Because such a great variety of minerals appears in metamorphic rocks, they are best studied with the petrographic microscope, aided by the principles of physical chemistry and, of course, by thorough field observations. Nevertheless, the more common groups of metamorphic rocks can be roughly distinguished without the microscope, as indicated in Appendix III, Table III-3.

Metamorphic rocks, like sedimentary and igneous rocks, are classified on the basis of texture and composition. The principal textures useful for determinations made without the aid of the microscope are listed and described in Appendix III.

FACTS, CONCEPTS, TERMS

SEDIMENTARY ROCKS; IGNEOUS ROCKS; META-
    MORPHIC ROCKS
UNIFORMITARIAN PRINCIPLE
CEMENTATION OF SAND; BURIAL AND PRESERVAL
    OF FOSSILS
LAW OF SUPERPOSITION; LAW OF ORIGINAL HORI-
    ZONTALITY
TEXTURE OF ROCKS
VOLCANIC AND PLUTONIC ROCKS
    Magma
ORIGIN OF BASALT
    Importance of field studies
ORIGIN OF GRANITE

INTERPRETATION OF CONTACTS
    Fragments of one rock in another
    Penetration of one rock by another
    Alteration of one rock by another
RECRYSTALLIZATION OF ROCKS BY METAMOR-
    PHISM
ORIGIN OF FOLIATION
    Relation of foliation to relic sedimentary and
      igneous features
STABILITY RANGE OF MINERALS
CHECKING PHYSICAL-CHEMICAL DEDUCTIONS IN
    THE FIELD
CRYSTALLINE SCHISTS AS INDICATORS OF DEEP
    EROSION

QUESTIONS (Based in part on Appendix III)

1. The bedding in sand dunes is commonly curved, with some parts sloping more than 15° to the horizon. How do you reconcile this with the Law of Original Horizontality?

2. According to the Uniformitarian Principle, geologists agree that large areas of South Africa and India, which now have a tropical climate, must once have been covered with glaciers. What kind of observations do you think have been made that lead to this conclusion?

3. The controversy over the origin of basalt in which Desmarest and Werner participated took place before the invention of the petrographic microscope. How would microscopic studies (if available) have helped in a solution?

4. If you observed two intersecting sets of structures in a rock, how would you decide which is the older?

5. The surface temperatures of lavas are considered to be as high as or higher than those of most intrusive magmas. Yet there are many evidences of metamorphism along intrusive contacts and few beneath lava flows. Can you suggest a reason?

6. Some limestones, otherwise quite normal, contain scattered well-formed crystals of feldspar. What evidence would you seek to determine whether these are from falls of volcanic ash or were developed in place by mild metamorphism?

7. How do you distinguish limestone from sandstone? basalt from limestone? phyllite from shale?

8. In examining a contact between granite and an overlying rock, how could you tell whether the granite had intruded the overlying rock, or had been eroded to form it?

9. Discuss the origin and significance of porphyritic texture.

10. What holds the sand and other mineral fragments together in a sandstone? What holds the mineral grains together in a granite? What holds the fragments together in welded tuff?

SUGGESTED READINGS

Cloos, H. *Conversation with the Earth.* New York, Alfred A. Knopf, 1953.

Geikie, Sir Archibald. *The Founders of Geology.* Baltimore, Johns Hopkins Press, 1901.

Huxley, T. H. *On a Piece of Chalk,* in *Discussions Biological and Geological.* New York, D. Appleton, 1895.

Mather, K. F., and Mason, S. L. *Source Book in Geology.* New York, McGraw-Hill, 1939.

4 | WEATHERING AND SOILS

Weathering

WE PAINT our houses every few years because, if we neglect to, the old paint peels off, the wood becomes etched and splintered, and it ultimately splits and rots. We say it is "weathered" or "weather-beaten." If we examine the gravestones in an old cemetery, or even the facings of some fairly new buildings, we also see that stones, originally smooth and polished, have become discolored, pitted, and cracked by exposure to the weather. For example, the surfaces of white sandstone blocks facing the buildings at Stanford University turned yellow in five to ten years, and where exposed to frequent wettings from garden sprinklers, began to crumble in twenty or thirty years.

Natural rock outcrops show these effects even more strongly. Deep road cuts commonly show that underlying firm rock, which had to be blasted to make the road, grades upward through a transition zone of discolored and broken rock into loose soil near the top of the cut. Moreover, excavations nearly everywhere show that rock near the surface is less firm and more easily crumbled than rock at depths of twenty to a hundred feet. Many rocks that are black or steel gray in the walls of deep mines, wells, or quarries, are yellow or brown in outcrops. In some, the yellow color is a mere stain on or near cracks, but in most it is

more pervasive and is accompanied by drastic changes in mineral composition and firmness of the rock. From this, we infer that exposure to air and moisture, aided by plants and animals that live on or near the ground surface, has brought about the changes. We call the altered rock **weathered** and deduce that much soil has certainly been formed from the weathering and crumbling of underlying rocks.

Soil

Soil consists, at least in part, of material that has weathered in the place where it is now found and is mixed with organic matter near the surface. These two features distinguish **soil** from such unconsolidated materials as gravel in a river bed, sand in dunes, or mud on a tidal flat. All these deposits are like soil in being easily crumbled into individual grains, but unless a deposit contains some organic matter and shows some signs of having decayed in place it is not properly called soil.

Although soils vary widely from place to place they tend to be similar in areas with similar climates, despite differences in **parental, or source rocks,** and they differ in areas of different climate even though the source rock in each may be essentially identical. Climate is partly a measure of the amount of rainfall and evaporation and hence controls the kind and amount of vegetation and other

43

organisms. These, in turn, strongly influence the geological processes that operate to break the rock down into soil. The differences between the soil in one climatic province and that in another are often so great that an ancient buried soil can give rather clear indications of the climate that prevailed when it was being formed.

Analysis of Weathering

Studies of soils and their parental rocks show that weathering usually includes both **mechanical disintegration** and **chemical decomposition.** Disintegration involves chiefly loss of coherence; it is a mechanical breakdown with little change in composition. It does not include abrasion and removal of the constituents —such movements are part of erosion, the wearing away of the land surface. Decomposition, or chemical weathering, is the term for decay of rock that is accompanied by changes in chemical and mineralogical composition. The complex silicates that make up the greater part of most crystalline rocks change into other substances, particularly into hydrous silicates, hydrous oxides, and carbonates.

Mechanical Weathering

FROST ACTION   When water changes to solid ice, it expands 9 per cent. The freezing of water in soil or in the cracks and pores of rocks is thus an effective disruptive force. This process, called **frost wedging,** breaks up the surrounding soil and rock. The colder the climate the greater the depth to which the water freezes. But because its effect is greatest where repeated freezing and thawing occurs, frost wedging is more marked in cool, temperate climates than in extreme arctic climates.

In soils especially, because of their high water content and complex pore systems, freezing causes notable expansion; thawing leaves the soil open and spongy. To break rocks, freezing water must be confined. Because water in a crack freezes from the surface down, it may be completely confined in the deeper parts of crevices, and repeated freezing will shatter rocks extensively. Most high mountain peaks are so mantled by rubble formed by frost wedging that solid, unbroken rock is difficult to find. Areas covered by a rubble of shattered rock are widely distributed even within parts of the temperate zone where frost action is now weak or no longer active. They give evidence, confirmed in many other ways, that in the geologically recent past the climate of much of the earth was far cooler than it is now. (See Chapter 13.)

PLANTS AND ANIMALS AS AIDS TO WEATHERING.   Organisms help to break rock down into soil, both mechanically and chemically. Growing plant roots powerfully wedge both soil and rock, as is shown by broken and heaved slabs of concrete in old sidewalks bordered by trees. Even tiny lichens and mosses pry open cracks in rock and loosen the bonds between mineral grains. Vegetation also affects the formation of soil in other ways. Roots bind the soil and retard its washing away, thereby inhibiting erosion and leading to a thicker accumulation of soil. When plants die and rot, their roots leave tubules in the soil into which water penetrates and freezes.

Burrowing animals move and mix the soil effectively. Darwin estimated that English earthworms spread their casts over the ground to a depth of 0.1 to 0.2 inch per year, thus loosening and aerating the soil and subjecting much of it to the chemical action of the worms' digestive processes. This mixing is a major factor in producing uniform soils in humid regions. There are practically no earthworms in arid regions, but ants, termites, and rodents fill a similar niche in the natural economy.

OTHER AGENTS OF DISINTEGRATION. Frost action and wedging by plant roots are the most effective disintegrating agents, but many other processes operate also: expansion caused by the crystallization of soluble salts as water evaporates within soil and rock pores in desert regions; the sudden intense heat of forest fires; the shock and heat of lightning; even the impact of rocks rolling or falling from above. All processes that give further access to moisture and air promote the fragmentation of the rock and expose additional surfaces to the attack of chemical agents.

Indeed, chemical decomposition itself may be a major cause of disintegration. Feldspars swell as they weather into clay and as many other minerals decompose they form substances that occupy more volume. In a granite composed of feldspar, quartz, and mica, the swelling of the altering feldspar and mica may disintegrate the solid rock into a loose pile of granitic sand. Alternate swelling and shrinking of the clay as it is wet by rains and heated by the sun aids in the disruption.

It is possible that the drastic day-to-night changes of temperature that take place in deserts may cause enough expansion and contraction to weaken or even break some minerals and rocks. Specimens of granite, however, have been heated and cooled in electric ovens through the daily temperature ranges characteristic of deserts for many thousand times without showing appreciable disruption. Without doubt, the swelling of decomposing minerals—slow as is chemical decomposition in deserts—is even there more effective in breaking down the rocks than are the daily temperature changes.

Chemical Weathering

Mechanical processes disrupt rock, exposing new surfaces to the action of the weather. Oxygen, carbon dioxide, and moisture from the air can then react with the minerals of the newly exposed rock, slowly decomposing them into new minerals, which are generally hydrous (chemically combined with water). Microscopic and X-ray studies show various stages of this process, and from the chemical changes revealed by these studies, it is known that one of the principal agents of alteration is carbon dioxide (CO_2), which, when dissolved in water, forms carbonic acid (H_2CO_3).

All rain dissolves some carbon dioxide from the air as it falls. In coal-burning industrial communities, the amount may be considerable, as anyone who has been in London may deduce from the corrosion of marble and limestone on even fairly new buildings. Most of the carbon dioxide dissolved in soil moisture, however, comes from decaying organic matter in the soil. Soil bacteria have been shown to play a most important part in this process; indeed, they are essential to the making of all soils. Most plant tissues are carbohydrates (compounds of carbon, hydrogen, and oxygen). Microscopic molds and bacteria, in the absence of oxygen, change the leaves, fruit, and wood in the soil of swampy areas to the dark organic substances called humus. In the presence of oxygen, the organic substances are broken down further into carbon dioxide and water. Water in the soil thus contains carbon dioxide derived from several sources. The water and carbon dioxide combine to form carbonic acid, and this, in turn, supplies ions of hydrogen and bicarbonate. In chemical notation this is written:

(1)

$$H_2O + CO_2 \rightleftharpoons H_2CO_3 \rightleftharpoons H^+ + HCO_3^-$$

| water | carbon dioxide | carbonic acid | hydrogen ion | bicarbonate ion |

As an example of chemical weathering let us consider the role played by carbon dioxide and water in the weathering of the chemically simple rock, limestone.

WEATHERING OF LIMESTONE. Limestone is mostly calcite, but it generally contains a little clay and other impurities. Calcite dissolves very slightly in pure water, but a few calcium ions (Ca^{++}) and carbonate ions (CO_3^{--}) do enter the solution:

(2)

$$CaCO_3 \rightleftharpoons Ca^{++} + CO_3^{--}$$

| calcite | calcium ion | carbonate ion |

But if calcite dissolves in water that has already dissolved some carbon dioxide, the carbonate ions formed by solution of calcite will react with the hydrogen ions derived from the reaction shown in equation 1 to form more bicarbonate ions:

(3)
$$H^+ + CO_3^{--} \rightleftharpoons HCO_3^-$$

hydrogen   carbonate   bicarbonate
ion   ion   ion

The removal of the carbonate ion allows still more calcite to dissolve, and thus water which contains carbon dioxide is a more powerful solvent of calcite than pure water. The basic reason for this is that water which has dissolved carbon dioxide contains hydrogen ions, carbonate ions, and bicarbonate ions (equation 1), but only the carbonate ions can react with calcium ions to produce calcite. Consequently any process that moves equations 1 and 3 toward the right will at the same time remove carbonate ions from the right side of equation 2, allowing this reaction to proceed toward the right, so that more calcite goes into solution.

In solutions, the combination and dissociation of ions is constantly proceeding at rates governed by the abundance of the several ionic species present. If the rates of reaction gradually adjust until no change is taking place in the total amounts of the various components while the reactions are still going on, the system is said to have reached equilibrium. At equilibrium, in equation 2, as much calcite is being precipitated from the solution within a given time as is being dissolved back again into ions within the solution. The weight of both the calcite and of the solution remain constant, and the solution is said to be saturated with calcite. But if the ions on the right side of equation 2 are selectively removed so that fewer are available to form the product on the left side (calcite), the reaction will proceed so as to yield more of these ions (calcite will dissolve). When limestone dissolves, equilibrium would soon be attained if the solution were unable to move. But the slow downward percolation of water through the limestone carries away the calcium ions and bicarbonate ions and allows new unsaturated water continuously to attack the limestone. Calcite is dissolved, not only at the surface, but along every crack and fissure through which the solutions percolate. Where the underground circulation is vigorous (see Chapter 14), the limestone may be extensively honeycombed, and large subterranean caves may even be formed in the rock. The clay in the limestone does not dissolve; it is left on the surface as the underlying rock slowly dissolves. A few inches of clay soil may thus represent the residue of many feet of dissolved limestone.

The soil that accumulates on the surface of the limestone contains practically the same minerals that were in the original rock—only their proportions have been drastically altered. Weathering merely changes the texture and mineral proportions; it does not produce a radically new set of minerals. The clay and other impurities are not chemically altered. This is readily understood when we recall that they were deposited under atmospheric temperatures and pressures, and accumulated in sea water which was constantly exchanging carbon dioxide with the atmosphere. In other words, the impurities, as well as the calcite of the limestone, were not far from being at equilibrium with the conditions existing on the surface of the land and were thus chemical compounds that are nearly stable under these conditions. Many other sedimentary rocks are also composed of minerals that are relatively stable under atmospheric conditions. These weather to soils composed of practically the same minerals as compose the rock itself, with merely their mutual proportions altered. But the changes in nearly all igneous and metamorphic rocks are far more drastic; their component minerals were formed under conditions in which the temperature and pressure were very different from those on the earth's surface, and hence many of them are unstable when exposed to weathering, breaking down into new and different compounds. To illustrate this, we will consider the weathering of a granodiorite.

WEATHERING OF GRANODIORITE. The individual minerals of granodiorite weather very differently from calcite and from each other. In the chemical reactions below we list only the products, rather than the ionic reactions through which they were largely formed.

1. *Quartz:*

Persists almost unchanged, except for staining and some mechanical breakdown. It does dissolve, but with extreme slowness.

2. *Potassium Feldspar:*

$$2KAlSi_3O_8 + H_2CO_3 + nH_2O \longrightarrow K_2CO_3 +$$
potassium   carbonic   water   potassium
feldspar   acid   carbonate
                                              (readily
                                              soluble)

$$Al_2(OH)_2Si_4O_{10} \cdot nH_2O + 2SiO_2$$
clay mineral   soluble
                           hydrated
                           silica
                           or finely
                           divided
                           quartz

3. *Plagioclase:*

$$CaAl_2Si_2O_8 \cdot 2NaAlSi_3O_8 + 4H_2CO_3 + 2(nH_2O) \longrightarrow$$
anorthite   albite   carbonic   water
                         acid

$$Ca(HCO_3)_2 + 2NaHCO_3 + 2Al_2(OH)_2Si_4O_{10} \cdot nH_2O$$
calcium   sodium   clay mineral
bicar-   bicar-
bonate   bonate
(soluble)   (soluble)

4. *Biotite:*

$$2KMg_2Fe(OH)_2AlSi_3O_{10} + O + 10H_2CO_3 +$$
    biotite   oxy-   carbonic
                      gen   acid

$$nH_2O \longrightarrow 2KHCO_3 + 4Mg(HCO_3)_2 +$$
water   potassium   magnesium
           bicarbonate   bicarbonate
           (soluble)   (soluble)

$$Fe_2O_3 \cdot H_2O + Al_2(OH)_2Si_4O_{10} \cdot nH_2O +$$
"limonite"   clay mineral

$$2SiO_2 + 5H_2O$$
soluble   water
silica
or quartz

5. *Amphibole:*

Alteration like that of biotite, with similar products, but goes to completion more readily.

Many examples show that the complete weathering of granodiorite in a humid temperate climate leaves residual quartz and new formed aluminum-silicate clay, stained yellow with a mixture of hydrated ferric oxides ("limonite"), as illustrated by these equations. Sodium and calcium and much of the magnesium and potassium go off as ions in the water draining from the soil, although some magnesium and potassium ions may remain in the clay minerals, held there by feeble electrical forces. As potassium is an important plant food, its retention is agriculturally significant.

Despite the differences in parental rocks, soils derived from limestone and granodiorite are both rich in clay. The clays of the original limestone were merely concentrated in the soil by leaching away of the calcite, but the clay in the soil on granodiorite is newly formed in place. The clay minerals are among the stablest under surface conditions, both in the temperate and arctic zones.

Exfoliation

The splitting away of scale-like layers of rock from an exposed or soil-covered surface of massive rock (not a platy rock such as shale or schist) is called **exfoliation.** The separated sheets or plates may be flat or curved, paper-thin or many feet thick, a fraction of an inch or many hundreds of feet long. Two kinds of exfoliation may be distinguished—small thin flakes of decomposed material that spall from massive, partly weathered rocks, and giant plates of fresh or only slightly decomposed rock, usually granite or granodiorite.

Most rocks are cut by cracks or **joints** that divide them into smooth-sided blocks whose dimensions may vary from a fraction of an inch to many feet. Dolerite, graywacke, arkose, granite, and many other medium- or coarse-grained rocks commonly show many thin concentric layers of crumbly weathered

Figure 4-1.   *Exfoliation in granodiorite. Note that the spheroidal forms have developed by rounding off the corners of angular blocks (lower part of picture) bounded by intersecting fractures, or joints. The corners are rounded because the weathering agents here had access from two or more sides. (Photo by Eliot Blackwelder.)*

Figure 4-2.

Granite dome showing coarse exfoliation, Sierra Nevada. The sheet-like slabs of rock are tens of feet thick. (Photo by G. K. Gilbert, U. S. Geological Survey.)

material (Fig. 4-1) which have been formed by weathering that has proceeded inward from the surfaces exposed by joints. During weathering, hydrated clay minerals form from the original minerals, causing the material to expand. As the outermost layer weathers and expands it pulls away from the fresher rock beneath, and other shells form in succession inward, the swelling due to chemical weathering bringing about the mechanical exfoliation of each.

The huge curved plates of fresh rock (Fig. 4-2) that have split away during the formation of the domes of the Yosemite in California, Stone Mountain in Georgia, and Sugarloaf at Rio de Janeiro, show that one kind of exfoliation may take place without much decomposition. These domes are all of granitic rock that originally consolidated deep in the earth's crust beneath a thick cover of overlying rocks. Perhaps the release of pressure caused by removal of thousands of feet of cover by erosion has allowed the rock to swell upward, thereby causing the curved cracks parallel to the surface.

Residual Soil and the Soil Profile

Soil scientists have traced the various stages of the change from bedrock to humus-rich soil. The whole series visible at any one place is called the **soil profile** (Fig. 4-3). Most soil profiles are divisible into three main zones. In the Sierra Nevada, for example, canyon walls expose hard gray granodiorite, composed chiefly of plagioclase, with smaller amounts of quartz, potassium feldspar, biotite, and hornblende, but on the rolling forested uplands between the canyons, the granodiorite is buried beneath a soil that is made up of three layers. The surface layer—called the *A-horizon*—is a red-brown sandy loam (a mixture of quartz sand, silt, minute clay particles, and decomposed plant residues). In the fine-grained reddish matrix are embedded

Figure 4-3.   Soil profiles on Sierra Nevada granodiorite (left) *and Kentucky limestone* (right).

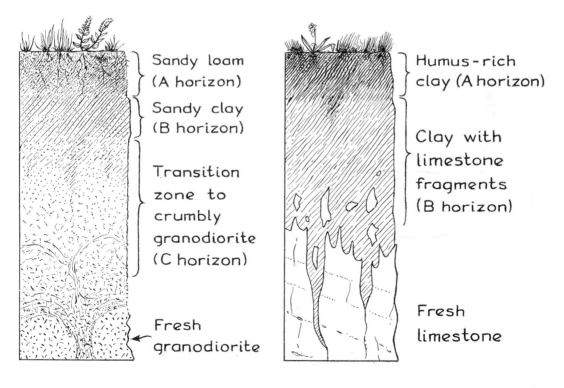

Sandy loam
(A horizon)

Sandy clay
(B horizon)

Transition
zone to
crumbly
granodiorite
(C horizon)

Fresh
granodiorite

Humus-rich
clay (A horizon)

Clay with
limestone
fragments
(B horizon)

Fresh
limestone

many irregular quartz grains, of the same size and shape as those in the granodiorite. At a depth of about a foot, the clay content increases. This sandy clay is the subsoil, or *B-horizon.* Apparently some of the clay formed by decomposition of feldspar near the surface has been washed downward from the A-horizon into the B-horizon. Two to four feet below the surface the soil becomes paler and sandier. The sand grains include not only quartz but abundant feldspar, some partly changed to clay but still readily recognizable by dulled cleavage faces, and some, a little deeper, by flashing cleavages nearly as bright as those of fresh granodiorite. Here also are many micaceous flakes—not jet black like the biotite of the granodiorite, but iron-stained pearly yellow scales sometimes mistaken for gold. Rusting and dissolving away of the iron has changed the color of the biotite from black to yellow. Still deeper, this loose material grades imperceptibly into harder, less-stained, but still crumbly material in which the texture and characteristic minerals of the granodiorite are identifiable. The transitional material between the zone of high clay content (B-horizon) and the bedrock is called the *C-horizon, or rock mantle* (Fig. 4-3, left). The conclusion is inescapable that the surface material has developed by weathering of the underlying granodiorite. Such a soil, still in place on its parent rock, is called **residual.**

Most soils show such characteristic profiles composed of two or more distinct layers, or soil horizons, that differ from place to place because of differing parental rocks, climates, and maturity (which depends on the length of time the soil-forming process has been operating on the material). The residual soil of the limestone region of Kentucky differs notably from that of the Sierra. The climate, though also temperate, is more humid and the underlying rock is mineralogically simpler. The A-horizon consists of black humus-rich clay, the B-horizon of light-gray clay containing fragments of limestone which passes downward into white limestone, with no intervening

C-horizon (Fig. 4-3, right). The clays are the residue left when the calcite in the limestone was dissolved. Although the parental rock in these particular examples clearly influences the profile, soil scientists have found that mature profiles are in general surprisingly similar in regions with similar climates, even though the soil has been derived from various kinds of rocks. If mature soil profiles can be recognized in ancient buried soils, they thus give strong clues to past climates.

Soils on Unconsolidated Transported Material

Many soils have developed, not on bedrock, but on unconsolidated material deposited by streams. Such materials have generally been at least partly weathered before deposition. After deposition, the loose material allows easy access to air and water, and so renewed weathering quickly forms typical A- and B-horizons when climatic conditions are favorable.

The soils of the Central Valley of California afford a typical example. The residual soil of the Sierra, largely derived from granodiorite, has been washed into streams and transported to the Valley. On leaving the mountains, some streams have spread debris from partly weathered rock over hundreds of square miles of the valley floor. In places, such sediments, including even coarse gravel, have been left undisturbed long enough to have rotted completely into brown soils with a characteristic profile. The brown, silty A-horizon, two or three feet thick, generally contains scattered quartz pebbles and groups of closely spaced angular quartz grains—probable remnants of decayed pebbles of granodiorite. The compact B-horizon, one or two feet thick, has been formed in part by minute clay grains washed down from the A-horizon. Such compact, clayey B-horizons, especially when cemented by iron oxide, calcium carbonate, or other bonding materials, are called **hardpan.** The term refers to any tough clay-rich deposit, it is not confined to soils developed on transported material, though it is commonest there. The C-horizon consists of relatively unaltered gravel or other parent transported material below the B-horizon.

Another soil developed on transported material may be wholly different. For example, a soil in eastern Massachusetts, derived from **rock flour** (very finely ground fresh rock), boulders, and clay transported by glaciers in the geologic past (see Chapter 13), has no B-horizon and an A-horizon consisting of only three or four inches of dark humus-rich material overlying unweathered rock flour and rock fragments. It should, however, be pointed out that this soil is doubtless much younger than the California soil; it has been forming only since the glaciers of the Ice Age melted away about twelve thousand years ago, whereas the California soil was beyond the reach of the glaciers and has been forming for a much longer time. In short, soils differ not only because of climate, original (parental) material, and the plant and animal life that has inhabited the soil, but also because of the length of time that the soil has been forming.

Colors of Soils

Most soil is colored either by minerals containing iron or by organic matter. The iron is combined with other elements and occurs in one of two chemical states: ferrous and ferric. A ferric ion may be formed from a ferrous ion by the loss of one electron, a process called oxidation (from the fact that a ferric ion can combine with more oxygen than a ferrous one). FeO is a ferrous, Fe_2O_3 a ferric, compound. When hydrous ferric oxide (limonite) is formed by chemical decomposition of a ferrous silicate such as biotite, the reaction is brought about by the addition of oxygen from the air. The finely divided limonite stains the soil yellow. If the soil is dried out repeatedly, as in a climate with a warm dry season, some of the limonite may lose its water and change to red hematite; the soil then becomes red.

Iron is reduced to the ferrous state as readily as it is oxidized. A pale-greenish or dark-gray soil generally indicates that the iron has been reduced by reactions with plant residues or other organic matter. Ordinarily this occurs where the pores of the soil are filled with water which excludes the air that would otherwise oxidize both iron and organic matter. Hence a black soil may indicate that swamp conditions existed at the time the soil was formed; the iron has been reduced and the soil is rich in humus. Although soils rich in organic matter are generally dark, forest soils of the temperate zone may contain so much plant acid formed by decomposing leaves that nearly all the iron is dissolved from the upper part of the soil, which becomes very light gray. The color of soils gives a clue to the conditions under which weathering took place and to the past abundance of organic matter, thus supplementing other characters of a soil profile in recording past climates.

Climatic Factors in Weathering

In moist temperate climates, as we have seen, the weathering of both limestone and granodiorite yields chiefly minute grains of one or more of the clay minerals. The main difference between the soils is the differing proportions of rock fragments and minerals residual from the parental rock that their B- and C-horizons contain. For this climate, a rough rule—with many exceptions—is that the more iron and the less silica a rock contains the more rapidly it weathers. Basalt and limestone weather readily, but granodiorite weathers more slowly, and quartzite is almost immune.

In Dry and Cold Climates

Disintegration, perhaps caused by slight chemical alteration, is apparently the chief weathering process in the driest deserts, such as those of southwest Africa. Because desert soils contain little organic matter and few bacteria, their moisture is less rich in dissolved carbon dioxide than that of humid soils. Hence there are few obvious chemical changes, but decomposition of the surface layer may cause enough expansion to break the slightly decomposed rock into a coarse, only partly weathered soil.

Chemical weathering of another sort, which yields soils rich in calcium carbonate and in clay minerals with a high silica content, operates in semiarid regions such as the western interior of the United States. Here crusts and irregular nodules of calcite precipitate in the pores of the B-horizon and in places cement this part of the soil profile into a nodular calcareous rock called **caliche.** The calcium carbonate accumulates because, during most of the year, the water in the soil evaporates within the small connected pores and there releases its dissolved carbonates, whereas in a humid region the soluble carbonate is continuously leached from the soil into permanent streams. Where, in arid regions, soil water rises almost to the surface, as along the shores of saline lakes and swamps in undrained desert basins, or where irrigation has been heavy and subsoil drainage poor, salts much more soluble than calcium carbonate may accumulate on and near the surface. This is the cause of the so-called "alkali-soils," many of which are covered with encrustations of sodium carbonate and sodium sulfate which are poisonous to most plant life. Such soils are useless for agriculture unless they can be drained and the soluble salts washed out of the surface layers.

Limestone affords a striking contrast between the effects of weathering in moist and semiarid regions. In a semiarid region like Arizona or Nevada it stands out as bold ridges, almost like those of quartzite, but in humid regions it dissolves to leave pockmarked valleys.

Disintegration is the most common form of weathering in polar latitudes and on the alpine heights of the temperate and torrid zones. In arctic regions frost action is the chief weathering agent. In subarctic regions such as Finland, however, chemical weathering of a special type, yielding very siliceous soils, appears dominant even over frost action, especially where the tundra supports fairly abundant vegetation. The acid formed from decomposing plant material leaches most of the calcium, iron, and magnesium from the soil.

In the Tropics

The soils of the rain forests of the Congo and Amazon Basins have not been adequately studied, but they appear to be similar to the aluminum-silicate clay soils of moist temperate regions.

LATERITE.   The wide belts of grass- and tree-covered savanna that lie north and south of the tropical rain forest are largely underlain by tough to thoroughly hard yellow and red-brown soils called **laterites** (from *later,* Latin for brick). The characteristic dark-brown upper layers of laterites dry to brick-like hardness and are sometimes used as building materials. Typical laterite areas are found in India, Nigeria, Brazil, the Caribbean region, and many other tropical areas.

Because laterites are so different from soils of the temperate climates, and because they illustrate one way in which a chemical element such as iron or aluminum may be concentrated into valuable ores, we will discuss them in some detail.

Laterites vary greatly in composition, but typically contain aluminum hydroxides and iron hydroxides and oxides, mixed with some residual quartz. A rare variety called **bauxite** is almost pure hydrous aluminum oxide ($Al_2O_3 \cdot nH_2O$) and hence valuable as an ore of aluminum. In laterites, practically all the silicon of the original silicates has been leached out by rain water, along with the easily soluble sodium and potassium and the acid-soluble calcium and magnesium. The leaching out of all these elements at the same time is hard to understand. Silica is only slightly soluble; it dissolves most rapidly in water containing many more hydroxyl (OH^-) ions than hydrogen ions—an alkaline solution. Calcium and magnesium, on the other hand, are not very soluble in alkaline solutions, but dissolve readily in solutions that contain more hydrogen than hydroxyl ions—acid solutions. Yet great quantities of all three of these elements have clearly been leached from the soils.

Most laterite regions have marked wet and dry seasons. It has been suggested that during the warm dry seasons organic acids are so completely oxidized to carbon dioxide, which escapes into the atmosphere as a gas, that the dry soil contains no acid-producing materials, but retains a little material that would produce an alkaline solution when dissolved. Hence, at the onset of the first rains, silica is carried off in the temporarily alkaline soil solution before the growth and decay of new vegetation again restores the supply of carbonic acid.

Moreover, it has been found that some of the complex aluminum and iron hydroxides found in laterite are not formed directly but first precipitate as other minerals that are easily soluble when first formed but quickly harden and become the highly insoluble minerals of laterite before the onset of the next wet season.

Residual laterite soils are characterized by a pale zone of leaching just above the parent rock, and a dark-brown concretionary zone at or near the surface (Fig. 4-4). Each zone is usually a few feet or a few tens of feet thick, but in places it may deepen to hundreds of feet. The concretionary zone is a concrete-like mass, composed chiefly of either dark-brown limonite or of many limonite nodules (concretions) the size of peas or marbles, more or less well cemented into a solid mass. The uppermost part of some lateritic soils contains enough unaltered quartz to make it crumbly or even sandy.

Leaching is so complete in many laterites

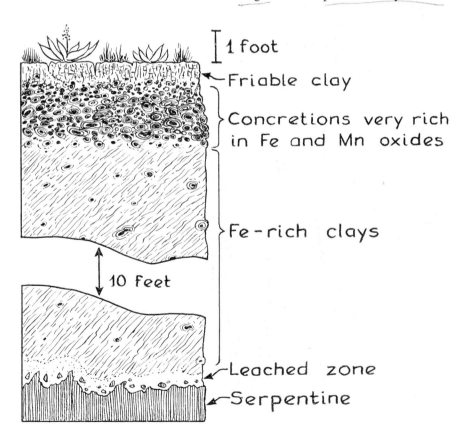

1 foot

Friable clay

Concretions very rich in Fe and Mn oxides

Fe-rich clays

10 Feet

Leached zone

Serpentine

Figure 4-4.

Profile of Cuban laterite. The concentration of iron in these soils is so great that they are mined as iron ore. (Data from H. H. Bennett and R. V. Allison, 1928.)

that some elements needed by plants are entirely removed, and others, such as phosphorus and iron, are precipitated as iron phosphates or other compounds so insoluble as to be practically unavailable to plants. Even though the lateritic soil of the Hawaiian Islands contains abundant iron, it is necessary to fertilize the pineapple plants grown there with soluble salts of iron and phosphorus.

What happens to the silica leached out during lateritization? No definite answer can yet be given because the subtropical distribution of even so abundant a substance as silica has been little studied. Extensive siliceous crusts have been reported from Angola, just south of the Congo Basin, and from other parts of tropical and subtropical Africa, but laterite is not definitely known to be forming near them. Possibly nodules of chert (a silica-rich rock) and silica concretions form beneath the lateritic soils. By comparing the silica content of certain rocks to the amount of silica in the streams that drain them, it has been shown that silica probably dissolves more

rapidly in tropical than in temperate climates. For example, the amount of silica carried by rivers in tropical British Guiana is about twice the world average for rivers draining the same kind of rocks in all climates.

Rates of Weathering

The rate of weathering varies greatly with different rocks and different climates. Surfaces of igneous rock polished by glaciers 10,000 years or more ago still glisten (Fig. 4-5) in the north temperate climate of New York; even the finely ground rock flour left by the same glaciers has little or no decomposed material in it. On the other hand, stream gravels of about the same age in Maryland have a fairly well-developed soil profile, and the upper layers (A-horizon) of soil that has developed on ash from the 1883 eruption of Krakatoa in Indonesia are as much as 5 per cent poorer in silica and 2 per cent richer in aluminum than the C-horizon. This suggests extremely rapid decomposition of the glassy pumice which was the parental

Figure 4-5.

Glacial polish on igneous rock, Adirondacks, New York. The polish is unscarred by 10,000 years of weathering. (Photo by Vincent Kelley.)

rock; a crystalline rock in the same setting would undoubtedly weather much more slowly.

Europe, southeast Asia, and Central America are dotted with ruins whose dates of building and abandonment are accurately known. A few of these have been studied by geologists and archeologists, and they give us scattered clues to the rates of weathering under different climates. Some of the data are conflicting, perhaps because of insufficient evidence about the rock involved. Most students consider that chemical weathering proceeds most rapidly in moist tropical climates. But the arched roofs of Angkor in Cambodia stand intact after seven centuries of neglect. Though the jungle crowds closely, and plants spring from every cranny, the sandstone and laterite of which the sculptured walls of the buildings were made show only slight signs of weathering. By contrast, a fairly well-defined soil profile has developed on the burial mounds left by the Huns in the Volga Valley eight centuries ago. But we should expect the stream deposits of the Volga to weather much more rapidly than laterite, which is itself a product of weathering.

Old gravestones also yield interesting data. In Edinburgh, within less than eighty years, the inscription on marble in memory of Joseph Black, the discoverer of carbon dioxide, was rendered illegible by the action of the gas he discovered and other acid-forming substances. There has also been marked disintegration of the marble by frost action because enlarging of the openings between the grains of the rock by solution allowed water to freeze within it. On the average, about a third of an inch of rock has been weathered away from faced limestone and marble in Edinburgh every hundred years. Slate, which is more immune to acid solutions, has been barely roughened in the same time. In small Scottish towns with less coal smoke, marble dissolves more slowly.

Weathering is slowest in a dry warm climate. Inscriptions carved between 3 B.C. and 79 A.D. above the doors of sepulchers in the crumbly sandstone cliffs of northeast Arabia can still be read. Forty centuries ago, not far from the present site of Assuan Dam in upper Egypt, a surface of red granite was smoothed and dated by an inscription. This surface, though exposed to the direct rays of the sun, is still firm. At various dates between 2850 and 313 B.C., colossal statues from this quarry were set up at Luxor and elsewhere in the somewhat moister climate of Middle and Lower Egypt, and blocks of the same rock were used to face pyramids near Cairo. Ancient structures built of this granite throughout Egypt were studied in 1916 by D. C. Barton, an American geologist. He estimated the average rate of exfoliation was about one or two millimeters per thousand years.

Two obelisks of the granite, each bearing many deep-cut hieroglyphics, and each now called Cleopatra's Needle, stood about 3,500 years in Egypt with only slight weathering. One, removed to London, has weathered appreciably but not disastrously. The other, brought to New York about 1880 and set up in Central Park, where it is exposed to frost, frequent wetting, and air rich in carbon dioxide and other acid-forming substances, disintegrated so extensively that by 1950 (despite the application of shellac-like preservatives in the 1920's and 1930's) part of the pictured story was completely erased (Fig. 4-6). Frost wedging alone had produced more weathering in seventy New York winters than all processes of weathering in fifty times seventy Egyptian winters.

Summary

Soil profiles develop through the rotting of rock. The minerals that form the crust of the earth are not immune to the attack of oxygen, moisture, and carbon dioxide from the atmosphere, nor to the disruptive forces of frost and other agents of disintegration. Hence most of the earth's surface is mantled by decayed rock of varying thickness.

Variations in soil profiles arise chiefly from differences in climate and in the original

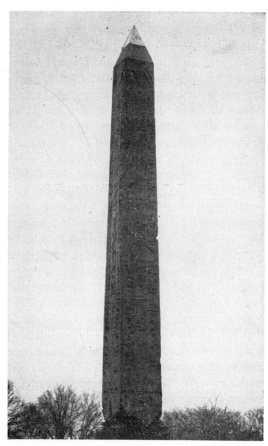

Figure 4-6.   *Cleopatra's Needle, in Egypt* (left) *and in Central Park, New York City* (right) (*Photos by courtesy of the Metropolitan Museum of Art.*)

source (parental) rocks, though there are many other modifying influences. In truly mature soils, differences due to differing source rocks become trivial compared to those due to climatic factors. Thus three great soil groups are the products of three differing climates:

  a. Soils of humid temperate regions, in which aluminum and iron are leached from the upper layers and silicon is concentrated there.

  b. Soils of the savanna tropics, in which iron and aluminum are concentrated and from which silicon as well as other elements are selectively removed.

  c. Soils of the arid and semiarid regions, in which the soluble salts are redistributed by water but mainly remain within the soil. This results in the formation of hardpan, alkali, caliche and other sub-surface accumulations of calcium, sodium and even of soluble potassium compounds.

  Source rock, whether bedrock or transported, governs the kind of material composing the soil while the soil profile is immature. After a long time, the soil shows less and less resemblance to the parental material. Ultimately, soils derived from such different rocks as sandstone, granite, and basalt may become almost identical, provided they have been formed under identical climatic conditions.

  Other factors that influence soil development include such things as topographic position (which influences drainage, growth of vegetation, humus accumulation, number of soil bacteria, and many other factors), the geologic environment (whether the soil is being slowly or rapidly eroded or buried, etc.) and time. The fact that it takes a long time for a soil to adjust to a change in climate allows us to use the characteristics of an existing soil as a clue to the prevailing climate during the time it was being formed. Such studies indicate that the prehistoric climates of many areas were much different from those of the present.

FACTS, CONCEPTS, TERMS

WEATHERING
  Residual soils
  Definition of soil
DISINTEGRATION, OR MECHANICAL WEATHERING
  Frost wedging
  Influence of plants and animals
  Decomposition
  Minor supplemental factors
DECOMPOSITION, OR CHEMICAL WEATHERING
  Main factors: oxygen, water, carbon dioxide
  Weathering of limestone
  Weathering of granodiorite
  Representative reactions during decomposition
    of rock minerals
EXFOLIATION
  Of decomposed material

Of nearly unaltered material
Influence of joints
THE SOIL PROFILE
  A, B, and C Horizons
  Variations with climate
  Soils on transported materials
  Hardpan
SOIL COLORS; OXIDATION; REDUCTION
SOILS
  Of moist temperate climates
  Of dry climates: caliche, alkali accumulations
  Of cold climates
  Of tropical climates
  Of savanna climates: laterite, bauxite, concretions

QUESTIONS

1. In much of Illinois, Iowa and nearby states, deep road cuts expose more than one soil profile, one above the other. The lowest is buried beneath material on which a second profile is developed, and this, in turn, is buried beneath material with still a third soil profile developed on it. In broad terms, what does this superposition of profiles indicate about the geologic past?

2. Western Nevada is semiarid, with dry summers; eastern Iowa is moist, with considerable summer rainfall. Assuming that the soils are derived from similar parental rocks, how should the characteristic soil profiles of the two areas differ, if at all?

3. Why does calcium accumulate in the A-horizon of some soils of Nevada, whereas it is practically absent from this horizon in soils developed on limestone in Kentucky?

4. Few of the soils of extreme West Texas are mature, whereas most of those of East Texas are mature. What hypotheses occur to you as possible explanations of this fact?

5. The Hagerstown Valley of Western Maryland is underlain by limestone; the Piedmont, to the east, by gneiss and schist. How would you expect the soils of the two areas to differ, if at all?

6. Name the chief minerals in granite, and tell what happens to each of them when granite weathers in a moist temperate climate.

7. Volcanic tuff containing abundant fragments of pumice is successfully used as a building stone in southern Arizona, but not in Alaska where similar volcanic rocks are widespread. Why?

8. In the great fire that destroyed much of

Chicago pillars of granite were greatly spalled and cracked, but pillars cut from limestone withstood the flames with much less damage. Can you suggest why?

SUGGESTED READINGS

Geikie, Archibald. *Rock Weathering as Illustrated in Edinburgh Churchyards,* Proceedings of the Royal Society of Edinburgh, Vol. 10 (1880), pp. 518-532.

Jenny, Hans. *Factors of Soil Formation.* New York, McGraw-Hill, 1941. [A thorough treatment of the formation of soils by weathering. Five principal factors are recognized: time, character of rock, topography, climate, and organisms.]

Keller, W. D. *The Principles of Chemical Weathering.* Columbia, Missouri, Lucas Brothers, 1955.

Reiche, Parry. *A Survey of Weathering Processes and Products,* Rev. Ed. Albuquerque, New Mexico. University of New Mexico Publications in Geology, 1950.

5 | EROSION

Weathering is a static process; clays, loams and other weathering products, if not removed, would eventually bury all rocks beneath a thick mantle of the products of their own decomposition. This does happen on flat ground in regions with a warm humid climate, where weathered rock may extend downward two hundred feet or more. Yet even here, rain water seeping through the soil constantly leaches away the soluble materials formed by weathering. On gentle slopes the insoluble clays and sands, too, are slowly removed by rainwash, rills, and streams. On many steep mountain slopes these erosional agents are so active that they have removed all the soil and are biting deeply into fresh rock. New rock surfaces laid bare by erosion are exposed to renewed weathering.

The loosening and carrying away of rock debris by moving agents operating at the earth's surface is called **erosion.** Erosion is a dynamic process; it requires transportation of the rock waste to a new location. Because the moving agents must eventually slow down or stop, the ultimate fate of all eroded material is **deposition.** Indeed, weathering, erosion, and deposition are the three main factors in an endless cycle of rock change: weathering prepares the rock for transport by decomposing and disintegrating it; erosional agencies transport the material to a different locality

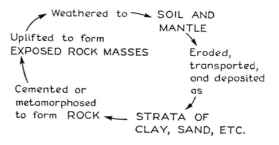

Figure 5-1.   The cycle of rock change.

(for example, the ocean), and there deposit it in strata which then may be cemented into rock. This rock may then be raised above sea level (see Chapter 8), exposed to the air and the rains, and again weathered and eroded to start a new cycle. The interrelations within this cycle, and its products, are schematically diagrammed in Figure 5-1. Analysis of these processes is the chief theme of Chapters 11 through 16, but we here give some brief examples as an introduction to other geologic processes.

Agents of Erosion

Anything that moves can carry rock waste. But although many different agents—as varied as earthworms, lightning, and avalanches—assist in the erosional process, nearly all transportation of rock waste on the lands is accomplished by five main agents: (1) Gravity —acting directly on solid or semiliquid masses of mud, soil, and rock; (2) wind; (3) glaciers; (4) ocean waves and currents; (5) streams.

To evaluate the effectiveness of these different agents in eroding the land requires analysis of many factors. Because of the size of the earth, the complexity of the erosional process, and the difficulty of measuring accurately the amount of debris in transit at any one time, it is not easy to determine either the rate at which erosion is lowering the land masses (the **rate of denudation**), or the amount of debris transported by any one agent of erosion. Yet despite the incomplete data we can make fairly reliable estimates of the relative importance of the different agents, and arrive at a rough but useful approximation of the rate of denudation of the lands.

Energy for Erosion

Most erosional processes are driven by gravity. Soil, rock, water, ice, and air—all are drawn by gravitational attraction toward the center of the earth's mass, and each particle tends to slide or flow to low areas on the earth's surface—as close to the earth's center as its nature and the earth's configuration permits. Because of gravitational attraction, loosened rocks fall or slide down steep slopes, streams flow downhill, and glaciers shear or flow outward. Winds result from the flow of dense air masses beneath masses of thinner air. Ocean currents, too, (as distinguished from the shallow roiling of the water by wind-generated waves) are caused by the flowing of huge bodies of water attempting to restore gravitational equilibrium between water masses of different density. Except for such trivial effects as those produced by the activity of plants and animals, the shattering of rock by lightning, and its spalling by forest fires, all erosion, in the last analysis, results from gravitational attraction.

But gravity is only the immediate driving force. Wind and water, the major erosive agents, depend upon solar radiation for their effectiveness. Radiation from the sun warms the air and ocean—more in tropical areas than in polar areas—thus causing different masses of air or water to differ in density. Because the gravitational attraction on dense air or water is greater than on an equal volume of air or water that is less dense, the denser masses flow beneath the lighter ones, generating the winds and water currents which then redistribute the heat. This heat transport from tropics to polar areas exactly compensates for the differences in heating; if it did not the equatorial zones would become steadily hotter and the polar areas colder. Measurements show that most of the heat is redistributed by the winds, but about 10 per cent is by ocean currents. More than heat is carried: dust storms could not arise from the land, nor could storm waves undermine the coast if there were no winds. Furthermore, this circulation of air and water has another important effect upon erosional processes: water evaporated from the oceans is carried to and precipitated upon the continents. Streams and glaciers could not form if the atmosphere did not transport water vapor. In a windless world the land would quickly parch to barren deserts of dust and rock. In a world without either wind or water no erosion other than that caused by the falling of rock downhill under the direct action of gravity would be possible—and we would not be here to see it. Instead of the stream-etched continents and sediment-filled seas that we see about us, the earth would probably have a pock-marked landscape like that of the moon, whose great craters stand stark and bare because there is no air or water to erode the high spots and fill the low areas with sediments.

Erosion on Land

Gravity

Gravity plays a dual role in erosion. We have already noted its indirect effects in keeping the air and water that envelops the earth in a constant state of motion. Climbers threading their way along the edge of a glacier are often forcefully reminded of its more direct action when a boulder loosened by frost wedging comes bounding down the mountainside and lands with a crash among a pile of similar fragments that have already tumbled from the cliffs and lie scattered over the margin of the glacier (Fig. 5-2). Larger rock falls or avalanches of cascading snow have dammed rivers and buried towns. Less spectacular examples of **downslope movements** (as the direct transportation of rock, soil, and mud by gravity is called) are all about us: Banks undermined by rivers or waves cave in; mud and wet soil slide downslope or are pushed downhill by the hooves of grazing animals; piles of sediment on the sea floor or at the edge of a steep delta give way and glide or squirt out in tongues under the water; avalanches roar down steep gulches, carrying trees, soil and all else before them; on almost every sloping surface loose material creeps

Figure 5-2.   *Gravity movements at the head of a glacier. Sunset Amphitheater, Mount Rainier, Washington. Length of view: one mile. Note the following features: (1) The arcuate crevasses (bergschrund) formed where the glacier pulls away from the steep snowfield and rock at the headwall; (2) The dark colored streaks and fans of broken ice and rock piled up by avalanches and rock falls tumbling from the cliffs. Much of this cascading rock and ice has been channeled down steep ravines (avalanche chutes) on the cliff face. (3) The precariously balanced blocks of ice at the edge of the 200-foot high ice cliff (in shadow) that caps the rock wall on the right edge of the photo. Fans composed of broken ice and rock that has tumbled from this ice cliff and the rock wall below it spill down across the bergschrund. (Photo by Miller Cowling, 116th Photo Section, Washington National Guard).*

gradually downslope, bit by bit, inch by inch, year after year.

If they acted independently, downslope movements would be relatively ineffective, as we have already noted. The configuration of the earth is such that gravity, acting directly, can roll or slide solid or semiliquid masses of rock and soil only to the bottom of a cliff or slope—there they must stop. But here other means of transportation take over. Loose rocks crash down upon the surface of a glacier, and the glacier carries them away; banks of streams cave in during floods, and the swirling waters swish the debris down to the sea; soil creeps slowly down a slope, and is whisked away by a brook at its base. Thus the chief role of downslope movements is to supply a continuous increment of rock waste to the agents of long-distance transportation.

Wind

Wind transports rock fragments—dust, sand, and silt—as any prairie housewife can testify. Among the best examples of its efficacy are the many dust storms that blew out of the so-called Dust Bowl of the southwestern Great Plains during the drought of the early 1930's.

When the Great Plains were settled, the natural grass sod was plowed under and the light soils were planted to corn and wheat. Even before settlement, parts of this area had undergone considerable wind erosion. The farmers who raced madly into the Cherokee Strip of what is now Oklahoma to stake out homesteads were greeted by blinding dust storms. As more and more land was put under the plow, these "black dusters" (Fig. 5-3) became larger and more frequent. In the early 1930's, a succession of dry seasons led to the terrible drought years of 1933 and 1934. Pulverized by tillage and parched by drought, the soil had lost not only its original protective grass cover, but much of its cohesiveness. The stage was set for one of the most spectacular and destructive events of modern agriculture.

On May 12, 1934, strong winds lifted a vast quantity of dust from the fields of Kansas, Oklahoma, Texas, Colorado, and other Plains States and drove it swiftly eastward in a

Figure 5-3.   A "black duster" rolling into Spearman, Texas on April 14, 1935. (Photo by F. W. Brandt, courtesy Sedimentation Laboratory, California Institute of Technology.)

gigantic dust storm. Sweeping out of the plains as a blinding, choking mass of particles so dense as to blacken the sky and change day into darkness, the seething dust cloud rolled rapidly across the well-watered lands east of the Mississippi. Here, where little loose soil could be gleaned from the forest and grass-covered landscape some of the dust settled to the ground, but the clouds retained enough dust to blot out the sun as they swirled around the skyscrapers of New York City and out over the Atlantic. Dense, dirty-brown clouds of dust engulfed ships more than five hundred miles from shore.

Measurements of the amount of dust in the air, reported by observers in widely scattered points over central and eastern North America indicate that more than 100 tons of dust per square mile fell in the areas covered by the dust cloud. Since the dust storm covered approximately two-thirds of the North American continent and much of the western Atlantic, it appears that more than 300 million tons of soil—enough to fill six million railroad cars—were removed from the Great Plains during this storm and strewn over the lands and sea to the east.

Wind winnows thoroughly the material it transports. Only the finest particles are swirled high in the air and carried far. Most of the material moved is not dust, but consists of grains of silt and sand that roll or skip along the surface of the ground. Studies by soil conservationists indicate that in the Great Plains about three-quarters of the soil moved by the wind does not rise into the air as a dust storm but drifts along the surface for a few yards, or at most a few miles, and then accumulates in ditches, around clumps of vegetation, and against fences, buildings, or other obstructions. For every ton of air-borne dust there are generally two or three tons of coarser debris piled in drifts of silt or dunes of sand near the source.

Although the great dust storms of the 1930's were intensified by changes in the soil cover brought about by man, wind erosion is constantly at work on all land surfaces, and is particularly potent in deserts. In the western Sahara the "Harmattan," a local name for the trade winds, sweep across the desert from north to south for about six months of each year. In exceptionally stormy years they are reported to deposit as much as a foot of silt, dust, and sand along the edge of the desert in northern Nigeria. One has only to watch this sand blowing off the surfaces of the large dunes to get a vivid picture of the effectiveness of wind as an agent of erosion.

Glaciers

Wind and water are mobile fluids that flow readily on application of even the slightest force. But solids can also flow under certain conditions of pressure and temperature. Glaciers supply excellent examples of how gravity can cause even a solid material to flow. As an ice mass slowly creeps and slides downhill under its own weight, it drags with it the soil and rock beneath. Thus glaciers transport great quantities of rock waste; indeed, they are among the most powerful agents of erosion.

The Nisqually Glacier (Fig. 5-4), easily reached by highway in Rainer National Park, has probably been visited by more people than any other in North America. The Nisqually is a pygmy among glaciers; less than five miles long and less than a thousand feet thick, it does not compare with the much larger Emmons and Winthrop glaciers in the more remote northeastern section of Rainier National Park—not to mention the sixty-mile-long ice streams of Alaska or the vast moving ice sheets that blanket Greenland and Antarctica.

Although it is a dwarf among its fellows, no visitor can examine the front of the Nisqually Glacier without being impressed by the tremendous erosive power of slow-moving ice masses. Near the glacier front very little ice is visible, most of it being obscured by blocks of rock that ride on the moving ice mass or are pushed forward in front of it. Many of these are huge fragments of a distinctive porphyritic andesite which crops out in ledges

Debris-covered ice

Meltwater

Figure 5-4. *Nisqually Glacier, Rainier National Park. The lobe in the central part of the picture is so heavily covered with rock debris that little ice is visible. Note the large streams of meltwater cascading from the base of this lobe; also the highly crevassed surface of the lobe at the left. (Courtesy Ross Bender, National Park Service.)*

far up the valley: the blocks were torn from these parent ledges and carried down the valley by the glacier. Smaller particles of rock and soil are mixed with the larger boulders. As the ice melts, this rock debris accumulates in hummocky piles in front of the glacier. Loose rock also accumulates on top of the glacier, especially at its edges, where boulders loosened by frost have rolled down from the cliffs above (Fig. 5-2). Snowslides and streams of meltwater also deposit debris on the glacier's surface.

Until 1956 the Nisqually Glacier had been slowly shrinking—more recently precipitation seems to have been enough to maintain its front at nearly the same place. Downstream, below the front of the glacier, lie irregular piles of debris left by the ice as it melted. The rock floor bared by the melting ice has been scored and polished by blocks of rock and finer material dragged across it by the moving glacier.

The meltwater that pours from tunnels at the base of the Nisqually Glacier (Fig. 5-4) is a dirty milky white. If we dip a glass of it from the stream, allow the sediment to settle, and examine it with a magnifying glass, we see that its cloudiness is not caused by suspended particles of clay, but by rock flour, obviously pulverized by the grinding of rock particles against one another and against the bedrock as they were rolled beneath the tremendous weight of the moving glacier and dragged forward by it—a striking example of the powerful erosive action of glaciers.

Ocean Waves and Nearshore Currents

At the shore the ocean vigorously attacks the land. Each oncoming breaker crashes against the beach, and as the wave recedes the water surges back toward the sea. Anyone who has watched the ceaseless play of the waves along an open coast (Fig. 5-5) need not be told that here is a powerful agent capable of picking up and transporting sand, gravel, and other rock waste. Houses, breakwaters, and seaside roads may be destroyed overnight by the onslaught of waves during a severe storm. Ships are driven against rocks and broken into matchwood, and boulders are rolled about like ninepins in the swirling water near the shore.

The effects of a major storm on an exposed open coast seem almost unbelievable. At Wick, in northern Scotland, a great storm in 1872 tore a concrete monolith (45 feet long, 26 feet wide, 11 feet thick, and bound by 3½ inch iron rods to the breakwater foundation) from its place, together with a huge piece of the foundation material, and dropped it unbroken inside the harbor. The total mass removed weighed 1,350 tons. The monolith was replaced by one weighing 2,600 tons, but five years later this, too, was torn away by the waves. At Tillamook Rock, on the Oregon coast, waves have repeatedly richocheted stones off a curving rock platform and broken plate-glass windows in the lighthouse, 130 feet above the sea. One fragment, weighing 135 pounds, crashed through a roof more than 100 feet above sea level. At Dunnet Head, in northern Scotland, lighthouse windows 300 feet above the water are occasionally broken by storm-driven stones.

The shore of the open ocean is clearly a zone of vigorous erosion. Storm-driven debris acts as a gigantic horizontal saw that bites ceaselessly into the land. Most ocean coasts are cliffed because the waves rapidly undermine the shore. Valuable beach property must be protected from erosion—or in some places from unwanted deposits of new sand or gravel —by breakwaters.

Detritus torn from the shore during a storm may be carried into deep water and deposited there, or nearshore currents may drift it along the coast and finally drop it to form spits and sandbars in protected areas. Sites of erosion and deposition shift with different storms, depending upon the direction of the wind, the velocity of the nearshore currents, and other factors. Sand that drifts along the

Figure 5-5.

Wave breaking on a rocky headland of the Oregon coast. (Photo by A. C. Waters.)

coast during one storm may completely block the mouth of a river; the next storm, driving in with more direct frontal attack, may sweep this accumulation far out to sea. Shallow currents also carry shore materials into deep water, where they settle to the bottom or are transported to even greater depths by currents of heavy sediment-laden water gliding down steep slopes on the sea floor.

Streams

RELATIVE IMPORTANCE OF DIFFERENT AGENTS.   Although wind, glaciers, and ocean waves perform spectacular feats of erosion, their total effect in eroding the land masses is minor. Streams, and slope processes including rill wash and downslope movements, are the great levelers. Flooding rivers cause dramatic examples of erosion, as when the Milk River of Montana undermined a railroad bridge, from which a great Mallet engine tumbled into the swirling flood and was rolled a half mile downstream. But the quantitative importance of streams is because rain falls on all parts of the land and carries rock waste from it. Even the driest deserts and the glacier-clad slopes of Antarctica bear imprints left by running water.

In the years since the middle 1930's, rainwash has almost completely obliterated the eroded hollows and the drifts of silt and sand made during the dust storm of May 12, 1934. Only in the driest of deserts are features due to wind erosion conspicuous, and even there the presence of numerous gullied slopes, dry stream beds, and sheets of water-deposited detritus shows that the rare rainstorms have left their stamp upon the desert landscape.

At present, glaciers are quantitatively unimportant. They are confined to high mountain ranges and to polar regions, and cover only 10 per cent of the land surface. Although they strongly abrade the areas they cover, their effect in wearing away the land as a whole is insignificant compared to the work of streams.

Ocean waves, too, are limited in scope and effect. The attack of the sea upon the land is confined to the shoreline and to the shallowly submerged margins of the land. On exposed open coasts, waves play a dominant role, but at many places where the coast is protected, or where storms are infrequent, stream deltas advance into the sea more rapidly than the waves can carry the stream-borne detritus away.

Analysis of Stream Erosion

As an indication of the role of streams in wearing away the lands let us look more closely into the source and amount of stream runoff, and into the amounts of debris actually carried by different streams. So great is the importance of streams as agents of erosion that this entire section of the chapter is concerned with these problems.

SOURCE OF THE RUNOFF.   "What is the source of the water in rivers?" This question could be answered reliably only in comparatively modern times. Aristotle and other early philosophers held that rainfall was entirely inadequate to account for the vast flow of water in rivers like the Danube and Nile, and that the earth's surface was too impervious to allow the percolation of rain water into the soil and rocks from which it could be returned as springs. Up to the middle of the seventeenth century, the general belief was that the amount of water rising in springs and flowing to the ocean in streams was so great that it could not possibly come entirely from rain and snow.

The modern concept of **hydrology** (the science that treats of water) began with the work of a Frenchman, Pierre Perrault (1608-1680). Perrault measured both the rainfall and the amount of water flowing in the Seine, during a three-year period. From the available maps, he then estimated the drainage area above the point where he had measured the flow of the river. His results showed that the Seine carried off only one-sixth of the water that fell within its basin as rain and snow. A few years later Edmund Halley, an English astronomer, showed by experiment that the moisture evaporated from the oceans entirely suffices to supply the runoff from streams. These measurements proved the fallacy of the old assumption that streams carry more water to the sea than falls on their drainage basins. Indeed, the problem of the streams was reversed—the question was no longer, "What is the source of the water?" but, "What has become of the vast volume of water, equivalent to five times the flow of the Seine, that has fallen in its drainage basin but is not being carried out by stream flow?"

THE HYDROLOGIC CYCLE. Various things happen to the moisture precipitated on the land as rain and snow (Fig. 5-6): (*a*) Some evaporates at once from the surface of the ground and from the vegetation on which it falls. (*b*) Some is absorbed by the roots of growing plants and is quickly transpired back into the atmosphere through their leaves, although a little enters the plant tissues and is trapped there until the plant dies and rots. (*c*) Some seeps into the soil and rocks where it may be temporarily stored as **ground water.** Ground water fills pores, cracks, and larger openings in the soil and rocks, and thus acts as a storehouse and equalizer for the flow of streams. From the ground some water returns to the surface by capillary action and evaporates, some is delivered to the roots of growing plants, and much reappears on the surface at lower elevations, gushing forth in springs or seeping into streams along their banks and bottoms. Finally (*d*) some of the water from rain and snow runs off in surface rills, brooks, and rivers.

Runoff is defined as the total discharge of water by surface streams. It includes not only the precipitation that flows across the surface immediately after rains, but also increments from the ground-water storehouse which swell the streams from springs and seepages. It is the runoff that erodes the lands.

The part of the precipitation that returns to the air by evaporation and transpiration is called the **evapo-transpiration factor.** Hydrologists generally simplify the hydrologic cycle by assuming that evapo-transpiration can be determined by subtracting runoff from precipitation. Actually addition or subtraction from the ground-water reservoir may render this assumption quite unreal for a short period, though it seems to balance out in the long run. The equation

Precipitation = Runoff + Evapo-transpiration

is only approximately correct, however, even when ground-water storage remains constant. It neglects many locally important (though generally unmeasurable) factors, such as the seepage of water through the soils and rocks directly into the ocean. For the land masses as a whole such seepage is not great, but in areas of highly permeable rocks such as the lava and cinders of the Hawaiian Islands, or the cavernous dolomites of Yugoslavia, it may dispose of most of the rainfall. Other minor factors are the amounts of water stored in the tissues of plants and animals, and the amounts that combine chemically with minerals when they are being weathered.

The hydrologic cycle is depicted graphically in Figure 5-6. The sun is the source of the energy that operates this great system of waterworks. Solar energy warms the ocean and the land, and evaporates water from their surfaces. It also stimulates the growth of plants which transpire water vapor into the atmosphere through their pores. Winds waft the water vapor inland and raise it to high altitudes, thus cooling and condensing it into rain. On falling to the surface, some of the rain water gathers into streams that sweep soil and rock debris to the sea.

FACTORS AFFECTING RUNOFF. The ratio of runoff to precipitation is not everywhere the 1 to 6 that Perrault calculated for the basin of the Seine. Measurements made by the Water Resources Division of the U. S. Geological Survey in many different drainage basins of the United States reveal wide variation in the ratio of runoff to precipitation. Among the factors that affect this ratio are the following:

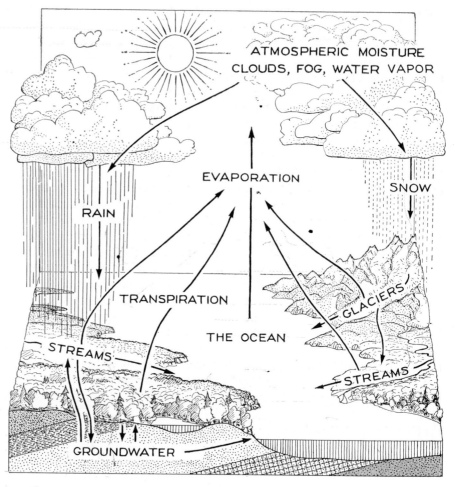

Figure 5-6.

The hydrologic cycle.

Amount and Duration of Rainfall.—The distribution of rainfall through the year greatly influences the runoff. Rain that is uniformly distributed in many small showers may be largely evaporated or absorbed by the ground before it reaches flowing streams, but during violent and heavy rainstorms, infiltration is too slow to capture a significant proportion of the water and evaporation is negligible. Rapid melting of the winter snowpack is a common cause of river flooding.

If the annual rainfall is high (80 inches or more), the ground generally becomes waterlogged and most of the rain runs off, even though it is uniformly distributed. In deserts, on the other hand, the scanty rainfall is quickly absorbed by the parched soil, or evaporated, and there is little runoff except after violent storms.

Permeability of the Ground.—Soils and rocks differ greatly in **permeability** (ability to transmit water). Most rain that falls on the porous ash of a young cinder cone sinks directly into the ground and becomes part of the ground-water storage, but nearly all that falls on a similar slope of shale runs off because the pore spaces in shale are so minute that the rock is almost impermeable, even though the shale, when saturated, can hold about as much water as the ash.

The ability of a soil to absorb rain or snow-melt depends on other physical conditions besides permeability. Water-logged soil, even though highly permeable, can hold no more water; neither can frozen ground. A highly permeable soil, once saturated, may also allow little more to sink in because the subsoil or bedrock a few feet below is impermeable. Permeability, then, does not alone control infiltration. Hydrologists use the term **infiltration capacity** to define the maximum rate at which soil, in a given physical condition, can absorb falling rain. Artificial tests of infiltration capacity, made by playing sprinklers on enclosed plots of soil from which the runoff is caught and measured, show, as would be expected, that the rate of absorption is high at the beginning of a rain, then diminishes rapidly—usually within half an hour—until a fairly constant rate is reached.

Vegetation.—Vegetation retards the runoff. Tangled stalks of grass or the mulch of decaying leaves and twigs in a forest absorb rain like a blotter. Earthworms and other burrowing animals that live in the plant-rich soil aid percolation by opening tunnels to the surface. Heavy coniferous forests may hold much snow on the branches of their trees, increasing the amount of moisture that evaporates back into the air.

Very striking increases in runoff have been observed in places where the forests were burned off, or where the natural sod has been plowed under, as in our Dust Bowl. Figure 5-8 summarizes some of the data for areas with differing vegetative cover.

Temperature.—Temperature profoundly affects the amount of runoff. Evaporation and transpiration are much greater in warm regions than in cold. Hence for a given amount of rainfall, the higher the temperature, the smaller the runoff. The data relating temperature to runoff in the United States have been summarized by Walter B. Langbein, a hydrologist of the U. S. Geological Survey, in Figure 5-7. The graph shows that, for an average annual precipitation of 40 inches, more than half (21.5 inches) runs off where the mean annual temperature is 40°F; but only 10.2 inches where the mean annual temperature is 60°F, and less than 3 inches where it is 80°F.

Slope.—Slope obviously influences runoff

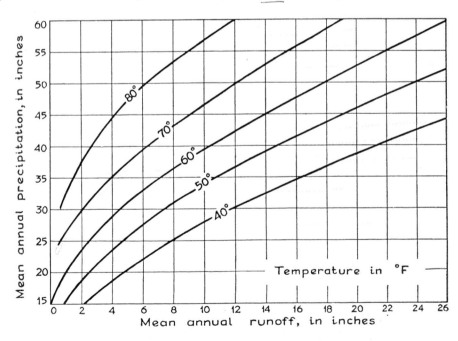

Figure 5-7.

The variation of runoff with rainfall and temperature. (*After W. B. Langbein, Annual Runoff in the United States, 1949.*)

strongly. Steep mountain slopes of barren rock shed nearly all their rain, but on flat ground, shallow puddles form and hold much of the rain water until it evaporates or is absorbed by soil and plants.

These variable factors result in marked differences in runoff in different stream basins. In the western United States, for example, runoff in different sections varies tremendously with differences in amount of rainfall, temperature, infiltration capacity, and other local conditions. The range is from less than 0.25 inch of runoff (about 6 per cent of the total rainfall) in the desert of southwestern Arizona to more than 80 inches (about 75 per cent of the total) on the western slopes of the Olympic and Cascade mountains in Washington.

AMOUNT OF WATER AVAILABLE FOR EROSION. The average annual rainfall of the United States, determined from thousands of rain-gaging stations, is 30 inches. The average runoff for the country as a whole is 8.6 inches. This gives a ratio of runoff to precipitation of approximately 1 to 3.5, as compared with the ratio of 1 to 6 determined by Perrault for the basin of the upper Seine. The

rivers of the United States, as determined by stream gaging, deliver water to the oceans at the rate of 1,800,000 cubic feet per second (about 330 cubic miles per year). Roughly one-third of this amount is carried by the Mississippi River.

Data for precipitation and runoff on other continents are less complete than for the United States. L'vovich, a Russian hydrologist, has made the most complete world-wide study of this. His results are summarized in Table 5-1: The world average runoff, as shown there, is 10.5 inches per year; other hydrologists give somewhat lower figures (around 7.5 to 9 inches).

Despite these uncertainties, we can make a fairly reliable estimate of the total amount of water available for erosion: The average annual precipitation over the land areas of the earth is about 40 inches per year. This means that each year approximately 35,000 cubic miles of water falls on the land as rain and snow. According to different estimates, the rivers return to the ocean from 7.5 to 10.5 inches per year. Using an average figure, this means that in round numbers *approximately 8,000 cubic miles of water courses off the lands and into the seas each year. This is the amount available for the erosion of the land.*

CONTINENT (or other Area)	AREA (Thousands of Square Miles)	RUNOFF (Inches)
Europe (including Iceland)	3,734	10.3
Asia (including Japanese and Philippine Islands)	16,321	6.7
Africa (including Madagascar)	11,510	8.0
Australia (including Tasmania and New Zealand)	3,075	3.0
South America	6,941	17.7
North America (including West Indies and Central America)	7,893	12.4
Greenland and Canadian Archipelago	1,499	7.1
Malayan Archipelago	1,012	63.0
Total Area and Average Runoff	51,985	10.5

TABLE 5-1

World Distribution of Runoff (from Langbein, after L'vovich).

ENERGY AVAILABLE FROM THE RUN-
OFF. On the average, the surface of the
land stands about one-half mile above sea
level. Therefore, the runoff falls an average
of one-half mile as it flows from its source to
the ocean. This, it must be remembered, is
only an average: runoff from a plain near sea
level may descend only a few feet to reach the
ocean, the meltwater from the snows on the
summit of Mount Everest falls over five miles.
A tremendous amount of energy is developed
by the world's streams during their descent to
the sea. Some idea of the amount can be
gained by imagining all the continental runoff to be concentrated in one gigantic river
pouring over a huge waterfall equivalent in
height to the average altitude of the land
masses. In other words, imagine 8,000 cubic
miles of water per year tumbling down a
waterfall half a mile high! Such a waterfall
could make available a continuous supply of
about 200 horsepower for each square mile
of land—enough to keep almost 60 million
bulldozers in continuous operation. All this
energy is available for erosion. Despite the
fact that very few streams work at full capacity it is easy to see why running water is the
great leveler.

AMOUNT OF DEBRIS CARRIED BY
STREAMS. The total load of debris actually
carried by a stream is difficult to measure and
it varies greatly for different rivers. Reliable
figures are available for only a few rivers, but
there are enough to indicate the general magnitude of erosion.

Each year the Mississippi River brings to
the Gulf of Mexico about 730 million tons of
dissolved and solid material. Yet the Mississippi, generally considered a muddy stream,
carries only about five thousand parts per
million (0.5 per cent) by weight of solid
material. Even the Missouri, often called the
"Big Muddy," rarely carries more than twenty
thousand parts per million (2 per cent). This
is a high load for a big river, though it is exceeded by the Colorado, the Yellow River of
China, and a few others. A series of careful
measurements of the silt load of the Missouri

River above Kansas City indicates that the
drainage basin of this river is being lowered
about 1 inch in 650 years, or 1 foot in 7,800
years. The Colorado River, which, between
1925 and 1935 carried an average load of
28,500 tons of silt and sand per hour past the
Grand Canyon gaging station, is removing
material from its drainage basin even more
rapidly. On the other hand, the Columbia,
though a dashing turbulent stream filled with
violent rollers and eddies, contains very little
silt and mud above the junction with its muddy
tributary, the Snake River. The Columbia
flows on smooth bedrock and coarse boulders
which supply little fine debris to be picked up
and carried off. In contrast, the Missouri flows
across the Great Plains, where the thick soil
cover and scanty vegetation yields abundant
fine-grained waste for transport.

Many small streams in arid or semiarid
regions carry enormously greater loads than
these large rivers. During floods as much as
30 per cent of their weight may consist of rock
debris. A sample from the San Juan River in
Colorado when in flood contained over 75 per
cent by weight of red silt and sand. There is,
of course, a complete gradation from such
highly loaded streams through mudflows to
landslides. Nearly all streams, however, work
far below their potential capacity as erosion
agents. If they used most of their energy in
quarrying out and entraining rock waste, few
slopes could retain a cover of soil. Nevertheless measurements such as those given above
support the estimate that the present rate of
denudation from stream erosion for the entire
United States is about 1 foot in 9,000 years.
If this rate could be maintained, and if there
were no compensating upward movements of
parts of the earth's crust, all the landmasses
would be eroded to sea level in about 23
million years. This is a long time by human
standards, but, as shown in Chapter 7, it is
short in terms of the total length of geologic
time.

CHANGES IN THE RATE OF EROSION.
There are many reasons for believing that the
loads of present-day streams are higher than

the average loads during the geologic past. Rivers in populous areas carry industrial and municipal wastes in addition to their normal loads. Enormous amounts of silt and mud are now washed into streams from cultivated fields that were once covered with forest and grass. That cultivation greatly increases the rate of erosion has been proved by the Soil Conservation Service of the United States Department of Agriculture, which made extensive tests of the amounts of soil and water running off plots of ground with identical areas and slope but with different vegetative covers. A few results from these tests are given in Figure 5-8.

Because such factors cannot be precisely evaluated, the rate of erosion during the whole of geologic time cannot be determined accurately. Certainly, the present rate of 1 foot in 9,000 years is too high.

Soil Erosion.—In many sections of the United States productive topsoil is rapidly disappearing. Once-prosperous farms are now barren wastes of deeply eroded gullies and exposed bedrock. It is estimated that about 282 million acres of former farmland have been so seriously eroded as to make farming unprofitable. The soil conservationist has difficulty in reconciling this striking evidence of damaging erosion with a rate of denudation

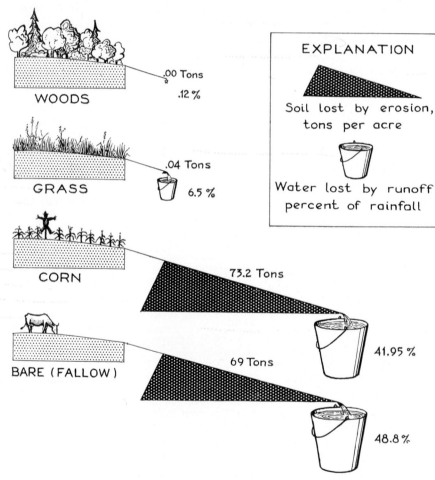

EXPLANATION

Soil lost by erosion, tons per acre

Water lost by runoff percent of rainfall

WOODS   .00 Tons   .12 %

GRASS   .04 Tons   6.5 %

CORN   73.2 Tons   41.95 %

BARE (FALLOW)   69 Tons   48.8 %

Figure 5-8.

Results of soil erosion tests on plots of ground with different vegetative covers. (Redrawn by permission from H. H. Bennett, Soil Conservation, *McGraw-Hill Book Co., 1939)*

of 1 foot in 9,000 years. Most of our productive soils are at least a foot thick: how can so much damage have been accomplished in the relatively short time since the sod of the frontier was plowed into farmland? Only after intensive investigations like those diagramed in Figure 5-8 were made on thousands of soil plots scattered all over the United States did the answer become clear: most of the soil removed from the fields by runoff is almost immediately redeposited at the foot of the slopes or along the stream channels; only a small part is transported directly to the sea. Thus the figure of 1 foot per 9,000 years for the rate of denudation, though a reasonable estimate of total lowering of the continent, does not give a picture of the much greater local erosion and redeposition that is of primary interest to the soil conservationist and to the farmer.

Erosion under the Sea

The sediment eroded from the landmasses ultimately reaches the ocean and is deposited in the shallow seas that border the continents or is drifted by waves and currents into deeper waters. Deposition of the products of erosion is an important process in the sea—"the oceans are the graveyards of the land." But deposition is not the only process that affects the lands beneath the sea. There is reason to believe that erosion is also proceeding even in the depths of the ocean. Before we can discuss this, it is necessary to describe some pertinent features of the topography of the sea floor.

The dark abyss of the ocean floor has always been difficult to study. Until recent years hydrographic maps were based wholly upon scattered soundings taken from shipboard. These soundings were made by paying out a wire with a weight on the end until the weight touched bottom. By this tedious and inaccurate method a few of the outstanding topographic features of the ocean bottom were crudely outlined during the nineteenth century.

Major Relief Features of the Ocean Floor

Just as the continents have mountains, plateaus, and plains, the sea floor also has its larger topographic features. Among these are continental shelves, continental slopes, and ridges or rises.

The **continental shelves** are the submerged edges of the continents (see Fig. 16-28, page 320). Off most coastlines the bottom descends gradually from the shore to a depth of about 600 feet, or perhaps somewhat less, before breaking off into the much steeper continental slope. The shallow continental shelves include more than 7 per cent of all the marine areas of the earth. They may be nonexistent (as off Alaska or Chile) or as much as 800 miles wide (off the Siberian coast in the Arctic Ocean), with an average width of about 30 miles for all coastlines. This makes their average seaward slope about 20 feet per mile.

At depths that may be as little as a few tens of feet or as much as a thousand, the gently sloping surface of the continental shelf plunges into the much steeper **continental slope** (see Figs. 16-1 and 16-28). Off mountainous coasts, the continental slope commonly drops off to the ocean floor at a rate of 300 feet or more per mile: off most wide coastal plains its slope is about half as great.

Great mountain ranges and mountain systems rise above the floor of the ocean. If they are long and relatively narrow they are called **ridges;** if broader and larger, **rises.** For example, one of the greatest mountain ranges on earth, the Mid-Atlantic Ridge, almost bisects the Atlantic basin from north to south. For its entire length the summit of the Mid-Atlantic Ridge rises approximately 10,000 feet above the floor of the Atlantic. Much of its summit is less than a mile below sea level, and a few peaks project as islands above the surface of the sea—among them the Azores, Saint Paul's Rocks, Ascension, Saint Helena, Tristan da Cunha, and Bovet. The Walfisch Ridge, a range that rises as high above the bottom as the Alps rise above sea level, and is three times as long, branches from the Mid-Atlantic

Ridge near its southern end and joins it to the west coast of Africa.

Minor Relief Features

Until the advent of sonic sounding (see Appendix I) the major relief features of the ocean floor were generally drawn with smooth uniform slopes, though it was recognized that in a few places there were steep canyons and abrupt peaks. It was reasoned that any minor irregularities would be obscured and smoothed by the constant rain of sediment pouring into the sea. But with the great wealth of data that became available following the widespread use of sonic sounding it soon became evident that at least some parts of the ocean floor are highly irregular. Figure 5-9 shows the change that took place in the interpretation of the bottom configuration of an area in the South

Atlantic when data from sonic sounding became available. It was also found that most parts of the steep continental slopes, and the sides of the ridges and rises as well, are cut by an intricate maze of canyons of all sizes, some of which are deeper and more precipitous than the Grand Canyon of the Colorado. Many can be traced down the steep submarine slopes to depths of more than 12,000 feet. A few large submarine canyons begin off the mouths of major rivers such as the Congo and Hudson; others, equally impressive, begin at the shoreline far from the mouth of any stream, and many more begin in steep submarine notches far from any land. The origin of such canyons is vigorously debated (the characteristics of the larger canyons and the various theories of their origin are given in Chapter 16). However, the fact that the sides of the Mid-Atlantic Ridge and of most steep

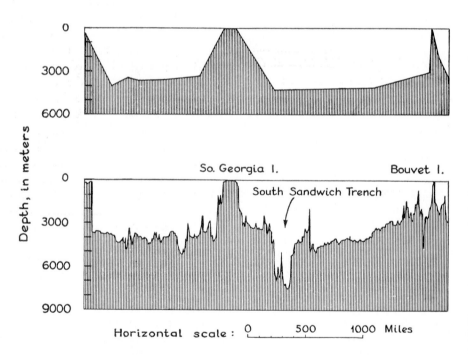

Figure 5-9.

Horizontal scale: 0 ___ 500 ___ 1000 Miles

Two profiles of the bottom of the Atlantic near the Southern Antilles. The upper profile shows the interpretation based on a few wire soundings; the lower that measured by sonic soundings. Note not only the greater detail but also that the great South Sandwich Trench was completely missed by the wire soundings. (After Stocks and Wust, redrawn from H. U. Sverdrup, M. W. Johnson and R. H. Fleming, The Oceans, *Copyright 1942, by Prentice-Hall, Inc.)*

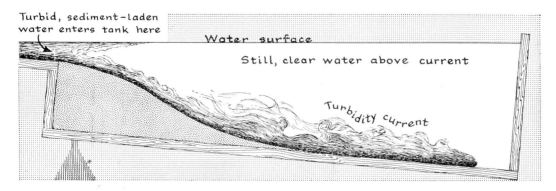

Turbid, sediment-laden water enters tank here

Water surface

Still, clear water above current

Turbidity current

Figure 5-10.   Turbidity current in a laboratory tank. (After photos by Hugh Stevens Bell, Sedimentation Laboratory, California Institute of Technology.)

submarine slopes, are scored by countless ravines and small canyons, not at all unlike those on land except that they have steeper gradients, raises the question of whether they cannot have been eroded by some kind of submarine current that courses down the steep slopes under the influence of gravity. Can masses of water on these submarine slopes become so heavily laden with sediment that the extra impetus given them by the entrained rock debris enables them to flow rapidly downslope beneath the clear water above? And can they pick up enough speed to erode the weakly consolidated sediments over which they glide? Such streams of sediment-laden water, flowing beneath a body of still water because of the higher density that the suspended sediment gives them, are called **turbidity currents.**

Turbidity Currents

Aviators in the Arctic report that some of the silt-laden streams of meltwater discharged from the front of the large Greenland glaciers do not halt or spread out when they enter the sea, but keep right on flowing *beneath* the clear water of the fjords.

Soon after the building of Boulder Dam, when Lake Mead was only half filled with relatively clear impounded water, it was noticed that, from time to time, outlet pipes more than 200 feet above the base of the dam discharged surges of muddy silt-laden water. At this stage

of reservoir filling, the Colorado River entered Lake Mead about 100 miles upstream from the dam. It is a sediment-laden river, but it was thought that its sediment should have settled out in a delta that had formed at the head of the lake. Much of it did settle there, but samples of water from the lake bottom, and data on currents obtained by use of a flowmeter, revealed that muddy river water was cascading down the steep slope at the end of the delta and continuing the full length of the reservoir as a turbidity current that had enough energy left on reaching the dam to boil up high enough to enter the outlet pipes. Similar turbidity currents have been observed in the Elephant Butte Reservoir on the Rio Grande, in Lake Leman in Switzerland, off the mouth of the Magdalena River in Columbia, and at many other places.

We can produce turbidity currents like those in Lake Mead or the Greenland fjords in the laboratory. If streams of water made heavy by dissolved salts or suspended sediment are poured into a tank of clear water which has a sloping bottom, turbidity currents are developed that closely resemble those found in reservoirs (Fig. 5-10). Experiments show that such currents have enough energy to pick up loose particles over which they flow, and they confirm the theory that currents of turbid water flowing down continental slopes with inclinations of 200 to 300 feet per mile could actively erode those slopes.

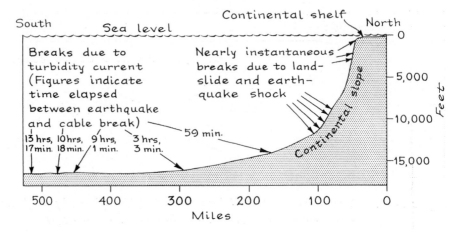

Figure 5-11.

Profile of the sea floor south of the Grand Banks showing (by arrows) the position of transatlantic cables broken by the landslide and turbidity flow started by the earthquake of November 18, 1929. (After Heezen and Ewing, 1952.)

THE GRAND BANKS TURBIDITY FLOW. In 1952, Heezen and Ewing presented evidence that a very large turbidity current once passed across part of the floor of the North Atlantic. On November 18, 1929, New England and the Maritime Provinces of Canada were rocked by an earthquake that centered at the edge of the Grand Banks off Nova Scotia. During the quake, and in the first thirteen hours following, thirteen transatlantic telegraph cables were broken: ten parted in two places and three broke in three places. The broken segment of each cable was more than a hundred miles long. All of the broken cables lay along the steep continental slope that descends southward off the edge of the Grand Banks, or on the gently sloping ocean floor below the slope and south of it. None of the many cables that lay on the Grand Banks (a part of the continental shelf) were broken.

Each break was timed accurately by the automatic machines that record the messages transmitted. The location of each break was determined by measurements of the electrical resistance of the cables, a method used by the telegraph companies to find cable breaks so that ships can bring them up and repair the damage.

When the information for times and positions of the breaks was studied, an interesting correlation was found (Fig. 5-11). Eight cables high on the slope were broken almost instantaneously during the earthquake. The remaining five were broken successively in the order of their positions downslope. The highest of these five broke 59 minutes after the quake, the lowest, 295 miles farther downslope, parted 13 hours and 17 minutes later. Heezen and Ewing concluded from this that the earthquake started a landslide in the poorly consolidated sediment of the continental slope. This broke the first eight cables. As the water-soaked sediment tumbled and cascaded down the steep submarine slope, the motion loosened the weak cement binding the mineral grains together and threw the unconsolidated material on the bottom violently into suspension. It then started to flow as a heavy turbulent liquid, and from the toe of the landslide, a turbidity current squirted forth on a hundred-mile front and rolled down the gently sloping ocean floor at the base of the slope, breaking each cable as it engulfed it. The velocity of flow could be calculated from the times when the cables were snapped and the distance between them. The current was traveling about 58 miles an hour near the base of the continental slope, but had slowed to a little less than 14 miles an hour when it snapped the last cable, 295 miles downslope.

Using the determined values for time, distance, and slope, Kuenen compared the turbidity flow with currents artificially produced in experimental tanks. He reasoned from its calculated velocity that it must have advanced far beyond the last cable break, even on the relatively flat ocean floor, and suggests, as a tentative estimate, that it may have transported fine sand 500 miles from the toe of the landslide, and spread it at great depths over approximately 100,000 square miles of sea bottom. This wide travel has been partly confirmed by the dredging of "clean sharp sand" from many points within the area.

Other Evidence of Submarine Erosion

At the foot of the Mid-Atlantic Ridge, also, cores taken from pipes driven into the bottom show coarse-grained well-stratified sand with cross-bedding and other features typically developed by currents. Underwater cameras lowered to the Pacific Ocean floor off Eni-

wetok show sand and gravel with perfect current ripples (Fig. 5-12) similar to those that develop on the beds of overloaded streams. A generation ago such deposits and features would have been pronounced the work of rivers flowing on land, but these come from depths of one to three miles below sea level! Evidence is rapidly accumulating that the depths of the ocean are not always lifeless and still; strong sediment-laden currents are known to sweep through the dark abyssal canyons and spread great aprons of coarse detritus at the base of submarine slopes. Strong currents doubtless sweep relatively less of the submarine areas than of the land. Erosion of mountains beneath the sea, however, may differ only in degree from erosion of mountains on land, perhaps both are accomplished primarily by streams of sediment-laden water. But the vast size of the sea and the relative inaccessibility of its depths makes it difficult to measure current flow and load, and leaves many questions still unanswered.

Figure 5-12.   Current ripples in calcareous sand on the ocean bottom at a depth of 6,600 feet. Southwest slope of Eniwetok Atoll, Marshall Islands. (Underwater photo by C. J. Shipek, U. S. Navy Electronics Laboratory.)

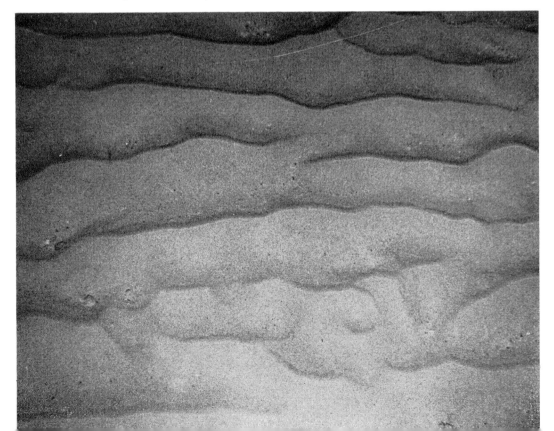

Basic Principle Underlying Erosion Processes

Our brief look at the processes that erode the earth's surface brings out one striking principle: *Gravity is the driving force of erosion.* Nearly all erosion is accomplished by fluids that move because of gravitational forces. During their flow they entrain rock waste whose added weight makes the flowing current seek even more vigorously its lowest possible level.

Although differing in some characteristics, there is a basic similarity between a dust storm in air, a turbidity current in the sea, a silt-laden river, or an ash flow of expanding pumice and gas racing down the slopes of a volcano. Each is a current of fluid, with entrained rock particles, and each is out of gravitational equilibrium with the less dense fluids that surround it. This fundamental principle applies even to glaciers. Ice is a solid whose threshold strength must be exceeded before flow begins, but once plastic flow has started it responds in the same way as a liquid.

Geologic Evidence of Erosion

Nearly all of the data on which this chapter is based became known during the past hundred years, and most of it only within the past twenty or thirty. Since the earliest days of the science, however, geologists have been aware of the vast changes in the landscape wrought by running water. Early geologists, however, were less concerned with the amount of silt being carried to the sea in streams and with the spectacular effects occasionally produced by catastrophic river floods, than they were with the etched surface of the earth itself (see Fig. 5-13; also Figs. 9-5 and 12-25).

Over 150 years ago John Playfair, a British mathematician and geologist, nicely summarized the evidence that streams have cut their valleys:

Every river appears to consist of a main trunk, fed from a variety of branches, each running in a valley proportioned to its size, and all of them together form a system of vallies, communical with one another, and having such a nice adjustment of their declivities, that none of them join the principal valley, either on too high or too low a level, a circumstance which would be infinitely improbable if each of these vallies were not the work of the stream that flows in it.

At first glance, the deep gash of the Grand Canyon (Fig. 5-13), or the cliffs bordering

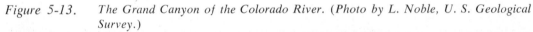

Figure 5-13.   *The Grand Canyon of the Colorado River. (Photo by L. Noble, U. S. Geological Survey.)*

Figure 5-14.   *Erosion of tilted sedimentary rocks. The drawing shows the rocks as they would appear if sliced vertically at the lower boundary of the photograph. The dashed lines represent only a small part of what erosion has removed. (Photo by U. S. Air Force.)*

the Nisqually Glacier on Mount Rainier (Fig. 5-4), seem to have been produced by some great catastrophe that rent the earth asunder. But look more critically into the relations. Although beds of flat-lying sedimentary rock at the Grand Canyon, and of gently inclined lava flows on Mount Rainier, are cut off abruptly by the canyon walls, they can be seen to continue across the canyon in the opposite wall. Evidently the rock layers must once have been continuous sheets, extending completely across the site of the canyon, but parts of them have been eroded as river and glacier slowly lowered their beds into the rock.

In many mountain ranges, strata of sandstone, shale, and limestone have been tilted from their original horizontal position. The edges of these tilted beds, etched out by erosion, project in ridges like those shown in Figure 5-14. Obviously the deeper and older beds in the sequence could only have been exposed by removal, through erosion, of the younger beds that once covered them. In several mountain chains such series of tilted beds are exposed in belts many miles wide; to strip away all of the overlying beds and expose the deepest layers in some of these ranges required the removal of two, ten, or even more miles of overlying rock. Were it not for such deep erosion, geologists would have only meager information about the internal structure of the earth's crust and about rocks such as slate and granite that form far below the earth's surface.

The study of this phase of erosion, however, is best deferred until we have learned about geologic maps and about movements of the earth's crust that raise the mountains so erosion can work on them. The most striking of all proofs of erosion are shown by the folded and eroded rocks themselves, but the complex relations among the strata can be grasped only after we have plotted them on geologic maps. Such maps are the subject of our next chapter.

FACTS, CONCEPTS, TERMS

EROSIONAL AGENTS
    Gravity; wind; glaciers; ocean waves and currents; streams; turbidity currents

RELATIVE IMPORTANCE OF THE AGENTS OF EROSION
    Streams, aided by downslope movements, are the great levelers

THE HYDROLOGIC CYCLE
    Source of the energy that powers the cycle
    Factors affecting the runoff
    Amount of runoff available for erosion
    Energy generated by the runoff

RATE OF DENUDATION
    Local, present total, and geologic rates of soil denudation

EROSION IN THE SEA
    Submarine ravines and canyons on steep slopes
    Coarse sand and gravel plains at depth
    Turbidity currents
    Evidence of current action at depth

ENERGY FOR EROSION
    Basic principle underlying nearly all erosion processes
    Respective roles of gravity and solar radiation

GEOLOGIC EVIDENCE OF EROSION
    Proof that streams cut their valleys
    Comparison of landscapes on the Earth and Moon
    Revealing of metamorphic rocks and granites by erosion

QUESTIONS

1. Why can a stream move larger particles than can wind moving with the same velocity?

2. Which of the erosional agents listed in this chapter could cut a valley to depths of 1,000 feet or more below sea level? Why?

3. Point Barrow, Alaska, and Yuma, Arizona, have about the same rainfall (5 inches per year). Yet Yuma lies in a parched desert whereas the country around Point Barrow is largely swamp. Explain.

4. In a temperate humid climate, which will erode more rapidly: a basalt cone composed of loose cinders, or a hill the same size composed of silt? Why?

5. In view of what has been said about infiltration, on what rocks would you expect the streams to be spaced closer together, assuming similar slope, vegetation, and precipitation: (*a*) basalt flows with numerous vertical cracks; (*b*) shale; (*c*) granite? Give reasons.

6. Where would you expect streams and gullies to be most closely spaced, assuming uniform granite bedrock: (*a*) steep slopes; (*b*) gentle slopes; (*c*) nearly flat terrain?

7. It has been said that "A turbidity current in the ocean is like a dust storm on the land." Analyze this statement in terms of (*a*) energy of motion, (*b*) entrainment of debris, and (*c*) nature of the medium surrounding the moving current in each of the two cases.

8. Rivers flow beneath air, turbidity currents beneath clear water. Assuming that turbidity currents actually do cut submarine canyons, does the above relationship help to explain why the gradient of submarine canyons is, on the average, about four times as steep as that of comparable canyons on land? Explain.

SUGGESTED READINGS

Bennett, H. H. *Soil Conservation.* New York, McGraw-Hill, 1939.

Brown, C. B., *Sediment Transportation,* in H. Rouse, ed., *Engineering Hydraulics.* New York, John Wiley and Sons, 1950.

United States. Department of Agriculture Yearbook: *Soils and Man,* 1938; *Water,* 1957. Washington, D. C.

6   GEOLOGIC MAPS

No TRAVELER can miss the contrast between a lava flow of black basalt and the prevailing light-colored granodiorite of the Sierra Nevada, or, on the opposite side of the earth, between a similar basalt flow and the gleaming white coral rock of Samoa. To show the outlines of such a flow on a map we must trace the contacts between the flow and the adjoining rocks that it touches. This is done by plotting on the map the positions of the contact (contact lines) in their proper relation to valleys and hills as shown by the contour lines, and to other features on the map, such as streams and roads. The result is a **geologic map.** Even so simple a map as one showing only basalt and granodiorite may be economically useful. If basalt is needed to surface a Sierran road, our map shows where it can be quarried, and, from the contours, we can estimate the thickness of the flow and thus calculate the available tonnage. Geologic maps, in conjunction with topographic maps, allow us to tell a great deal about the size and shape of rock bodies hundreds or even thousands of feet below the surface.

A geologic map may consequently be a powerful economic tool, useful in locating supplies of oil, water, coal, iron ore, and other valuable substances hidden beneath a cover of soil and rocks. Though there may be no surface indications of these, a geologic map often reveals where tunneling or drilling might

be successful. The accuracy of such predictions has been proved again and again by discovery of valuable materials. Further, the geologic map is our principal tool in deciphering the history of a mountain range, the sequence of the evolution of fossil organisms, the changes in local climates—indeed, the history of the earth itself.

Difficulties of Geologic Mapping

The distribution and relationships of rock bodies are not ordinarily so obvious as they are on the peaks of the Sierra Nevada or along the shores of Samoa. Indeed, in a fertile agricultural area such as Illinois or the Ukraine, it is difficult to perceive any systematic arrangement of the strata, because the rocks are nearly everywhere masked by soil or recent stream deposits. Unweathered rock can be found only in stream banks and deep ravines, or in artificial excavations such as roadcuts and quarries. To make a geologic map in such regions is not easy; it often requires digging pits and trenches at critical spots, or drilling holes and examining fragments of the rocks penetrated by the drill.

Early Geologic Maps

The principles of geologic mapping were developed chiefly in western Europe, where the rocks are seldom well exposed. Among the earliest geologic maps that showed the relations of sedimentary strata over a considerable area are two maps of the region around Paris, France, published jointly by the French naturalists Georges Cuvier and Alexandre Brongniart in 1810 and 1822. At about the same time (1815) William Smith, an English surveyor, published a geologic map of England which was one of the milestones in the development of geology.

Long before the work of Cuvier and Brongniart, French scientists knew that the rocks near Paris are gently tilted layers of limestone, clay, gypsum and sandstone. These rocks could be seen in many natural and artificial exposures, notably in the pits dug by the makers of pottery and porcelain in their search for plastic clay. As early as 1782, Lavoisier took time from his epochal discoveries in chemistry to demonstrate that quarry after quarry near Paris showed the same succession—from the base upward—of clay, limestone, gypsum, impure limestone and sand, with a siliceous limestone forming a cap at the top. But Cuvier and Brongniart went much further. They demonstrated that certain characteristic fossils are present in some of the layers, that some beds change in character both laterally and vertically, and that the different strata near Paris can be grouped into mappable units called formations whose thickness and physical characteristics are sufficiently distinctive to allow them to be traced continuously for long distances.

Succession of the Rocks near Paris

East of Paris a series of low hills and narrow lowlands (Fig. 6-1) curves in a broad arc, partly encircling the city. The hills have steep slopes on the side away from Paris and gentle slopes toward the city. The lowland just beyond the first row of curving hills, though largely covered with soil, contains scattered rock **outcrops** (natural exposures) and also man-made excavations, all of which expose chalk, a variety of limestone.

The lowland underlain by chalk almost completely encircles Paris. On the side of the lowland farthest from Paris, the chalk is gray, and contains many thin layers of pale green sandstone; but on the side nearer Paris it is white and porous, and some of its thin layers are crowded with potato-shaped nodules of black flint. Between the flinty layers lie beds of massive chalk, 15 to 20 feet thick, containing no flint nodules. The layering in both gray and white chalk inclines gently downward toward Paris; from this Cuvier and Brongniart concluded that the white chalk rests upon the gray. They were thus able to separate the chalk into two distinct formations: the Lower Chalk, chiefly gray chalk and greensand (a sandstone rich in a green iron-bearing mineral, glauconite); and the Upper Chalk, a massive white chalk containing layers of flint nodules. It is the Upper Chalk that appears across the English Channel in the "White Cliffs of Dover."

Cuvier and Brongniart found more than fifty different kinds of fossil shells and other animal remains in the Upper Chalk, all of which resemble, although they are not identical with, those of animals now living in the sea.

The steep slopes of the hills on the Paris side of the chalk lowland expose scattered outcrops of a plastic clay along the bottoms of little ravines where the thin soil cover on the steep hillside has been washed away by the rains. This clay rests upon the chalk. Ravines farther up the slope show loosely consolidated sandstone resting on the clay. Still higher are exposures of limestone and marl (clayey limestone). In all these beds, the stratification is distinct and each stratum slopes gently toward Paris.

The clay that overlies the chalk yielded no fossils, leading Cuvier and Brongniart to conclude that although both chalk and clay were originally deposited in water, they were formed under different environmental conditions—the chalk in the sea, the clay in fresh water. Apparently the animals that flourished while the chalk accumulated could not live in the fresh water from which the clay settled.

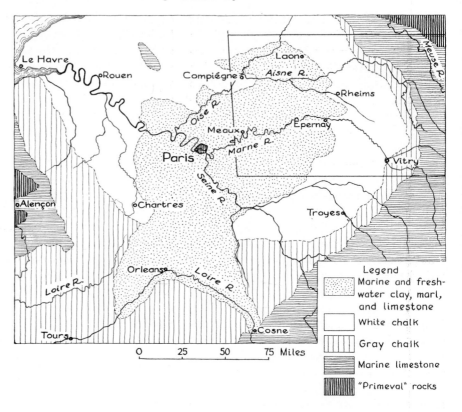

Legend

Marine and fresh-
water clay, marl,
and limestone

White chalk

Gray chalk

Marine limestone

"Primeval" rocks

0   25   50   75 Miles

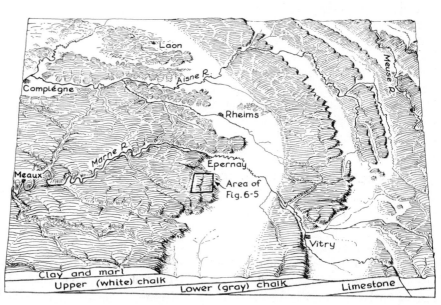

Figure 6-1.

Top: *Map of the Paris Basin showing the rock formations as mapped by Cuvier and Brongniart.* Bottom: *Relief diagram of the area east of Paris, outlined on the map. Note how the topography indicates the distribution of the inclined formations. (After W. M. Davis.)*

In some places, near the contact between chalk and clay, fragments of chalk were found within the lowermost bed of clay. Cuvier and Brongniart concluded that the chalk must have been a coherent rock when the deposit of clay began to form, and hence that considerable time had elapsed between the accumulation of the chalk and that of the clay.

Eventually Cuvier and Brongniart systematically worked out the succession of the formations all the way to Paris. They consist of several beds of limestone, sand, clay, and gypsum: some contain marine shells, others contain bones of land mammals and birds, skeletons of fresh-water fish, and impressions of the leaves of land plants. Each formation shows particular physical features and most of them also contain distinctive fossils.

The larger features of the succession remain the same throughout the Paris Basin, but not every bed nor even every group of beds making up a formation could be followed all the way around the basin. Some beds had been partly eroded away before the overlying beds were deposited; others had been deposited as lenses in discontinuous small basins, or built up by water currents just as spits and sand bars are being built at the present time.

Identifying Formations by Fossils

The great variety of rocks made Cuvier and Brongniart's task of mapping difficult: for example, the distinction of one limestone from another, among so many, could not always be made on the basis of color, details of bedding, thickness, or other physical characteristics. Not all of these difficulties were solved by Cuvier and Brongniart in their pioneer studies. Modern geologic maps of the Paris Basin show many refinements in the subdivision and mapping of the formations, but the basic principles they established have served well in all later studies. Perhaps the most important conclusion they reached was that: *Each closely related group of strata contains its own characteristic assemblage of fossils.*

This generalization has proved funda-mental in correlating isolated outcrops of strata, even across seas and oceans. It has been checked again and again by the Law of Superposition. For example, approximately the same succession of fossils occurs in the same order as one compares the sequences of strata in England, France, and North Africa.

William Smith's Geologic Map of England

The first geologic map of England, published in 1815 by William Smith, also gave great stimulus to the wider use of fossils in geologic mapping and correlation. His map represented a notable advance over the maps of Cuvier and Brongniart. Smith, a surveyor, took great pains to locate the contacts of his formations accurately and to plot their positions correctly on the map with reference to streams, roads, and other features. Starting with the exposure of a contact on a canal or river bank, he would follow its approximate position across a soil-covered hill, using as guides small rock fragments in the soil or at the mouths of rabbit holes, until he could again locate the contact accurately where it was again exposed, perhaps on a stream bank in the next valley.

Smith was employed as a surveyor on many canals throughout England. On the Somersetshire Coal Canal, for example, he superintended the excavation work for more than six years, observing the details of the strata in many miles of cut. In all his travels he noted the succession and kinds of rocks. Finally, after twenty-four years of observation, he published his colored geologic map of England, which has taken its place among the great classics of geology.

This map profoundly influenced the development of geology. A text outlining the results of Smith's twenty-four years of labor would have been so bulky that no one could have read it through with comprehension, but once the observations were plotted on the map, the principal relations could be quickly grasped and their implications deduced. Scientists saw that many problems could be answered by the careful plotting of the position of rock masses: Smith had already shown what could be done by predicting the kind and thickness of rock masses that could be found in a particular excavation or tunnel, and maps such as his also allowed the thickness of overburden over a coal bed or other valuable rock to be computed. Men began to think of other economic applications of geology and of the many practical ways in which a knowledge of the succession of rock strata might be used.

Smith's great contribution, however, lay in determining the **stratigraphy,** the order of succession of the different sedimentary formations, for an entire country, and thus proving the continuity of individual formations over great areas. He showed conclusively that if a given bed or stratum occurs above another distinctive formation in one locality, it never occurs below it elsewhere unless a later structural disturbance has affected the rocks. This is of course simply one aspect of the Law of Superposition. The succession of strata that he established was found to be valid not only in England, but also in much of Europe. Eventually, the subdivisions that he and other pioneers established were extended and refined into the Standard Geologic Column to which we now refer sedimentary formations throughout the world. (See Table 7-1.)

This brief account of early geologic maps gives us hints of the methods and principles used in geologic mapping. We will now summarize these principles, consider their validity, and show how they are applied.

Four Fundamental Postulates of Geologic Mapping

Four fundamental postulates underlie the making of a geologic map. Two of these, the Law of Superposition and the Law of Original Horizontality, have already been discussed (Chapter 3). The third, the **Law of Original Continuity,** is merely a common-sense deduction from these two, and, like them, was first stated by Steno: *A water-laid stratum, at the time it was formed, must continue laterally in all directions until it thins out as a result of nondeposition, or until it abuts against the edge of the original basin of deposition.* An important corollary of this law, not fully appreciated by Steno in 1669, but well known to the geologists of France and England at the beginning of the nineteenth century, may be stated: *A stratum that ends abruptly, at some point other than the edge of the basin in which it was deposited, must have had its original continuation removed by erosion, or else displaced by a fracture in the earth's crust.*

These four postulates—(1) *superposition* (the higher bed is the younger), (2) *original horizontality* (stratification planes are formed roughly parallel to the earth's surface), (3) *original continuity,* and (4) *truncation by erosion or dislocation*—are the basis for many of our interpretations of the relations of strata. They are not absolute rules that can be rigidly applied. For instance, some beds once horizontal have been highly tilted and even overturned by movements of the earth's crust (Chapters 8 and 9), so that a stratum formerly beneath another may now lie on it upside down. Other strata, as at the front of a delta, may have been deposited on appreciable slopes; many landslides end abruptly instead of thinning out to a feather edge. Such exceptions, though, are not common and can generally be easily recognized by the geologist.

Although these basic principles are commonplace a geologist still meets problems in applying them. What, for example, does a geologist select to map in a thick sequence of strata containing hundreds of thin beds of rock, many of which closely resemble one another? Obviously he cannot map each separate stratum, but how is he to group them?

Formations

The basic unit of the geologic map is the **formation.** *There are two criteria for deciding what constitutes a formation; first, its contacts (i.e., the top and bottom of a sedimentary* *formation) must be recognizable and capable of being traced in the field, and second, the formation must be large enough to be shown on the map.*

Cuvier and Brongniart noticed faint stratification surfaces within the Lower Chalk. The chalk above and below such stratification surfaces, however, was so nearly identical in appearance and fossil content that the beds of chalk were not regarded by the two geologists as either significant or capable of being successfully traced in the field or shown individually on their map. The contact between the Upper Chalk and the overlying Plastic Clay, on the other hand, was mapped as a formation boundary because of the marked contrast in the rocks. A still more cogent reason for selecting this contact to map was the evidence that it represented a considerable span of geologic time—enough for the underlying chalk to have become firmly coherent, so that it could be incorporated as pebbles and fragments in the lowermost bed of clay.

The beds above the Plastic Clay posed a still more difficult problem. Here were many different kinds of rock in relatively thin layers—limestone, shale, sandstone, gypsum, and clay. At some outcrops, an individual bed —perhaps a layer of clay only a foot thick— could be seen to thin out and disappear within a few tens of feet: or the overlying sandstone, perhaps fifteen feet thick, could be seen to thicken when followed across country in successive outcrops, and then to thin again and perhaps ultimately disappear. Only on a map of a very large scale could each thin layer be shown, and it would take a prodigious amount of time to trace the contacts. Such a series of thin, variable beds, often including very diverse types of rock, were grouped together by Cuvier and Brongniart as a single formation. Although individual thin beds of such variable formations may be discontinuous and are even indistinguishable from similar beds in the same formation or adjacent ones, nevertheless the group of beds as a whole constitutes a unit recognizably different from formations above and below it.

The scale of the map, the number of exposures, the character of the beds, the purpose for which the map is intended, and, not least, the discrimination of the geologist, determine the selection of map units (formations). Any differences are adequate to justify calling a particular bed, or any closely related group of beds, a formation, provided the differences allow the formation to be recognized in scattered outcrops, and provided the top and bottom of the formation can be traced in the field.

In the United States, the name given a geologic formation is nearly always that of a geographic locality near which the formation was first identified, followed by the name of the dominant rock variety composing it, or, if it is composed of a great variety of rocks, by the word "formation." Examples: Austin chalk, Columbia River basalt, Chattanooga shale, Denver formation. In Europe, the practice is less formal; many formations are named from some characteristic fossil (Lingula Flags, a thin-bedded sandstone containing abundant fossils of the genus *Lingula*), from some economic characteristic (Millstone Grit), or even from a folk name (Norwich Crag).

Mapping of Poorly Exposed Formations

On the barren walls of the Grand Canyon (Fig. 5-13), the strata are beautifully displayed for scores of miles, and contacts between the several formations can be readily traced. But in most areas soil covers most of the surface, and natural outcrops, roadcuts, and quarries are scarce. On William Smith's geologic map of England, lines representing the contacts between different rock formations are drawn for distances that represent hundreds of miles. Yet, in tracing an individual contact for a hundred miles, Smith probably found, on the average, less than fifty exposures where the actual contact could be seen on a clean rock face. How, then, can his map record the real distribution of the rocks? Can it represent anything but a guess? The eyes of a geologist are no more capable of seeing the bedrock through a cover of soil and turf than those of any other observer. How can the geologist make inferences about the position of the bedrock underground that will withstand objective tests, such as those provided when wells are drilled or mine shafts dug?

The succession must be pieced together from scattered outcrops. Although, in an area of several square miles, a geologist may find only one or two outcrops in which he sees the actual contact between two formations, he will doubtless find a hundred or more outcrops composed entirely of rock belonging to one formation or the other. Each outcrop gives a clue to the position of the contact and he is often able to "bracket" its position closely. The problem is a little like that of drawing a contour line to conform to elevations determined at a hundred or more control points (Appendix I). To use scattered rock outcrops in this way, however, requires that the separate formations be correctly identified in each outcrop, and correlated from outcrop to outcrop, and this is not always easy. How is it done?

Correlation of Rock Outcrops

Modern geologists use essentially the same methods of correlation as Cuvier, Smith, and the other pioneers. In a ravine on a grassy hillside we may see a bed of clay with well-marked horizontal stratification; we assume that it continues horizontally into the hill at the same elevation, for how else can its horizontal stratification be extended? If we go a few hundred yards along the same level without seeing an outcrop, and then find a clay bed at the same elevation in another ravine, we may suspect that it is the same bed. If both are gray, the probability is heightened. If both show lines of concretions (nodular lumps) along the stratification planes and if the size and spacing of the concretions is about the same, we can be still more confident

of our correlation. If both rest on red limestone, are overlain by fine-grained brown sandstone, and contain the same kind of fossils, we can be almost sure of the correlation. We are now justified in assuming that the bed is continuous beneath the soil between the exposures. If we go on a little farther and come to a deep ravine that exposes not merely a few feet of strata but several hundred, and if in this section there is only one clay bed with features identical with those we saw in the two small outcrops, we have still further assurance that our correlation has been correct. We can now map the clay, for the contacts of the bed with those above and below, being horizontal planes, will run parallel to the contours. We have, furthermore, gained information about the red limestone below and the brown sandstone above the clay bed, because in this larger outcrop they are exposed through a much greater thickness. For example, we may find that the brown sandstone is 180 feet thick and is overlain by a bed of distinctive black limestone containing many fossils.

If, now, we go to a distant outcrop and find there a clay bed that is a little thinner than in the last outcrop, a bed that instead of resting on red limestone rests on pink limy sandstone and is overlain by a pebbly green sandstone instead of the fine-grained brown sandstone, we might be doubtful that we could correlate it with our original bed, though we would certainly not regard correlation as impossible. To check, we might go to a lower elevation and study the limy sandstone in various outcrops. If we found it gradually changing to pink sandstone in one direction, but to sandy red limestone and then to pure red limestone in the other, our correlation would be strengthened. It would be further confirmed if we walked up the hill and found that the pebbly green sandstone above the clay was overlain by a black limestone full of fossils exactly like those in the limestone that overlay the brown sandstone in the large exposure.

This example illustrates the use of three most important factors in the correlation of rock formations. These are:

1. *Lithology.*—The more nearly alike are the kinds of rock in scattered exposures—in such features as grain-size, composition, bedding, and any other recognizable physical characteristics—the more likely their correlation.

2. *Sequence.*—Similar sequences of strata suggest correlation.

3. *Fossil content.*—William Smith found that, "Each stratum contained fossils peculiar to itself, and might, in cases otherwise doubtful, be recognized and discriminated from others like it by examination of them." Cuvier and Brongniart reached the same conclusion. Fossils can be used in correlation very much as though they were particularly distinctive pebbles, but as we shall learn in the next chapter, they provide an even more significant guide to correlation.

A fourth method of correlation is obviously the best of all: *tracing a continuously exposed contact from one area to another.* But only where rocks are not covered with soil can this be done for any considerable distance. The determination of similarities in physical characteristics of rocks, sequence of strata, and fossil content—all of which call for the exercise of judgment—are generally required in geologic mapping because of the limitations in exposure of the rocks.

Thus, in geologic mapping there is invariably an element of judgment. Some correlations are certain, others are reasonably sure, and about others there may be a reasonable doubt. Two geologists may disagree about the doubtful ones, just as two equally qualified physicians sometimes disagree in the diagnosis of identical but ambiguous pathological symptoms. But nearly all such differences in interpretation concern minor features in a stratigraphic succession. Most thick groups of beds show enough peculiarities to lead two careful observers to identical conclusions.

Geologic Sections

Geologic sections are used with geologic maps in nearly all economic applications of geology. A **geologic section,** also called a **structure section,** shows how the rocks would appear on the side of a trench cut vertically into the land surface. The edge of a slice of layer cake illustrates the layers and the filling between layers; a geologic section is a similar illustration of rocks in depth. As an example, let us make a geologic section of the horizontal clay bed shown in Figure 6-2, taking our data from the geologic map, which shows the relation of a clay bed to other beds in a deep branching ravine. In Figure 6-2, the completed section is shown below the geologic map; the figure also shows the construction lines used in drawing the section.

This geologic section portrays the strata as they would appear on the wall of a trench dug along the line from A to B on the geologic map. The section was drawn by making use of the contour lines on the map and relating the outcrops to them. First, to simplify our task, it was decided to make the horizontal scale of the section the same as that of the map. Then lines were dropped perpendicularly from A and B to the place below the map where the section was to be drawn. A vertical scale showing the range in elevation from 1,120 to 1,260 feet above sea level was laid off on the line dropped from B. In this particular example we used the same scale as the map, so as to avoid distortion. Horizontal lines were then drawn across the section through these points; each line represents the elevation of the corresponding contour line on the map. From each point where the line AB intersects a contour, a perpendicular line was dropped to the horizontal line corresponding to that contour on the section; the ends of the perpendicular lines provided a guide for sketching the **surface profile,** the irregular line connecting A' and B' in the section. Perpendiculars were now dropped to this profile from each intersection

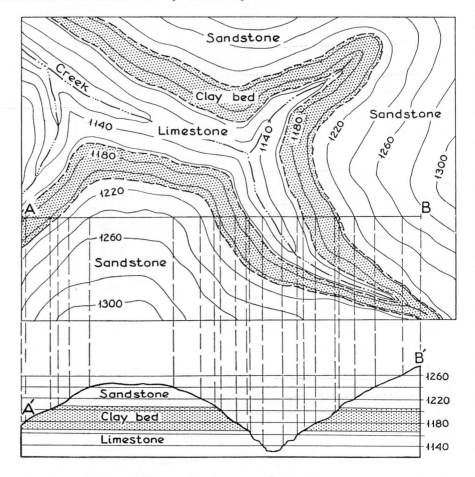

Figure 6-2.

Construction of a geologic section from a geologic map.

of the map line AB with the top and bottom of the clay stratum. There are five such intersections—three with the top of the clay stratum, two with the base. Lines drawn through the points on the surface profile that represent respectively the top, and the bottom of the stratum (in this example, the beds are horizontal) complete the cross-section, and show the relations of the clay bed to the underlying limestone and overlying sandstone.

Geologic sections have many practical uses. If the clay shown in this one is suitable for brickmaking, we can determine from the section how much worthless soil and rock must be removed at any point along the section line to uncover the clay. If a subway tunnel

is to be driven, we can foresee difficulties that may arise during excavation, such as problems of roof support and water disposal. Mines, tunnels, and wells all test the validity of our geologic maps and sections, and of the assumptions underlying their construction.

Rock Structure and Geologic Mapping

In most places, strata are no longer horizontal, as they were when deposited; they have been warped and folded (Chapter 8). We mentioned that the beds of the Paris Basin are tilted gently toward Paris. In mapping tilted beds and plotting them on sections, the same principles apply as with horizontal beds, but since a tilted bed rarely runs parallel to a contour line, and then only for short distances, its outcrops will generally be found at different elevations when it is traced along a hillside. How are the amount and direction of its tilt to be determined?

Dip and Strike

The slope of a tilted plane is fixed if we know the direction and amount of inclination of the steepest line that can be drawn on its surface. This is most simply illustrated by the slope of a roof—the direction in which a drop of water runs down that slope is the **direction of dip** of the roof surface. The acute angle between the track of the water and a horizontal surface, measured on a vertical plane through the track, is the **angle of dip** of the roof. But in natural exposures of rocks it may not be possible to determine these directions so easily. We usually do it indirectly by determining the **direction of strike,** which is the direction of a horizontal line in the surface of stratification. Such a horizontal line is, of course, at right angles to the direction of dip. To revert to our roof example, it is obvious that the ridge pole is a horizontal line and that it lies in the plane of the roof. The compass direction of the ridge pole is thus the direction of strike for the roof. Moreover, the compass direction of the ridge pole is at right angles to the compass direction of the direction of dip of the roof.

In a more natural example, we may visualize the relations shown in Figure 6-3. If a tilted stratum intersects the surface of a lake, the trend of the water's edge where it intersects the stratum—that is, the bearing, or compass direction, of the line of intersection of the lake surface (a horizontal plane) with the stratification (a tilted plane)—forms a definite line of reference, the **strike** of the stratum. We know that the bed will project horizontally in this direction unless it becomes bent, or is cut off by erosion or in some other way. Strike is measured in the field with a compass equipped with a level-bubble so that it can be held horizontally. With the level-bubble cen-

tered, the compass is sighted along the bedding plane and the compass bearing read. The line in the bedding plane thus determined is a **strike line.** Thus a bed that intersects a lake surface along a line running exactly northwest–southeast is recorded as having a strike of N45°W (which is, of course, the same as S45°E, or northwest–southeast). A bed on which a horizontal line trends 10° east of south would be recorded as having a strike of N10°W or S10°E.

As we noted in the example of the roof, the **dip** of a bed is *the maximum angle between a horizontal surface and the stratification plane.* In our example of the lake and the inclined stratum, the dip is the angle between the surface of the lake and the line on the submerged continuation of the tilted bed that lies at right angles to the strike (Fig. 6-3). Dip angles are measured with a clinometer, which is a pointer with a level-bubble attached to its top. This pointer is attached to the inside of the compass, and its lower end swings freely against a scale graduated in degrees (Fig. 6-4). With the compass held in position and the bubble on the clinometer leveled as illustrated in Figure 6-4, the angle of dip is read directly from the graduated scale. The direction of dip must not be confused with the angle of dip. The direction of dip is the compass direction toward which

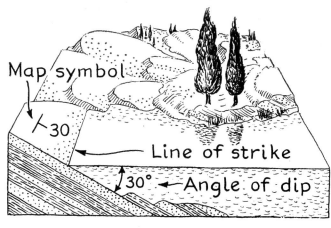

Figure 6-3.   The strike and dip of an inclined bed exposed along a lake shore.

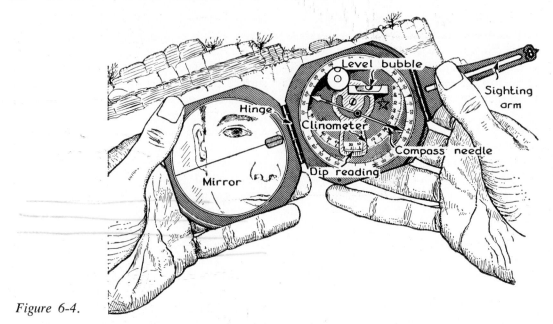

Figure 6-4.

Determining dip with the Brunton compass. The clinometer is rotated by a lever on the back of the compass until the bubble is centered, then the dip is read directly on the inner half circle.

the tilted bed slopes into the earth; in our example, it is the direction (not the inclination) taken by the water that runs down the surface of the roof. *The direction of dip is always at right angles to the direction of strike.*

In recording strike and dip on a map, a symbol consisting of two lines is used. The symbol ⟋⟍ indicates that the stratum to which it refers has a strike of north 45° east and a dip of 60° to the southeast at the indicated point. On most maps, the letters and figures indicating the strike are omitted; thus ⟋55 indicates a bed striking north 45° west and dipping 55° to the northeast. The "N45W" is omitted because the top of a map is always north unless specifically marked otherwise; the direction of strike can thus be determined from the trend of the strike line, which is always accurately plotted with respect to the north line on the map. Similarly the direction of dip need not be given because the dip line points in that direction, but the angle of dip in degrees must always be given.

Topography, Inclined Beds, and Geologic Mapping

A dipping bed can be projected along a contour only when the trend of the hillside parallels the strike. If the strike is not parallel to the contour, the trace of the bed along the hillside will lie either higher or lower than the first outcrop, depending on the direction in which the bed is followed. This fact is the basis for determining the attitude of most beds with low dips, for it is difficult to read a measurement of less than 1° by a clinometer, but it may be relatively easy to locate two points on the surface of a bed that each have exactly the same elevation, although they may be a thousand feet apart on opposite sides of a stream valley. The bearing of a straight line between the two points is, of course, the strike of the bed. This relationship is also the basic clue to reading the succession of beds and their structure on a geologic map.

In the Paris Basin, most streams drain to the Seine. East of Paris (Fig. 6-1) they flow westward, cutting at approximately right angles through the arcuate ridges. Applying our knowledge of the relation between the dip of a bed and its trace on the land surface, we find that if we select a particular stratum, such as one of the thin layers of greensand in the Lower Chalk, or one of the thin limestones that lies above the Plastic Clay, and trace the outcrops of this bed westward along the walls of a valley, the bed decreases gradually in elevation until it reaches the level of the stream; thereupon it crosses the stream bed, reverses its direction and climbs higher and

higher when followed eastward on the opposite valley wall. In other words, the outcrop pattern is a V with the point of the V directed downdip (Fig. 6-5).

The fact that the Upper Chalk crops out farther west in the valley of the Marne and Aisne rivers (Fig. 6-1) than it does on the intervening divides proves that the contact of the chalk with the overlying Plastic Clay dips west. By using such facts, the east-west section forming the lower edge of Figure 6-1 (*bottom*) was drawn, although each forma-

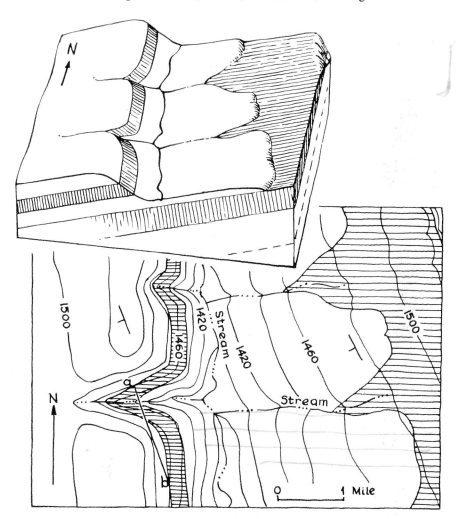

Figure 6-5.

Relief diagram and geologic map of the small area south of Epernay (See Fig. 6-1, bottom). Note the strong V in each contact where it crosses a stream valley, whether the stream flows east or west. The strike of the beds can be determined by joining points, as a and b, where a contact intersects a contour line. (Why?)

tion shown on this section is projected to much greater depths within the earth than we can actually observe in the field. The basic principle of original continuity is the same as for horizontal beds, but in projecting the bed to a geologic section, account must be taken of the dip of the beds.

RELATION OF TOPOGRAPHY TO UNDER-LYING ROCKS.   As shown in Figures 5-13 and 6-1, there is generally a relationship, quite close in areas of little soil but less definite in areas of deep soil, between the landscape of a country and the underlying bedrock. Weathering and erosion etch the surface into relief, forming lowlands on the less resistant beds and leaving the more resistant ones standing as hills. This differential erosion produces a landscape that reflects differences in rock character and structure. In the Paris Basin (Figs. 6-1 and 6-5) the curving ridges mark outcrops of resistant strata such as sandstones, but only porous chalk and other easily eroded rocks are found in the lowlands. The curving pattern of these hills and lowlands also shows that the rocks of the Paris Basin have been warped into a shallow saucerlike basin. Indeed, the whole succession of strata resembles a pile of saucers of diminishing size, with Paris near the center of the smallest and uppermost saucer.

The correlation between topography and structure in the Paris Basin is by no means perfect—much closer adjustment is common in deserts, where the soil cover is thin or absent (Fig. 9-6). Usually, however, the topography indicates the general trend of the underlying rocks. Sandstone is generally more resistant to erosion than shale, and hence in a dipping sequence of beds it forms ridges where the two are interstratified (Fig. 5-14). It is also more permeable to rain, so that where it rests on shale there is likely to be a line of springs, or a strip of flourishing plants, along its base. Thus the minor topographic features of an area nearly always furnish clues to the characters and trend of the underlying bedrock. If we find conglomerate on top

of a ridge at one point, it suggests that conglomerate may continue along the ridge throughout its entire length. This is easily checked by seeking other outcrops along it. A road may expose chalk in a lowland. Perhaps a well has been dug in the same lowland a thousand feet away. Does it show chalk on its walls? By piecing together such information, the geologist can generally establish the stratigraphic succession, discover the variations in thickness of beds, and ultimately plot their positions on a map and structure section.

Even in country with thick soil, it is still possible to apply the principles of geologic mapping and correlation by using data gained from excavations and well borings, or by geophysical methods (Chapter 21).

Limitations of Scale

Geologic maps, like all other maps, require a rigorous selection of data; they emphasize some features at the expense of others. The smaller the scale of the map, the fewer details that can be shown. In Figure 6-5, which shows only a few square miles of the Paris Basin near Epernay, details of thin layers above the chalk are shown that could not possibly be indicated on a map with the small-scale of Figure 6-1. The geologist must select his geologic map units to fit the scale of the map. The larger the map scale and the better the exposures, the larger the number of formations that can be shown within a given area, although the number per square inch of map remains about the same (compare Figs. 6-1 and 6-5).

The geologic map is a powerful tool, but in general, its preparation is only the first step in the geologic study of an area. The geologist, with map in hand, can interpret much of the geologic history recorded in the rocks—their mutual relations and attitudes and the episodes these features record. Other problems, such as those of determining the environments of deposition of the various strata and their ages, can often be solved only after further work, and particularly after careful study of the fossils contained in the rocks. Fossils are one subject of our next chapter.

FACTS, CONCEPTS, TERMS

USES OF GEOLOGIC MAPS

To simplify and enable us to visualize complex relations among rocks

To find valuable minerals hidden beneath soil or rock

To clarify the geologic history of an area

FUNDAMENTAL POSTULATES IN GEOLOGIC MAPPING

Law of Superposition (Chapter 3)

Law of Original Horizontality (Chapter 3)

Law of Original Continuity

Truncation by erosion or dislocation

GROUPING OF STRATA INTO FORMATIONS

CORRELATION OF OUTCROPS

Lithology

Sequence

Fossil content

Tracing of beds

STRUCTURAL ATTITUDE OF ROCK STRATA

Dip and strike

Relation of horizontal contacts to contours

Relation of dipping contacts to contours

V-ing of contacts in crossing stream valleys

Construction of geologic sections

TOPOGRAPHIC EXPRESSION AS AN AID IN MAPPING

In desert regions

In areas partially masked by soil

QUESTIONS

1. What differences in landscape would you expect if the rocks of the Paris Basin had been warped into a dome instead of a saucer-shaped basin?

2. Express a general rule relating contours and outcrop patterns of horizontal beds.

3. If you traced a thick lava flow for a mile and could not find its continuation, what possible explanations of its termination could you suggest?

4. What map pattern would a bed dipping vertically and striking north make across a ridge trending due east?

5. If you follow the contact between a shale bed and a sandstone bed across nearly level country for several miles and it leads you in an oval path back to the starting point, what inferences can you make, about the dips in the area?

6. Some of the buttes of the New Mexico desert are capped by basalt flows; others are volcanic plugs. How would you expect the map patterns of these igneous rocks to differ?

7. Draw a hypothetical geologic map showing a series of tilted beds that have been invaded by a sill and that also contain a buried lava flow. Indicate on the map a locality where you would expect to find fragments of the lava flow as inclusions in a sedimentary bed.

8. When a geologic contact V's downstream the direction of dip is always downstream also, but if the stream is a rushing mountain torrent a contact which dips *downstream* may actually V *upstream*. Show how this might happen, and frame a general law expressing the relation between the angle of dip of the contact and the gradient (slope) of the stream bed.

SUGGESTED READINGS

Adams, F. D. *The Birth and Development of the Geological Sciences*. Baltimore, Williams and Wilkins, 1938. [Especially Chapters 7 and 8.]

Mather, K. F., and Mason, S. L. *Source Book in Geology*. New York, McGraw-Hill, 1939. [Especially pp. 181-191, 194-204.]

7 STRATA, FOSSILS, AND TIME

FEW DISCOVERIES have had as much influence on the development of geology as the establishment of the principle that fossils can be used both in determining the succession within a rock series and in correlating rock outcrops that are widely separated, even those on opposite sides of an ocean. That many fossil shells found far inland are the remains of marine animals has been known for centuries, but their significance in earth chronology was not recognized until the early years of the nineteenth century. At first Cuvier, Brongniart, and Smith used fossils to identify beds in different outcrops very much as one might use unusual varieties of chert nodules or characteristic kinds of pebbles. But much more than this developed as they continued their work. Cuvier was one of the first to explore systematically the biologic relations among fossils, and the place of fossil organisms in the history of life on the earth. His studies of the fossil animals and plants of the Paris Basin have earned for him the title of "Father of Paleontology." **Paleontology** (derived from the Greek words for "ancient" and "existing things") is the name for the scientific study of ancient life. Some of Cuvier's conclusions about fossil relationships have proved incorrect, but others, more firmly based on field evidence, are basic to modern stratigraphy.

Correlation and Faunal Succession

The great advance made by Cuvier and Brongniart was to recognize that the differences in the fossils of the strata in the Paris Basin were systematic. When they arranged the fossils collected from various strata in the same order as that of the beds in which the fossils were found, they noticed that the fossil assemblages differed from one group of beds to another, and that the fossils from the lower (older) beds were invariably less like animals now living than those from higher (younger) beds. This was broadly true of all fossils—clams, sea snails, and all other kinds of organisms. Thus fossils were not only aids to correlation, but they also constituted a record of the changes in life forms throughout geologic time.

Cuvier's recognition that the older fossils differ more from modern forms than do younger ones implied two things: extinction of old forms of life and the development of new forms through geologic time. Neither of these conceptions was generally accepted before his day. In fact, the great Swedish naturalist Linnaeus, who established the systematic classification of animals that is used today, had only a few years before declared that "the existing species of animals are now as they were created in the beginning."

Cuvier's discoveries disproved Linnaeus' idea but raised a new question: How did the new species arise? Cuvier answered this question incorrectly, as we shall see, but his discovery of extinction of old species and the rise of new ones was a significant step in the history of science, and led the way to other fundamental discoveries in both biology and geology. Among these were Darwin's theory of evolution and the establishment of a biologic basis for geologic chronology.

Geologic Chronology

Naturalists working in other regions soon found many other fossil species, as well as most of those described by Cuvier from the Paris Basin. And, learning from Cuvier to seek for faunal changes, they confirmed his discovery of a progressive change with time—the more ancient the fossil, the more it differs from a living form.

Intensive studies by paleontologists and geologists eventually showed two important facts about fossil species:

1. Once a species died out, it never reappeared in younger strata.

2. No two species are identical; a new species is thus never exactly like any extinct one.

These two discoveries are the basis of the most important key to geologic history, the **Law of Faunal Assemblages:** *Like assemblages of fossil organisms indicate like geologic ages for the rocks that contain them.*

Once Cuvier's and Smith's work had established the systematic changes in fossil assemblages in their areas, other students quickly spread the work over much of the earth. Parallel successions became known from many lands. Such successions, partly identical and partly supplementary, furnish the basis for the standard geologic column.

The Standard Geologic Column

Simple Early Column

As early as the middle of the eighteenth century, Italian and German geologists had classed their local rocks into three groups: Primary (rocks like granite and gneiss, with neither bedding nor fossils), Secondary (cemented sedimentary rocks, generally exposed in the mountains), and Tertiary (weakly consolidated sedimentary rocks of the lowlands, which rested upon the Secondary rocks). Though fossils from both Secondary and Tertiary rocks were known, distinctions among them from bed to bed were not used in the eighteenth century classification.

Standard Column

The present **standard geologic column** is made up of sequences of European formations because it was developed by expanding the stratigraphic sequences worked out by Smith, Cuvier, and Brongniart. It was pieced together in the nineteenth century from strata exposed in various parts of Europe. Its fossil assemblages form the standard of comparison for all parts of the world. Correlations that may extend across a continent, or even to another continent, are based on assemblages of fossil plants and animals. Such correlations are sometimes handicapped by the restriction of some kinds of fossils to specific environments of deposition so that they are found only in one part of the world, or in one kind of rock. On the other hand, many fossil species were cosmopolitan in distribution and of great population density. Correlation is greatly facilitated by the large number of former living things; thousands upon thousands of varied species are preserved in the fossil record.

The major subdivisions of the column are called **rock systems.** Most of the systems are represented, at least in part, in the area mapped by Smith and his early followers. Smith grouped the oldest strata in his section as the Old Red Sandstone. These rocks contain few fossils, being, in fact, largely landlaid beds, but to the south in Devonshire they interfinger with fossiliferous marine beds. The Old Red Sandstone is therefore now considered a part of the Devonian System named from Devonshire. Resting on the Old Red

Sandstone is a group of strata called by Smith the Mountain Limestone, and this series is in turn overlain by a succession of sandstones, shales, iron ores, and coals which Smith called the Coal Measures. These rocks and the underlying Mountain Limestone are now grouped together as the Carboniferous System, so named because of the abundance of coal in the rocks. Above the Coal Measures, Smith recognized a series of beds called the Magnesian Limestone, followed in turn by the New Red Sandstone. Both these formations contain few fossils and are largely of continental rather than marine origin. The Magnesian Limestone is now considered part of the Permian System, named from a province in Russia just west of the Ural Mountains, where marine fossiliferous rocks occupy a similar stratigraphic position. The New Red Sandstone, on similar grounds, is now regarded as part of the Triassic System, named from the three (triad) formations that are found just above the Permian System in Germany.

Overlying the New Red Sandstone, is a series of richly fossiliferous beds which Smith divided into many formations, partly because the abundant fossils facilitated correlations, and partly because the canals he constructed lay across these beds so that he had ample time to work out the details of their succession. Some years later, many identical fossils were found in the rocks of the Jura Mountains of Switzerland and France, whence the Jurassic System derives its name. Jurassic rocks also underlie the Lower Chalk of the Paris Basin.

Toward London, the Jurassic strata are overlain by greensand, and this in turn by chalk. This series is grouped as the Cretaceous System (from the Greek word for chalk). The fossils are identical to those in the chalk of the Paris Basin. Overlying the chalk, Smith found the London Clay, a group of beds rich in fossils like those in the beds above the chalk of the Paris Basin. These beds, both in England and France, are now regarded as part of the Tertiary System, a name that has survived from the classification of the eighteenth century.

More than a generation after Smith, the stratigraphy of the highly disturbed rocks below his Old Red Sandstone was worked out. Three new systems were recognized: in descending order Silurian, Ordovician (both names of old British tribes), and Cambrian, from the Latin name for Wales.

The Cambrian strata are the oldest rocks that contain fossils in any abundance, although sedimentary rocks thousands of feet thick are found beneath them in some regions. In this book, all older rocks beneath the Cambrian are grouped together as the Precambrian. They have great bulk and complexity and are not easily divided into formations according to age, although they can be classified in various ways despite their lack of fossils (Chapter 18). Perhaps refinements in the dating of rocks by radioactivity, as mentioned later in this chapter, may some day enable us to classify the Precambrian rocks in an orderly chronological sequence, just as fossils have permitted us to classify the Cambrian and younger systems.

The systems of rocks in the standard geologic column are listed in Table 7-1.

Geologic Time Scale

The standard geologic column is the basis for the **geologic time scale.** The names applied to the systems of rocks are also used for the periods of time during which the respective systems of rocks were deposited. Thus, we use the term Carboniferous Period for the time during which the Carboniferous System —the Mountain Limestone and Coal Measures of Smith—were laid down. **Periods** (time) and **Systems** (beds) are further divided into **Epochs** and **Series,** respectively. For example, we say that the Comanche Series of Texas was deposited in the Early Cretaceous Epoch. More subdivisions are recognized among younger rocks than among older. Just as in human history, the data are more numer-

TABLE 7-1. *Geologic Column and Time Scale (as recognized by the U. S. Geological Survey); approximate ages from Holmes, 1947, Marble, 1950, and Knopf, 1957.*

ERA	SYSTEM OR PERIOD	EPOCH	APPROX. AGE IN MILLIONS OF YEARS FROM RADIOACTIVITY
CENOZOIC (*recent life*)	QUATERNARY (An addition to the old tripartite 18th-century classification)	RECENT PLEISTOCENE (*most recent*)	
	TERTIARY (Third, from the 18th-century classification)	PLIOCENE (*very recent*) MIOCENE (*moderately recent*) OLIGOCENE (*slightly recent*) EOCENE (*dawn of the recent*) PALEOCENE (*early dawn of the recent*)	17 (Miocene ?) 60 (Paleocene, New Jersey)
MESOZOIC (*middle life*)	CRETACEOUS (*chalk*) JURASSIC (Jura Mts., Europe) TRIASSIC (from tripartite division in Germany)		62 (Late Cretaceous, New Jersey)
PALEOZOIC (*ancient life*)	PERMIAN (Perm, a province in Russia) CARBONIFEROUS SYSTEMS (from abundance of coal in these rocks) 　PENNSYLVANIAN* 　MISSISSIPPIAN* DEVONIAN (Devonshire, England) SILURIAN (An ancient British tribe, the Silures) ORDOVICIAN (An ancient British tribe, the Ordovices) CAMBRIAN (Roman name for Wales)		230 (end of early Permian) 270 (Late Middle Devonian, Saskatchewan) 350 (end of Ordovician) 440 (Upper Cambrian, Sweden) 470 (Late Lower Cambrian, Alberta)
PRECAMBRIAN	Many local systems and series are recognized but no well-established worldwide classification has yet been attained.		600 (Late Precambrian, Africa) 2500 (Precambrian, Manitoba. At least 2700, possibly 3300, Rhodesia)

NOTE: Many provincial series and epochs have been recognized for the Mesozoic and older strata but the generally recognized subdivisions are Lower, Middle and Upper series (Early, Middle and Late epochs) of the respective Systems.

* Pennsylvanian and Mississippian Systems are not generally recognized outside the United States; elsewhere the Carboniferous System is regarded as a single system, on a par with Devonian or Cretaceous. Definitions in italic are from the Greek.

ous and the gaps in the record fewer the more recent the period with which we deal.

The periods are grouped into still larger categories called **Eras.**

Table 7-1 presents the column and time scale used by the United States Geological Survey. It gives also the sources of the names, as well as the ages of the periods as inferred from the radioactive minerals discussed later in this chapter.

Gaps in the Standard Column

Divisions of the standard column are based on abrupt changes in the fossil assemblages of the strata in Europe. These points of division, which mark the boundaries between different systems, were naturally those indicating long periods of erosion or nondeposition in the European stratigraphic series. The longer the period of erosion or nondeposition the more prominent the differences between fossils in adjacent systems would generally be. As stratigraphic work was extended to other continents, however, fossil assemblages intermediate between those of adjacent systems as recognized in western Europe were discovered.

With more and more stratigraphic work, the gaps in the column have continued to narrow. Beds containing fossil assemblages that pose "boundary problems"—that is, uncertainty about their correlation with the upper part of one European system or the lower part of the next higher—are thus present at one or more places on the earth for nearly every systemic boundary. Even the gap between the Paleozoic and Mesozoic Eras, long thought to represent an interval of time during which none of the present continents received deposits, is apparently bridged by nearly complete successions of beds in Nevada and in the Himalayas. Even in Europe, where the divisions were first established, further research has served to narrow the gaps in the record. For example, the Paleocene was established to designate strata that could not be referred with certainty to either the typical Eocene or the typical Cretaceous. Now we find that different paleontologists refer the

same strata (in Wyoming, for example) to the Cretaceous or to the Paleocene, depending on their appraisals of the relative affinities of the fossils of these beds with those found in one or another of the European sections.

The uncertainties posed by "boundary problems," however, are concerned largely with form instead of fact. Such disputed strata, it is generally agreed, must fill, or at least partly bridge, gaps in the sequence of formations in those areas of Europe that supplied the data on which the standard geologic column is based. Further detailed stratigraphic work is sure to fill other gaps. This is indeed a tribute to the precision of correlation by fossils instead of a criticism of its uncertainties. It seems likely that the gaps between systems in the standard column will ultimately all be bridged by fossiliferous strata at one place or another around the earth. The systemic divisions are purely arbitrary and convenient, rather than natural divisions applicable the world over.

Intercontinental Correlation

Thus, although the original divisions of the geologic column were based on stratigraphic relations of the beds, our *correlations of distant strata are necessarily based on a comparison of fossils,* not strata. Showing that there is an interruption in stratigraphic succession in the type area does not help correlate beds in a distant part of the world. A stratigraphic break in Texas, for example, cannot be used as evidence that the beds above it are Permian and those below Carboniferous. Such assignments of age to the Texas strata can be made only on the basis of comparison of fossils with those of the type sections of the geologic column.

Many difficult problems arise in trying to use fossils to correlate strata. Some of these will now be discussed.

LONG-RANGING FOSSIL SPECIES. In the century and a half since Cuvier and Brongniart began their work, studies of thousands of different species of fossils have shown that some shells, even from very ancient rocks, differ little from the shells of organisms now living. But such stable, long-enduring species of organisms are very few. Though a long-enduring species may be found to range throughout a thick series of strata, some of the fossils of other species associated with it generally change from bed to bed, until finally none of the original companions of the long-enduring species that were found in the lower (older) part of the series are present in the higher. Conversely, an abundant species may disappear in higher strata, though its associates persist. Individual species range through different thicknesses of beds, which must mean that the different organisms persisted unchanged through different spans of time (Fig. 7-1).

Obviously, short-ranging species are more useful in correlation than the persistent ones. But only occasionally can enough short-ranging forms, each with a slightly differing time-span, be found to supply clear-cut evidence for accurate correlation within a small part of an epoch. The most suitable fossils for correlation over wide areas are obviously those of species that lived in nearly all parts of the ocean or whose shells drifted far before sink-ing—that is, fossils of free-swimming or drifting oceanic organisms. The organisms must also have been abundant: unless they were, their chances of preservation as fossils in widely different environments is remote.

SEDIMENTARY FACIES AND FACIES FOSSILS.   In correlating rock strata by comparison of fossils, it is important to keep in mind the limitations to the spread of organisms imposed by their natural habitats. Many different depositional environments exist: floodplains of rivers, estuaries protected from the open sea, ocean beaches, coral reefs, and hundreds more. Each environment has its characteristic group of animals and plants, that live contemporaneously with the more or less different but equally characteristic groups of organisms found in other environments. For example, we do not expect to find the bones of antelopes in a coral reef, nor coral in a desert sand-dune. Similarly, during a particular span of past geologic time, we would not expect to find the same fossils entombed in all the varied deposits formed.

By analogy with similar modern organisms, we assume that some of the marine fossils represent free-swimming forms that could live in almost any part of the sea. Their shells, how-

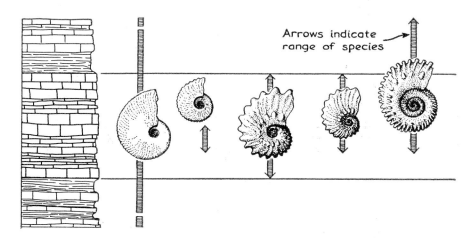

Figure 7-1.

Using fossils to date beds. The long-ranging species on the left is of no value in dating the limestone beds between the two horizontal lines, but the short ranges of the other species make them good time markers. The actual specimens were collected in England. (Data from S. W. Muller.)

ever, might be battered to pieces in the breakers and hence be preserved only rarely in deposits formed near the shore. On the other hand, some fossil organisms were bottom dwellers living only on muddy bottoms; their remains would not normally be found in limestone, or conglomerate, for they could not live in environments that permit such rocks to accumulate. Thus the fossils in ancient rocks of even the same age may differ because of variations in the conditions of deposition. Rocks of the same age that were formed in different sedimentary environments are said to represent different **sedimentary facies.**

Most fossil organisms could live only in one kind of environment and hence the fossils of each tend to occur in rocks of a particular sedimentary facies. The term **facies fossils** is generally used for groups of fossils found only in particular kinds of sediments. Thus we speak of one assemblage of fossils as the "limestone-reef facies." Along the bedding the limestone may change to shale containing a fossil fauna that lived on a mud bottom, a "shale facies fauna." Although the deposits were contemporaneous the two facies faunas may have no species in common.

One relationship that may occasionally be found between two facies fossils is shown in Figure 7-2. A fossil of a long-ranging species

(Fossil A) occurs above that of a shorter-ranging kind (Fossil B) in one region, but below it in another. Such reversals are generally the result of differences in the environment of deposition of the two fossils, but they may occur simply because of the greater time range through which one fossil species survived, or even because of accidents of preservation. Likewise, a particular fossil may be absent from a certain bed containing a second kind, though it is found both below and above that bed. The environmental conditions (sedimentary facies) might have changed during the life-span of the longer-ranging form, excluding it temporarily from the area of deposition, but allowing it to return when conditions again became favorable for its existence.

Despite these complexities—and there are still others—Cuvier and Brongniart's generalization has been abundantly justified: The older the rocks, the less their fossils resemble living forms; the younger the rocks, the more their fossils resemble living forms, particularly those found in similar depositional environments. The accumulation of data from many parts of the world now makes it possible to assign almost any collection of more than a few species of fossils—and some containing only a single species—to a fairly restricted part of the standard geologic column.

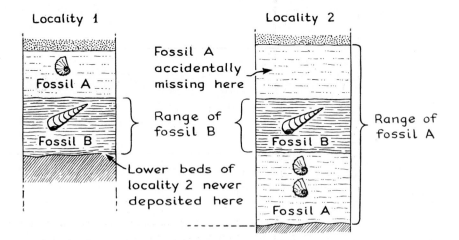

Figure 7-2.

The reversal of fossil sequence between two localities owing to differences in depositional sequence and accidents of preservation.

Early Estimates of Geologic Time

Cuvier's discovery of the extinction of some species of animals and the rise of new ones led him to the erroneous conclusion that there had been a series of catastrophes in geologic history. These, he believed, destroyed all existing life, and following each a whole new fauna was created: this doctrine, called Catastrophism, was doubtless in part inspired by the Biblical story of the Deluge. Buffon, a French naturalist, had earlier estimated from some crude experiments that it would have taken the earth about 75,000 years to cool from the white heat he assumed it must once have had to its present temperature. Only during the last 40,000 of these years would its temperature have been low enough for life of the sort we know to exist. Cuvier, who accepted Buffon's estimate, thought he could recognize four distinct faunas, and so assumed that during the past 40,000 years there had been at least four catastrophes that had destroyed all existing creatures. Following each a new creation had repopulated the earth. The creation described in Genesis was thought to be the most recent in the series, and occurred about 6,000 years ago—a date obtained by adding the genealogical ages from Adam to Christ as given in the Old Testament.

But even as Cuvier expressed this belief, the evidence was already at hand to disprove it: evidence showing that all concurrently existing species do not die out simultaneously, but that the individual species change and become extinct in an overlapping sequence. One fossil species may die out, but its contemporaries continue on until they too, each in its own time, are succeeded by others. There is no basis for the belief that a catastrophe destroyed all existing species, nor that new species all arise at once. Part of Cuvier's error lay in confusing facies faunas with new creations, for in the Paris Basin a continental environment commonly succeeded a marine one —but part of the confusion, no doubt, was due to the human predilection to fit his ideas into those current at the time. This trait is still with us, in science as well as other activities, and serves too often to color judgments that should be objective.

Cuvier's theory was short-lived; Hutton and Lyell urged the Uniformitarian view, and on this basis students soon arrived at a wholly new and more accurate way of assessing evidence of the earth's age, and of the changes in its fossils.

Modern Estimates of Geologic Time

With the building of the geologic column came a growing appreciation of the vast duration of geologic time. Contemplation of even the time required to lay down the 500-foot thickness of chalk in the Paris Basin is disturbing to the man who thinks of time only in terms of the span of human life. The strata of the chalk are composed of the skeletons of minute animals and plants. Similar deposits are accumulating today at rates so low as to defy measurement—certainly no more than a few inches per century and probably much less. Yet the chalk represents only a small fraction of the Cretaceous system, and the whole Cretaceous period is a small part of geologic time.

It was not only the great thickness of sedimentary deposits that impressed geologists with the immensity of geologic time, but also the vast parade of life recorded by the fossils —the development of thousands upon thousands of new species and the gradual dying out of whole fossil assemblages and their replacement by new ones can only be conceived of as involving millions of years, unless the rate of development and spread of new species was far more rapid in the past than at present.

One simple and obvious way to measure the duration of geologic time, it would seem, is to add the greatest thicknesses of the strata representing each period to obtain the total thickness of strata for all geologic time and divide this total by the present annual rate of sedimentation. This might be thought to give the length of geologic time in years.

But so many doubtful assumptions are involved in this approach that it is meaningless. How can we find an "average" rate of sedimentation when we know that it may take a century to lay down less than an inch of chalk, whereas a desert cloudburst may deposit forty feet of gravel in an hour? Rates of sedimentation vary so greatly and have been measured so seldom that an "average" annual rate can only be guessed at. Therefore, this method can give only a rough approximation of the length of geologic time; by using it the British geologist Sollas estimated (1899) that the length of time since the beginning of the Paleozoic could have varied from 34,000,000 to 75,000,000 years. His larger figure included a guess at the length of lost intervals in the record: such guesses are interesting but far from reliable, as we shall see.

Age of the Ocean

The Irish scientist Joly was more ingenious. He reasoned that the salt in the sea must have been weathered from the rocks and carried to the oceans by streams. As little is blown out by the wind or deposited by sea water evaporating in desert lagoons or on tide flats, the oceans must be growing saltier; if we could measure their present salt content and compare it to the annual increment, we might determine the age of the sea. From the many ions contained in sea water, Joly selected sodium as the one best suited for such a measurement.

The approximate volume of the sea has been determined from its mean depth and area, and its composition is known from thousands of analyses (Appendix IV, Table 4). Its sodium content can be roughly computed. Similarly, we have thousands of analyses of river waters, and from stream gages we know fairly well how much river water flows annually to the sea. From these figures, Joly estimated the annual increment of sodium. Dividing the amount of sodium in the sea by

the amount added annually by rivers, he found the age of the ocean:

$$\frac{15,627 \times 10^{12} \text{ tons of Na}^+ \text{ in the oceans}}{15,727 \times 10^4 \text{ tons of Na}^+ \text{ added annually}} = 99,400,000 \text{ years.}$$

Joly, of course, knew he was disregarding many factors. For one thing, river discharge has probably not been constant throughout geologic time. Furthermore, not all the sodium in present-day rivers is directly derived from weathered rocks, as it may have been in the geologic past: much comes from sewage and industrial waste, some in the water near river mouths is windblown from the sea, and much is leached from old marine sedimentary rocks that were once deposited in ancient seas. The present annual increment is surely higher than the average for the geologic past, but how much higher cannot be ascertained.

On the other hand, there are great deposits of rock salt derived from evaporated sea water among the stratified rocks. If returned to the sea, they would increase the oceanic tonnage of sodium, but we do not know how much. Furthermore, sodium ions react with clay and so are removed from sea water in muds. Finally, much sea water is trapped in the pores of marine sedimentary rocks and thus the sodium contained in it has been removed from the ocean.

Clearly, Joly's 99,400,000 years is far too short a time, but we cannot make a quantitative correction; we can only conclude from this argument that the ocean has existed for a very long time.

The Radioactive Clock of the Rocks

When Becquerel discovered radioactivity (1896), he opened new vistas in every science. Among these was the discovery that it is possible to establish some points on the geologic time scale in terms of years by a study of the rate of decay of radioactive minerals contained in some rocks. This method proved that all previous estimates of the duration of geologic time were far too short.

A few elements, among them uranium and

thorium, disintegrate spontaneously into other elements. The atomic nuclei of such elements are intrinsically unstable and emit alpha particles (charged helium atoms) and beta particles (electrons). Each nuclear emission, whether of an alpha or beta particle, transforms the atom into a different element. Starting with uranium 238 (U^{238}), there are 15 steps in this natural process: 8 alpha particles and 7 beta particles are emitted, yielding ultimately an isotope* of lead (Pb^{206}) which does not disintegrate further.

The rate of spontaneous disintegration varies tremendously with different elements. It is expressed in terms of the element's "half-life," which is the time required for half its atoms to disintegrate. The half-life of some members of the U^{238} series is only a fraction of a second; for U^{238} itself it is 4,500 million years. If we start with one gram of U^{238}, in 4,500 million years half a gram will be left; in another 4,500 million years, only a fourth of a gram remains and so on. The other half (or three-fourths) has changed into lead, helium ions, electrons, and very small amounts of intermediate elements in the decay series. In no experiment has the disintegration rate been changed by heat, pressure, state of chemical combination of the element, or time. The half-life of a radioactive element is thus considered a constant, that is, a fundamental property of the element.

Many minerals, most of them comparatively rare, contain measurable amounts of uranium. By analyzing such minerals and finding the ratio of the uranium-derived lead to the uranium still remaining, their age can be computed, provided that certain conditions are fulfilled.

The analyses are difficult. The proportions of the different isotopes of lead must be determined, so that lead of radioactive origin may be distinguished from any ordinary lead

---

* Isotopes are atoms of the same chemical element which have different atomic weights. The heavier isotopes contain additional neutrons in the nucleus, giving the extra weight, but the isotopes of one element all contain the same number of protons.

that may be present. Ordinary lead is a mixture of four isotopes, with an atomic weight of 207.21. Uranium-bearing minerals contain U^{235} as well as the more abundant U^{238}, and many contain thorium. Each of these three disintegrates to yield a lead having a different atomic weight: Pb^{207}, Pb^{206}, and Pb^{208}, respectively. Common lead contains these, and also Pb^{204}, which is of nonradioactive origin. The many isotopes make it difficult to find the ratios accurately. The minerals analyzed must be absolutely fresh, for solutions circulating long after the mineral was formed might leach out the lead and uranium at different rates, thus producing great errors in the calculated age. Though hundreds of determinations have been made, relatively few meet the rigid requirements of analytical accuracy and freshness of material.

Many radioactive minerals crystallize from magma. Thus, dikes or other intrusive bodies that cut, say, Devonian rocks, and contain radioactive minerals, give us a minimum age for the Devonian in years. Pebbles of these intrusives found in younger strata give us in turn a maximum age for the younger beds. Unfortunately, few of the hundreds of analyses that have been made in trying to apply this method have yielded internally consistent analytical results—doubtless mainly because of differential leaching or metamorphic changes in the minerals. Nevertheless, enough have given roughly consistent results (5 to 10 per cent variation when different isotopes have been used) to make possible a crude dating of many of the geologic systems by this method. Some of the best of these are given in Table 7-1.

Although the present development of this method leaves something to be desired—differential leaching of lead and uranium isotopes or addition of extraneous atoms quite often result in different ostensible ages computed from U^{238}/Pb^{206} and from U^{235}/Pb^{208} ratios—still we have here a fairly consistent method of dating some geologic events in years, and one that, in spite of its shortcomings, is extremely useful. Radioactive analyses are, indeed, the only method available for interregional correlation of Precambrian rocks. In addition to the disintegration of U to Pb, similar radioactive pairs such as K^{40}/A^{40} (potassium to argon) and Sr^{87}/Rb^{87} (strontium to rubidium) have been used for dating. Indeed, it seems likely that the potassium-argon ratio may ultimately prove widely applicable to many rocks because it can be determined from mica, a common and widespread mineral.

The oldest mineral thus far measured from North America (2,500 million years) came from southeast Manitoba; some from Rhodesia are about 800 million years older. The oldest minerals analyzed were collected from igneous rocks that have invaded rocks that are clearly still older. Since some meteorites have given ages as great as four and a half billion years, many scientists consider it likely that this may be the approximate age of the solar system.

RADIOCARBON, THE "SWEEP-HAND" OF THE RADIOACTIVE CLOCK. Uranium and the other radioactive elements we have discussed are naturally radioactive. Certain other elements can be made radioactive by bombardment with other charged particles. Among these, the most significant for use in geologic dating is carbon. Most carbon, such as that in coal, is the isotope C^{12}, with a constant small admixture of C^{13}. But carbon in the carbon dioxide of the air also contains a small amount of C^{14}. Cosmic rays from outer space bombard the nitrogen of the air to produce this isotope. Radiocarbon, as C^{14} is called, disintegrates spontaneously to N^{14}. It has a half-life of only about 5,570 years. The fact that the ratio of isotopes in the carbon from living matter is the same as that of the carbon in the air means that a measurement of the C^{14} content of an old piece of wood or

shell may give a measure of the time elapsed since the organism died and hence ceased to acquire new carbon from the air or water.

The half-life of C^{14} is so short that within a few tens of thousands of years even the most accurate analyses can no longer measure the amount remaining; hence the method is valueless with materials more than about 40,000 years old. In fact, experimental errors in measurement are so great, compared with the small quantities to be measured, that ages greater than about 30,000 years cannot be considered accurate. The existence of radioactive carbon, however, gives us a way of measuring the age of wood or carbonate shells that are only a few thousand years old—so young that Pb/U ratios are useless, as the small amount of lead produced cannot be measured accurately. By the use of C^{14} ages, considerable advance has been made in working out the details of the history of the most recent geological times (Chapter 13).

All these methods, it must be remembered, give only approximate results. The possibility of differential leaching of uranium and of lead; of the addition of new lead or uranium; of the addition of new organic material to a buried carbon deposit by roots or soil bacteria, and many other factors—entirely aside from experimental errors of measurement—all introduce uncertainties into such age determinations. Unquestionably, many of them are in error. Yet there remains a consistent group of measurements—consistent not only among themselves but also with the geologic record—that makes it possible to give the ages of certain geologic events with considerable confidence. It is nearly certain that geologic time encompasses at least a few billion years. Organisms comparable to many we know today have existed at least since the beginning of Cambrian time—a time span of nearly half a billion years.

FACTS, CONCEPTS, TERMS

QUESTIONS

1. Most of the standard geologic column is based upon strata deposited in the sea. What relations between these strata and land-laid strata might be found so that correlations can be made between widely separated land-laid deposits?

2. Inasmuch as all paleontologists agree that new species arise suddenly by mutation, why do they reject Cuvier's Theory of Catastrophism and New Creation?

3. Why do we find that gaps in the Standard Column of western Europe are commonly bridged by transitional fossil assemblages (and accompanying rock strata) in some other part of the world?

4. In attempting to correlate two limestone sequences, one in Kansas, the other in Pennsylvania, would a comparison of the physical characters of the limestones or of their contained fossils be most useful? Why?

5. Most radioactive minerals used in age determinations are derived from intrusive igneous rocks. How can these give data about the age of adjacent sedimentary or metamorphic formations?

6. Many geologic formations contain no fossils, even though they are obviously of sedimentary origin. What relations might they show to other rocks which would permit determination of their geologic age?

7. In selecting material for age determinations by the radiocarbon method, why must we be very careful to choose material that could not have been penetrated by roots, or infested by insects or bacteria after it was deposited?

SUGGESTED READINGS

Brown, Harrison. *The Age of the Solar System,* Scientific American, Vol. 196 (1957), pp. 81-94.

Knopf, Adolph. *Measuring Geologic Time,* Scientific Monthly, Vol. 85 (1957), pp. 225-236.

Mather, K. F. and Mason, S. L. *Source Book in Geology.* New York, McGraw-Hill, 1939. Pp. 12-13, 47-48, 174-175, 192-200.

Simpson, G. G. *The Life of the Past.* New Haven, Yale University Press, 1953.

Zeuner, F. E. *Dating the Past: An Introduction to Geochronology.* 3d ed. London, Methuen, 1952.

MOVEMENTS OF
THE EARTH'S CRUST

IN CHAPTER 5 we noted that many different moving agents erode away the surface of the land. In Chapter 7 we reviewed evidence for the very great antiquity of the earth. Clearly, if some other process did not counteract erosion, the land would long since have been reduced to plains near the level of the sea. Do the rocks reveal evidence of changes of level? What raises the mountains and plateaus so that erosion can work on them?

A miner deep in an Illinois coal mine who unearths a fossilized tree stump with roots spreading in the position in which they grew can only conclude that this tree—now hundreds of feet underground, even below sea level—once grew on the surface of the earth. Similarly, in copper mines of northern Michigan, ore comes from typical stream-deposited conglomerates and from the scoriaceous upper part of basalt flows now a mile underground. The land surface must have been warped downward since the basalt was erupted and the stream gravel deposited. On the other hand, the marine fossils that Cuvier and Brongniart found in the Paris Basin clearly suggest that a former sea floor has been uplifted. Climbers in the Himalayas bring back pieces of marine limestone full of fossil shells from altitudes greater than 20,000 feet. These and many other examples show that land and sea are not always fixed in position; in some

places they must have risen or fallen and even changed place during the geologic past.

How are such changes of level brought about? No one has ever seen a single convulsion that caused movement of a thousand or several thousand feet of the earth's crust. Can it be that repeated movements of only a few inches or feet at a time might, over a long period of time, raise or lower the earth's surface enough to account for total displacements measured in thousands of feet?

Measurable Displacements of the Earth's Crust

Displacements during Earthquakes

Spectacular but relatively small earth movements have accompanied many earthquakes. In Chapter 19 some earthquakes that devastated densely populated areas are described. During these earthquakes the ground cracked open and the earth's crust was visibly displaced along the cracks. Roads, fences, strata, and other features that formerly extended straight across the site of the break were separated and offset in position (Figs. 8-1 and 19-2).

Breaks in the earth's crust along which slipping has taken place are called **faults.** Fault displacements observed during even the most severe earthquakes have been small—

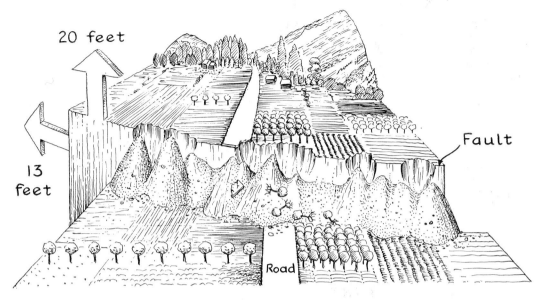

Figure 8-1.   *Cliff formed during the Mino-Owari earthquake, Japan. The displacement, as measured on the offset road, was 20 feet vertically and 13 feet laterally. (From a photograph by Koto.)*

seldom more than a few feet. In some the movement was vertical, producing a small cliff (Figs. 8-1 and 8-2); in others (for example, the destructive San Francisco earthquake of 1906) the fault walls slipped laterally, offsetting roads or fences; and in still others (for example, the Mino-Owari earthquakes in Japan), the slipping was oblique, with both vertical and horizontal components (Fig. 8-1). Table 8-1 lists some of the largest single displacements observed during historic earthquakes.

Perhaps a few recorded earthquakes may have caused even greater fault displacements on the sea floor than those recorded for land areas in Table 8-1. After an earthquake near Disenchantment Bay, Alaska, in 1899, the beaches stood 47 feet above the sea, and a wide expanse of sea floor became dry land. This is the greatest well-authenticated earthquake displacement known. The great Japanese earthquake of September 1, 1923, which destroyed much of Yokohama and Tokio with a loss of over 140,000 lives, was at first be-

LOCATION	DATE	MAXIMUM VERTICAL DISPLACEMENT (Feet)	MAXIMUM HORIZONTAL DISPLACEMENT (Feet)
Assam, India	1897	35	0 (?)
Owens Valley, California	1872	23	12
Mino-Owari, Japan	1891	20	13
San Francisco, California	1906	3	21
Sonora, Mexico	1887	20	0
Pleasant Valley, Nevada	1915	16	0

TABLE 8-1

Visible Fault Displacements Associated with Historic Earthquakes.

Figure 8-2. *Fault scarp (white line), 12 feet high, at the base of the Sonoma Range, Nevada, formed during the 1915 earthquake. (Photo by B. M. Page.)*

lieved to have been accompanied by a much greater displacement, but the evidence is inconclusive. Comparison of soundings in Sagami Bay made before and after the earthquake showed local changes of more than a thousand feet in the depth of the water. Detailed study suggests, however, that most of these changes were not a result of fault displacement but were caused by large slides set up in the unconsolidated muds and silts on the floor of the bay by the earthquake vibrations.

Thus the historic record indicates that no single observed fault displacement accompanying an earthquake has been great enough to account for marine shells in the rocks of high mountains, or for rooted stumps in mines below sea level.

Are these small displacements but minor steps in the recurrent growth of a fault? Examinations of the structure of the rocks on either side of earthquake fissures proves that they are. Although new faults with a few feet of displacement are known to have formed during earthquakes, most displacements have merely rebroken an old fault. The Pleasant Valley earthquake, which rocked the almost uninhabited desert of central Nevada in 1915, offers a good example. After the earthquake, the western base of the Sonoma Range was marked for 17 miles by a low cliff 1 to 16 feet high where none had existed before (Fig. 8-2). Figure 8-3 shows the break at one point along this new cliff. The 1915 displacement is clearly shown by the vertical offset in the surface of the alluvium. The small patch of alluvium clinging to the surface of the upthrown Sonoma Range block is 12 feet higher than the alluvial surface of the downdropped Pleasant Valley block. But the total displacement on the fault must be much greater, for the dolomite of the upthrown block (the range) abuts against the alluvium on the downthrown block (the valley) for a vertical distance far greater than 12 feet. Furthermore, a short distance away, gullies cut in the Pleasant Valley alluvium show that it rests not on dolomite like that across the fault, but upon lava flows. Immediately across the fault, however, dolomite and other sedimentary rocks extend to the crest of the Sonoma Range, which is more than 2,000 feet above the valley floor. Farther north, the dolomite and other sedimentary rocks at the summit of the range are capped by lava flows identical to those on which the valley alluvium lies. Obviously, therefore, the total vertical displacement along the fault has been at least 2,000 feet; perhaps it has been enough to account for the entire difference in level between valley and range—in some places more than 3,500 feet. Apparently, the 1915 displacement was only the latest of many similar ones.

Nearly all faults along which displacements have occurred within historic time show similar relations. Structures in the rocks on the two sides of the fault would not match if they

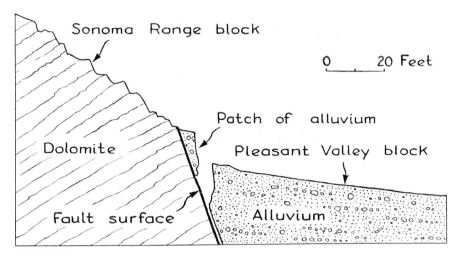

Figure 8-3.

Cross section showing the relation of the new 1915 scarp to the old fault surface, Sonoma Range, Nevada. (After B. M. Page.)

were merely restored to the positions occupied before the earthquake.

Measurable Slow Movements along Faults

The Buena Vista oil field is on a rounded hill that rises above the flat San Joaquin Valley in California. Soon after the first oil wells were drilled, a road was built across the hill, and several pipelines were buried in shallow ditches near it. A few months later the road-bed cracked, and a vertical displacement of less than an inch appeared. The road was patched, but broke repeatedly at the same place. Within a few years, eight of the buried pipelines had buckled up out of the ground, and they continued to arch upward slowly, a few inches each year (Fig. 8-4). In fifteen years each pipeline had been shortened by an amount that varied from 9 to 19 inches. Cleaning tools lowered into some of the wells stuck at different depths, thus showing that the steel well casings in the wells were slowly being bent out of line. In some, bending continued until the casing collapsed; in others the steel casings, when pulled from the ground 10 or 12 years after the wells were drilled, were found to have been bent about 15 inches horizontally. The casing failures in different wells occurred at depths ranging from 76 to

794 feet. What caused these curious phenomena?

By plotting on maps and sections all of the points where such disruptions occurred, it was found that they lie along a smoothly curving surface. This surface slopes downward into the ground at a low angle, cutting and offsetting the rocks (Fig. 8-5). Both the disturbance of man-made structures and the offset of the rocks prove that the surface is a fault. Apparently the rocks above the fault surface are moving slowly upward and south-

Figure 8-4. Buckling of heavy pipeline in the Buena Vista oil field, California. (Photo by T. W. Koch, courtesy of the American Association of Petroleum Geologists.)

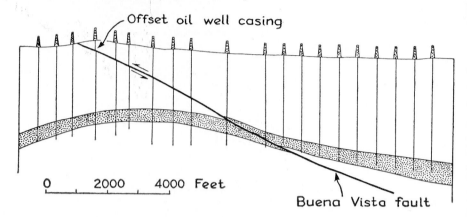

Figure 8-5.

Cross section showing the fault at the Buena Vista oil field. The half arrows indicate the relative movement. (From T. W. Koch, 1933.)

ward relative to those below, breaking the roadbed, bending the well casings, and buckling the pipelines out of the ground. The average rate of movement is 1½ inches per year. No earthquake shocks arising from this fault have been detected, even by seismographs.

Other examples of slow continuous movement along faults have been detected by re-surveys of the position and elevation of points established by precise triangulation and leveling (see Appendix I). Along a 90-mile stretch of the northeast coast of the island of Honshu, Japan, for example, differences between leveling surveys made in 1900 and 1933 show that the earth's crust in this area is sinking relative to sea level. The amount of sinking varies at different points, apparently because of the difference in movement between various fault-bounded blocks.

Measurable Slow Movements not Connected with Faults

So far we have described only displacements along faults, but there are other widespread and important slow movements of the earth's crust that are in no way related to faults. Although the rate of such movements is slow, it has been measured in a few places. The classic and perhaps best known example is that of an ancient Roman ruin, the so-called "Temple of Jupiter Serapis" on the seashore near Naples.

Only three upright columns and part of the floor of the original building are still in place. About 18 feet above the floor there is a line on the columns (Fig. 8-6): above this line the columns are smooth, below it they have been bored full of holes by marine rock-boring clams, some of whose shells can still be seen in the holes. It is reasoned that the building was built on dry land, that slow downward movements lowered the floor until it was 18 feet below sea level, allowing the marine clams to bore into the columns, and that later movements caused the land to rise again.

Along the shores of the Baltic Sea in Sweden and Finland a still more striking change of level has been observed for many years. The farmland and fresh-water marshes fringing the sea are littered with marine shells identical with those in the Baltic today. Over 150 years ago these conditions were correctly interpreted to mean that the land had risen out of the sea, and in order to find out whether the movements were still going on, monuments were set up at high-tide line along the shore. Today many of these monuments are a few feet above sea level, and some are as much as a mile inland. The maximum rate of uplift—3 to 4 feet per century—is along the northern Baltic. In some parts of Scandinavia there is little or no movement, and southern Denmark appears to be sinking about 2 feet per century. The rate of movement also appears to vary somewhat with time, as considerable differences from one decade to the next have been revealed by accurate tide gage records at many Baltic ports.

What causes this uplift? When the measured changes along the Scandinavian coast are compared with the obvious prehistoric evidence of uplift shown by raised marine beaches and terraces, an interesting relation appears. During the Pleistocene Scandinavia was covered by a huge sheet of ice like that which mantles Greenland today. The Scandinavian uplift is greatest along the northern Baltic, where the Pleistocene glacier was thickest (as determined by evidence that will be discussed in Chapter 13). In the approximately 12,000 years since the ice melted—dated by varved clays in glacial lakes (see Chapter 13) and radiocarbon analysis—the

northern Baltic has risen about 900 feet, an average rate of uplift of approximately 7.5 feet per century (Fig. 13-29). This close coincidence between ice thickness and uplift in Scandinavia is strong geologic evidence that removal of heavy loads on the earth's crust is accompanied by a flow of deep-lying rock to adjust the load. Much more evidence of the interrelation between some earth movements and changes of load are given in Chapter 10, but we shall also find that many earth movements cannot be explained by local loading.

There are many examples of similar crustal movements. Off Denmark and Japan, garbage heaps left by primitive man and accumulations of charcoal and ashes marking the position of ancient camp-fires have been found 5 to 40 feet below the surface of the sea. Obviously no one could have built a campfire beneath the sea. Tide gages show that some

Columns of the so-called "Temple of Jupiter Serapis," Italy, with high-water marks about one-third of the way up. (Photo by E. F. Davis.)

Figure 8-6.

harbors in Chile, Denmark, Japan, and elsewhere are slowly deepening. Other Japanese harbors are growing shallower, a few at the comparatively rapid rate of 1 to 3 feet every fifty years. Ships can no longer enter them, and formerly submerged rocks are now visible. These changes have been recorded for so short a time, however, that their evidence of the rate of crustal movements is inconclusive. A few reliable measurements extending over 75 years or more indicate that such movements are very, very slow. Nevertheless, since many significant features in the landscape clearly result from such movements, they must have been under way long before human history began.

Geologic Evidence of Displacements of the Earth's Crust

Emergence and Submergence along Coasts

Along most of the world's coastlines there is evidence of geologically recent (although prehistoric) crustal movement. The lobster fisherman who sets his traps off the Maine coast now and then brings up fragments of peat composed of the remains of fresh-water plants like those in swamps on the nearby land. Almost every New England stream ends in a tidal estuary. Dredgings from the bottom of many of them reveal river-deposited silts filled with decomposed grass roots, and thinly stratified clays that were formed in fresh-water lakes and marshes. All of these must have been deposited above sea level.

On a clear day, a person flying over the shallow southern part of San Francisco Bay can see former stream channels on the bay floor. These channels, though interrupted by deltas or small wavecut features at the shore, are clearly underwater continuations of the streams now entering the bay. They have been submerged either by subsidence of the land or by a rise of the sea. Not far away, near Stockton, California, water wells drilled to depths of more than a thousand feet below sea level penetrate buried soils, river silts containing grass roots, peat that once accumulated in fresh-water marshes, and other land-laid deposits, throughout their entire depth.

High above the reach of present waves, along the shores of Alaska, Newfoundland, Oregon, Italy, and many other lands, are abundant relics of former shore-lines—barnacle shells still attached to the rocks on which they grew; rocks bored by marine clams (many with shells still in the holes); sea cliffs, sea caves, and other erosional features carved from solid rock by former waves; and deposits of shell-strewn sand drifted along ancient beaches by longshore currents. Conspicuous marine terraces border many sea coasts (Fig. 8-7 and Fig. 16-16). Although in many places they are covered by sand and other detritus washed down from the hills, or have been partly cut away by streams since their uplift, most of them preserve sands that contain abundant marine shells, proving that they are upraised beaches of ancient seas.

Figure 8-7.   Uplifted marine terraces, Palos Verdes Hills, California. (Airplane photo by John Shelton and R. C. Frampton.)

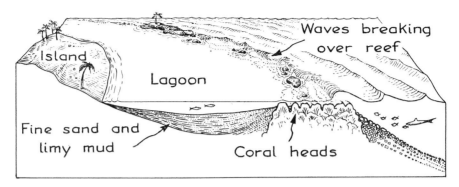

Figure 8-8.

Diagrammatic sketch of a typical coral reef.

Some striking examples of geologically recent changes of level are found in Indonesia, particularly in the region north of Sumatra, Java, and the southern Moluccas (Figs. 8-10 and 8-11). Coral reefs abound in the warm clear seas bordering these tropical lands (Fig. 8-8). These fringing reefs generally have relatively flat tops whose surfaces are mostly submerged, but are less than 150 feet below sea level. The reef-building coral animals cannot survive depths greater than 200 feet and are killed by a few hours' emergence. Coral limestone, however, is by no means confined

to the present depth of coral growth. Far above the reach of the highest storm waves are great terraces of white coralline rock exactly like that accumulating off the present shore. Some of these uplifted reefs are only a few feet above the sea, others surround mountain tops 3,000 feet high (Fig. 8-9).

Some uplifted reefs form continuous level collars around the smaller islands (Fig. 8-10). Others have been tilted, for if a reef that is a hundred feet or more above the sea on one side of an island is traced around to the other side, it may slope down until it passes below

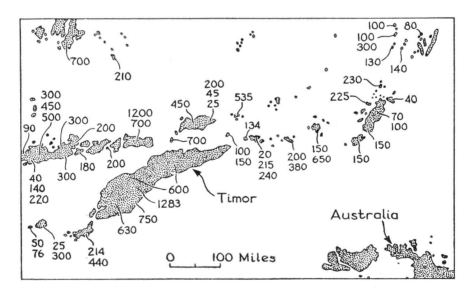

Figure 8-9.

Height, in meters, of uplifted coral reefs and stream channels in the southern Moluccas. (Redrawn from J. H. F. Umbgrove, Pulse of the Earth, *Martinus Nijhoff, 1947.)*

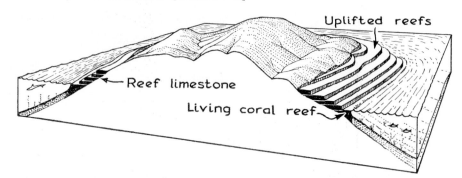

Figure 8-10.

Uplifted coral reefs on the island of Kissa, southern Moluccas. (After Ph. H. Kuenen, redrawn from J. H. F. Umbgrove, Pulse of the Earth, Martinus Nijhoff, 1947).

sea level. Still other uplifted reefs have obviously been displaced by faults.

Each of these raised reefs, of course, testifies to uplift of the land relative to the sea. But there is equally clear evidence that some former land areas are now submerged beneath the sea. The chief evidence comes from two sources: (1) examination of samples dredged from the sea bottom, and (2) detailed contour maps of the sea floor prepared from sonic soundings. Though coral reefs form only in comparatively shallow water, the dredge brings coralline deposits from depths of more than a thousand feet at various places in Indonesia. It also brings up muds that can have accumulated only in freshwater marshes or mangrove swamps, and poorly sorted silts and sands that must have been formed on river floodplains.

Soundings also prove that some of the shallow Indonesian seas were once dry land. The Sunda Shelf, between Borneo and Sumatra just west of the area of uplifted coral reefs shown in Figure 8-9, is a shallow sea, most of it less than 250 feet deep. Detailed sonic sounding shows clearly that the Shelf is a recently submerged land surface that was drained by two large rivers. The headwaters of these drowned rivers were the streams that still drain northern Sumatra and Java and southern and western Borneo (Fig. 8-11). Further proof of the existence of this submerged river system lies in the fact that the

fresh-water fishes and other stream-dwelling animals of southwestern Borneo are identical to those of eastern Sumatra, although a wide salt sea now separates the two areas.

Thus a fairly small part of Indonesia yields clear geologic evidence of both submergence and emergence within comparatively recent time. Side by side lie the submerged topography of the Sunda Shelf and the uplifted, tilted, and faulted coral reefs of the southern Moluccas. Elevated reefs are also found in Java and Sumatra, pointing to uplift that took place before the drowning of the river system

Figure 8-11. The rivers of Borneo, Sumatra, and Java, with their submerged extensions. (Redrawn from Ph. H. Kuenen, Marine Geology, John Wiley and Sons, 1950.)

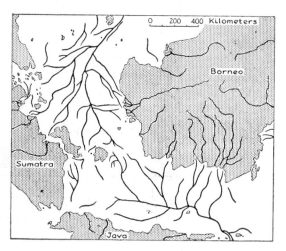

on the Sunda Shelf. Obviously, the movements that are now going on in this active part of the earth's crust are far from simple. They involve not merely vertical uplift and subsidence, but concurrent bending and folding of the rocks. Indeed, many of the tilted reefs fit into a regional pattern of folds in the basement rocks. Study of the rock structures of the islands shows that most of the long curving island arcs are complex upfolds or arches in the rocks, separated by basins and downfolds that in most of the area still lie beneath the sea. The movements that produced these upfolds and basins are still going on, warping the fringing coral reefs above the sea at one point, deeply drowning the reefs and the land-laid deposits enclosed by them at another, and forming a complex but slowly growing system of folds in the crust of the earth.

Contemporaneous Folding, Erosion, and Deposition

The folding of the earth's crust disclosed by uplifts and submergences in Indonesia suggests that possibly such movements are related to the formation of mountain ranges. Many mountains show warped and bent strata that must have been deposited as nearly horizontal sheets. They are now distorted into patterns far more complex than the Indonesian warps, but suggestive of them. Can we find geological links between the broad warping of Indonesia and the more intense localized folding of mountain ranges such as the Alps and Appalachians? Let us consider first the relatively simple warps and folds in the lava flows that make up the eastern foothills of the Cascade Mountains in the northwestern United States.

In central Washington and northern Oregon the walls of the canyons of the Columbia River and its tributaries reveal flow upon flow of black basalt. The flows are 50 to 300 feet thick, and, unlike those seen by Werner at Stolpen have relatively little interbedded sedimentary material. Here and there, however, thin sheets of river gravel separate the flows, showing that streams did advance onto the barren volcanic plain after some eruptions, only to be overwhelmed by new lava flows. Elsewhere, thin layers of ancient red or black soil containing petrified (silicified) logs and tree stumps, some of the latter with their roots still spreading out in the soil, appear between the flows (Fig. 8-12). Time enough had elapsed for the scoria on the surface of the flow to weather into soil and for a forest to grow on it before a new sheet of lava devastated the area. In other parts of the

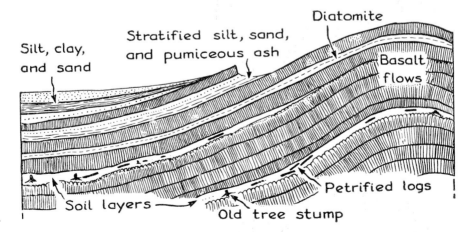

Figure 8-12.

Cross section of lavas and interbedded sediments near Yakima, Washington. The length of the section is one mile, its height 1,000 feet.

canyons thin layers of a brilliant white rock with paper-thin stratification contrast strikingly with the basalt. Petrographic examination shows that this white rock is made up almost entirely of the siliceous skeletons of minute one-celled plants called **diatoms.** Similar white diatomaceous deposits are being laid down today on the bottoms of shallow ponds and lakes nearby. In a few places, river gravels, floodplain silts, and diatomaceous deposits have buried the basalt flows under several hundred feet of river and lake deposits.

The point to be emphasized is that at many places these basalt flows and associated sedimentary rocks are no longer horizontal (Fig. 8-12). They rise and fall in great arches and troughs. On the flank of an arch, the scoriaceous top of a basalt flow and the diatomaceous strata above it may dip at an angle of 20 degrees (Fig. 8-12). At another place beds of gravel and sand between basalt flows dip at 70 to 85 degrees. No stream tumbling down a 70-degree slope could deposit gravel and sand upon it, nor could a molten basalt flow drape itself over a steep-sided arch and maintain a uniform thickness, nor paper-thin sheets of diatomite accumulate on a 20-degree slope in a lake. Each must originally have been nearly horizontal. Clearly, they were folded into the present arches and troughs long after they had been deposited.

What is the relation of these arches and troughs to the present topography? Central Washington is exceptional among mountainous areas in that the major topographic ridges coincide with arches in the rocks beneath. The flanks of the arches are scored by ravines extending straight down the slopes. Turbulent floods course down these ravines in the wet season. Aided by rillwash and downslope movements, they have removed most of the weakly consolidated river and lake deposits from the steep flanks of the arches, but the edges of these beds, cut off by erosion, can still be seen on the gentler slopes at the base of the ridges. In some places a few of the much more resistant basalt flows also have

been eroded, and in a very few localities the folds have almost been erased as topographic features. In general, however, the smooth curving surface of the arches, intact except for ravines, indicates that erosion has only started its task of erasing the uplifts. Many ravines do not have the usual concave-upward profiles of normal streams (see Fig. 12-19). The stream canyons and folds have been growing at the same time, and slow continuous arching of the lava sheets has modified the development of a normal stream regimen.

What is the relation of these topographic ridges to the troughs beside them? Conditions vary from place to place, but some of the partly dissected arches lie half buried in unconsolidated sediments deposited by streams and lakes on the floors of the troughs. The uppermost beds deposited in these troughs are nearly horizontal, abutting against the tilted rocks of the arches at high angles. In a few places, younger lava flows are interbedded with these young sediments, but they do not extend over the arches. They were erupted after the folding had started, and poured down the troughs (Fig. 8-13).

In a few of the larger river canyons we can see—and elsewhere, from records of wells drilled in the troughs, we can infer—that the older beds deposited in these troughs have also been somewhat folded. Where they abut against the neighboring basalt arch, they dip with the basalt, though at a lower angle (Fig. 8-12, upper left). Beds higher in the unconsolidated series dip similarly, but at still lower angles. In some troughs only the uppermost beds are nearly horizontal. These relations confirm the conclusion reached from a study of the erosion of the arches: While the troughs were being downfolded, sedimentation was also going on. In a few places, sediments were deposited on the trough floors almost as fast as the floors sank, and they were progressively warped as the fold developed.

Some of the sediment deposited in the troughs was eroded from the adjoining growing arches, but most of it was brought in by rivers from the rugged Cascade Mountains to

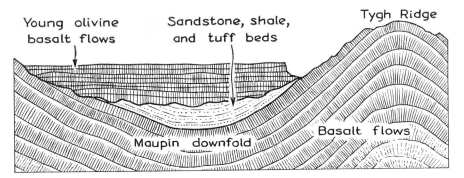

Young olivine basalt flows

Sandstone, shale, and tuff beds

Tygh Ridge

Maupin downfold

Basalt flows

Figure 8-13.

Cross section showing the relation of folded lavas and sediments to younger horizontal lavas. Near Maupin, Oregon.

the west, as shown by the abundant fragments of quartz, pumice, and andesite, materials which are not found in the rocks of the adjacent arches.

Such evidence of simultaneous erosion and sedimentation must mean that the folds grew very slowly. Flows originally horizontal have been so greatly folded that the surface of a particular flow at the crest of an arch is thousands of feet higher than the level at which it is cut by the drill on the bottom of an adjoining trough. But the folds did not grow to full size overnight. The first stage of the folding blocked out the respective areas of erosion (arches) and sedimentation (troughs). The rising folds dammed streams and impounded lakes in the troughs, interfering with normal stream development. In many places sedimentation was interrupted by tilting of already deposited beds. There is evidence that the folding movements are still continuing. Small streams in the area show abnormal gradients (Fig. 12-19), and patches of unconsolidated gravel cling to tilted slopes that are too steep to have originally received such deposits. Evidence from old surveys, although not wholly conclusive, suggests that the observed slowing of the flow of water in irrigation canals built 10 to 50 years ago may have been caused by folding movements that are slowly changing the gradient of the canals.

We could cite many other examples to show that warping and folding go on slowly, along with erosion and deposition. This has certainly been true in the young and growing mountain ranges bordering the Pacific Ocean on both sides, and in the Alpine-Himalayan belt across southern Eurasia.

Folds That Have Ceased to Grow

An older mountain range such as the Appalachians shows both contrasts and similarities to the structural features of Indonesia and of the Cascade foothills.

Figure 8-14 shows a cross section of the folded rocks of central Pennsylvania. This section depicts the position and attitude of the rocks deep underground as compiled from surveys of the many coal mines and from the evidence gained from exploratory drill holes.

The relation between the folds in the rock and the topography suggests immediately that the Appalachian folds, unlike those of Indonesia and the Cascade foothills, are not growing today and have not grown in the recent past. The Pennsylvania folds have obviously long been dead, for the arches are no longer ridges and the troughs are no longer receiving sediments. In fact, throughout the folded Appalachians, it is common to find that erosion-resistant rocks along the axis of a downfold now form a mountain summit, whereas adjacent upfolds with more easily erodible rock cores have been eroded to lowlands. Figure 8-15 shows a typical example. In the Appalachians, the topography is closely adjusted

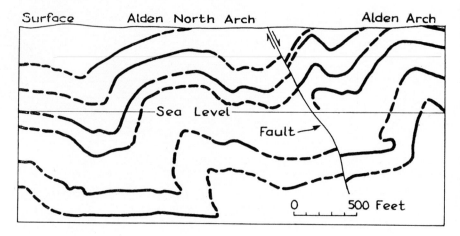

Figure 8-14.

Folds and fault in the coal measures of Pennsylvania. The solid lines are mined coal beds; the dashed lines are their plotted continuations. The actual thicknesses of the individual coal beds is from 2 to 15 feet. (From N. H. Darton, 1940.)

to the rock structure, but the adjustment is of a kind quite different from that of Indonesia and the Cascade foothills. In the Appalachians all of the ridges are underlain by resistant rocks and the lowlands by easily eroded rocks, a situation typical of old mountain regions where folds have ceased to grow. Stream erosion, uninterrupted by folding and warping, has had time to etch out the easily eroded rocks and leave the resistant ones standing in relief. This contrasts sharply with Indonesia and central Washington, where soft sedimentary rocks cap many mountain summits.

Can slow crustal movements that went on in the far-distant geologic past, long before the present streams developed their courses, explain the folded beds of the Pennsylvania coal mines? Erosion has clearly bitten much more deeply into the rocks of Pennsylvania than into those of central Washington or Indonesia. This deep erosion long ago removed any sediments that may have been deposited in the troughs while the folds were growing, or any shoreline features such as the coral reefs of Indonesia that might once have clung to the initially rising arches. We can easily measure the displacements by folding and faulting as revealed by the structure of individual coal beds in the mines, but we cannot tell whether these displacements took place in a few seconds or in the course of millions of years.

However, nothing in the Appalachian structure differs fundamentally in form from its counterparts in the Cascades or Indonesia. If deeply eroded, the Indonesian topography would resemble that of the Appalachians. In the higher and more rugged parts of the Cascades, northwest of the foothills area, erosion has already worn down some of the

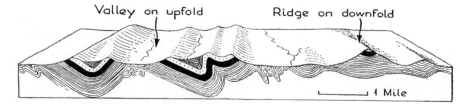

Figure 8-15.

The relations between folds and ridges in the Appalachians near Rogersville, Tennessee. (From Arthur Keith, 1905.)

basalt arches and stripped so much sediment from intervening troughs that the best evidence of their slow growth has already disappeared. Such transitional areas show that slow movements of the crust, like those now going on in Indonesia and Japan, are entirely adequate to explain the folds of Pennsylvania as well as those of the Cascade foothills. Again, we see another application of our fundamental postulate: "The present is the key to the past." Fossil shells at the tops of mountains, and soils and fossil plants in deep mines are only what we should expect and predict from the evidence of slow but measurable changes of level

taking place in different parts of the world today.

Furthermore, we can observe that, in some places and at certain times, the earth's crust has broken along clearly defined faults, just as a brittle rock might be expected to break. Elsewhere the rocks have folded like plastic dough. In places both kinds of deformation have occurred at the very surface of the ground. The reasons for this differing behavior and the ultimate cause of the deformation are both obscure. The questions they raise are discussed in Chapters 9, 10, and 20. They are among the greatest problems of earth history.

FACTS, CONCEPTS, TERMS

CRUSTAL MOVEMENT
  Fault displacements associated with earthquakes
  Fault displacements not associated with earthquakes
WARPING OF THE CRUST NOT ASSOCIATED
  WITH FAULTS
  Slow vertical movements

  Bending and folding of the crust
WARPING AND FOLDING IN RELATION
  TO MOUNTAIN STRUCTURE
  Characteristics of growing folds
  Time relations between erosion and folding
  Erosional patterns on growing folds versus
    those on dead folds

QUESTIONS

1. You are examining a fault in the field. What evidence would you look for in the landscape to tell whether this fault is still active, or long since dead?

2. Would you expect earthquakes to be more common in Indonesia or in the Central Atlantic States? Why?

3. In a certain mountain range all of the ridges and peaks are composed of erosion-resistant rocks that have been tilted, folded, and faulted. In another mountain range the rocks show about the same structure, but easily eroded rocks are locally exposed at the summits of the peaks, and many streams flow along the axes of downfolds. What can you say about the relative age of folding in the two regions? Explain.

4. As many as 13 nearly level marine terraces have been recognized at heights ranging between 100 and 1,300 feet above sea level in the Palos Verdes Hills near Los Angeles, California (Fig. 8-7). Suppose you were sent to examine this area. How could you tell whether these terraces were caused by folding and faulting of the earth's crust, or by removal of water from the ocean, perhaps to form ice sheets on the land during glacial epochs?

5. The rocks of the Swiss plain, just north of the intensely folded rocks of the Alps, show much gentler folds. The oldest rocks of the plain are marine, and about the same age as the youngest rocks of the Alps. The youngest rocks of the plain are nonmarine river gravels

and sands which do not appear in the Alps. The Alps, like the Appalachians, show no direct relation between folds and topography. What suggestions occur to you to account for the differences in the two areas?

6. The dolerite sill composing the Palisades of the Hudson, across from New York City, is several hundred feet thick where exposed along the west river bank. Sandstone beds above and below the sill dip to the west. How can you account for the absence of the sill on the east side of the river?

7. Cincinnati is built on Ordovician marine rocks. Both to the east and to the west, Silurian, Devonian, and Carboniferous rocks are exposed, dipping away from Cincinnati. What is the simplest explanation for this that occurs to you?

8. Draw three geologic sketch maps to represent the evolution of one of the folds in the Cascade foothills. In the first map, show an almost uneroded arch in the basalt lavas and overlying sedimentary rocks, with a little new sediment deposited in the adjoining troughs. In the second, show the fold after the sedimentary rocks and some of the lava have been stripped from the crest of the arch, and the adjacent troughs are half filled with new sediment. In the third, show the area after erosion has completely erased the arch as a topographic feature.

SUGGESTED READINGS

Daly, R. A. *Our Mobile Earth*. New York, C. Scribner's Sons, 1936.

Gilluly, J. *Distribution of Mountain Building in Geologic Time,* Geological Society of America Bulletin, Vol. 60 (1949), pp. 561-590.

Umbgrove, J. H. F. *The Pulse of the Earth*. 2d ed. The Hague, M. Nijhoff, 1947.

9 | RECORDS OF EARTH MOVEMENTS

EVIDENCE PRESENTED in Chapters 5 and 8 indicates that the earth's crust is affected by a constant interplay between processes of destruction (erosion) and processes of construction such as volcanism and uplift. Most folds and other crustal structures that we see today are not complete—they have been modified or even almost destroyed by erosion. In areas of strongly deformed rocks, if we are to read the record correctly, we must know not only the kinds of rocks, but we must also be able to analyze and understand their structure, for in structural features lie keys to an understanding of the changes that have taken place in the rocks since their original deposition as sediments or solidification from magmas. This chapter describes the geometry of the more common rock structures, and points out how they may be used in helping to unravel events of the past.

H. B. de Saussure (1740-1799), a Swiss geologist who was also an ardent mountain climber, did much to develop interest in **structural geology.** This branch of geology is concerned with the deformation of rock bodies and with interpretation of structural features in terms of the forces that caused them.

"Original Horizontality": The Key to Structure

It sometimes happens that a fundamental law of nature discovered by an early worker is forgotten by later generations. It must then be rediscovered anew. We have seen (Chapter 3) that by the middle of the seventeenth century Nicolaus Steno had proposed the Law of Original Horizontality—that strata are deposited in nearly horizontal layers, parallel or nearly parallel to the surface on which they accumulated. But another century passed before geologists became aware of the significance of Steno's law in interpreting the structural features of the stratified rocks.

While climbing in the Alps, de Saussure noted that the strata there appeared to be crumpled into folds like those formed when a rug is pushed together in a heap on the floor (Fig. 9-1), but he did not immediately interpret the folds in the light of the law advanced by Steno more than a hundred years before; instead, he at first assumed that the rocks had crystallized in the contorted forms in which he found them. It was not until he had carefully studied beds of typical water-deposited conglomerate projecting vertically from the ground that he recognized how absurd it is to believe that sheets of pebbles interlayered with sand, and all layers standing on end, could have been deposited in that position. The beds must have been tilted to the vertical after they were deposited and consolidated.

NW

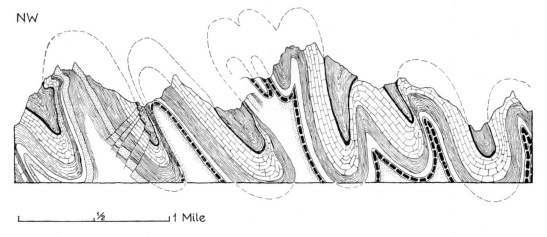

L_____½_____ 1 Mile

Figure 9-1.   Folded sedimentary beds, Saentisgebirge, Swiss Alps. (After A. Heim, 1922.)

Warps and Gently Tilted Strata

Over much of the earth the sedimentary strata still appear to be horizontal. If, however, we determine the elevations of several widely separated points on the upper surface of a seemingly horizontal bed, we generally find that the horizontality is not perfect. Either the bed had an original slope or else it has been slightly warped. But the rise and fall of such a bed is so irregular that its departures from the horizontal cannot be explained entirely by original dip; the bed must have been tilted since deposition.

The rocks of the Mississippi Valley afford good examples of such broad warps. In small exposures, the beds seem horizontal, but if we determine the elevation of many different points on the upper surface of a widespread formation, we find notable differences. For example, in oil wells drilled in southern Illinois, the Chattanooga black shale of Devonian age lies about 4,500 feet below sea level. When followed eastward, it rises steadily until it finally appears at the surface about 500 feet above sea level near Louisville, Kentucky. It also rises, though less steeply, to the north, south, and west. As another example, well records and mapping reveal that the bottom of the Colorado shale, a widespread marine formation of Cretaceous age, is about 3,000 feet below sea level near Williston, North Dakota, but rises to 2,000 feet or more above sea level near Shelby, Montana, and to 1,000 feet above sea level near Sioux City, Iowa. Such differences must have been caused by movements of the earth's crust.

Showing Warps on Maps

How can we represent broad warps on maps and sections? If the topography is rough, ordinary geologic maps and cross sections like those shown in Figure 6-2, may suffice. However, in areas of gently dipping beds and low relief, few beds will crop out at the surface, and hence a geologic map may be ill adapted to the needs of a mining or quarrying operation.

If we are mining a coal bed by open-pit methods (stripping away the overburden of barren rock and soil above the coal), a dip of only a few feet per mile may be critical to our operation. Suppose that at one place 25 feet of overburden must be stripped off to lay the coal bed bare. If the ground is flat and the coal bed dips 100 feet per mile (a little more than 1 degree), half a mile down-dip the overburden will have increased to 75 feet. Up-dip, in a little more than a quarter of a mile, the coal will have risen to the surface and been eroded away. If the ground is hilly, as in the Wasatch Plateau coal field of central Utah

(Fig. 9-2), or if the coal bed is irregularly warped instead of dipping uniformly, it may seem difficult to compute just what part of it can be mined economically by open pits and what part could better be mined from underground tunnels and shafts. To help solve such a problem we construct a structure contour map of the coal bed.

STRUCTURE CONTOUR MAPS. A **structure contour map,** like a topographic map (see Appendix I), uses contours to represent lines of equal elevation. But whereas a topographic map depicts the surface of the ground, a structure contour map shows the surface of a single bed as it would appear if all the rocks above were stripped away. If we removed all the overburden from a coal bed and then made a topographic map of the newly exposed surface of the coal, the result would be a structure contour map of the coal.

But how is it possible to make a structure contour map without actually excavating down to the coal? Figure 9-3, a map of the area sketched in Figure 9-2, illustrates some steps that will enable us to get control points for the structure contours. Figure 9-3 is a combined topographic and geologic map upon which the structure contours of the coal bed have been superposed. The outcrop of the Hiawatha coal bed is shown by a heavy black line. Notice that the contours showing the ground surface do not quite parallel the outcrop of the coal—the strata have therefore been tilted since deposition. For example, there are seven places (numbered 1 to 7 on Fig. 9-3) in the ravines north of Miller Creek where the 8,250-foot contour crosses the top of the coal bed. At each of these points, the top of the coal is 8,250 feet above sea level. Thus we have seven control points upon the surface of the coal through which to draw the 8,250-foot structure contour. The structure contour is thus a line on the surface of the coal bed where it is 8,250 feet above sea level (or was before erosion removed part of it). On the south wall of Left Fork Canyon, there are ten points where the coal bed intersects the 8,000-foot topographic contour, giving us ten control points for drawing the 8,000-foot structure contour. Other control points can be obtained by marking the intersections of other

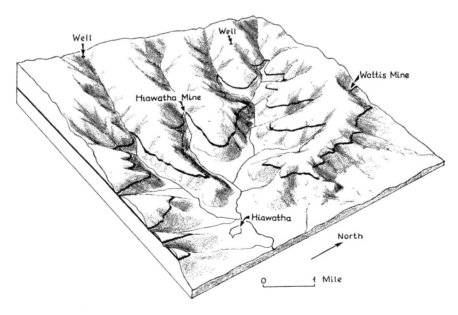

Figure 9-2.

Relief diagram of a part of the Wasatch Plateau coal field, Utah. (From a map by E. M. Spieker, U. S. Geological Survey.)

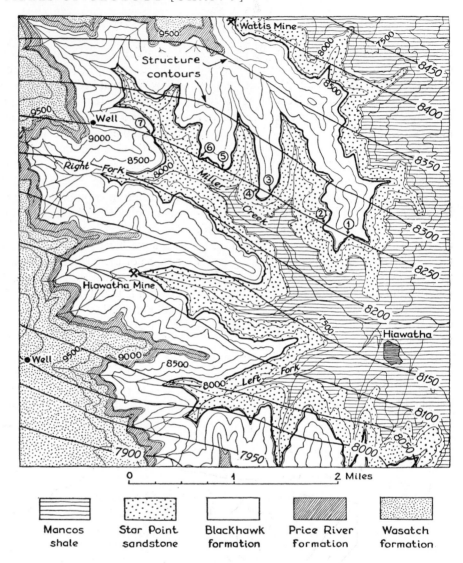

Figure 9-3.

Mancos shale | Star Point sandstone | Blackhawk formation | Price River Formation | Wasatch formation

Topographic, geologic, and structure contour map of the area shown in Figure 9-2. (Modified from E. M. Spieker, U. S. Geological Survey.)

topographic contours with the coal. Still other points can be obtained from borings and wells. For example, a well drilled on the ridge north of the Right Fork of Miller Creek penetrates the top of the coal bed 750 feet below the surface. Since the curb (top) of this well is on the 9,000-foot topographic contour, the coal bed directly below must be at 8,250 feet, giving us another point through which to draw the 8,250-foot structure contour.

The coal bed is overlain by the Blackhawk formation. The thickness of this formation can be measured on the walls of several of the canyons. Five such measurements in different parts of the area give its thickness as 750, 775, 725, 740 and 760 feet. The variation is not systematic in one direction, so we can accept 750 feet as the average thickness. Therefore, at any point where a topographic contour intersects the top of the Blackhawk formation we can obtain the approximate elevation of the coal bed directly below by subtracting

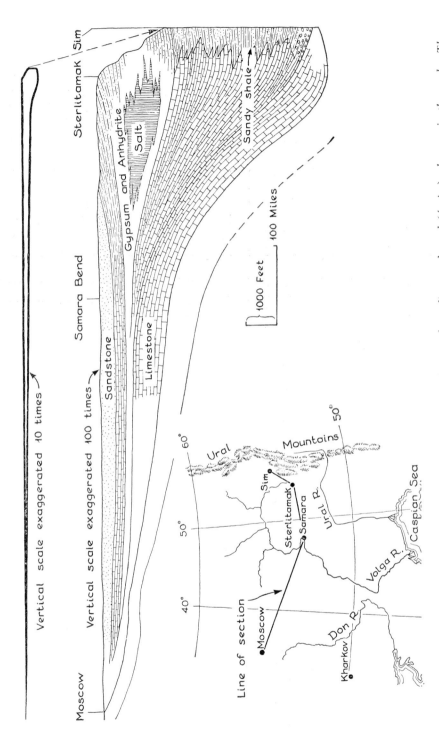

Figure 9-4. Cross section of the Moscow Basin, Russia, showing long-distance lateral (facies) changes in the rocks. These can be plotted only because of the greatly exaggerated vertical scale. (After C. O. Dunbar.)

750 from the elevation of the topographic contour. The position of the 8,000-foot structure contour near the west edge of the map was determined in this way: A well drilled on the 9,750-foot topographic contour is not deep enough to penetrate the coal, but at a depth of 200 feet it does cut the top of a thin bed of limestone which, from measurements on canyon walls, is known to lie 550 feet above the base of the Wasatch formation. The Price River formation, which lies between the Wasatch formation and the Blackhawk formation, is 250 feet thick, as determined by measurement at several points. Thus, at the site of the well, the coal bed must lie 200 feet (depth to the limestone), plus 550 feet

(distance from top of limestone to base of Wasatch formation), plus 250 feet (thickness of Price River formation), plus 750 feet (thickness of Blackhawk formation)—a total depth of 1,750 feet—below the surface. Since the elevation of the surface is 9,750 feet, that of the coal is 8,000 feet at this point; and we have another point through which to draw the 8,000-foot structure contour. Many other elevations can be determined by similar methods; enough to draw structure contours on the Hiawatha coal with reasonable accuracy.

Once such a structure contour map has been prepared, it is easy to find the amount of overburden above the coal at any particular point. This is done by subtracting the

Figure 9-5. *Airplane view of an eroded plunging anticline in Iran. The plunge is away from the camera. Note how the beds dip away from the axis of the fold. (Photo by Aerofilms, Limited, through courtesy of John Shelton.)*

Figure 9-6.   *Airplane view of an eroded plunging syncline in northwest Africa. The plunge is*
to the left. Note how the ridges formed on resistant beds clearly indicate dips
toward the axis of the fold. (Photo by U. S. Air Force.)

elevation shown by the structure contour from that shown by the topographic contour for the point on the surface directly above.

CROSS SECTIONS WITH EXAGGERATED VERTICAL SCALE. For certain purposes, geologic cross sections drawn with a greatly exaggerated vertical scale are useful in depicting gently dipping rocks. Such exaggeration, of course, distorts the form of the features shown. It gives a wholly erroneous idea of the dip by oversteepening it, and also a false impression of the size of the structures, but it does permit us to plot thin formations that could not otherwise be shown and to emphasize lateral changes in the sedimentary rocks. Such sections emphasize, even though they distort, slight changes in dip, small basins, local upwarps, and other minor structures. For example, Figure 9-4 shows the structure beneath the Moscow Basin. The large cross section is plotted with a vertical scale that is 100 times that of the horizontal. The lateral gradation of limestone to shale, and of salt to various other kinds of rock is clearly shown,

although such gradations could not have been plotted on the section with a 10 to 1 exaggeration shown in the same figure. Had the section been drawn to true scale (vertical equal to horizontal), the entire thickness of all the beds would have fallen within a single pencil line. It must be kept in mind, however, that when the scale is exaggerated 100 times, beds that have a true dip of not more than 1 degree will appear to dip 45 degrees or more in the section.

Folds

The records left by intense crustal movements can be seen clearly in the great mountain chains—for example, the Alps, on which de Saussure did his pioneering work. But steep folds, large faults, and other records of strong deformation are not confined to lofty mountain ranges of the present day. In some areas, repeated and long-continued periods of erosion have destroyed mountain ranges that must once have towered as far above their surroundings as the Alps and Sierra Nevada do today. One of the triumphs of structural

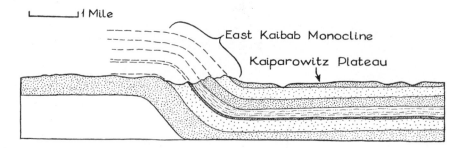

Figure 9-7.

Cross section of the Kaibab monocline, Utah. (After H. E. Gregory and R. C. Moore, U. S. Geological Survey.)

geology has been the tracing of vanished mountain chains across such relatively flat areas as Finland, eastern Canada, and Brazil by the remnants of their deeply eroded structural features.

Folds are the most common structures in present and former mountain chains. They range from microscopic crinkles to great arches and troughs fifty or more miles across. Upfolds or arches in rocks are called **anticlines** (Figs. 9-5, 9-12, and 8-12); downfolds or troughs are **synclines** (Fig. 9-6). A **monocline**

is a flexure in a series of beds which are nearly horizontal on either side of the flexure (Fig. 9-7).

The young anticlines of the Cascade foothills still form ridges, but in the Appalachian landscape all ridges are underlain by resistant rock irrespective of the position of this rock in an anticline or syncline. The terms anticline and syncline apply only to the structure of the strata and have no reference to topographic form. The original forms of most folds have been greatly obscured by erosion (Fig. 9-8).

Figure 9-8.   *Deeply eroded limb of an anticline, Flaming Gorge, Green River, Utah. (Photo by W. H. Jackson, U. S. Geological Survey.)*

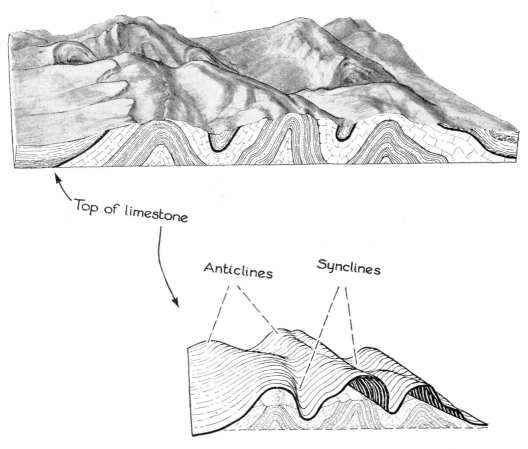

Figure 9-9.   Top: *Relief diagram of a part of the Jura Mountains, Switzerland. The top of a resistant limestone bed is shown by a heavy line.* Bottom: *Sketch of the top of the limestone bed as it would appear if the beds above and below it were removed. (After A. Heim, 1922.)*

To visualize these forms, we often sketch the eroded beds, reconstructing them by drawing dashed lines beyond the truncated ends of the strata. In the monocline shown in Figure 9-7 and the anticlines and synclines shown in Figure 9-1, the eroded upper parts of the structures have been partly restored in this way.

Another way of showing the form of eroded folds is illustrated in the lower part of Figure 9-9. The upper sketch shows part of the Jura Mountains in Switzerland. One bed of limestone, more resistant to erosion than the others, forms cliffs and bold ridges. The top of this limestone is shown on the cross section as a heavy black line. In the lower sketch, the top of this resistant stratum is drawn as it would appear if suspended in space, entirely detached from the beds above and below it, thus making it easy to visualize the form of the folds.

Structure Symbols

One of the best ways to portray a simple fold is by structure contours (Fig. 9-10). If we do not have enough information to draw structure contours. however, **structure symbols** placed on the geologic map help bring out details of the fold. Figure 9-11 shows some of the more common symbols used to depict structure on geologic maps.

The block diagram and geologic map (Fig.

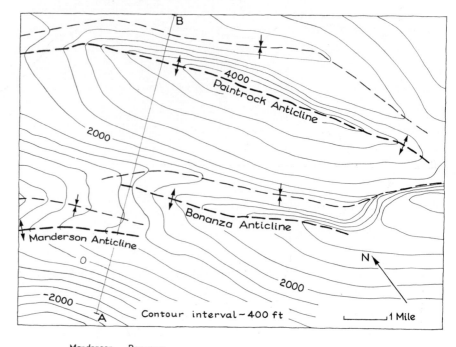

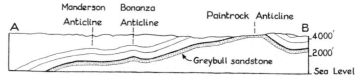

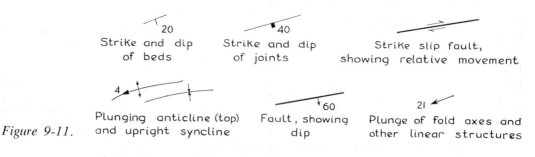

Figure 9-10.

Structure contour map and cross section of folds in the Big Horn Basin, Wyoming. *The structure contours are on the top of the Greybull sandstone. (After D. F. Hewett and C. T. Lupton, U. S. Geological Survey.)*

9-12) of a small fold in the Jackfork formation of Arkansas shows how various kinds of structures can be shown by symbols. On the geologic map, the strike and dip of the beds are shown at several places by **strike and dip symbols** (see Chapter 6, and Fig. 9-11). While the geologist is mapping, he plots these symbols on his base map wherever he determines strike and dip.

Note in the block diagram that two layers of shale interbedded with the prevailing sandstone of the Jackfork formation have been crinkled into a series of small puckers that roughly parallel the major fold. In mapping,

Strike and dip of beds	Strike and dip of joints	Strike slip fault, showing relative movement
Plunging anticline (top) and upright syncline	Fault, showing dip	Plunge of fold axes and other linear structures

Figure 9-11.

Chart of common structure symbols.

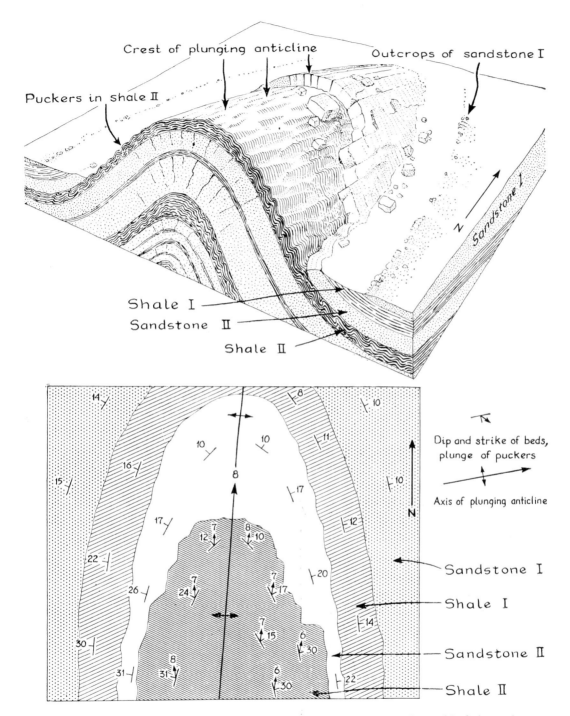

Figure 9-12. Relief diagram and geologic map of a small fold in the Jackfork formation near Amity, Arkansas.

it is important to avoid mistaking the dip of the strata in one of these minor puckers for the general dip of the beds in the major fold.

Another feature easily plotted on a geologic map is the position of the **axis** of an anticline. This is the line of opposed dips, or, in other words, the line on the surface of the ground along which each bed exposed at the surface reaches its highest point as it arches over the top of the fold. On a geologic map the axis of an anticline is represented by a line crossed by arrows pointing in opposite directions (see Figs. 9-10 and 9-11). The axis of a syncline —the line separating the converging dips in each bed at the surface—is shown by a line with converging arrows.

Another measurable feature shown in Figure 9-12 is the inclination of the top of a fold, or its **plunge.** Note that on the crest of the anticline shown in Figure 9-12 each warped bed plunges northward into the ground. The measured inclination, determined in degrees from the horizontal, is 8 degrees; this is the amount of the plunge. Plunge is shown on maps by an arrowhead showing direction, and numerals that give the amount of plunge (Figs. 9-11 and 9-12).

Kinds of Folds

Anticlines and synclines may be either plunging or nonplunging. Clearly, though, every fold must somewhere die out, and here it must plunge. A little study of Figures 9-6 and 9-12 will demonstrate why, after a plunging fold is eroded, the different strata that compose it show a curving or canoe-shaped pattern at the surface of the ground. Erosion etches the resistant beds into relief, and the curving ridges strikingly reveal the structural details (Fig. 9-6). If the fold does not plunge, and if the topography is nearly flat, the beds will crop out as roughly parallel bands on either side of the axis.

A very short anticline whose crest plunges in opposite directions from a high point is called a **dome.** A doubly plunging syncline forms a **basin:** the Paris Basin is a typical example. Domes and basins need not be

circular, they are usually two or three times as long as they are wide.

Many folds, such as the Paintrock anticline (Fig. 9-10) are **asymmetrical**—the strata on one side, or **limb,** of the fold dip more steeply than those on the other limb. In regions of intense deformation, such as the Alps, many folds are **overturned**—the beds on the lower limb of an overturned anticline have been tilted beyond the vertical (Fig. 9-1) so that the strata on both limbs dip in the same direction, though they may differ in amount of dip. Still other folds are **recumbent** (Fig. 9-18)— in a recumbent anticline the beds on the

Figure 9-13.   Columnar jointing in basalt lava. The long six-sided columns formed by shrinkage in a thick lava flow as it cooled from the base upward. The upper two-thirds of the flow has been removed by erosion. Columbia River basalt, Maury Mountains, Oregon. (Photo by A. C. Waters.)

lower limb are upside down; in a recumbent syncline the beds in the upper limb are inverted. If the beds on the two limbs of a fold are nearly parallel, the fold may be called **isoclinal,** no matter whether it is an upright, overturned, or recumbent fold. Many of the folds shown in Figure 9-1 are properly called overturned isoclinal folds.

Joints and Faults

Fractures in rocks are classified by geologists as joints or faults. By definition, **joints** are fractures that have merely opened, without slipping and offset of the rock along the fracture; **faults** are fractures along which there has been movement. In mapping, this distinction is made only if the displacement can be shown on the map. Fractures showing slips of only a few feet are generally ignored or are mapped as joints. The faults shown on most geologic maps are features with displacements large enough to show offset of the rocks at the scale used in mapping. Many faults have displacements of thousands of feet, or even scores of miles.

Almost every rock outcrop shows numerous joints (Figs. 9-13 and 9-14). Because of their profusion and irregularity, they are generally omitted from geologic maps. If there is some economic or other reason for showing them (for example, valuable ore veins may be developed along joints), the most common method is to plot their strike and dip by the symbol shown in Figure 9-11.

Joints and small faults may be formed in several ways, but large faults that can be traced for miles (Fig. 9-15) and which displace their walls hundreds or thousands of feet have certainly been formed by crustal movements.

Kinds of Faults

Faults are common in all parts of the earth's crust, but particularly so in the highly deformed rocks of mountain ranges. Geologists recognize several kinds; the distinction among them is based on the direction of apparent movement along the fault fracture. A **dip-slip fault** is a fracture along which the apparent movement has been predominantly vertical (Fig. 9-16, A and D). A **strike-slip fault**

Figure 9-14.   Rectangular joint pattern in massive sandstone, near Needles, California. (Photo by Vincent Kelley.)

Figure 9-15. *Aerial view of a fault near Great Bear Lake, Canada. The fault extends for 80 miles. In the photo, sandstone strata lie to the left, granite is on the right. Note the small faults and joints that cut the granite at acute angles to the main fault. (Data from A. W. Jolliffe, photo by Royal Canadian Air Force.)*

is a fracture along which the apparent movement has been predominantly horizontal (Fig. 9-16, *F*). Most strike-slip faults show a little vertical movement, and many dip-slip faults show some horizontal movement. If the vertical and horizontal components of the movement are about equal the fault may be called an **oblique-slip fault.**

In nearly all dip-slip faults the fracture surface is not vertical, it has an appreciable dip. The predominant direction of slippage is along the dip of the fault, from which, of course, the name dip-slip is derived. But, depending on how we view the fault, the direction of movement may be up the dip, or down the dip. This leads to a further classification of dip-slip faults into two kinds. A **normal fault** is an inclined fracture along which the rocks above the fracture have apparently moved *down* with respect to those beneath the fracture (Figs. 9-16, *A* and *D*, and 9-17). A **thrust fault** is an inclined fracture

along which the rocks above the fracture have apparently moved *up* with respect to those beneath (Fig. 20-2, bottom). Some geologists reserve the name thrust for faults dipping at angles less than 45°; those of steeper dip are called **reverse faults.**

It is also convenient to describe the apparent direction of horizontal movement on a strike-slip fault. M. L. Hill has recently proposed that we call strike-slip faults by the simpler name **lateral fault,** and that we distinguish two kinds. In a *right lateral fault* the apparent direction of relative movement of the side of the fault opposite the observer is to the right (Fig. 19-1). In a *left lateral fault* the direction of apparent relative movement of the opposite side is to the left (Fig. 9-16, *F*).

Fault definitions must be carefully and precisely used or serious ambiguities will arise. Note the presence of the words "with respect to," "apparently," and "relative movement" in the above definitions. The reason we cannot use more direct and positive language is that we do not actually observe the movement itself, but only the effects of movement. The **offset** of strata severed by a fault can be measured, but the direction of movement with respect to a definite reference plane such as sea level can rarely be determined. In a normal fault, for example, both sides of the fault could have moved up (but the rocks above the fault surface not as far) relative to sea level; or both could have moved down; or the rocks above the fault surface could have moved down and the rocks beneath the fault surface up. The study of the geometric relations of the rocks on either side of a fault gives us only the *apparent* movement *relative* to the rocks *on the other side* of the fracture. Abrupt bending of the strata as they approach the fault (called **drag**) may show us the direction of relative displacement, or we may be able to tell by the offset of the beds at the fault plane. Both drag and offset are well shown on the normal faults illustrated in Figure 9-17.

In areas of uniformly tilted strata, it is not always possible to tell from the offset whether dip-slip or lateral movement occurred along a fault. Either kind of movement can, after erosion, produce the same apparent displacement. Consider the examples sketched in Figure 9-16. Block A shows a series of tilted strata cut by a normal fault. Block B shows the same faulted terrain after erosion has removed the elevated block. Note the offset of the beds at the fault surface. Block C shows a similar series of beds displaced by a left lateral fault. Compare B and C and note that the same offset can be produced either by dip-slip movement followed by erosion or by strike-slip movement alone. Mere examination of the offset of the beds in block B would not enable us to tell which kind of faulting produced the final result, or whether it was produced by a combination of the two.

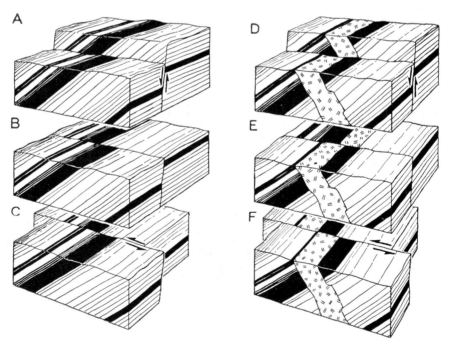

Figure 9-16.

Diagram showing how dip-slip and strike-slip (lateral) faults can produce identical outcrop patterns (A, B, and C), and how these faults can be differentiated under ideal conditions (D, E, and F).

W

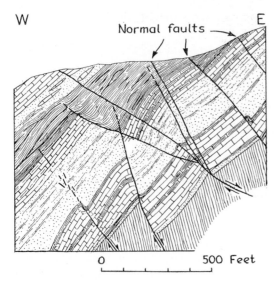

E

Normal faults

0   500 Feet

Figure 9-17.   Cross section showing drag and offset on normal faults. Magdalena mining district, New Mexico. Extensive underground mine operations aided the accurate plotting of these faults. (After G. F. Loughlin and A. H. Koschmann, U. S. Geological Survey.)

If, however, two or more kinds of rock masses with different dips intersect, and are cut by a fault, we can definitely tell the direction and amount of relative motion. A simple example is illustrated by block D, E, and F of Figure 9-16. Here there is a clear difference between blocks E and F. After elevation of part of block D by normal faulting, erosion has caused outcrops of both dike and strata to migrate down the dip, producing offsets in

opposite directions, as shown in block E. With lateral movement (block F), all offsets are in the same direction, despite the difference in dip of beds and dike.

Such measurements, when they can be obtained, are invaluable. In many mines (see Fig. 9-17, for example) careful matching of beds across faults, and determination of the exact amount of offset along each fault, is of great importance both in seeking faulted segments of known ore bodies and in planning the position of shafts and tunnels to extract ore whose location is already known.

Examples like those illustrated by D, E, and F in Figure 9-16 are rare; on most faults there is no dike or other intersecting structure, and we cannot tell the direction of relative motion. The word "apparently" in our definitions calls attention to this ambiguity.

The whole classification of faults, however, is artificial; not only are there all transitions between dip-slip and strike-slip faults, but many high-angle thrusts, when traced along their strike, steepen in dip, eventually become vertical, and then dip in the opposite direction. Thus a thrust fault may change along its course to a normal fault. A well-known example is the Uinta fault that extends sixty miles along the north side of the Uinta Mountains in Utah. It is a thrust fault at the west end, but becomes a normal fault toward the east. Fault classification is also ambiguous if the fault planes have been folded and warped after faulting. If we held strictly to

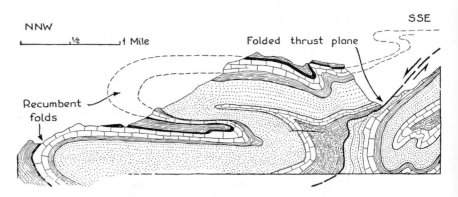

NNW

SSE

Folded thrust plane

0   ½   1 Mile

Recumbent folds

Figure 9-18.

Recumbent folds and a folded thrust surface, Swiss Alps. (After A. Heim, 1922.)

the definitions given above we would have to call the irregular fault shown in Figure 9-18 a normal fault, for the rocks above the fracture (left side of section) have apparently moved down with respect to the rocks beneath (right side of the section). Detailed study of a wide area beyond that depicted in the section has shown, however, that the fault formerly dipped southward at a low angle. It is really a thrust fault that has been warped and folded either during the thrusting or after thrusting had ceased. Such intense deformation, however, is rare.

There are many exceptions, but most normal faults dip steeply—commonly ranging from 65 degrees to vertical. Among thrust faults all gradations occur, but most can be grouped into either high-angle thrusts or low-angle thrusts—the distinction is based on whether the dip is greater or less than 45 degrees, but generally the dip of a low-angle thrust is less than 30 degrees and that of a high-angle thrust greater than 60 degrees. Low-angle thrusts are conspicuous in some mountain zones. Many have displacements measured in miles and attest to great horizontal shortening in the visible part of the crust. Some lateral faults also show displacements of many miles.

Folds and faults are related structures and may grade into one another. Some normal faults die out into monoclines along their strike. Some thrust faults are merely broken anticlines, although others show no evidence of having grown from folds.

Unconformities

Figures 9-19 and 9-20 illustrate a common relationship between rock masses. In Figure 9-19 the well stratified sandstones that form the cliff rest on granite. Examination of the contact shows that the granite did not invade the sandstone, for there has been no metamorphism of the sandstone by heat, nor does the granite penetrate the sandstone in dikes. On the contrary, the basal layer of the sandstone contains many pebbles and grains of

Figure 9-19.   Unconformity between granite and sandstone, El Paso County, Colorado. (Photo by N. H. Darton, U. S. Geological Survey.)

Figure 9-20.

An angular unconformity, Wyoming. Tilted and eroded beds of sandstone are overlain by flat-lying clay and sandstone. (Photo by C. J. Hares, U. S. Geological Survey.)

quartz and feldspar that were derived from the granite, proving that the sandstone is younger. The contact clearly is not a fault, for such evidences of movement as drag and offset are missing. The pebbles of granite in the basal layer of sandstone are not angular fragments sheared from the granite by fault movement but are smoothly rounded from wear in turbulent water. Moreover, the sandstone has filtered down into the granite along joints, indicating that it was unconsolidated sand when first brought into contact with the granite. It is evident that the sandstone rests on an *ancient erosion surface carved across the granite and later buried by deposition of the sandstone upon it.* Such a buried erosion surface is evidence of a lack of continuity in deposition, and is called an **unconformity.**

The production of an unconformity requires a reversal of the local process of erosion or sedimentation. The lack of continuity between the rock masses separated by an unconformity supplies proof of a gap in the local geologic column. The interval of time between the formation of the rocks below an unconformity and those above it is not represented in the local rock record. At another locality, where deposition was continuous, no unconformity will appear at the same position in the column.

In Figure 9-20, an unconformity appears as a conspicuous dark line, about a third of the way down the hill. The tilted beds of sandstone forming the lower part of the hill are cut off abruptly at the surface of the unconformity. Above the unconformity and roughly parallel to it, lie beds of much less consolidated sandstone and clay, whose basal layers contain fragments of the underlying tilted rocks. Obviously, the younger, poorly consolidated sediments rest on an old erosion surface that had developed across older sediments long after they were laid down, consolidated, and tilted by movements of the earth's crust.

From these two examples, it is clear that extensive unconformities record at least three important geologic events: (1) formation of the rocks below the unconformity, (2) erosion of these rocks to a comparatively flat surface, (3) burial of the surface beneath younger strata. Most unconformities also record crustal movement between 1 and 2 which gave the elevation necessary for erosion, but under some conditions—the erosion of a volcanic cone, for example—no crustal movement was necessary. Unconformities buried beneath marine rocks may also record a second movement of the crust between erosion (2), and burial, (3)—the warping of the eroded surface below the sea—but a land area might be buried by river-borne sediment without downwarping of the crust.

Landscapes Preserved Beneath Unconformities

In a few localities the soil and minor irregularities of a former landscape are preserved in their entirety beneath an unconformity but generally such features are eroded during burial. Erosion surfaces buried under lava flows or volcanic ash commonly preserve every detail of the former landscape, including such features as tree stumps still rooted in the position of growth (Fig. 8-12). Soils and weathered bedrock also may be found beneath stream deposits but such features are almost never found when the rocks above an unconformity are marine. Under exceptional conditions they may be preserved by rapid subsidence beneath an inland arm of the sea sheltered from the strong waves of the open ocean. In Chapter 8 we mentioned the drowned drainage channels on the floor of the southern end of San Francisco Bay. Twenty-five miles west of these are the gravel and coarse sandy beaches of the Pacific. The same subsidence that lowered the floor of San Francisco Bay also affected the coast, but strong wave attack along the beaches as the land submerged has obliterated all evidence of subaerial topography. All the soil has been removed and a wave-cut platform covered with coarse gravel and sand is developing across the bedrock.

Basal Conglomerate

When a broad erosion surface of low relief is warped beneath the sea the rate of submersion is generally so slow that the ocean shore moves inland perhaps no more than a few yards per century.

Waves are powerful agents of erosion (Chapter 5). During the slow advance of the sea upon the land, they strip away the soil and perhaps even some of the bedrock beneath. They plane down irregularities on the erosion surface, finally producing a nearly flat rock floor strewn with storm-swept gravel and sand: finer debris is carried into deeper water. The thin layer of conglomerate and coarse sandstone directly overlying the smooth rock floor is called a **basal conglomerate.** Such conglomerates, the nearshore deposits of slowly advancing seas, are common but by no means ubiquitous records of slow marine transgressions over erosion surfaces.

Kinds of Unconformities

Cross sections of six simple unconformities from different areas are sketched in Figure 9-21. Note in A and C that the beds above and below the surface of unconformity are parallel. Such unconformities are called **disconformities.** Many disconformities are difficult to recognize; the series of beds may appear to be **conformable,** that is, to have been deposited continuously without erosional breaks. In C, however, disconformity is certain because Silurian strata are absent, as proved by fossils collected from the beds immediately above and below the unconformity. Very likely this area was land during Silurian time, for if it had been under the sea it would have received Silurian marine deposits. If it was below the sea, the Silurian deposits formed must have been uplifted and eroded before the Devonian shale was deposited— hence, in either case, the disconformity records a former land surface. In A, the break between the beds above and below the unconformity is vastly greater, embracing nearly all of geologic time since the Cambrian.

Unconformities in which the beds above the unconformity transgress the eroded edges of folded and tilted beds, as do those shown in Figure 9-20 and B and D of Figure 9-21, are called **angular unconformities.**

In another common kind of unconformity —Figure 9-19 and E and F of Figure 9-21 show examples—bedded rocks rest on an eroded surface of plutonic or metamorphic rocks such as granite, gneiss, or gabbro. The term **nonconformity** has been used for this kind of unconformity.

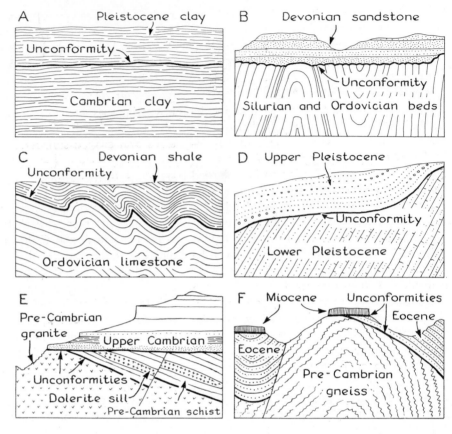

Figure 9-21.

Cross section showing different kinds of unconformities. (A) Baltic region of Russia; (B) Siccar Point, Scotland; (C) central Alabama; (D) Palos Verdes Hills, California; (E) Grand Canyon, Arizona; (F) central Washington.

Dating Geologic Events by Unconformities

The examples sketched in Figure 9-21 also illustrate how unconformities can be used to date various geologic events. For example, at Siccar Point, Scotland (B of Fig. 9-21), the Ordovician and Silurian beds were obviously folded before the unconformity was formed, since the overlying Devonian sandstone is un-affected by the folds. On the other hand, the beds in central Alabama (C of Fig. 9-21) were folded after the development of the un-conformity, for both sets of beds as well as the unconformity itself have been arched by the folds. The folding is thus known to have taken place later than the period in which the Devonian shale was deposited. At Siccar Point, however, the folding must have oc-curred after the deposition of the Ordovician and Silurian strata but before the Devonian sandstone had accumulated. The uncon-formity shown in D, Figure 9-21, definitely proves that the lower Pleistocene beds of southern California were tilted during the Pleistocene, for undeformed Pleistocene beds lie above the unconformity.

In part E of Figure 9-21, we see that the tilted rocks beneath the Upper Cambrian sedi-ments in the Grand Canyon were invaded by a dolerite sill and cut by a normal fault before Upper Cambrian time, because the noncon-formity at the base of the Upper Cambrian truncates the sill, the tilted beds, and even the granite upon which the tilted beds them-selves rest nonconformably.

Similarly, the relations of the two different unconformities shown in F—one beneath the Eocene beds, the other at the base of the Miocene lava flow—tell us that the fault cutting these unconformities has undergone at least two periods of movement, one during post-Eocene but pre-Miocene time, the other after the faulted area had been eroded to a plain and the Miocene lava spread out over it.

Time Significance of Unconformities

Every unconformity marks an interval of time not represented by sedimentary deposits at the particular spot where the unconformity occurs. Either no strata were deposited there during this time because the land was being eroded, or, if any deposits were laid down during that time they were eroded completely away before the overlying beds were deposited. In Chapter 7, we noted that the breaks in the geologic time scale, as built up in Western Europe, represent times of local non-deposition, although many of these times are recorded by "transitional series" elsewhere. These breaks correspond with the major unconformities in the Western European section.

It is important to try to estimate the time represented by an unconformity. A common fallacy is to assume that an angular unconformity necessarily implies a greater lost interval of geologic time than a disconformity. In some areas, it is true, the unconformities with the greatest time span are angular, but this generalization is not valid. Contrast, for example, the unconformities shown in A and D of Figure 9-21. At several places in the Baltic region (A) clays laid down in Pleistocene lakes rest directly upon marine clays that contain Cambrian fossils. The interval of time represented by the disconformity includes all of the Mesozoic and nearly all of the Paleozoic and Cenozoic—a gap of more than 400 million years. Yet, in some places, the unconformity can hardly be located, so similar are the Cambrian clays to those of the Pleistocene. In D, however, the marine sediments both above and below the angular uncon-

formity are of Pleistocene age, as shown by their abundant fossils. Thus the events during Pleistocene time in southern California included deposition of lower Pleistocene strata; folding, upturning, and then erosion of the newly deposited beds to a comparatively flat surface; sinking of the erosion surface below the sea; and deposition of upper Pleistocene strata. All of these local events took place in perhaps not more than a few thousand years—almost surely less than a million.

Unconformities, and the historical record they reveal, are not easily destroyed. Many are recognizable even after the rocks have been folded and metamorphosed. Only widespread uplift and deep erosion can obliterate them completely.

Regional Groupings of Structural Features

We have described the more common structural features of the earth's crust. How are they associated in time and space? We noted that thrust faults and overturned folds occur together in regions of intense crustal deformation; we would not expect recumbent folds in areas of horizontal or gently warped strata. Are certain broad belts of the earth's crust characterized by definite associations of structural features?

Continental Plates

Broad warps, monoclines, and normal faults of small displacement are the main structural features in the relatively stable parts of the continents. These stable land areas are called **continental plates.** The great area of low relief between the Appalachians and the Rockies (except for the Ouachita, Arbuckle and Wichita Mountains), and extending from the Gulf of Mexico to the Arctic, is the continental plate of North America. Another huge continental plate extends from eastern Germany to the Urals, and then beyond the Urals far into Outer Mongolia and Turkestan. In parts of the continental plates ancient metamorphic and plutonic igneous rocks appear at the surface, elsewhere the continental plates are covered with horizontal or gently warped sedimentary rocks. Drilling for petroleum shows that the sedimentary rocks of the continental plates are generally only a few hundred, or at most a few thousand, feet thick, and that they rest nonconformably upon a basement of granite and metamorphic rocks.

Folded Belts

The strata of the mountain belts that adjoin the slightly deformed sedimentary rocks of the continental plates are strongly folded and faulted. Steep, even overturned, folds and thrust faults characterize these belts, just as broad warps characterize the continental plates. Moreover, these strongly deformed rocks occur in linear belts that contrast sharply with the broad rounded outlines of the continental plates. Most mountain chains are composed of rocks that have been deformed into bundles of closely packed parallel anticlines, synclines, and thrust faults. In many of them closely appressed isoclinal and overturned folds and great thrust faults have squeezed and mashed the rocks tightly together.

These features contrast with the little-deformed sedimentary rocks that form a thin cover on the continental plates. The broad warps and monoclines of the continental plates could have been formed by differential vertical movements alone; the formation of the bundles of overturned and recumbent folds and associated thrusts of the great mountain chains required great horizontal compression of the shallow crustal zones. Rocks that formerly occupied wide belts now lie crowded together in a much narrower zone.

Where deep erosion has revealed the cores of large mountain chains it is common to find that the folded and faulted rocks along the edges of the mountain belt grade gradually into metamorphic rocks in the more deeply eroded cores of the ranges. Furthermore, many mountain ranges contain large masses of plutonic rocks that invade the sedimentary and metamorphic rocks along the core of

the range. These relations suggest that when the crust is squeezed and shortened to form a mountain belt, rocks near the surface are faulted and folded, but farther down, beneath a heavy load of overlying rock, where the temperature is higher, the rocks are slowly transformed to metamorphic varieties by granulation and recrystallization. Perhaps, indeed, the temperature may rise high enough to melt some of the recrystallizing rock into magma.

Broader Implications

The picture of the earth that has been developed in this chapter is a lively one. The earth's crust is not static and dead. Clearly recorded in its structure is the evidence that many rocks do not long remain in the horizontal position in which they were deposited. They have been warped upward and downward, bent into folds, broken and displaced by faults, invaded by igneous bodies, and crushed and recrystallized into metamorphic rocks. Unconformities allow us to date many of these events, and they also show that the earth movements responsible for the complex structure of the crust did not occur all in one great paroxysm, but have been going on throughout geologic time.

The mountain belts are key areas in the understanding of earth history. How were the rocks deformed? What conditions govern metamorphism, the origin of magma, and the emplacement of granite masses? The structures still left in the roots of old mountain chains after deep erosion give us glimpses into the results of processes that occur deep within the crust. To try to comprehend the movements now going on, and to understand those of the geologic past, we shall return again and again to the structure of the earth's mountain chains. Some are young and growing, others have long since ceased to grow, but reveal, in the deeper levels laid bare by erosion, chapters of history that may be paralleled in the younger growing ranges.

Other questions arise from the study of the

structures of mountain systems. The crowding together of wide areas of rocks into intensely deformed narrow mountain belts means great horizontal transfer of mass. How is this accomplished? Does the deformation go deeply into the body of the earth or did the mountain folds slide over a solid basement, like the wrinkles in a rug crumpled across the surface of a smooth floor? Can the earth's crust support a huge load of crumpled rocks heaped upon it in this way? What are the consequences of the great transfer of load that must occur when erosion erases a great mountain chain and spreads its detritus in an adjacent sea? In the next chapter we attempt to answer these difficult questions.

FACTS, CONCEPTS, TERMS

WARPS
  Structure contour maps
  Exaggerated scale cross-section
  Continental plates
FOLDS
  Plunging, asymmetrical, overturned, and recumbent folds
  Folded belts
  Mountain roots

JOINTS AND FAULTS
  Normal, thrust, and strike-slip faults
  Right lateral and left lateral faults
  Apparent versus real displacements on faults
UNCONFORMITIES
  Disconformities, angular unconformities, nonconformities
  Basal conglomerate
  Dating events by unconformities
  Time involved in an unconformity
STRUCTURE SYMBOLS

QUESTIONS

1. How do you know that the 5,000-foot difference between the elevation of the base of the Colorado shale at Shelby, Montana, and its elevation at Williston, North Dakota, is the result of warping since deposition of the shale, rather than the result of uniform deposition in an ocean which was shallow near Shelby and 5,000 feet or more deep near Williston?

2. On pages 125-129, the method of getting control points for drawing structure contours on a deeply buried bed is described. Describe how it would also be possible to get control points that would enable you to project above the ground surface the former position of a bed that has been completely eroded from the top of an anticline.

3. Draw a geologic map showing two anticlines and an intervening syncline that have been eroded to an almost flat surface. All three folds plunge to the north, and all are asymmetrical. Four sedimentary formations are exposed on the map.

4. Draw a geologic map showing a syncline plunging to the south which has been cut by an east-west normal fault that dips north. Assume that erosion has reduced the area to an almost flat surface.

5. Why is it more common to find overturned folds grading into thrust faults along their strike than into normal faults?

6. In the field, what criteria would you use to tell an angular unconformity from a thrust fault?

7. In the field, what criteria would you use to distinguish between a nonconformity developed across a granite mass and an intrusive contact formed by invasion of the sediments by molten granite magma?

8. An extensive but thin basal conglomerate contains Lower Jurassic fossils in one locality

but Middle Jurassic fossils when traced westward 230 miles. How is this possible?

9. Why are broad warps difficult to detect in former mountain belts?

10. Draw *one* cross-section showing *all* of the following features:

a) A series of folded marine sediments that lie nonconformably on granite and metamorphic rocks.

b) A series of nearly flat lava flows that lie with angular unconformity on the folded sediments.

c) Two thrust faults that are older than the lava flows but younger than the sedimentary rocks.

d) A normal fault that is younger than the lava flow.

e) A dike that is younger than the thrust faults, but older than the normal fault.

SUGGESTED READINGS

Bucher, W. H. *The Deformation of the Earth's Crust*. Princeton, N. J., Princeton University Press, 1933.

Hutton, James, in K. F. Mather and S. L. Mason. *Source Book in Geology*. New York, McGraw-Hill, 1939, pp. 92-100.

Umbgrove, J. H. F. *The Pulse of the Earth.* 2 ed. The Hague, M. Nijhoff, 1957.

10 GRAVITY, ISOSTASY, AND STRENGTH

WE HAVE SEEN in Chapters 8 and 9 that forces within the earth fold and crush rocks together and greatly change their elevations relative to sea level. In Chapter 5 we also noted that erosion is constantly removing rock waste from high elevations and transporting it to the sea. Are there still other factors that influence the relief of the earth's surface, and perhaps even dictate the amount of the earth's departure from a perfect spherical form? How, indeed, do we know that the earth is roughly spherical, as all of us were taught in grade school?

The Earth's Size and Shape

Early Measurements

The ancient Greeks noticed that the earth casts a round shadow upon the moon during eclipses. They also saw that the surface of the sea is curved, for only the upper part of a ship's mast is visible at a distance, and the ship appears to rise gradually out of the water as it approaches. From these observations, the Greeks correctly inferred that the earth is roughly spherical. Today this conclusion is commonplace; the earth's curvature shows plainly in photographs taken from rockets; airplanes circle the globe in a few days and man-made satellites circle it in a few hours.

A few of the early Greeks even made some measurements and calculations about the earth's form and size. More than two thousand years ago, Eratosthenes, a Greek geometer and astronomer, first measured the curvature of the earth and computed its dimensions. Though measuring techniques have been greatly refined, his reasoning is still used in modern geodesy. (**Geodesy** is the science of measuring the earth, its dimensions and curvature and the distances and directions of points on its surface from each other.) Eratosthenes learned that in southern Egypt, at Syene (now Assuan), the sun shines vertically down a well only at noon on the longest day of the year. At Alexandria though, a part of every well is always in shadow. Alexandria lies 500 stades (the ancient Egyptian stade equals about 6,000 feet) north of Syene. Eratosthenes measured the angle between a plumb line and the edge of the shadow cast by the sun at noon in a well at Alexandria on the longest day of the year (Fig. 10-1). He then calculated the size of the earth on these premises:

a. That the sun is so distant that its rays to Syene and Alexandria are parallel.

b. That Alexandria lies due north of Syene, so that a plane through Alexandria, Syene, and the center of the earth also includes the noon sun.

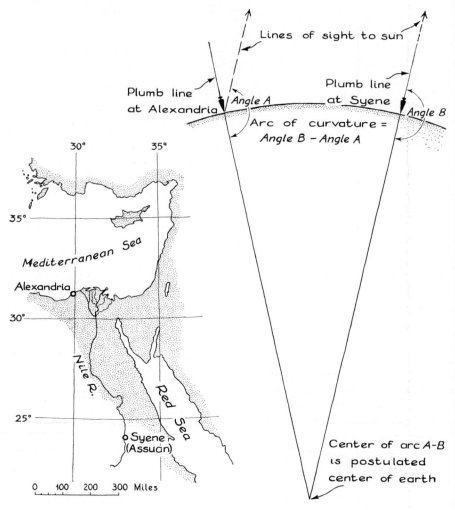

Figure 10-1.

Eratosthenes' method for measuring the size of the earth. Note that Syene does not lie south of Alexandria, so that the distance between Syene and Alexandria was not measured along a meridian, as he assumed. His result was therefore too large.

c. That the plumb line points directly toward the center of the earth.

d. That the earth is a sphere.

On these assumptions, the angle between the plumb line and the shadow at Alexandria is equal to the arc of the earth's curvature between the two points (Fig. 10-1). The circumference of the earth is, therefore, given by solving the equation:

$$\text{Circumference} = \frac{360°}{\text{Angle of sun's rays to vertical at Alexandria}} \times 500 \text{ stades.}$$

Eratosthenes' result was, in modern measure, about 28,000 miles. This is nearly 4,000 miles (about 14 per cent) larger than the figure now accepted. About a century later, Poseidonius, another Greek philosopher, applied the same method to another arc, but was not so favored by compensating errors. The size of his earth was a quarter too small, and this error may have led to Columbus's error in mistaking America for India.

In these early crude measurements, it was assumed that the earth is a sphere. We shall see that later more accurate measurements forced several modifications of this assumption. Few better examples of scientific method, and of successive improvements in theory made necessary by additional observations, can be found than are afforded by the history of the investigation of the shape of the earth.

Modern Measurements

In the seventeenth and eighteenth centuries, as navigation expanded, accurate charts became more important and Eratosthenes' method came into wider use. North-south lines at several different localities were measured and the angle of arc that they represented were calculated. These measurements showed that a degree of latitude is longer near the poles than at the equator. Or, stated in another way, if we hold to the assumption that the earth is a sphere, its radius as deduced from observations near the pole is somewhat greater than that deduced from observations near the equator. This is shown, greatly exaggerated, in Figure 10-2. Here the dashed circle, with the center P, illustrates the size of the earth deduced from observations near the pole. The dotted circle, with the center E, shows the size deduced from observations made near the equator. Note the discrepancy in size. If Eratosthenes' assumption that the earth is a sphere is accepted these measurements cannot be explained. The simplest way of reconciling the differences between the polar and equatorial measurements is to assume that the earth is not quite spherical, but is, instead, slightly flattened at the poles—or, in technical words, that it is an ellipsoid. The solid line in Figure 10-2 is an ellipse with its center at C. This line fits the data from both the polar and equatorial observations.

The simplest model of the earth that conforms with these measurements is an oblate ellipsoid, the solid figure obtained by revolving an ellipse about its shorter axis. In the ellipse indicated by the solid line in Figure 10-2, the short axis would be a straight line connecting the North Pole with the South Pole. In the drawing, the flattening at the

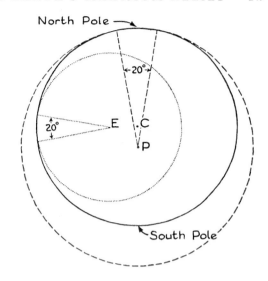

Figure 10-2. Diagram showing how unequal circular arcs measured in different latitudes require an ellipsoidal figure for the earth.

poles is much exaggerated, for the earth does not depart greatly from a sphere. The measurements now accepted, and used internationally as the basis for official mapping are:

Equatorial radius..	6,378,388 meters (3,963.5 miles)
Polar radius.......	6,356,912 meters (3,950.2 miles)
Difference.......	21,476 meters (13.3 miles)

What is the meaning of this difference of 13 miles between the polar and equatorial radii? And how closely does the oblate ellipsoidal figure that we now substitute for a sphere really fit the actual surface of the earth? Certainly in mountainous areas the peaks and gorges must represent real departures from a smooth ellipsoidal surface. How much do these departures amount to?

The Earth's Maximum Relief

Sea level is the conventional surface of reference with which we compare heights on the earth (see Appendix I). The earth's highest peak, Mount Everest, towers 29,141 feet—nearly 5 miles—above sea level; the greatest oceanic depth thus far reported lies between Guam and Yap, where an abyss in the western Mariana Deep descends to 35,400 feet—

about 6.75 miles below sea level. Great as are these distances by human standards, they are insignificant in comparison with the radius of the earth. If the largest circle (or ellipse) that can be drawn on this page represented the earth, a pencil line of moderate weight would, on the same scale, include within its width all of the irregularities of the earth's surface, ranging from Mount Everest to the Mariana Deep. Actually, therefore, in comparison to its size, the irregularities of the earth's surface are no greater than those on a billiard ball, though to a Tibetan, living amidst the peaks of the towering Himalayas, this must seem a gross oversimplification.

The areas of these extreme heights and depths are also insignificant compared to the areas of the continents and the ocean basins, which are, of course, the major relief features of the earth. Analysis of the best maps and charts available shows the following:

Area of the sea.......	361,059,000 sq. km.	70.8%
Area of the land.....	148,892,000 sq. km.	29.2%
Total............	509,951,000 sq. km.	100.0%

Land and sea are very unevenly distributed. The earth can be divided into two hemispheres: four-fifths of all the land lies in one and nearly nine-tenths of the other is covered by water. Figure 10-3 summarizes our knowledge of this distribution.

What are the differences in elevation between the continents and the ocean floors? From the best maps and from other data careful estimates have been made of the total areas of the land surface that lie between various altitude limits. These are summarized in Figure 10-4, which brings out clearly two important relations already noted: (1) The high mountain peaks and the abyssal depths of the sea are very small in area. (2) Within the extreme range represented by the Mariana Deep and Mount Everest, the altitudes are not evenly distributed by area. Instead, two altitude ranges are especially prominent. One is the range between 4,000 and 5,000 meters (13,120 to 16,400 feet) below sea level, which includes nearly one-fourth of the earth's surface. The other is the range from 200 meters below sea level to 500 meters above sea level, which includes approximately one-fifth of the earth's surface. The part of this second level that lies beneath the sea is the continental shelf. The ocean basins are overfull; sea water spreads beyond their confines and inundates the continental shelves, which are really parts of the continents. At the outer edge of the continental shelf the sea floor descends rapidly in the continental slope to the ocean floors proper, which lie within the first altitude range mentioned, about 4,000 to 5,000 meters below sea level.

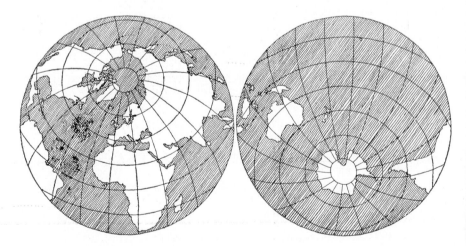

Figure 10-3.

The land and water hemispheres.

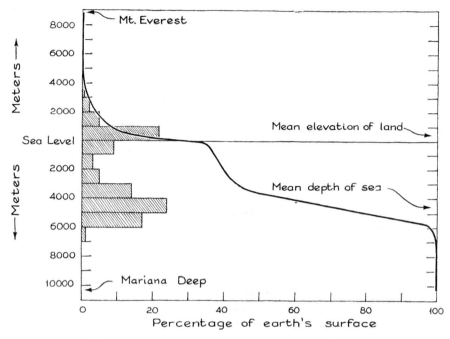

Figure 10-4.

Graph showing the percentage of the earth's surface lying between various levels above and below the sea. The bars at the left represent the percentages lying between the respective contours at intervals of 1,000 meters. Note the two broad flat areas in the curve, one near sea level, the other 4,000 to 5,000 meters below sea level. (Redrawn from H. U. Sverdrup, M. W. Johnson and R. H. Fleming, The Oceans, Copyright 1942, by Prentice-Hall, Inc.)

Why are there two dominant levels in the architecture of the earth? Why is the boundary between continental shelf and ocean floor so marked? And why, despite the great folds and faults that we see in the earth's crust, whose relief is several times as great as that of the earth's surface, is the maximum difference in elevation so insignificant compared with the radius of the earth? Before we can even start to answer these difficult questions we need to know more about our plane of reference, the surface of the sea. Does the sea's surface everywhere correspond to the smooth surface of an oblate ellipsoid, or does it, like the surface of the land, show real departures from this form? If it does, how can we account for them? Some inkling of the answers, and of the reason for the difference of 13 miles in the polar and equatorial radii as well, can be obtained from a study of gravity and of the

centrifugal force of rotation upon the body of the earth.

Gravity

Water in a pond and coffee in a cup both assume a level surface. If we hang a plumb bob above this surface, we find that the plumb line is exactly perpendicular to it. Both the plumb bob and the liquid are responding to the force of gravity. Each has approached the center of the earth as closely as its nature will permit— the liquid by flowing to the lowest level possible, and the plumb bob by hanging as close to the earth as the string which suspends it will permit. The earth evidently has an attraction for each particle of the liquid, and for each particle of the plumb bob. Moreover, the attraction on a particular volume of material must vary as the mass of the material contained within it, for if we drop a heavy stone in water it sinks at once to the bottom, displacing an equal volume of the lighter liquid upward, but if we uncork a bottle of air beneath water, the air bubbles upward to the surface because the water, being denser than air —that is, containing more mass in an equal volume—more forcefully seeks its lowest level.

The Law of Gravitation

The attraction of the earth for a plumb bob, for water, for air, and for all other objects in the universe illustrates the universal **Law of Gravitation,** first formulated by the great English scientist Isaac Newton (1642-1727). This generalization is usually stated: *Every particle in the universe attracts every other particle with a force that is directly proportional to the product of their masses, and inversely proportional to the square of the distance between them.*

The mathematical statement of this law is as follows:

$$F \propto \frac{M' \times M''}{D^2}$$

In this expression, F is the force of attraction, M' is the mass of one body, M'' that of a second body, and D the distance between the bodies, the symbol $\propto$ means "varies as."

As a numerical example of the way in which the law operates, consider the earth's attraction for a plumb bob that weighs one pound. At sea level, the distance of the plumb bob from the earth's center is approximately 4,000 miles. If this distance were doubled, the attractive force would be only one-fourth as great, for the denominator would be $8,000^2$ instead of $4,000^2$ ($8,000^2 \div 4,000^2 = 4$). In other words, if it were possible to suspend the plumb bob in space 8,000 miles from the earth's center (4,000 miles above the earth's surface), it would weigh only ¼ pound. Because of this relation, instruments on artificial satellites must be so designed that the pull of gravity is not necessary for their functioning, as it is for so many laboratory instruments on earth.

Gravity and a Level Surface

In making a topographic map, or in setting the floor joists of a building, what do we mean when we speak of a level surface? The surface of a quiet pond is level, and it appears to be a plane, but in fact it is not: it is curved, as we know the surface of the ocean to be curved. A level surface is, therefore, not a true plane; instead it is a surface that, at every point, is exactly perpendicular to the direction of the plumb line. All plumb lines converge toward the earth's center. The direction of the plumb line is also the vertical—its projection overhead defines the **zenith,** the point directly above us among the stars. When Eratosthenes set out to measure the size of the earth he determined the angle between two such vertical lines and thus could calculate the earth's curvature.

Weighing a Mass

Careful measurements of the exact force of gravity at various points on the earth's surface yield valuable information about the size and form of the earth. Before proceeding to the results of these measurements we must first outline the methods by which we can weigh an object. The **weight** of any mass is the measure of the force of attraction between the earth

Figure 10-5. Two common weighing instruments. Left: *Spring scale.* Right: *Beam balance.*

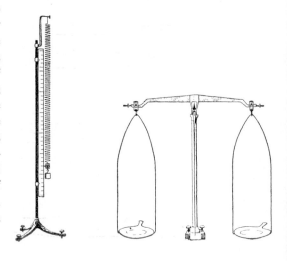

and itself. There are two common methods of weighing—the spring scale and the beam balance (Fig. 10-5).

A spring scale measures weight by the stretching of a spring; it is calibrated by marking the stretching produced by the earth's pull on a series of standard weights. By international agreement, such calibrations are based on the standard kilogram mass preserved at the International Bureau of Weights and Measures at Sévres, France. At Sévres, we calibrate our spring scale so that the pointer reads exactly one kilogram when the standard kilogram mass is placed on the scale.

A second weight that brings the pointer to the same mark weighs, of course, exactly one kilogram and will counterpoise the standard kilogram mass when the two are placed in opposite pans of a beam balance. But if we move our equipment from Sévres to some other point on the earth's surface, we generally find that these relations no longer hold.

EFFECT OF ALTITUDE.   If, for example, we take scale, weights, and balance to a pass in the Alps, two miles above sea level, we find that on the spring scale our kilogram weight will no longer weigh one kilogram but

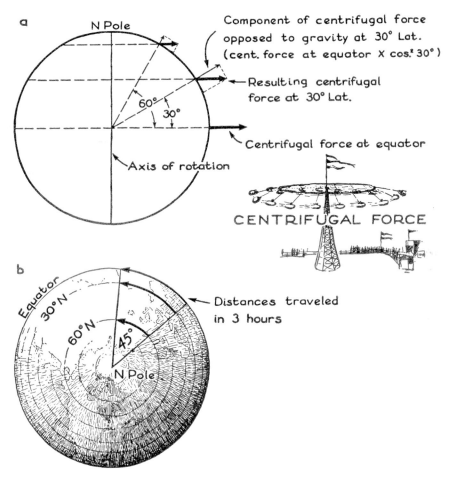

Figure 10-6.

Diagram showing a familiar demonstration of centrifugal force and (a) *how the centrifugal force due to rotation varies from equator to pole, or, stated differently,* (b) *how the linear velocity varies from equator to pole.*

slightly less, although it will still exactly counterpoise the standard kilogram mass in the beam balance. All our equipment is identical with that at Sévres, but, at the Alpine pass, the distance to the earth's center is roughly 4,002 miles, whereas at Sévres, nearly at sea level, it is only 4,000 miles. The product of the masses of the earth and our kilogram weight must be divided, at Sévres, by $4,000^2$ and, at the Alpine pass, by $4,002^2$. This is a difference of nearly 0.1 per cent, or 1 gram. Newton's law thus shows us immediately that the distance from the earth's center must be considered when we weigh on a spring scale.

EFFECT OF THE EARTH'S ROTATION. Because the earth spins on its axis, objects near the equator tend to be thrown off, just as mud is thrown from a spinning automobile wheel, or sparks from an emery grinder. This force is the **centrifugal force of rotation,** and it tends to counteract a part of the force of gravity. But it is very small compared to the force of gravity, and hence solid objects do not fly off the equator into space. Yet the centrifugal force is not negligible (Fig. 10-6). As Newton showed long ago, it should

produce an equatorial bulge and a polar flattening in the shape of the earth. Thus is explained the 26 miles difference between the polar and equatorial diameters actually found if Eratosthenes' method of measuring arcs of meridian is used.

Since the poles are 13 miles closer to the earth's center than the equator, the force of gravity is greater at the poles. Even if the earth were a perfect sphere, however, an object at the pole would weigh more than the same object transported to the equator, for the centrifugal force of rotation is greatest at the equator and steadily diminishes until it becomes zero at the pole (Fig. 10-6). The actual difference that results from both these factors is approximately 0.5 per cent, so if a polar bear weighing 1,000 pounds in his natural habitat were transported to an equatorial zoo, he would there weigh only 995 pounds.

EFFECTS OF LOCAL VARIATIONS IN ROCK DENSITY. Still another factor causes variations in the weight of an object at different points on the earth's surface; this is the local distribution of rock masses of different

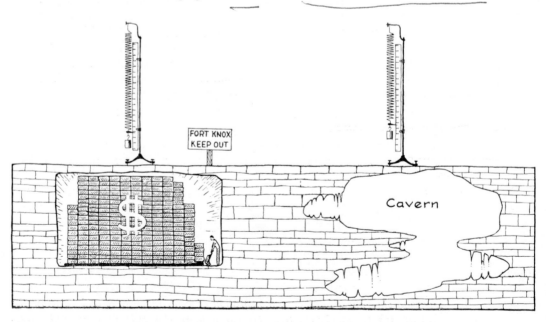

Figure 10-7. *The effect of differences in density of nearby masses on weight.*

density. Let us imagine that the gold buried at Fort Knox, Kentucky, as part of the United States Treasury reserve, formed a single huge block of pure metal (Fig. 10-7). A cubic foot of gold weighs more than 1,200 pounds. The inverse-square relation in the Law of Gravitation tells us that an object immediately on top of the gold should weigh a little more than the same object would if it were weighed on the roof of one of the great limestone caverns nearby. Although the latitude and altitude are the same, the dense gold immediately beneath the object exerts far more pull on it than does the air of an empty cavern. As we know, the rocks at the earth's surface do differ considerably in density from place to place, though not, of course, to the extreme degree of our artificial example at Fort Knox. Clearly, the force of gravity at each point must vary with the density of the immediately underlying rocks.

The Gravity Pendulum

To summarize, the force of gravity at any point on the earth's surface depends on (1) altitude, (2) latitude, and (3) variations in density of the underlying rocks. The actual effect of each of these factors is small. In order to study them we need a very sensitive instrument that will detect minute variations in weight—an instrument far more sensitive than even the best spring scale. The **gravity pendulum** is an accurate but simple instrument which fills this need.

A free-swinging pendulum—that is, one not driven by clockwork or other external means —oscillates to and fro because of the force of gravity. If we suspend a heavy weight from a string, pull back the weight and release it, the weight falls toward the center of the earth, following the arc controlled by the length of the string. The force of gravity pulls the weight downward along its path, but the weight's **inertia**—the resistance any object offers to any change in its motion—carries it past the low point of its swing and thus causes it to rise against the force of gravity. It continues upward along the arc until its

inertia is overcome by gravity, whereupon it reverses and falls back again toward the lowest point, repeating this process again and again. But with each swing it rises to a little less height because of friction with the air. Gradually the oscillations die away until finally the pendulum hangs straight down, perpendicular to a level surface. It has become a plumb bob.

We borrow from physics the law that relates to the **period of oscillation** (the time for one complete to-and-fro movement) of a pendulum: *The period varies inversely with the square root of the local acceleration of gravity, and directly with the square root of the length of the pendulum.*

Newton demonstrated that this relationship explains why even the best pendulum clocks show systematic gains or losses in time when moved about from place to place. (It is for this reason that all such clocks have adjustments permitting slight changes in the length of their pendulums). A pendulum clock that keeps good time at Paris would systematically lose time at a high Alpine pass because the force of gravity is less there. This relationship between the force of gravity and the period of a pendulum allows us to measure the force of gravity by using a pendulum of known length. To determine gravity we count the number of oscillations of the pendulum in a measured time and calculate the force from the law for the period of oscillation.

Modern gravity pendulums are so constructed that they are almost frictionless. They are hung on knife-edge jeweled bearings, and are swung in chambers from which nearly all the air has been evacuated. The number of swings is counted by precision chronometers accurate to 1/10,000 of a second. Such equipment enables scientists to measure the force of gravity within a few parts per million.

Ordinary gravity pendulums cannot be used on shipboard because of wave disturbances, but a Dutch geodesist, F. A. Vening-Meinesz, has modified the instrument so that it can be used in a submarine below the zone of strong wave motion. Thus, in recent years we have obtained thousands of measurements from the sea as well as the land. From these measurements of the force of gravity, as we shall see later in this chapter, geologists and geodesists have made important deductions concerning the relations between topography and differences in density of the earth's crustal materials.

Other important interrelationships, supplementing and confirming those obtained with the gravity pendulum, were discovered during attempts to explain some puzzling systematic errors that arose during triangulation. **Triangulation** (described in Appendix I) is the method of locating a third point by sighting on it from each of two points of known position. But a point can also be located without recourse to triangulation by determining its latitude and longitude astronomically, as is done in navigation. Astronomical determinations of longitude and latitude involve reading angles between the horizon and lines of sight to the fixed stars. Such angles at any point allow us to determine the zenith—that is, the direction of the vertical—because, of course, this is everywhere at right angles to the horizon, like the plumb line. If the plumb line invariably pointed directly to the earth's center, determinations of position made by astronomical methods would coincide exactly with determinations made by triangulation. The plumb line, however, does not everywhere point exactly to the earth's center. According to the Law of Gravitation, a plumb bob is attracted by a given mass one mile away with a force one hundred times greater than it is attracted by an equivalent mass ten miles away. We ought, then, to find the plumb line deflected sideward toward a nearby mountain. The zenith determined astronomically at a point near a mountain should, therefore, be deflected away from the zenith determined directly over the mountain. And it is.

Consider the situation in a deep Norwegian fjord. A narrow arm of the sea lies between massive cliffs 4,000 feet high. A plumb line suspended near one side of the fjord will be deflected toward the nearby mountain mass.

The sea surface as well will be tilted slightly upward toward the mountain and downward toward the middle of the fjord. (Fig. 10-11, *bottom.*) Such tilts are very small, generally only a few seconds of arc, but they lead to appreciable errors in determining the position of a point by astronomical methods. Moreover, we now see that the concept of an earth shaped like an oblate ellipsoid, though closer to the truth than the concept of a spherical earth, still is not precise. In detail the true shape of sea level over the entire earth's surface is not exactly an oblate spheroid. Because of these local attractions, the surface that is everywhere horizontal—that is, at right angles to the plumb line—is vastly more complicated than a simple oblate ellipsoid.

Isostasy

The mass of even the largest mountain, however, is very small compared with the mass of the earth as a whole. Despite their being close at hand, we can expect their deflection of the plumb line to be small. To calculate the theoretical deflections at any one station requires considerable mathematical labor, for it is usually necessary to calculate the gravitational pull of many irregular topographic masses lying in different directions and at different distances from the station. When this is done for a large series of stations, however, an exceptionally interesting relation appears: *Mountain masses do not deflect the plumb line sideways as much as it would be deflected if the mountain were actually a load resting on top of an otherwise uniform crust.*

This somewhat surprising conclusion is also confirmed by measurements of the force of gravity with the gravity pendulum. If a mountain were really a load heaped on a perfectly rigid crust, the force of gravity (after being corrected for the effect of the added altitude) should be greater on the top of a mountain than on an adjacent plain because of the added gravitational pull of the mass of the mountain. The results of many investigations with the gravity pendulum show, however, that over large areas there is no such close relationship between topography and the force of gravity.

From these relations, geologists and geodesists have inferred that *the major irregularities of the earth's crust are sustained, not as loads borne up by the strength of a rigid earth crust, but instead are buoyed up by flotation upon a dense plastic interior.* The idea is that the gravitational effect of the material contained in a mountain range is balanced, or compensated for, by a lower density of the material beneath it as compared to the material beneath a plain. The earth's interior must yield to equalize the loads on areas of equal size.

The flotation may take place in either of two ways (or by a combination of them). One is illustrated by the different heights at which planks of the same size but of different density—say oak and pine—float in a pond. The lighter pine plank will float much higher out of the water than the heavier oak. Thus, it is possible that the mountains are higher than the continental plates because the rocks composing them are less dense, and that, in turn, the rocks of the main continental masses are less dense than those beneath the oceans. The second possible explanation of flotation calls for the assumption that all the materials under mountain, plain, and ocean floor are of the same density, though less dense than a plastic layer that underlies them all. In this case, the surface relief might be the result of thick masses of light rock standing higher than thin masses of the same rock. The analogy would here be with icebergs, which float with nine-tenths of their volume submerged. A berg that projects 10 feet above the surface may extend 90 feet below it; one that is twice as thick will stand 20 feet above the surface (See Fig. 10-10.)

Such a condition of flotational equilibrium between large blocks of the earth's crust is called isostasy (from the Greek, "equal standing"). The theory of isostasy is one of the most fruitful concepts in geology—one that we will refer to again and again. It will

be well, therefore, to explain in some detail the kind of evidence on which it is based. Perhaps the best example of all is the one that first led to the discovery of the condition of isostasy in the earth's crust—the analysis of some puzzling deflections of the plumb line encountered during an early survey of the landmass of India.

The Trigonometrical Survey of India

In the middle of the nineteenth century, the Trigonometrical Survey of India was organized under Sir George Everest (for whom Mount Everest is named) to locate precisely the control points needed for mapping that great subcontinent. These points were established by very careful triangulation (see Appendix I) which gave highly accurate distances between stations. Scores of points were located, and, for many, the latitudes and longitudes were also carefully determined by astronomical observations.

If the latitude and longitude, plus the direction of a north-south line, at any one station in a triangulation net are known, it is a relatively simple matter to calculate the latitudes and longitudes of all the other points with respect to the known one. Such calculations do not, of course, depend in any way on astronomical observations, except at the reference station (though they do depend on assumptions about the curvature of the surface of the earth). But, if an astronomical determination of the latitude and longitude of a second triangulation station is made independently, it can be compared with the position as computed from triangulation.

In the survey of India, it soon became apparent that, for some stations, relative positions determined by triangulation did not agree with those determined by astronomical methods. It was first thought that errors might have crept into the triangulation, but, when checked, the results were consistent. Moreover, several of the apparent "errors" were far too large to be accounted for by inaccuracies in surveying.

Two such stations, Kaliana and Kalianpur

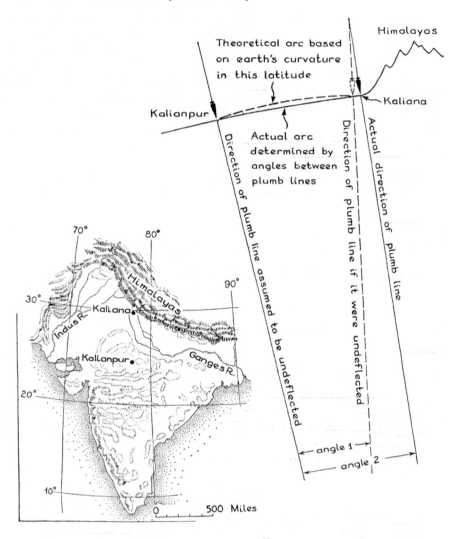

Figure 10-8.

The effect of the Himalaya Mountains on the computed distance between Kaliana and Kalianpur. Note the difference in the arc distance between the two cities produced by the deflection of the plumb bob, so that angle 1 is greater than angle 2. The deflecting angles are very greatly exaggerated in the diagram.

(Fig. 10-8), are among those discussed by Archdeacon J. H. Pratt, a British cleric who became interested in the problem and who, in seeking an explanation, discovered the isostatic relationship. Kaliana is on the Indo-Gangetic plain, immediately beside the towering Himalayas. Kalianpur lies far to the south, near the center of the Indian peninsula. Archdeacon Pratt surmised that the plumb line at Kaliana would be appreciably deflected northward by the gravitational pull of the mountain mass and that therefore the difference in latitude between the two stations given by the astronomical observations would be less than that calculated from triangulation. This proved to be true. The difference in latitude between the stations as determined by each method was:

Difference in latitude
Measured by triangulation.........5° 23′ 42.29″
Measured astronomically..........5° 23′ 37.06″
Discrepancy...................5.23″

The discrepancy of 5.23 seconds of arc corresponds to a distance of about 500 feet—far more than can be attributed to surveying errors.

Archdeacon Pratt decided to test whether the horizontal gravitational pull of the Himalayas might account for this discrepancy. Enough was known of the height and position of the principal peaks for Pratt to compute the approximate volume of the mountains above sea level and their average distance north of each of the two stations. Enough was also known about the kinds of rocks that compose the mountains to estimate the average density of the mountain mass. Assuming that the mountains rested on an otherwise uniform crust, Pratt next computed how much the plumb line should have been deflected northward at each station, and then computed the difference in astronomical latitude that should result from this deflection. The results at first seemed surprising; according to his calculations the plumb line should have been deflected far more than the actual deflection he was trying to account for. On his assumptions the plumb line should have been deflected northward 27.853 seconds at Kaliana and 11.968 seconds at Kalinapur. The difference is 15.885 seconds—more than three times the 5.23 seconds discrepancy actually determined by the Trigonometrical Survey—and far greater than could be explained either by errors in triangulation or in Pratt's estimate of the volume and mass of the Himalayas.

Pratt's Theory of Isostasy

Pratt saw that his assumptions must be wrong. One of the assumptions was that the density of the material constituting the earth's crust was uniform, regardless of whether the material lay beneath the plain of India or beneath the Himalayas. He had assumed that the mass of the Himalayas, from their highest peaks to sea level, was a load heaped on a crust that was everywhere uniform in density below sea level. Pratt saw that the discrepancy might be explained if the rock extending to a certain depth below the Himalayas were of less mass (lower density) than that extending to the same depth beneath an equivalent area of the plain of peninsular India. He suggested that both the mountain and plain are "floating" on a deep layer of denser material, and that the heights to which their surfaces rise above this layer are inversely proportional to the densities of the material composing the two "blocks." In other words, the high-standing mass of the Himalayas is "compensated," or balanced, by a corresponding deficiency in the mass of the rock beneath them. This rock is less dense than that underlying the plain.

A simple illustration of Pratt's idea is shown in Figure 10-9. In the upper diagram, blocks of four different metals, each of which weighs exactly the same amount and each of which has the same horizontal cross section, are shown floating in a pan of mercury, a liquid of very high density (13.6 grams per cubic centimeter). The heights of the metal blocks are inversely proportional to their densities. The blocks sink in the fluid until they displace enough mercury to equal their weight, and since their weights and cross sections are equal, they sink to the same depth but they project to different heights above the surface of the mercury. For example, the antimony block (density 6.6 grams per cubic centimeter) is about twice as tall as the lead block (density 11.4 grams per cubic centimeter), because its volume must be nearly twice that of the lead block in order for it to weigh the same. Consequently it will project nearly twice as high above the surface of the mercury as the lead. Similarly, zinc rises higher than iron. Pratt assumed that mountains, plains, and ocean floors showed essentially comparable relations. Mountains, he thought, are like the antimony block (Fig. 10-9, *upper*): they project higher above the surface of the "fluid" substratum because they are composed of (and to a considerable depth are underlain by) a material less dense than that which underlies plains.

Pratt's suggestion was the first formulation of the theory of isotasy, and his scheme of "compensating" for differences in elevation above sea level by variation in density of the blocks below sea level is known today as the **Pratt Theory of Isostasy.** Pratt did not use the word "isostasy"; some thirty-four years later the American geologist C. E. Dutton gave this name to the condition of equilibrium which Pratt had discovered.

Airy's Theory of Isostasy

The same volume of the *Transactions of the Royal Society* (1855) that contains Pratt's formulation also contains a brief contribution by G. B. Airy, the Astronomer Royal of Great Britain. Airy accepted most of Pratt's reasoning, saying that this conclusion should have been anticipated because it could be shown that if masses as great as plateaus and high mountains were loads on a solid earth, no rocks would be strong enough to sustain them.

The rocks beneath would break and flow out laterally until a state of balance was restored. The only possibility, then, is to regard mountain chains as floating masses, as Pratt did.

Airy, however, suggested a different mechanism of flotation. He saw no reason to believe that the density of the material immediately beneath a mountain is any different from that directly beneath a plain. If both blocks are of the same density, but of unequal thickness, the difference in surface height may still be readily explained. The thick block (mountain block) will float higher above the surface, but it will also sink deeper into the heavier "fluid" below. The height of the mountain block is compensated by a "root" of material that projects into the underlying "fluid" layer and displaces it. Airy's view is called the **Roots of Mountains Theory of Isostasy.** It accounts for the "errors" in the India Survey just as well as Pratt's theory, and accords much better with what we know about the composition of the rocks beneath the surface as revealed by deep mines and drill holes. It is much more widely accepted by geologists, but, as we shall see, Pratt's theory may also

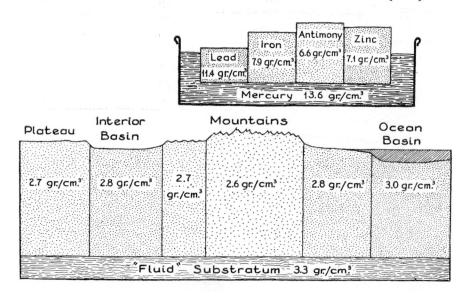

Figure 10-9.

Pratt's theory of isostasy. The densities shown in the lower diagram were not specified by Pratt but are based on modern estimates. (Modified from W. Bowie, Isostasy, *E. P. Dutton, 1927.)*

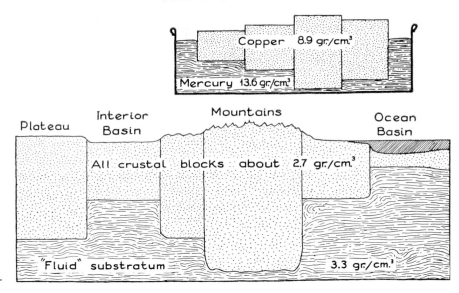

Figure 10-10.

Airy's theory, also called the Roots of Mountains Theory of isostasy. The densities shown in the lower diagram were not specified by Airy but are based on modern estimates. (Modified in part from C. R. Longwell, Geographical Review, 1925.)

have merit in explaining the differences between continents and ocean basins.

A simplified view of the Roots of Mountains theory is shown in Figure 10-10. In the upper diagram, several blocks of copper, all having the same density but differing in weight because they are of different heights, float in a pan of mercury. The tallest block projects highest above the surface and also sinks deepest into the mercury. The lower diagram shows how blocks of the earth's crust, all composed of the same kind of material, may nevertheless float to different heights provided they differ in thickness.

The diagrams shown in Figures 10-9 and 10-10 are, of course, greatly oversimplified. Good evidence will be provided in later chapters to show that the earth's crust is not divided into simple blocks free to move past one another along frictionless boundaries. The substratum, also, is not a fluid, although it may respond by plastic flow to heavy loads of long duration, reacting to these large stresses essentially like a viscous fluid. We know, furthermore, that the strength of the earth's crust is very great; loading must reach a certain intensity before this strength is overcome and the rock beneath gives way and begins to flow.

The Geoid and the Spheroid

We have seen how the modern measurements of arcs of meridian at different latitudes changed our concept of the "Figure of the Earth" from Eratosthenes' sphere to an oblate ellipsoid. But a moment's thought about the facts just discussed shows that still further refinement is necessary.

Though nearby mountain ranges do not deflect the plumb line as much as one might expect—a fact explained by the concept of isostasy—they nevertheless do deflect it. Even the surface of the sea, therefore, cannot be a perfect oblate ellipsoid. Near shore it is warped upward by the gravitational pull of the adjacent lands. This irregularly warped surface of the sea, which is, of course, everywhere at right angles to the plumb line, is

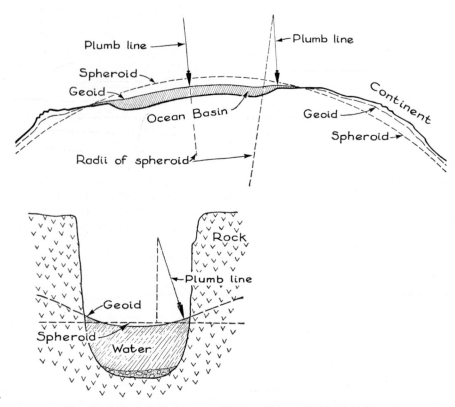

Figure 10-11.

The relations between spheroid and geoid, tremendously exaggerated to show the qualitative effect of irregular topography. Top: *Broad view of their relations as between continental and oceanic segments.* Bottom: *The hypothetical relation (greatly exaggerated) in a Norwegian fjord.*

called the **geoid** (Fig. 10-11). The geoid may be thought of as the surface of the ocean, and in continental areas, as the surface of the water in a system of narrow sea-level canals which we might imagine to be cut through the continents.

The geoid—in other words, the level surface corresponding to sea level over the whole earth—obviously does not correspond to any regular mathematical figure; unlike the ellipsoid, for example, it cannot be formed by rotating an ellipse on its axis. It has irregular bumps and warps and, hence, offers great mathematical difficulties to geodesists, who need a precise and definite surface to which they can refer observations and thus make comparisons between different measurements.

To get around this difficulty, geodesists have accepted a mathematical figure called the **spheroid** which corresponds approximately to the world-average form of the geoid. The spheroid is the ellipsoid of revolution that most closely fits the geoid. When we recall that the oceans cover 71 per cent of the earth, it should not be surprising that the spheroid, or world-average geoid, is only slightly different from the ellipsoid that was calculated from polar flattening. The spheroid lies very slightly above the geoid in oceanic areas and somewhat below it in continental areas, as the oceans are less dense than the rocks at the same level. These relations are illustrated in tremendous exaggeration in Figure 10-11.

conclusion reached from the plumb-line observations: *the excess mass of the rocks above sea level is compensated for by a deficiency of mass below sea level.* Either of the two explanations—lower density of the same thickness of rocks (Pratt), or equal density of a variable thickness of rocks (Airy) could account for this.

Conversely, the positive anomalies at sea stations are explained by the error involved in assuming that the oceans are underlain by material of the same density as that beneath the continents. If we replace this assumption with another—that oceanic segments are underlain by denser material than the continents—the anomalies are greatly reduced.

Both the deflections of the plumb line and the relations between gravity measurements and the earth's relief thus indicate the same thing: the larger segments of the earth are roughly in floating equilibrium (isostatic balance) one with another. Large areas of high land stand above large areas of lowland because, either (1) they are composed of less dense materials than underlie the lowlands (Pratt), or (2) if they are made of the same material, it is thicker beneath the highlands (Airy).

Strength

The preceding discussion of isostasy assumes that the earth has a plastic interior that buoys up irregularities of the crust by flotation. What does this mean? Ordinary rocks seem rigid and do not behave at all like fluids. The great mountain ranges do not seem to be flattening out under their own weight; as far as we can see they are made of strong, rigid rocks capable of maintaining their present shape. Furthermore, we shall see in later chapters that there is good evidence that in some areas of limited size—say a small mountain range or a moderate-sized delta—isostatic equilibrium is far from complete. Some areas are actually held lower or higher than their theoretical equilibrium position by the strength of the earth's crust.

Must we conclude from these evidences of surface strength and bodily weakness that the earth has a strong solid crust floating on a liquid interior? As we shall see in later chapters, there is cogent evidence that the subcrust is not really liquid—that under some short-term stresses it behaves as though it were twice as strong as steel.

Perhaps a part of our dilemma might be resolved if we consider carefully just what we mean by "strength," and also how we visualize the property of strength in huge masses the size of the earth. Airy gave us a very significant clue when he emphasized that a solid or rigid core, no matter how strong we think the strongest rocks are, could not possibly be strong enough to support the earth's crust: the core must behave plastically, almost as though it were a fluid. Furthermore, in areas where metamorphic rocks have been exposed by deep erosion, we have visual evidence in their foliation and fantastically complicated fold patterns that rocks deeply buried in the crust have flowed, bent, and recrystallized in patterns like those that we can form in putty or toothpaste at the surface.

Definition of Strength

The **strength** of a body is defined as the force (load) per unit area that is required to deform the body permanently—that is, to break it or make it yield continuously.

Thus, we say that a cube of granite an inch in diameter that breaks under a weight of 30,000 pounds has a compressive strength of 30,000 pounds per square inch. A steel cable with a cross section of one square inch that does not break until a weight of 150,000 pounds is suspended from its end has a tensile strength of 150,000 pounds per square inch. For each solid substance there is a definite force per square inch that must be reached to cause it to rupture or flow.

Fluids, both liquids and gases, have no strength; they yield continuously under the slightest load or stress, though they vary tremendously in the speed with which they yield. At first glance, tar seems "stronger" than water—an iron bar will not sink into it so quickly. Yet the bar does gradually sink in the tar and eventually it will reach the bottom; the tar is simply more viscous than water—it has no true strength to support the bar.

Solids, too, can be made to flow—that is, yield continuously without rupture—under particular conditions of temperature and pressure. But a solid, unlike a fluid, requires application of a definite force per square inch before its strength is overcome and continuous yielding begins.

Effect of Temperature

Whether a particular solid will break or will flow under a given load depends partly on its temperature when the load is applied. At red heat, a bar of iron is solid, but it will flow under stresses much weaker than those needed to make it bend at room temperature—a fact utilized in forging iron.

As shown in earlier chapters, there is clear evidence that many solid rocks buried deep within the earth's crust have flowed and bent in response to the heat and pressure of the earth's interior. The same rocks at the surface deform only by breaking. The flow and recrystallization of solids should not be confused with liquid flow; the rock does not melt, and a definite stress (equivalent to the strength of the material under the prevailing environment) must be applied before continuous yielding begins. The general rule is that *any particular solid is weaker at high temperature than at low.*

Effect of Size, or Scale

In everyday life we seldom think of the effect of size upon the strength of material. The earth, however, is a very large structure. How are we to think of rock strength in such a huge mass? A dramatic illustration of the effect of size has been given by M. King Hubbert in the quarry operation illustrated in Figure 10-14.

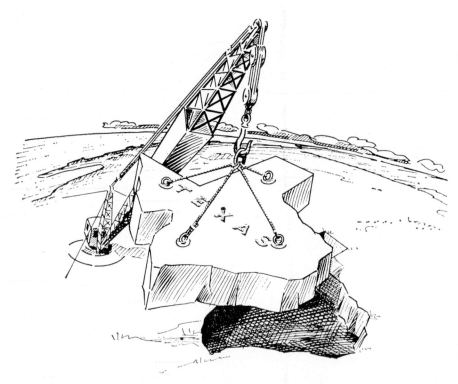

Figure 10-14.

Quarrying the State of Texas. (After M. King Hubbert, reproduced by permission, American Association of Petroleum Geologists, Bulletin, 1945.)

Suppose we are to quarry a single block of granite the size of the State of Texas. It is roughly 720 miles (1,200 kilometers) across, and we want to hoist a piece one-quarter as thick as it is broad—that is, 180 miles (300 kilometers) thick. Grant that we have a quarry crane capable of hoisting it. The rock is assumed to be flawless and to have the crushing strength of average granite, about 30,000 pounds per square inch. Will it be strong enough to allow itself to be hoisted without disintegrating? Obviously it is impossible to test such a problem directly, but we can investigate the properties of such a block by using a scale model.

What would be the properties of a model reduced to a size suitable for our experiment? To obtain a convenient size for our model of the State of Texas, we could reduce the true length of 1,200 kilometers to 60 centimeters (about 2 feet). Our model would then be on a scale of 1 to 2,000,000. On this scale, the 300-kilometer thickness would be reduced, in the model, to 15 centimeters (about 6 inches). Both original and model are at the earth's surface so the force of gravity will be the same on both. We can also use material of the same density as the original, about three times that of water. What other factors must be considered?

If the model is to act in the same way as the original—that is, if its mechanical behavior is to be the same—it is clear that the strength of the material used should be reduced in the same ratio as is the size. Hence, if the ratio of strength to load is to be the same in the model as in the original, we must use material whose strength is 1/2,000,000 that of granite. The material in our model then must have a strength of 1/2,000,000 of 30,000 pounds per square inch, or .015 pounds per square inch.

In Hubbert's words:

It is difficult to envisage a solid of this weakness. A crushing strength of .015 pounds per square cm, which, for the density of 3 grams per cubic cm, would be the pressure at the base of a column ⅓ of a cm high. Any column higher than this would collapse of its own weight. Yet the size of the reduced block would be such that its thickness would be about 15 cm (6 inches) and its total weight about 180 pounds. The pressure at its base would be about 45 grams per square cm or 45 times the crushing strength of the materials.

Consequently, if we tried to lift such a block in the manner indicated in the figure, the eyebolts would pull out; if we should support it on a pair of saw-horses, its middle would collapse; were we to place it on a horizontal table, its sides would fall off. In fact, to lift it at all would require the use of a scoop shovel. That this is not an unreasonable result can easily be verified by direct calculation upon the original block (the State of Texas). For it, too, the pressure at its base would exceed the crushing strength of its assumed material by a factor of 45. The inescapable conclusion, therefore, is that the good State of Texas is utterly incapable of self-support!

Effect of Confining Pressure

The strength of a substance is increased when it is placed under pressure from all directions simultaneously—that is, when it is under **confining pressure** (hydrostatic pressure).

Laboratory experiments show that the crushing strength of limestone from Solnhofen, Germany, is six times as great under a confining pressure of 10,000 atmospheres (147,000 pounds per square inch) as it is under ordinary conditions. Under a confining pressure of one atmosphere (14.7 pounds per square inch), its strength is 25,000 pounds per square inch; under 10,000 atmospheres, 150,000 pounds per square inch. Such a pressure is equal to the weight of a column of granite about 22 miles high. Presumably, then, it is also equal to the hydrostatic pressure at a depth of 22 miles within the earth. Despite the increased strength due to the confining pressure, Solnhofen limestone should yield by rupture or flow at this depth.

From temperature measurements in drill holes and mines, we know that the earth is hotter inside than at the surface. It is clear, then, that factors of opposite tendency affect the strength of rocks deep in the earth: on the one hand, increased hydrostatic pressure increases their strength; on the other, the higher temperatures weaken them.

We see, therefore, that confining pressure due to the weight of the overlying rock is a great factor in the earth's strength. In short, there is nothing really inconsistent in the apparent incongruity of an earth whose rocks are so "rigid and strong" that they are capable of maintaining large relief features on the surface, yet at the same time so "weak" that, in the long course of geologic time, they react almost like a liquid to such large differential loads as those imposed on them by a mountain chain. Our chief difficulty lies in visualizing the way in which a substance must act in very large masses or under pressures and temperatures unfamiliar to us.

FACTS, CONCEPTS, TERMS

THE EARTH'S GROSS FORM
  Sphere? Oblate ellipsoid?
  Measuring an "arc of meridian"
  The geoid and the spheroid
GRAVITATION
  Law of gravitation
  Mass, weight, density
  Relation of level surface to plumb line
  Measurement of gravity
    The gravity pendulum
  Influences affecting force of gravity
    Altitude, latitude (centrifugal force), density of underlying rocks
  Deflection of plumb line by mountains

INFERENCES FROM GRAVITATIONAL DATA
  Effect of nearby differences in rock density
ISOSTASY
  Evidence from deflection of the plumb line
  Effect of nearby topographic features
  Pratt's theory of isostasy
  Airy's theory of isostasy
  Evidence from gravity anomalies
    Free-air anomalies
    Bouguer anomalies
STRENGTH
  Solids and fluids
  Effect of temperature
  Effect of scale or size
  Effect of confining pressure

QUESTIONS

1. What evidence can you give that the earth is approximately an oblate ellipsoid and not shaped like a football or a doughnut?

2. What assumptions underlie Eratosthenes' measurement of the earth? Neglecting measuring errors, are there reasons for doubting the validity of these assumptions?

3. When we sight along a telescope accurately adjusted to a level position, are we sighting parallel to the (1) geoid, (2) spheroid, or (3) ellipsoid? Where, in general, would you expect all three of these surfaces to be most nearly parallel?

4. How would you expect the plumb line to be deflected from the line at right angles to the spheroid at Denver, just east of the Rockies? If surveys failed to show any such deflection what might you suspect as the cause?

5. It is often stated in geologic writing that the hydrostatic pressure at depths of a few tens of miles is equal to the weight per unit area of the overlying rocks. How can this statement be justified?

6. There is a very large negative anomaly (Bouguer) at Seattle, nearly at sea level. Within less than 20 miles east or west of Seattle, measurements show practically no anomaly. What suggestions can you offer to explain this fact?

7. What difference would there be between the rate of swing of a gravity pendulum at a station at the surface and the rate at a second station at the bottom of a 5,000 foot mine? Between the rate of swing at a station at Seattle (see Question 6) and that at another station 20 miles west of Seattle?

8. In a certain valley in Turkestan the plumb lines are actually deflected *toward* the center of the valley instead of away from it, toward the mountains. Suggest a possible explanation of this anomalous behavior.

9. Account for the fact that rocks that are brittle and break under stresses in the laboratory have obviously been folded and have flowed under stresses in the earth.

10. Why don't the continental masses spread out over the ocean floor?

SUGGESTED READINGS

Daly, R. A. *Strength and Structure of the Earth*. New York, Prentice-Hall, 1950. [Especially the Introduction and Chapter 1.]

Hubbert, M. K. *Strength of the Earth,* Amer. Assoc. Petroleum Geologists Bull., Vol. 29 (1945), pp. 1630-1653.

The Planet Earth. (A Scientific American Book) New York, Simon and Schuster, 1957.

Poynting, J. H. *The Earth*. Cambridge, England, Cambridge University Press, 1913.

11 | DOWNSLOPE MOVEMENTS OF SOIL AND ROCK

CHAPTER 5 outlined the role of gravity in causing erosion. Chapters 12 to 16 will describe the erosive effects of geological agencies such as streams, glaciers, waves, wind, and ground water. In this chapter we consider the ways in which gravity moves rock directly.

Varieties of Downslope Movements

Masses of rock or soil that glide or roll directly downslope because of gravity range from small patches of water-soaked soil that creep slowly down hillsides to great landslides that crash down mountains.

Creep is the term for slow movements that bulge and distort the soil downslope. Typically, creep takes place in unconsolidated materials on grass-covered slopes. Movement is usually so slow that there are no obvious surface indications of it, but over a period of years noteworthy changes occur.

Slow slides and **debris flows** differ from creep by showing distinct boundaries of the individual slides or flows at the surface. Slides and debris flows move as units bounded by well-marked slip surfaces, and gaping cracks or rough scars mark their sources. The fragments of a debris flow are jumbled together during movement, and the debris generally advances in tongues or broadly rounded masses. Debris flows range from a few feet to several miles in length.

Rapid debris flows, landslides, and **rock falls** are characterized by rapid movement. They vary from small fragments that rattle down fissured cliffs to great rock falls and landslides that may destroy villages and dam rivers.

Rainwash

Rainwash on hill slopes marks an initial stage in the flow of the surface waters that are later gathered into well-defined streams and rivers. It is considered here because its effects cannot always be distinguished from the sliding of water-soaked soil, or even from the slow downslope creep of soil and rock.

During a heavy rainstorm, hill slopes may be covered by a thin sheet of moving water heavily charged with mud, silt, and humus that have been churned up by the pelting rain drops. Some of the water soaks into the ground; some moves down the slope. Generally, the flowing water quickly unites to form numerous shallow rills that course almost straight downslope, often dividing and reuniting before they finally lose their individuality at the edge of a stream or on a nearly flat valley floor (Fig. 11-1). Most of these shallow rill courses are short-lived furrows that may be filled and obliterated in a single

Figure 11-1.

Rill furrows in fresh volcanic ash from Paricutin Volcano, Mexico. (Photo by Konrad Krauskopf.)

season, but some grow into larger, steep-walled permanent **gullies.**

Creep

Creep is the most widespread of all down-slope movements. Typically, it consists of slow downhill distortion of soil and mantle rock, or of poorly consolidated sediments. Observations extending over several years show that creep is most active during the wet season and at the beginning of the dry season. Ordinarily the movement does not extend far below the surface, and a slip surface seldom develops between the creeping mass and the rock beneath. Distortion by creep is shown by many rock bodies whose previous shape or structure is known. For example, decayed boulders (Fig. 11-2) that once must have been nearly round are stretched downhill into thin ribbons of varicolored soil. Creep is also well displayed in the bending of thin-bedded, steeply inclined strata as they come to the surface on a steep hillside (Fig. 11-3). On

Figure 11-2.

Decayed boulders stretched into long spindles by creep. (Photo by S. Capps, U. S. Geological Survey.)

Figure 11-3. *Bending of thin vertical strata by creep, Washington County, Maryland. (Photo by George Stose, U. S. Geological Survey.)*

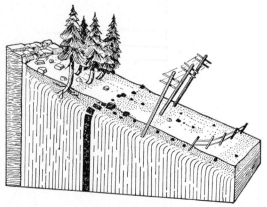

Figure 11-4. *Common effects of creep. (After C. F. S. Sharpe, Landslides and Related Phenomena, Columbia University Press, 1938.)*

many slopes, creep is perceptible through its effects on rock structures, trees, posts, or buildings (Fig. 11-4).

The mechanisms of creep are somewhat conjectural. Wetting of clay-rich soil or freezing of water contained in its pores causes the soil to swell upward, as shown in Figure 11-5. A particle of soil at *a* is pushed upward at right angles to the surface by the swelling, and comes to rest at point *b*. When the clay dries, or the ice melts, the soil contracts, but the particle does not return to point *a,* instead it is lowered vertically to *c*. If the soil is wet enough to flow slightly under the action of gravity, the particle may even glide still farther down the hillside. By repeated wetting, or freezing, it is moved, step by step, farther and farther downslope. Because water expands 9 per cent on freezing, the upward swelling is very noticeable in regions with cold winters. Soil crusts may be raised several inches and paved roads may be bulged upward and broken into rubble by the **frost heaving.** When the soil thaws, the shrinkage does not take place along the original path of expansion; the pull of gravity causes a net movement downslope.

Other processes that commonly cause creep include wedging by plant roots; the moving of soil by earthworms, rodents, and other burrowing animals; and the pushing of soil downslope beneath the feet of animals such as sheep or cattle (Fig. 11-6). Any random movement of loose material gives gravity a chance to cause a displacement downslope.

Creep passes imperceptibly into downslope sliding of definitely bounded masses. In the California Coast Ranges a black sandy clay soil develops on several types of sedimentary rock. On many moderate slopes (e.g., 15 to

Figure 11-5. *One mechanism of creep. The arrows show the gradual downslope migration of a particle with alternate swelling and contraction.*

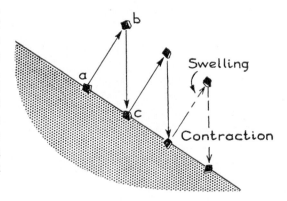

Figure 11-6.

Paths formed by grazing animals on a steep hillside in central Oregon. After each rain hooves push the softened soil a little further downslope. (Photo by A. C. Waters.)

20 degrees) this soil and the weathered rock are intimately mixed, but are sharply separated by a smooth slip surface from the fresh rock beneath. The surface layer, in slow downslope transit, has scraped the underlying rock clean. Marked movement in the past forty or fifty years is shown by the tilting of fence posts and telephone poles, but the lack of scars or irregularities on the surface indicates that the movement is general and not concentrated in landslide tongues.

Solifluction

In arctic and subarctic regions, and above the timber line in temperate zones, there are slow downslope movements called **solifluction** (literally: "soil flow") which are intermediate between creep and debris flows. Frost action and other forms of weathering produce abundant rock fragments of all sizes, including some material fine enough to be called soil. When this debris is saturated with water,

it spreads slowly in sheets, lobes, and tongues down moderate slopes and along the floors of steep valleys. A. L. Washburn, an American student of the Arctic, has suggested, from studies on Victoria Island, northwest of Hudson Bay, that most of the movement takes place immediately after the thawing of the frost-heaved surface in spring. Rows of stakes Washburn had driven in the lobe shown in Figure 11-7 proved that there was slight local tilting and forward movement during the spring and summer of 1940. The seasonal forward movement totaled only 1¾ inches and almost all of it took place in the 33 days following June 14. Apparently solifluction is caused by very slow seasonal flow of water-saturated soil, year after year.

Rock Glaciers

In southwestern Colorado the flat floors of large natural amphitheaters are strewn with fine rock fragments heaped in lobate ridges

Figure 11-7.

Solifluction lobe on Victoria Island, Canada. The rows of stakes were used to measure the rate of flow of the lobe. (Photo by A. L. Washburn.)

Figure 11-8.   Rock Glacier, Engineer Mountain, Colorado. (Photo by W. Cross, U. S. Geological Survey.)

(Fig. 11-8) somewhat like those on solifluction slopes, but also resembling the ridges that form on rock falls. These ridged debris piles have been called **rock glaciers,** perhaps because the ridges resemble the debris covering the ends of some glaciers. Rock glaciers are probably a result of large-scale frost heaving and solifluction. The debris ridges are sinuous and irregular, like solifluction lobes, and the material consists of fragments small enough to be readily moved by frost. Not much is known of the details of their motion, however.

Slow Slides and Flows

If part of the soil and loose rock on a hillside moves downslope at a rate a little more rapid than that of the general hillside creep, it is set off from its surroundings by a gaping crack

Figure 11-9.   *Slide near Orinda, San Francisco Bay region, California. Four-lane highway and large dump trucks give scale. (Photo by Bill Young, courtesy* San Francisco Chronicle.*)*

at its upper edge, and by cracks or ridges at its sides (Fig. 11-9). Many such masses are slides that glide more or less as a unit upon a sharply defined basal slip surface, but others are debris flows whose constituent parts are broken up and jumbled together during movement. Many masses start as slides and become debris flows farther downslope.

Gros Ventre Debris Flow

The Gros Ventre River is a tributary of the Snake River south of Yellowstone Park. In the spring of 1909, the Gros Ventre River was dammed in midcourse by rock debris that, as early as May, 1908, had begun to flow slowly down the moderate slope (10 to 20 degrees) of the Gros Ventre Mountains on the south

side of the river (Fig. 11-10). The rocks that slid were soft shales, with some interbedded layers of thin sandstone and limestone. The shales had been thoroughly soaked by heavy rains. Some of the strata probably slipped along the bedding planes, which almost parallel the land surface. The sliding was imperceptible to an observer but wrought notable changes in the landscape within a few weeks. Telephone poles tilted slowly downhill, snapping the wires. A wagon road paralleling the river soon became so hopelessly twisted and broken that repairs were futile; eventually it was so churned up by the movement that traces of it were hard to find.

Numerous gaping fissures opened at and near the places of initial movement on the

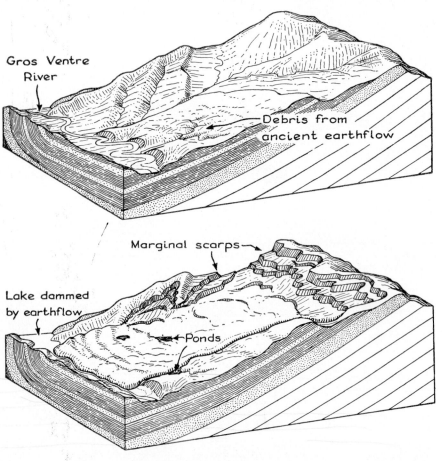

Figure 11-10.

The south slope of the Gros Ventre River valley before (top) *and after* (bottom) *the 1909 debris flow. (After Eliot Blackwelder, 1912.)*

east and south sides of the Gros Ventre debris flow. Farther down, where the material of an earlier flow (see Fig. 11-10) was set in renewed motion, earth domes swelled up and broke open in broad cracks. The flow thickened toward the river, developed a very irregular surface, and was churned into a jumbled mixture of clay and coarser material.

The flow did not move in one mass, but in sections, beginning at the east side and spreading week by week. The sliding and crumbling debris moved fastest in the wet spring months of 1909 and slowed noticeably by autumn. Movement continued through 1910 but had almost entirely ceased by 1911. The river was then able to cut 10 feet down into the debris dam and partly drain the lake that had formed on the upstream side.

Slow Slides

Many slides break up far less completely than did the Gros Ventre flow. A mass of rock may break away from a cliff and slip along a sloping water-lubricated surface for many

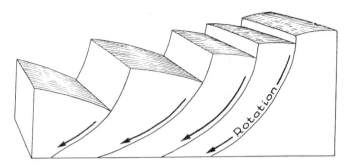

Figure 11-11.   Rotation of slide blocks on curved soles.

feet without breaking up at all, leaving only a gaping fissure on its upper side as evidence of movement. In weak materials, small slide blocks commonly rotate slightly on curved slip surfaces, forming a depression at the head of each slide unit as shown in Figure 11-11.

Rapid Slides, Flows, and Falls

Small Rapid Slides

The great majority of rapid gravity movements involve only small volumes of soil or

Figure 11-12.   Talus slope at the base of a basalt butte, Grand Coulee, Washington. (Photo by courtesy of the Washington Department of Conservation and Development.)

rock, but the aggregate effects are large. In humid temperate regions, small rapid slides are extremely common in soil or weak sedimentary rock, especially on steep grassy slopes after unusually heavy rains. The depression, or scar, left at the head of a typical slip may be more than ten feet wide. At the base of the scar, the soil piles up in more or less crumpled and disordered masses (Fig. 11-9).

Talus Piles

In total quantity, the most important falls of rock are countless small fragments, from a fraction of an inch to a few feet in diameter, that drop from cliffs or steep rock surfaces and accumulate in **talus piles** at the bases of steep slopes or cliffs (Fig. 11-12). A talus pile maintains a fairly steep surface slope as it grows. The slope angle, commonly about 30 degrees, is called the **angle of repose** because it is the steepest slope on which the material will rest without rolling downward. The widening of steep-walled valleys in arid regions is largely accomplished by the fall and continued downward rolling and sliding of large and small talus fragments.

RATE OF TALUS FORMATION. Those who often climb steep slopes of closely jointed rock in lofty snow-clad mountains know well the sound of, and also the danger from, rock fragments that tumble from cliffs and bound erratically down long talus slopes. Talus piles grow rapidly where frost action works on well-jointed rocks (see Fig. 5-2). The mere presence of talus, however, is no proof of rapid change in the configuration of the cliffs above. Great talus piles at the foot of granite cliffs in southern Arizona are composed of huge blocks so thoroughly weathered that they could not, in their present state, have withstood the impact of fall. They must have weathered in place after accumulation on the talus pile. Their presence is one indication that Arizona formerly had a wetter and colder climate.

Large Rock Falls and Mudflows

Large rock slides occasionally crash down steep slopes and huge rock masses may even break loose and hurtle through the air. Large rapidly moving mudflows also occur, and if well lubricated they may glide swiftly over very gentle slopes. Several such rapid slides, flows, and falls have destroyed villages or portions of cities. From the many such catastrophes, we select for description a rock slide and fall in the Swiss Alps, and mudflows in Norway and Switzerland.

ELM ROCK SLIDE AND FALL. Perhaps the best known rock fall occurred at Elm, a village in the northeastern Swiss Alps, in 1881. A steep slope 2,000 feet high that

Figure 11-13.   Cross section of the rock slide and fall at Elm, Switzerland, showing the original position of the slide block. (After A. Heim, 1882.)

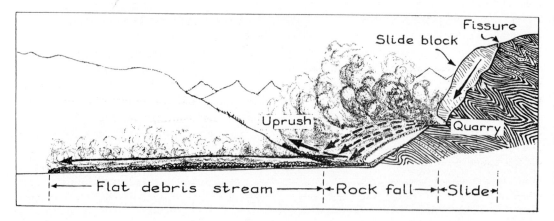

formed the prow of a ridge between two valleys, had been undercut half way up in quarrying for slate. In the course of a year and a half, a curving fissure 30 feet deep slowly formed along the top of the ridge 1,100 feet above the quarry (Fig. 11-13). This fissure was approximately perpendicular to the stratification and foliation of the rocks. In the late summer of 1881, the local runoff from heavy rains poured into the fissure, saturating the shattered rocks. Late one September afternoon, two small earth slides occurred, starting just above and on either side of the quarry. A few minutes later, the whole mass outlined by the fracture crashed down, filled the quarry, and shot forward into the narrow valley as a free-falling rock avalanche (Fig. 11-13). On striking the valley floor, it rushed obliquely up the opposite slope to a height of 300 feet, turned almost 90 degrees and shot down the valley in a debris stream that destroyed houses and everything in its path and killed 115 people. Thirteen million cubic yards of rock fell an average of about 1,450 feet, and spread as rubble over a third of a square mile to a depth of 30 to 60 feet. A dense cloud of dust covered the scene for several minutes.

All observers agreed that after the mass gave way and slid on the fissure to the quarry floor it shot forward into free fall. The villagers could see the hillside across the valley beneath the cascading torrent of shattered stone.

From eyewitnesses' reports, it was estimated that the debris at the front of the tongue traveled one and one-half miles in a little less than one minute. Calculations based on the acceleration of gravity make this appear reasonable. In free fall, the acceleration, or increase of velocity, of the falling object is 32 feet per second in each second. The short preliminary sliding and the free fall at Elm are calculated to have taken about 17 seconds, and the velocity of the falling rock when it hit the valley floor was about 186 miles per hour. Including the time it took the rock to come to a stop down valley, the whole dura-

tion was calculated at roughly 53 seconds —in good agreement with estimates by eyewitnesses. The average velocity of the blocks that traveled farthest was calculated to have been 93 miles per hour.

The Elm debris was composed largely of fragments a few inches in diameter, including much intermingled soil and rock dust. Larger blocks, up to 20 feet across, were scattered through it, especially in the central and higher parts of the debris tongue. The margins were abrupt. The top of the debris stream was hummocky and irregular, and low ridges festooned its surface. By 1928, 47 years after the event, almost all the devastated area had been restored to pasture and potato fields.

Elm was not the largest historic rock fall, by any means. Early in 1911 an enormous mass of broken rock plunged down the slope of the Pamir Mountains in central Asia and formed a giant dam, about 2,500 feet high and with a volume of some three billion cubic yards. It blocked the Murgab River, and the water that accumulated behind the dam formed Lake Sarezkoye, now 45 miles long and 1,650 feet deep. The lake discharges by seepage through the slide, thereby making a new source for the Murgab, 495 feet lower than the lake level. A balance has been reached between the flow of water into the lake and its seepage through the dam.

RAPID MUDFLOWS. The Elm fall affected hard rocks, and was made possible by a steep slope. Masses of mud, on the other hand, may break through weak barriers and flow fairly rapidly for long distances even on gentle slopes.

In northwestern Europe and eastern Canada, many valleys are floored with unconsolidated clays and sands that extend many miles inland and rise to elevations of several hundred feet. During the spring thaw, these soft sediments become saturated with water and a mass of mud as much as a square mile in area may suddenly break through a slightly more solid barrier, and roll down valleys as a destructive mudflow. The front of the flow

Figure 11-14.

Small lobate mudflow caused by heavy rains, Cape Fear River, North Carolina.

often moves as much as 6 miles in a single hour, then piles up, forming a temporary dam of sandy clay behind which water collects until it overflows and breaches the dam. At its head, such a mudflow leaves a clean-cut scar, with rough floor and steep walls a few feet or a few tens of feet high. One night in 1893, a mudflow of this kind moved down a Norwegian valley so fast that 111 persons were caught by it and lost their lives; others escaped after being jostled about in their wooden houses as the mudflow carried them down the valley.

In arid regions, still another kind of mudflow takes place. A thick mass of silt, sand, and coarser debris scoured from the walls and floor of a canyon by an exceptionally heavy rain may roll forward for miles, damming, piling up, breaking through, and gradually coming to a stop as it thickens through loss of water, or spreads out over a plain.

Small lobate mudflows are common at the base of steep slopes in unconsolidated material after heavy rains (Fig. 11-14).

Some of the largest and most destructive mudflows develop in the loose pyroclastic ejecta from active volcanoes. They are described in Chapter 18.

UNDERWATER FLOWS. Of all downslope movements of solid or semiliquid material the most obscure and difficult to study are those which take place on the floors of lakes or seas. One thoroughly studied example started at the shore of the Lake of Zug, in Switzerland, and squirted out under water along the lake floor.

The source of the flow lay within the city of Zug. It extended from a lake-front retaining wall to a street lined with buildings about 200 feet inland (Fig. 11-15). In the two years after the retaining wall was built, water began to appear in previously dry cellars behind it, and, in the spring of 1887, the ground settled and the pavements cracked slightly. The first disastrous movement, on July 5, dropped a small section of the retaining wall and three houses beneath lake level, causing several deaths. Half an hour later, wooden piles from the broken retaining wall suddenly rose to the lake surface a hundred yards offshore, showing that lateral movement as well as sinking had occurred. The main flow came three hours later; streets and many houses suddenly settled beneath the lake. The average drop was about 25 feet, and some buildings moved 30 to 60 feet toward the lake.

The material that flowed out into the lake from beneath the source area was water-saturated silt and fine sand from the submerged part of a small stream delta. The flow

excavated a trench 200 feet wide and up to 20 feet deep that extended almost 1,000 feet along the lake floor in the similar silt and sand on the bottom of the lake. At the end of the underwater trench, a new deposit of sandy silt extended out onto the lake floor as a thin debris tongue 2,500 feet long, with an uneven hummocky surface (Fig. 11-15 *lower*). The end of the tongue was 140 to 150 feet lower than the land surface in the area where the flow began, so the slope on which it flowed was less than 3 degrees. The deposit was more than 15 feet thick in places, and it contained about 200,000 cubic yards of material. Less than half came from the land, the remainder was eroded from the lake floor by the flow. The Zug flow, like the turbidity currents described in Chapter 5, was a gravity current of silt and sand, heavier than the lake water.

Figure 11-15.   Map and cross section of the underwater flow at Zug, Switzerland. (After A. Heim, 1888.)

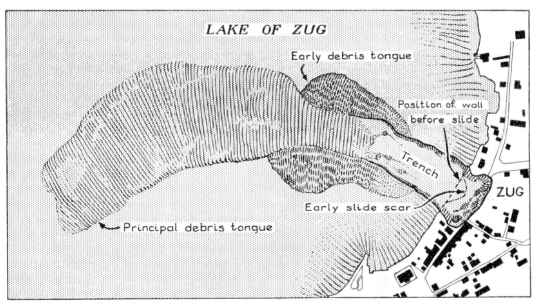

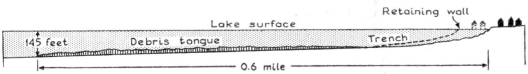

Prehistoric Slides and Debris Flows

Thousands of ancient slides have been recognized in all parts of the world. One is just over the hill from Elm; it is the enormous Flims landslide, at least 15,000 million cubic yards—a thousand times as big as that at Elm and five times the volume of the Pamir landslide. This mass probably started to move as a unit, but gradually broke up, especially those parts that traveled farthest. Long ago, probably in late Pleistocene time, it glided down along the slip plane of an old thrust fault and blocked the valley of the upper Rhine, forming a lake. Then the Rhine eroded the landslide dam, cutting a gorge 2,000 feet deep and 9 miles long. All these events left traces that can still be clearly seen: the hummocky surface of the great slide,

somewhat modified by erosion; the well-marked margins of the landslide dam; and the sudden change in the Rhine valley, from its broad and open upper reaches to a steep-walled gorge through the slide, and then to an open valley below. One thing remains uncertain: Did the slide move rapidly or slowly? A hint is perhaps furnished by the hummocky surface, much like that of the slow Gros Ventre debris flow.

A more complex lobate mass of debris is found where the San Bernardino Mountains rise above the southern margin of the Mojave Desert in southern California (Fig. 11-16). A partly eroded landslide mass is spread out below the outcrops of two thrust faults. On the lower of these faults, granite overrides Late Tertiary sediments; on the upper, crystalline limestone overrides the granite. The landslide also lies on Tertiary sediments; it may

Figure 11-16.   Dissected breccia lobe on the Mojave Desert. Note how the breccia laps up against the range of hills at the left. The lobe is 2½ miles across at its near end. (Photo by Robert C. Frampton, Claremont, California.)

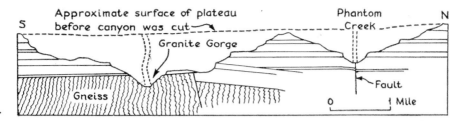

Figure 11-17.

Section across Grand Canyon. The vertical dashed lines above Granite Gorge and Phantom Creek indicate the narrow trenches that would have been made by stream cutting alone. (*Bright Angel quadrangle, U. S. Geological Survey.*)

have reached its present position in Late Tertiary or Pleistocene time. The most puzzling element in the assemblage is a broad lobe of poorly cemented breccia that extends four or five miles out over the flat desert floor, and that in most places is made up exclusively of small limestone blocks. The breccia is somewhat eroded—one stream has cut entirely through it—but its margins are still 25 to 100 feet high and sharply marked. Can this be the debris from a giant rock fall, perhaps a hundred times as large as that at Elm? Several features suggest this: first and foremost, it consists almost exclusively of limestone with no admixture of other rocks of the region; second, the breccia has piled up against low hills far out on the desert, with a slight deflection around the hills somewhat like that at Elm; and, finally, at the edge of the low hills erosion has exposed an underlying breccia composed of sheared and crushed Tertiary sediments. The material of this breccia was probably gouged out as the front of the lobe of limestone debris poured over a low ridge and cut into the soft Tertiary rocks below. A somewhat similar but less sharply defined segregation by rock types was present in the Elm debris. The corrugations of the breccia surface, unlike the lobate ones at Elm, are almost straight. They are nearly parallel to the trend of the partly overridden low bedrock hills to be seen at the left in Figure 11-16, and may represent waves set up by these barriers. The differences between this and the Elm deposit, however, raise some

doubt as to the exact origin of the limestone breccia.

Slides or Flows Preserved in Sedimentary Rocks

The form and textures of certain breccias, or brecciated strata, now parts of Paleozoic, Mesozoic, and Tertiary formations, suggest that they are ancient slides or debris flows. Most convincing are distortions in thin-bedded marine sediments and lenses of heterogeneous debris that lie in troughs which seem to be like that developed in 1887 on the lake floor near Zug. Such features have been recognized in strata from many parts of the world.

Significance of Downslope Movements

Grand Canyon Example

The Grand Canyon of the Colorado River (Fig. 5-13) not only gives evidence of extensive erosion, but makes possible at least a rough estimate of the parts played by different erosional processes in forming it. Figure 11-17 is a structure section across the Grand Canyon and its tributary, Phantom Creek, approximately from south (left) to north (right). The section shows the wide upper canyon cut in nearly horizontal strata, and the inner Granite Gorge cut into the gneiss that nonconformably underlies the sedimentary rocks. The canyon of Phantom Creek is eroded entirely in the overlying strata. The total depth of the canyon is about one mile, and the width from rim to rim about seven and a half miles. The inner Granite Gorge is about 1,300 feet deep at the line of section. The profiles of the side slopes of the Granite Gorge are relatively straight; those of the upper canyon and of Phantom Creek are in steps, with the harder strata forming cliffs above more gentle slopes cut on the less resistant strata. Phantom Creek furnishes an especially favorable example for analysis of the relative roles of stream transport and downslope movements. The stream follows a normal fault of about 150 feet vertical displacement. The position of the stream was apparently determined by the fault; presumably it has eroded downward along the fault, fixed in position by the ready erosion of the shattered rock along the fault zone. The dashed vertical lines on the right in Figure 11-17 indicate a trench as wide as the creek bed and represent the downcutting ascribed to the stream. But if the stream directly eroded only this narrow vertical slot, what processes account for the much wider valley? Judging the past in terms of the present, these other processes include rainwash coursing down the canyon walls in minor rills and deep gullies, and several kinds of downslope movements, among which the fall and continual streamward movement of talus fragments is perhaps a particularly important cause of the widening of Phantom Creek valley.

The Grand Canyon itself has been cut by the Colorado River and widened by rainwash and downslope movements in the same manner. Since the course of the Colorado was not determined by a fault line, however, the river may have wandered somewhat to reach its present position as indicated by the dashed lines in Figure 11-17, instead of following a straight path like that of Phantom Creek. A similar development seems probable for streams and stream systems in other regions. We assume that the depth of a rock-walled canyon whose floor is little or no wider than its stream is a measure of downcutting by the stream, whereas a valley's width is an indication of the amount of material carried downward by rainwash and various kinds of downslope movements.

Downslope movements of rock and soil are, of course, not limited to the matched sides of valleys. They are equally effective in reducing the steepness of single slopes or cliffs, as along shores. Gravity movements extend to the very summits of ridges, reducing their height. Rocky summits are lowered by the fall of fragments loosened by weathering or frost action (Fig. 5-2). This process has contributed to the reduction of the summit ridge between Phantom Creek and the Grand Canyon, so that it now lies well below the level of the plateaus to north and south. Rounded hills with soil-covered divides, on the other hand, are lowered chiefly by creep and rainwash.

Effect of Plant Cover

Downslope movement of material varies with the plant cover, which, in turn, is dependent primarily upon climate.

Even in humid regions, the density of the plant cover varies widely, being thin on cold moors and thick in tropical areas with year-round rainfall. Where trees, shrubs, and grass cover almost the whole surface, topographic forms are smoothly rounded, and creep is the principal variety of downslope movement. Minor differences in rock resistance on a single slope are commonly masked by the almost continuous cover of soil and vegetation, but major differences are made apparent by differences in the steepness of the slopes and in the general pattern of ridges and valleys.

In arid regions, trees and shrubs are few and grass may be absent. As a result, there is no soil on the resistant rocks, which stand out in knobs, ridges, or cliffs. Weak rocks are reduced rapidly by downslope movements and rainwash, and their outcrops are obscured by talus accumulations derived from the resistant rocks (Fig. 11-12). The etching out of weaker rocks, as shown in Figures 9-6 and 8-15, is called **differential erosion.** Differential erosion brings out even slight differences in rock resistance, as shown in Figure 5-14. Hence, the underlying rock structure stands out much more sharply in arid than in humid regions.

Conclusions

Considered in terms of the areas affected, downslope movements and rainwash are actually the most important of all processes of erosion. For every square foot that is directly subject to erosion by a permanent flowing stream there are hundreds of square yards over which soil is slowly creeping— flowing an inch or two downhill after frost heaving or clay hydration, being pushed downslope by burrowing rodents or by the feet of grazing animals, and gliding and falling in debris flows, slides, and talus.

The critical factor for most gravity movements is the presence of enough water to lubricate slide surfaces or to produce a semiliquid flow mass. Many rocks that are relatively strong when dry become weak and plastic when wet. If great volumes of rock so weaken, gliding may take place on a gigantic scale, even though individual parts of the mass may move as units.

Downslope movement is a very important and widespread process of erosion, but it rarely goes on alone. Streams cut valleys, downslope movements widen them, and the streams carry away the debris. Glaciers gouge valleys deeper, and gravity movements load the glacier margins with rock fragments that the ice transports away. Waves driving on shore undermine cliffs, whose upper portions then fall into the sea, to be broken up and carried away by wave-generated currents. In brief, the role of gravity movements is to provide a continuous supply of material to the agents of long-distance transportation.

Downslope movements differ from most other erosional processes in that they can operate beneath the sea as well as on land. Though the buoyant effect of the water lessens the effective pull of gravity on material immersed in it, the soaking of the material is complete. As a result, even though weathering is thought to be slight below the sea, downslope movements should be common there. As we saw in Chapters 5 and 8, such movements are known to have taken place within historic time. The record of their existence in the geologic past is found in disturbed beds and brecciated areas in the marine sedimentary rocks. Downslope movements on land bring debris to the streams, and the streams in turn push the shorelines seaward. Downslope movements in the oceans tend to reduce submarine heights to the level of the ocean floor. Thus, downslope movements contribute to the formation of both of the two broadest levels of the earth—one near sea level, the other on the floor of the ocean (see Fig. 10-4).

Engineering Applications

Gravity movements of soil and rock affect many man-made structures, such as roads, dams, and houses. In the United States alone, clearing highways of the debris that slides or rolls from the slopes above, and the repair of sections of roadbed that have settled and slumped downslope, costs millions of dollars annually. Many newly built railroads and highways have had to be rerouted within a few years in order to bypass slide areas, or cliffs that shed many talus fragments.

Expensive repairs and reconstruction can often be avoided by careful geologic inspection of the ground along the right-of-way. Areas of active sliding show readily recognized features: the hill slope is generally hummocky and contains undrained depressions, the rock may show slip surfaces roughly parallel to the surface of the hill, landslide scars and curving debris ridges are likely to be present, fences and telephone poles are tilted downhill, and tree trunks bend uniformly as they enter the ground.

A cut made for a highway or railroad obviously increases the danger of sliding because the excavation removes support from the slope above. Many an ancient landslide or debris flow that had not moved for tens or even thousands of years has been reactivated by the removal of debris from its toe during the construction of a roadbed.

Although highways and railroads can generally be relocated to detour a dangerous slide area, it is obviously impossible to move some structures endangered by gravity movements. Geologists and engineers must then take steps to stop, or at least to slow down and minimize, the sliding. An oil field near Ventura, California, affords a typical example. Oil wells drilled through a slide were slowly bent out of line as it moved. Some of the well casings were completely sheared off at a slip surface along the base of the slide. Movement was most rapid in the winter when the ground was saturated by seasonal rains. Unless the slide could be controlled, this valuable oil field would have to be abandoned. The problem was solved by paving the entire hillside with asphalt and digging and boring galleries along the base of the slide and installing drain tile to carry off the seepage from the rains. Most of the rain now runs rapidly off the pavement, and the little that does penetrate to the bottom of the slide is drained off. By thus preventing access of water, which transformed the clays into a lubricant, the slide was stopped.

During the building of the huge Grand Coulee Dam on the Columbia River, construction work was threatened when a tremendous mass of watersoaked silt started to creep into the excavation dug for the north abutment of the dam. To stop this threatened slide, engineers hit on the ingenious idea of penetrating the silt with numerous pipes in which a refrigerant was circulated. The refrigerant froze the water in the pores of the silt, thus cementing its particles and increasing its strength. This effectively stopped the movement, and the area was kept refrigerated until the concrete for the dam was poured, and the excavation thus filled and stabilized.

Similar problems have to be met when heavy structures such as large bridges and dams must be built on soft clay or on creeping ground. Many soils behave plastically when loaded, and will flow radially outward from beneath the load. One of the piers of the San Francisco Bay Bridge was purposely made extra large at its base so that the weight of the heavy structure could be distributed over a wide area of the hard clay on which the pier was set. Many kinds of laboratory tests have been devised to determine the load that various kinds of sand, clay, and other loose foundation materials will bear. These tests are the basis of a relatively new branch of engineering science called **soil mechanics.** It includes the study of such field conditions as the attitude of stratification or other slip planes, amount of contained water, slope, and other factors, as well as of the laboratory characteristics of the materials. With such knowledge, it is often possible to forestall or control gravity movements, even in places where weak materials are covered by massive structures.

FACTS, CONCEPTS, TERMS

GRAVITY MOVEMENT OF ROCK

CREEP; SLIDES; DEBRIS FLOWS; ROCK FALLS;
   TALUS

RAINWASH

CAUSES AND EFFECTS OF CREEP

SOLIFLUCTION; ROCK GLACIERS

SLOW DEBRIS FLOWS

RAPID SLIDES AND ROCK FALLS

UNDERWATER FLOWS
RECOGNITION OF ANCIENT SLIDES AND ROCK FALLS
  On land
  In the sea

RELATIVE ROLES OF DOWNSLOPE MOVEMENTS
  AND STREAM EROSION
ENGINEERING APPLICATIONS

QUESTIONS

1. What is the lowest level to which downslope movement on land can deliver material? Downslope movements in the sea?

2. On steep mountain slopes that receive a heavy snowfall even trees that are rooted in rock crevices have trunks that are bent downhill as they emerge from the ground, then straighten to a vertical position a few feet above the surface. Why?

3. In warm humid regions, compact clay-rich soils are more subject to creep than sandy or gravelly open soil, but the latter move readily in arctic regions. Why?

4. Describe the structures you might find in a marine sedimentary rock that would indicate that the area had been the site of an ancient underwater flow.

5. A symmetrical, almost perfectly round soil-covered hill is underlain by vertical soft shales containing two thin beds of hard sandstone. One sandstone is red, and it exactly bisects the center of the hill. The other sandstone is white, and it extends through the hill about halfway down from its summit. Draw a map or sketch showing the two sandstone beds and indicate on the sketch the areas of the hill over which you would expect to find (a) numerous loose fragments of red sandstone, (b) numerous loose fragments of white sandstone.

6. Building sites on a hill with a fine view are restricted to two locations: Both are underlain by soft shale, but at one site the stratification dips steeply into the hill, at the other it dips roughly parallel to the hill slope. Which site would you choose, and why?

7. Basalt cliffs on the Columbia Plateau have large piles of coarse talus at their base. On the Colorado Plateau, where climatic conditions are similar, equally large cliffs of crumbly sandstone have little or no talus. Can you suggest an explanation?

SUGGESTED READINGS

Eckel, E. B., editor. *Landslides in Engineering Practice*. Highway Research Board, Special Report 29. Washington, D. C., National Research Council, 1958. (Of special interest because of applications to highway and construction problems, but also contains an excellent chapter by D. J. Varnes, *Landslide Types and Processes*.)

Heim, Albert. *Bergsturz und Menschenleben*. Beiblatt zur Vierteljahrsschrift der Naturforschenden Gesellschaft in Zurich, No. 20, 1932. (Data concerning Swiss and other landslides, rock falls, and debris flows, including Elm and Flims.)

Howe, Ernest. *Landslides in the San Juan Mountains, Colorado, Including a Consideration of Their Causes and Their Classification*. U. S. Geological Survey, Prof. Paper 67. Washington, D. C., Government Printing Office, 1909. (Many photographic illustrations.)

Sharpe, C. F. S. *Landslides and Related Phenomena*. New York, Columbia University Press, 1938.

12 | STREAM EROSION AND DEPOSITION

RIVERS HAVE PLAYED an important role in human history. Western civilization began with an agricultural economy made possible by the life-giving waters of the Tigris, Euphrates, and Nile. Rivers were easy routes of access into new territory, and the trails of the explorer soon became the arteries of commerce and the pathways of the invader. The energy of rapids and waterfalls was harnessed to turn the early millwheels that sparked the first flickering flames of the Industrial Revolution. Today rivers are relatively less important as media of transportation, but the rich agricultural bounty of our arid lands still depends on irrigation just as in the days of the Pharaohs. Water from rivers supplies most of our factories and municipalities, furnishes electric power, and carries industrial and municipal wastes to the sea. The control and authority over water often spells the difference between poverty and wealth for individuals, states, or even nations.

To a geologist, rivers have many other features of interest besides the effects they have had on commerce and history. As indicated in Chapter 5, streams, aided by downslope movements, play the dominant role in the erosion of the lands. Stream deposits, too, are widespread in many places where no river flows today. Let us turn to an analysis of how streams perform their work, and how the results of their labors can be seen nearly everywhere in the landscapes about us.

To begin our study, let us visit—if only in imagination—the bank of a typical river and watch its activities. What do we see that sets a river aside from other bodies of water? Some obvious things are:

1. It flows downhill.
2. The flow is not uniform; swirls and eddies appear and disappear and some parts move downstream faster than others.
3. It carries a load. In places the water is muddy, and particles of sand or gravel are rolling along the bottom.
4. It is contained within a definite channel, generally bounded by steep banks.

Taking these items as points of departure, let us enlarge our investigation of each.

Stream Flow

Flowing streams are powered by gravity. It is convenient to use a simple graphical representation, the "resolution of forces" (Fig. 12-1), to determine the component of the force of gravity effective down the particular slope of a stream's surface. Consider a mass of water poised at the top of a uniform slope (point *a* of the figure). Its total energy is measured by the potential energy of vertical

Figure 12-1. Resolution of gravity for a stream of uniform slope.

fall (energy of position), and hence the final velocity after movement down the slope would, if there was no friction, be the same as for direct vertical fall, though the time required to attain the velocity would be greater because the component of gravity operating parallel with the slope is less. The acceleration of gravity (an increase in velocity of 32 feet per second in each second) is represented by the hypotenuse (*ab*) of the right triangle *abc*. If flow were frictionless, the mass of water would move down the slope AC with an acceleration *ac* (an increase in velocity of about 5 to 6 feet per second in a second for the slope shown in the figure) and would travel the distance *ac* in the same time that it would fall freely through the vertical distance *ab*. Even for the much flatter slopes of typical streams, the acceleration, if flow were frictionless, would normally be as much as 0.5 feet per second in a second. As there are 3,600 seconds in an hour, the stream, if it moved down an ordinary slope without friction, would after an hour's time attain the astounding velocity of 1,800 feet per second—more than 1,200 miles per hour!

No such velocities are even remotely approached in natural streams. They commonly attain and maintain velocities of only a few feet per second (generally less than 5 miles an hour). We conclude that the energy of fall is mostly converted to heat energy by friction of the particles of water against one another, against the bed and banks of the stream, and against the particles of debris carried by the stream.

If there is no increase in velocity, then the force of the water flowing down the channel must be just balanced by the frictional resistance. This balance is shown in Figure 12-2. The downvalley force is the product of the *weight of the water* times the *slope;* the weight being given by multiplying the *area, A,* by the *length, L,* and the *unit weight of water, w.* The force of friction or the *total drag* is obtained by multiplying the *drag per unit area, T,* times the *surface area of the bed and banks;* the surface area, as shown in Figure 12-2, being the product of the *wetted perimeter, p,* and the *length, L.* In an equation then:

$$wALs = TpL$$

or

$$T = w\frac{A}{p}s$$

It is known that the drag is proportional to the square of the velocity. As one would expect, however, natural streams differ widely in average velocity, and a single stream may fluctuate greatly in velocity over short periods of time. The factors causing these variations are many, but the chief ones are the *gradient* (the *slope, s*) of the stream; the *shape* of its channel A/p; the *amount* of its *discharge,* which influences both the *area,* A, and the *wetted perimeter, p*; and the *roughness, r,* of the bed and banks of the stream. We borrow from hydraulics the equation that relates vel-

Figure 12-2. Cross section of flow in a stream channel.

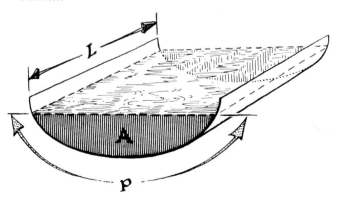

ocity to each of these factors (the symbol $\propto$ means "is proportional to"):

$$V^2 \propto \frac{A}{rp} s$$

The **gradient** of a stream is commonly stated as the number of feet of fall of the surface of the stream per mile of stream course. It is a measure of the slope down which the stream flows: the steeper the slope, other factors being equal, the greater the velocity (Fig. 12-1). The lower Mississippi River near Baton Rouge has a very flat slope, less than one foot per mile, whereas mountain torrents often have slopes exceeding several hundred feet per mile.

Velocity also varies with the nature of a stream's cross section. Figure 12-3 shows three channels with cross sections that are equal in area but are of different shapes. It can be proved mathematically that the channel of semicircular cross section A exerts less friction against the moving water because its rubbing surface per unit area is less than that of either B or C. Water flowing in a deep and narrow channel drags against the walls and tends to widen them by erosion. Water flowing in a wide but shallow stream drags against

Figure 12-3. *Three channel cross sections of equal area. Section* A *contains this area within the smallest possible wetted perimeter, and therefore opposes the least frictional surface to running water. (After W. W. Rubey, 1952.)*

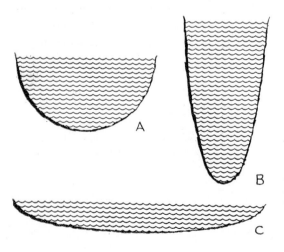

the bottom and is so slowed, particularly along the shallowest margins, that deposition of material carried by the stream is likely to occur on these margins, narrowing the channel and deepening its central part.

Mountain torrents flowing at several feet per second over hard resistant rock tend to assure channel shapes roughly similar to A. As tributaries enter and the flow increases downstream, the channel enlarges, generally increasing somewhat more in width than it does in depth. The cross section shown in A is also the one developed by engineers in their attempts to construct stable irrigation canals—open canals in erodible material in which the water and load are transported with a minimum of silting and a minimum of bank erosion.

The *discharge*, Q, is the quantity of water passing a given point on the stream bank in a unit of time (generally measured in cubic feet per second, abbreviated as cfs). Clearly the discharge which a stream is capable of carrying must be a function of the gradient, velocity, and the size of the channel.

Discharge = Area of Cross Section *times* Mean Velocity of Flow, or in equation form:

$$Q = AV_m$$

But since the area of channel cross section is equivalent to the surface width of the channel, W, times the mean depth of the channel, D_m, we can also write:

$$Q = AV_m = WD_mV_m$$

The mean velocity of the channel, as we have seen, is also influenced by the *roughness* of the channel boundaries as well as by the *amount and grain size of the rock debris* that the stream carries. Many of these variables are closely interrelated and thus, for example, a change in slope at one point along a stream channel may cause an increase in erosion which in turn will change the size and shape of the cross section. Downstream from the point of erosion, material may be deposited, thus decreasing the slope as well as the depth.

Some of these factors may fluctuate greatly

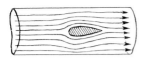  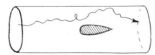

Figure 12-4.

Left: *Laminar flow.* Center *and* right: *Turbulent flow.*

even within periods of a few days. This is notably true of discharge. Floods rage through a river's channel during periods of heavy seasonal rainfall, rapid melting of snow, or even after brief cloudbursts, whereas during droughts the river may dwindle to a series of stagnant pools. These changes in discharge are accompanied by corresponding adjustments in velocity and in the size and amount of sediment load carried.

Turbulence in Natural Streams

Although we have been considering only the average velocity of the stream channel, it is important to realize that the velocity at every point in the cross section of a river is not the same. If streams of dye are injected into the flows of most natural rivers, instead of advancing downstream in parallel lines and at a uniform speed from the point of contamination as they will do in water flowing very slowly through a glass tube (Fig. 12-4, *left*), the colored threads swirl about and are rapidly mixed by the flow. This mixing indicates that flow is **turbulent** (Fig. 12-4, *center* and *right*) rather than laminar. Viscous fluids, such as honey or sticky molten lava, flowing at low velocities, commonly exhibit laminar flow. In natural rivers the low viscosity and high average velocities and depths cause the flow to be turbulent—tangled threads of flow

swirl in all directions and with highly variable speeds.

Turbulence is particularly great near the bed and banks of the channel. Although in a thin film immediately adjacent to the walls and floor of the channel the velocity may be almost zero and flow is laminar, the velocity increases abruptly and the flow becomes strongly turbulent a few feet from the margins. Farther toward the center of the river the velocity changes are less rapid (Fig. 12-5). The thread of maximum average velocity is usually near the middle and above the deepest part of the stream. In broad straight channels, the velocity may be nearly constant across most of the central part of the channel. Figure 12-5 shows the regions of most prominent turbulence in relation to the average velocity distribution. In crooked or meandering channels, as we shall see later, the position of the maximum velocity is not in the center but is shifted far to one side near the outside of each bend. This is an important factor in the differential erosion of the river bank.

It should be clear that the interrelations between gradient, velocity, channel shape and sediment load are extremely complex. Study of them is greatly aided, however, by the wealth of engineering measurements that have been made in the past fifty years. In order to utilize rivers for navigation, irrigation, indus-

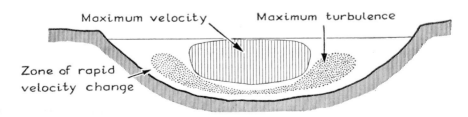

Figure 12-5.

Distribution of velocity and turbulence in a symmetrical channel. (After John Leighly, 1934).

trial or municipal water supplies, hydroelectric power, and many other purposes, we need to know their discharge, depth, rate of flow, sediment load and other characteristics at various points along their course. We also need these data for different seasons of the year if we are to cope intelligently with problems of flood control, river-bank erosion, sewage disposal, bridge and dam stability, seasonal fluctuations in hydroelectric power, and a host of other problems. Hence measurement of streams, including also the amount of rainfall and the ratio of precipitation to runoff within their drainage basins, are now routine. Voluminous files of such data for the watersheds of the United States have been published by the Water Resources Division of the United States Geological Survey.

Stream Loads

The Suspended Load

The turbulence in a stream accounts largely for its ability to sweep up and carry away a load of fine silt and clay particles suspended within the moving water. Whether the particles are brought to the stream by rainwash and creep or are eroded directly from the stream's channel, it is the *upward* currents of turbulence that allow them to be picked up and transported. Once a grain has been lifted by an upsweeping eddy, it is kept from falling out again only by the force of other upward moving currents. True, there are as many downward currents as upward, but since both are distributed at random a particle may be held up for a long time before it is dropped to the bottom by a downward swirl. Other grains will simultaneously be set in motion by upward moving currents. The important result is that, in the time during which a grain is picked up, jostled around, and deposited again, it has moved downstream. An underwater observer moving with the current would see the grains rise, gyrate, bob, and fall, although to an observer on the bank the stream may appear to be an almost homogeneous mixture of water and sediment, all flowing uniformly downstream. Because turbulent currents seem actually to suspend sediment in the stream, this part of the stream's load is called the suspended load.

The Bed Load

Only swiftly flowing rivers develop enough turbulence to lift particles larger than medium-size grains of sand from their beds. Coarser material, however, is pushed or rolled along the bottom by the swirling currents of the boundary zone, thus becoming part of what is called the bed load. Except during floods, when stream velocities are high, the material constituting the bed load generally does not move continuously but progresses downstream with many stops and starts. Consequently, the bed load moves much more slowly than the suspended load.

Moving bed loads have been observed through windows in the walls of experimental flumes. Most of the grains roll, though some slide along the bottom and others bounce along or momentarily vault into suspension. As the velocity of a stream flowing on a bed of sand is gradually increased, the motion of particles on the bed progresses from (1) short leaps of a few individual sand grains to (2) spasmodic movement and deposition of groups of grains, and finally to (3) smooth, general transport of many grains. When the velocity is great enough to produce uniform motion the scour and deposition of grains causes ripples on the bed (see Fig. 3-2). At higher velocities, large numbers of grains spring into temporary suspension, proceeding as such dense clouds that a distinction cannot be made between the bed load and the more rapidly moving suspended load. This gradation of the bed load and suspended load for the Missouri River is indicated graphically in Figure 12-6.

The Dissolved Load

Streams also carry material in solution. Transport of this material does not depend in any way on the nature of stream flow, for the dissolved material is actually part of the liquid. The dissolved load comes chiefly from inflow-

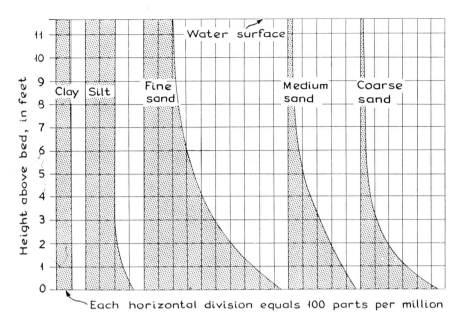

Figure 12-6.

Each horizontal division equals 100 parts per million

Graph showing the variations in sediment content with depth, Missouri River, near Kansas City, Missouri. From samples taken on January 3, 1930. Note the great concentration of the coarser grains near the bed and the nearly equal distribution of the suspended clay and silt. (After L. G. Straub, in Hydrology, courtesy of Dover Publications.)

ing ground water that has percolated slowly through the weathered mantle of soil and rock. Probably very little is dissolved from the channel walls except where streams flow on limestone.

Thousands of chemical analyses show that few rivers carry more than a thousand parts per million (0.1 per cent) of dissolved materials. A general average for many American rivers is about two hundred parts per million. In clear sluggish streams, however, this may form the major part of the total load that the stream delivers to the sea.

Competence to Erode and Capacity to Transport Load

A stream moving at a given velocity exerts a force on the particles on its bed. The force tending to set the particles in motion may be considered basically in two ways. (1) The impact of the flow against the exposed face of the particle, and (2) the frictional drag of the current across the exposed surface of the particle. For the grain to move, the sum of these forces must exceed the grain's inertia, which depends upon its weight. If one equates the impact or momentum of the flow with the weight of the grain, it can be shown that the diameter of a grain which can be moved is proportional to the square of the velocity of the flow striking the particle. That is, if the velocity is doubled, the diameter of grains that the stream can move is increased four fold. If the velocity is tripled, the diameters increase nine fold, and so forth. Similarly, if one equates the tractive force or drag with the weight of the particle, it can be shown that the diameter of the particle which can be moved is directly proportional to the product of the depth and slope. This relation has already been suggested in showing the factors which influence the velocity in a channel (Fig. 12-2). In both cases it is clear that as the impact and frictional drag of the current increase, the size of particles which can be moved by the flow will increase. The maxi-

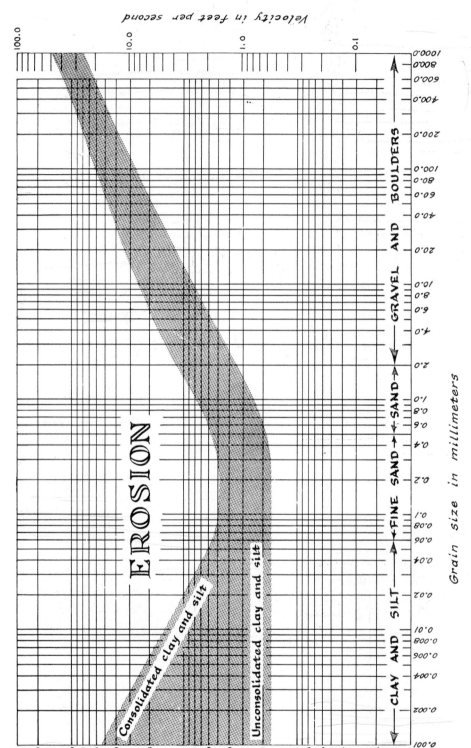

Figure 12-7. Curve showing the slowest velocity of flow at which particles of quartz of different sizes begin to erode. The width of the dark band indicates approximate variations, depending on the depth of the stream and on the cohesiveness of the material. Note that fine sand (0.06 to 0.5 mm. in diameter) is easiest to erode; silty loam and clay, as well as coarser sand and gravel, require greater velocities. (After A. Sundborg, Geografiska Annaler, vol. 38, 1956.)

mum size of particle that a stream can move under a particular set of conditions is defined as the **competence** of the stream. Figure 12-7 shows the velocity required to move quartz particles of various sizes. The competence of many natural streams when in flood is enormous. For example, there are numerous records of the movement of boulders more than 10 feet in diameter. When the St. Francis dam in southern California broke in 1928, the great mass of water that was suddenly released tumbled blocks of concrete that weighed as much as 10,000 tons apiece (63 by 54 by 30 feet) for half a mile downstream. It is interesting to note (Fig. 12-7) that particles of fine sand—from about 0.06 mm. to 0.5 mm. in size—are most easily moved. The same velocity or even a slightly greater velocity is required to move smaller grains. A particularly significant fact is that a still greater velocity is required to erode fine silt or clay-

size particles if these are closely packed or slightly consolidated.

The competence of a stream should not be confused with its **capacity** which is the total load a stream can carry. Capacity depends not only on the velocity (which governs competence), but also on the total volume of flow, the discharge of the stream.

Mechanics of Stream Erosion

Abrasion of Bed and Banks

The particles that a stream carries are constantly jostling each other and dashing against the bed and banks of the channel. Sharp corners of joint blocks and cobbles are broken or rubbed off as they grind against one another and against the floor of the stream channel. Soon the fragments are worn into the spherical or subrounded shapes characteristic of stream gravel. The longer the transport the

Figure 12-8. *The bed of the Susquehanna River, during the drought of 1947, showing potholes and pitted, abraded surfaces. The location is Conewago Falls, Pennsylvania, where a sill of resistant dolerite has produced a rapid in the river's course. (Photo by* Lancaster Intelligence Journal; *courtesy of Herbert H. Beck, Franklin and Marshall College.)*

more perfect the rounding, although tiny grains of silt or fine sand are rounded little, even by long transport, because the water film around them, combined with their small mass, protects them from violent impacts.

Particles rolled or bounced along the bed of a stream actively abrade the bedrock. Below Great Falls, Maryland, where the Potomac River rages through a gorge, fifteen-inch boulders have been lifted as high as sixty feet above the channel bottom during floods. The impact of such missiles shatters both bed and banks. In slower streams, swirling currents armed with coarse sand and small pebbles strongly abrade both the other moving rock fragments and the exposed bedrock. Even fine sand is an effective abrasive in swift currents. Streams in flood produce eddies of great erosive power whose visible effects are conspicuous during low-water (Fig. 12-8). Among them are rounding of the projecting rock, fresh angular scars where blocks have been torn from channel walls, and cylindrical pits (potholes) drilled in solid rock by stones caught in holes on the bed of the stream and whirled about in the swirling water. In the words of G. K. Gilbert, an American geologist who was one of the first to analyze and describe the sculpture of land masses by running water:

. . . —the chief work is performed by the impact and friction of hard and heavy particles moved forward by running water . . . They are driven against all sides of the channel, but their tendency to sink in water brings them against the bottom with greater frequency and force than against the walls. . . . [Therefore, in a swiftly flowing stream] downward abrasion of the rock is so much more powerful than the lateral that the effect of the latter is practically lost, and the channel of the stream, without varying the position of its banks, carves its way vertically into the rock beneath.

The strong turbulence at waterfalls gives an extreme example of the erosive power of flowing water. The swirling currents may pluck and carry away large joint-bounded blocks of bedrock from the brink of the waterfall. Water falling freely is accelerated by gravity; its velocity increases about 32 feet per second (20 miles per hour) during each second of fall. At Niagara Falls the water and entrained rock debris strikes the base of the 150-foot high fall at about 50 miles per hour —at such falls the water scours deep **plunge pools** that undermine the brim of rock over which the water tumbles, making this rock easily susceptible to caving (Fig. 12-9). Upstream migration of waterfalls by undercutting at the plunge pool and caving of the walls above may contribute greatly to the erosion of a stream valley. Below Niagara Falls, for instance, the gorge between Queenston and the Falls, about 7 miles long, was cut principally by headward migration of the waterfall, not by slow downward erosion along the entire channel.

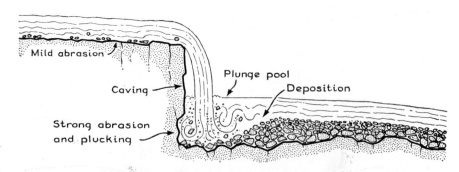

Figure 12-9.

Erosion at a small waterfall.

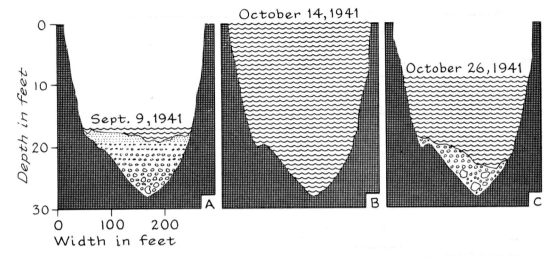

Figure 12-10.   Changes in the channel of the San Juan River, near Bluff, Utah, during the flood of October, 1941. Three stages are shown (A) on September 9 before the flood, when the river was discharging only 635 cubic feet per second, and was flowing over a shallow channel floored with silt, sand, and gravel, (B) at the height of the flood on October 14, when the discharge was 59,600 cubic feet per second and the river had removed all loose debris from its channel, and (C) during an early stage in the recession of the flood on October 26. (After L. Leopold and T. Maddox.)

Importance of Flood Erosion

The interrelations between discharge, velocity of flow, and erosion are strikingly evident during floods. The flood discharge of most rivers is many times that at low water. The Ohio River, notorious for its destructive floods, has a ratio of annual maximum to minimum flow of 313 to 1. As the discharge increases so does the velocity. The Columbia River, 170 miles above its mouth, had a measured mean velocity of 1.9 feet per second and was discharging 78,000 cubic feet of water per second on March 12, 1945. Following the snow melt in early May, the flood discharge was about thirteen times as great (1,018,000 cubic feet per second) and the mean velocity had risen to 11 feet per second. The increased velocity greatly increased the competence of the stream and the added discharge and velocity also greatly increased the stream's capacity.

In the course of such floods streams transport huge loads and rapidly abrade the bed-rock; slackening water leaves the coarser debris stranded on the stream bed. Changes in the channel of the San Juan River at Bluff, Utah, during a flood in 1951 were carefully measured by the United States Geological Survey (Fig. 12-10). On September 9, the river was discharging only 635 cubic feet per second and was flowing over deposits of sand, silt, and gravel that nearly filled the deep bedrock channel (Fig. 12-10, A). By mid-September, the discharge had increased to 6,650 cfs and the increased velocity enabled the river to set in motion parts of the coarse fill in the stream channel. As the flood rose to its peak discharge of 59,600 cfs on October 14, it swept the channel completely free of sand and gravel (Fig. 12-10 B), and the impact of the material in transit actively abraded the bedrock floor. As the flood receded and the velocity slackened, the stream was no longer able to move some of the coarse material brought down from upstream, and the bedrock was again mantled by new gravel deposited in the channel. By the next low-water period the river channel had essentially the same cross section it had on September 9— but a huge quantity of gravel, sand, and mud had been moved downstream, including much coarse material that the river was utterly incompetent to carry during low water.

Ultimate Source of a Stream's Load

Particles abraded from the bedrock add to the load of a stream, but as indicated in Chapters 5 and 11, most of the load is not derived from abrasion of the bedrock under the stream channel, but from rainwash and downslope movements over the entire drainage basin. In the great transportation system that erodes away the landmasses, the permanent river channels serve as the main trunk arteries of long-distance transportation, downslope movements supply the produce, and the ephemeral rills and gullies developed during heavy rains are the loading depots. Permanent stream channels occupy far less than 1 per cent of the land surface, but weathering, downslope movements, and rill-wash operate over all the rest. Both the load a stream carries and the water it discharges are almost wholly derived from upstream sources. The size and geologic nature of the drainage basin control the discharge, and also the kind, size, amount, and degree of weathering of the particles transported. But the stream itself has some ability to control and adjust the shape and gradient of its channel to this load imposed on it from above. It does this by downcutting where its velocity is high and its load small, or by depositing sediment and building up its bed where it is unable to carry the detritus. If the load and discharge provided by the watershed are relatively constant, the river may in time achieve a kind of balanced condition in which it is just able to transport the sediment and water along the slope within the channel that has been developed.

The Long Profile and the Concept of Grade

Thus far we have considered only the nature of a stream's activity as viewed from a point on its banks. There are also many things we can learn by studying the entire length of a stream—particularly the changes in gradient, stream pattern, discharge, and load—from the headwaters to the mouth. Let us take a trip along the full length of the Arkansas River.

The **long profile** (also commonly called longitudinal profile) of a stream is a graphic outline of the stream's gradient over long portions of its course. The profile is made by plotting the elevation of points on the surface of the river against distances along it and connecting these points with a line (Fig. 12-11). The vertical scale on such a plot must be

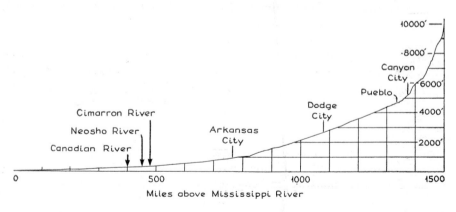

Figure 12-11.

Miles above Mississippi River

Long profile of the Arkansas River, from Tennessee Pass, Colorado, to the Mississippi River. Note the great vertical exaggeration. (Modified from Henry Gannett, U. S. Geological Survey.)

greatly exaggerated, if we are to read it, for the length of almost every stream is many thousand times greater than its vertical fall.

Shape of the Long Profile

The long profile of the Arkansas River is representative of most streams, although every stream has a profile different from that of every other, not only because of differences in discharge, load, and the other factors we have mentioned, but also because of more subtle differences related to the geologic history of the area traversed. The Arkansas River rises in the central Rocky Mountains and flows across the Great Plains, joining the Mississippi about 440 miles from the Gulf of Mexico. Above Canon City, Colorado, the gradient is steep and irregular: the river plunges swiftly through deep mountain canyons, including the awe-inspiring chasm of the Royal Gorge that the river has worn into the resistant granites and gneisses of the Front Range. By contrast, the gradient of the lower 200 miles of the river is very low and regular, nowhere greater than a fall of one foot per mile: here the river winds in serpentine bends (like those shown in Figure 12-20) on a gently sloping plain, composed of sand and silt that resembles the load now being carried by the stream.

Between these two extremes the gradient of the middle course of the river varies regularly and gradually, so that the entire profile approximates a smooth concave-upward curve. The curve steepens notably near the river's head. The entire profile roughly resembles a segment of a hyperbola, but in detail it is far from a perfect mathematical curve.

The Concept of an Ideal Graded Profile in Relation to Stream Gradient

Most large streams show concave-upward profiles generally like that of the Arkansas, although there is infinite variation in detail. What does this similarity in long profiles among the large streams mean? Is the concave-upward form of the profile an equilibrium curve toward which the stream tends con-stantly to adjust its gradient? We have seen that an underloaded stream sweeps the loose debris out of its channel and actively downcuts into its bed, thus flattening its gradient and decreasing its velocity. We also noted that a stream which is incompetent to handle the debris dumped into it builds its bed higher and higher upstream and thereby steepens its gradient. Therefore, by eroding from parts of its course and depositing in others, a stream does adjust its gradient to conform to the average amount of water it discharges and the average amount and size of sediment being supplied to it from upstream. Eventually it may make such an adjustment through most of its length. Thus we come to the basic theorem that ideally the **graded profile,** which the stream is attempting to achieve, is a gradient of equilibrium—a gradient nicely adjusted to the particular discharge and load inherent in the stream's drainage system. Although the true profile contains many irregularities, and local changes in slope, the conclusion is that the stream itself creates its concave-upward profile by cutting or filling until it approaches an equilibrium curve. But, as stated, such a concept of an ideal graded profile is entirely too simple; more than adjustments in gradient are necessary before a stream can attain a truly graded condition. Before we delve into these complexities, however, let us look into the factors that seem to compel a stream to adjust its gradient toward a long profile that superficially resembles a hyperbolic form. Among the most important of these are (1) the limitations imposed by base level, (2) the increase in discharge downstream, and (3) the changes in the grain size and the amount of load downstream.

BASE LEVEL. A stream, of course, cannot normally deepen its channel more than a few feet below the level of the ocean. This limiting level, below which a stream cannot erode, is called **base level.** The permanent base level of the ocean helps to account for the general flatness of a stream's profile near its mouth: the stream is approaching the definite limit below which it cannot lower its bed.

Although the ocean is the ultimate base level for stream erosion, a lake along a stream's course, or a particularly resistant mass of rock through which it can cut only with extreme slowness (for example, the gneiss at the Royal Gorge on the Arkansas) may form a **temporary base level.** Such levels are called temporary because in the long course of geologic time even large lakes are drained by downcutting of their outlets or are filled with sediment, and even the hardest rock ledge will ultimately be sawed through (as the gneiss at the Royal Gorge is being sawed) by the abrading action of the bed load of a swiftly flowing stream. But until such an obstruction is removed from the stream's course, it causes the profile to flatten upstream from the obstruction.

INCREASE IN DISCHARGE DOWN-STREAM. If the Arkansas' profile, steepening upstream like the segment of a hyperbola, is indeed a graded profile of equilibrium, how can it be that the river is in balance on a slope of less than one foot per mile in the area near its mouth, but is apparently also balanced on the much steeper slopes between Pueblo and Dodge City (Fig. 12-11)? And particularly, why are the gradients characteristic of different parts of the river's course transitional, steepening headward along a more or less uniform curve? A partial answer to these questions is that the profile of Figure 12-11 does not represent a stream of constant size throughout. The Arkansas, like most rivers,

grows in size by the confluence of tributaries and the seepage of underground waters.

There is a decrease in the ratio of friction surface to channel cross section as a stream grows. Consider, for example, the junction of tributaries in Figure 12-12. If the channels were all one foot deep with nearly vertical banks, the result of the union would be the removal of four feet of cross-sectional friction surface—in the diagram, a 30 per cent reduction. The energy previously dissipated in friction against these banks is available to speed up the water, causing erosion of the channel and hence a lowering of the gradient below the junction.

CHANGE IN GRAIN SIZE AND AMOUNT OF LOAD DOWNSTREAM. Confluence of two streams affects the amount and kind of load as well as the discharge. If, because of a very steep gradient, the competence of a tributary is considerably greater than that of the trunk stream, the confluence will force a change of the trunk stream's gradient. The huge load of sand dumped into the Missouri River by the Platte causes a hump in the Missouri's profile. An extreme example is that of the Colorado River of Arizona. Its steep tributary canyons are dry through most of the year, but during the seasonal floods their swift streams dump great quantities of coarse debris into the main river. Much of this material consists of huge boulders too heavy to be moved by the Colorado despite its roaring flood. Accumulations of boulders and coarse gravel pile up at the mouths of the tributaries forming **debris dams** (Fig. 12-13). Since these boul-

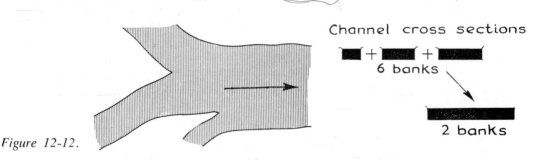

Figure 12-12.

Decrease in channel frictional area due to confluence of tributaries.

Figure 12-13. Rapids over a debris dam at the junction of Tapeats Creek (lower left) with Colorado River, Arizona. (Photo by Freeman, U. S. Geological Survey.)

ders can be transported only after they have been slowly ground down by abrasion, debris dams cause very persistent convexities on the main river's profile.

Though the debris dams of the Colorado provide striking examples of the effect of grain size on a river profile, they are abnormal. Changes that are more characteristic, though more subtle, are found in the meandering lower courses of most large rivers. A careful study of the bed material of the Mississippi River shows a marked decrease in the size of the particles downstream. The change in grain size of 600 samples that were collected between Cairo, Illinois, and the Gulf of Mexico is indicated by the data of Table 12-1.

The average composition of delta sediments, which are 70 per cent silt and clay, also confirms this general change. On the Rhine, between Basel and Bingen, a marked decrease in pebble size downstream is closely correlated with a flattening of the river profile, but it is noteworthy that the river's total discharge increases only slightly over this stretch. Thus the wearing down of the bed load by friction so that the grain size decreases downstream seems to be a factor in allowing many streams to flow on an ever-decreasing grade. Indeed,

MILES BELOW CAIRO ⟶	100	300	500	700	900	1,000
Gravel	29	8	14	5	trace	none
Coarse sand	30	22	9	8	1	none
Medium sand	32	50	46	44	26	9
Fine sand	8	19	28	41	70	69
Silt	trace	trace	2	1	2	10
Clay	trace	trace	1	trace	1	10

TABLE 12-1

Percentage of Different Grain Size Fractions of Lower Mississippi River Sediments, 100 to 1000 Miles Below Cairo. (After Charles M. Nevin; from data of the U. S. Waterways Experiment Station, Vicksburg, Mississippi.)

the velocity of most large graded rivers increases as they approach their mouths even though their gradient lessens. The reason for this apparent paradox is that the increased discharge and depth, combined with the diminishing grain size of the load the river must carry, and the lessened friction against smooth banks containing much sticky clay in proportion to easily entrained silt and sand, outweighs the effect of the lessened gradient.

The Concept of Grade in Relation to Cross Section and Stream Pattern

We have seen that a stream can adjust its gradient to conform to variations in discharge and load. Nevertheless, because the transporting power of a stream cannot be expressed in terms of slope alone, the graded condition of a stream cannot be rigorously defined solely by its gradient. The profile is not independent of the shape of the cross section of the stream nor of the stream pattern. In reaching equilibrium a river adjusts not only its gradient, but its cross section as well. Its channel must be neither too deep nor too shallow for the amount of discharge and for the particular size and kind of load that passes through it. Moreover, in addition to changing its gradient and cross section, a stream also adjusts its channel pattern, flowing in serpentine bends or some other pattern depending on the local conditions of discharge, gradient, load, and the kind of material that forms its beds and banks.

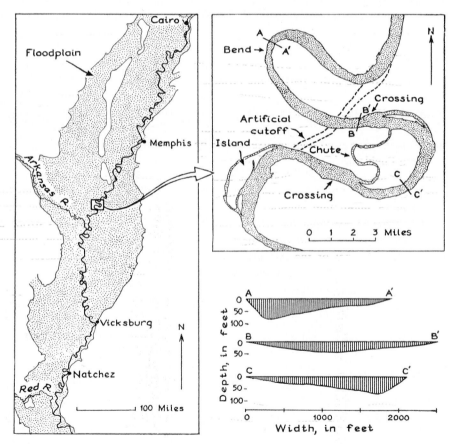

Figure 12-14.

Left: *The meandering course of the Lower Mississippi River.* Right: *Map and cross section of three bends. The artificial cutoffs are man-made channels, dug in 1941 and 1942. (After H. N. Fisk, Mississippi River Commission, 1947.)*

railroad please, my dear

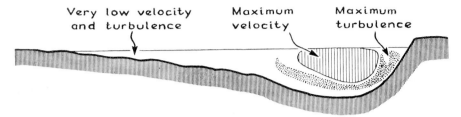

Figure 12-15.

Cross section showing distribution of velocity and turbulence at a bend in the Mississippi. (After John Leighly, 1934.)

Furthermore all such adjustments must, from the very nature of a stream, be transitory. It is evident that erosion does not stop with the attainment of equilibrium. The river still transports material to the sea, and so constantly lowers the landmass upstream and thus imposes changes in sediment load and discharge that must inevitably be reflected by changes in gradient and other parameters.

PATTERNS OF RIVER CHANNELS. As already noted, the lower part of the Arkansas River winds in serpentine bends, called **meanders.** Disdaining the shortest route to the sea, it follows an intricate path that is many times longer than a straight course would be. Between Pueblo and Dodge City, however, the river is **braided,** that is, it subdivides and detours in a plexus of interconnected small channels around many low islands made up of sand and gravel bars that the stream has deposited in its bed. In still other parts of its course, the channel of the Arkansas is relatively straight, though only for short stretches and under the most unusual conditions is any river completely without bends and kinks. The Mississippi River, from Cairo, Illinois, to the mouth of the Red River, has a typical meandering course (Fig. 12-14); the lower Amazon braids intricately between numerous low alluvial islands. But meanders are also common in small creeks, and braids appear in sediment-loaded rills that form after every rainstorm.

ORIGIN OF MEANDERING CHANNELS. Why should streams meander within their valleys instead of flowing in straight channels directly to the sea? Consider our example of the lower Arkansas River where it flows on a bed of loose silt and sand similar to the material which the stream is transporting. Here, with banks of easily erodible material, the stream is not able to maintain a narrow cross-section such as shown in Figure 12-3, A. Instead the stream constantly undermines the soft banks and develops a cross section that is notably wider than the theoretical semicircle. Even more important is the strong tendency toward lateral erosion at bends. The sidecutting power of the stream is greatly increased as it rounds a bend because centrifugal force causes the moving water to crowd against the outer side of the channel, just as a passenger is swayed to the side when a speeding automobile rounds a curve. Thus the water speeds up on the outside of the bend and the increased velocity causes strong undermining of the bank; on the inside, however, the velocity simultaneously decreases, so that the water deposits sediment.

Soundings of the Mississippi's curves reveal marked changes in the shape of the channel from bend to bend. As shown in Figure 12-15, the channel is deepest near the outer bank of each bend. The inner bank slopes gently or is even convex, and commonly consists of shifting sand bars which the stream is depositing. In the short straight stretches between bends, the river shallows considerably, and the channel is more or less symmetrical. These shallows between bends, called crossings, troubled the old-time river pilots. Some are less than 10 feet deep at low water, whereas at the bends the river may be more than 45 feet deep.

During a flood, when velocity and turbulence are greatest, the channel deepens and the outer banks cave in rapidly. The fine-grained material caved from the banks is quickly carried off in suspension, but the coarser material moves more slowly as a part of the bed load. Experiments show that almost all the coarse debris cut from a bend is deposited on the next crossing or on the inside slope of the next bend (Fig. 12-16).

Erosion of the outer banks and deposition on the inner slopes causes the meanders to shift their positions. This migration of the meanders causes a stream to wander widely over its valley floor. In the course of time the stream reworks the deposits left in previous meander channels and deposits new material that is later cut away as the channel continues to migrate. Thus a meandering river moves its coarser sediments only slowly toward the sea.

Studies of the gradient, load, and velocity of natural rivers have contributed much to our knowledge of flow in meandering channels, but many variables are so intricately interrelated that they cannot be examined separately, and hence their effects on stream patterns are difficult to evaluate. Because of the variability of natural rivers, investigators are turning more and more to stream models for help in solving both the theoretical and practical problems of stream flow. Simple wooden

troughs, used by early experimenters, have been replaced by carefully constructed scale models that not only reproduce channel and valley shapes exactly, but also have devices to control and measure nearly all the variables of flow.

Models were used in studies of meandering made at the United States Waterways Experiment Station at Vicksburg by the Mississippi River Commission. The models were not mere table-top arrangements, but were of considerable size (Fig. 12-17). In one of the most revealing experiments a straight channel was carefully molded in uniform Mississippi River sand, and water was allowed to run in it for three days. The stream quickly developed a sinuous course, whose bends (Fig. 12-17, *right*) swept evenly downstream in the homogeneous, easily eroded material.

During the experiments, discharge, valley slope, load, and erodibility of material were individually varied, in an attempt to ascertain their effects on the pattern of the artificial river. With increased discharge, the meanders widened in a regular and predictable way, verifying the general rule that big rivers have big bends, little rivers little ones.

The valley gradient, likewise, directly and predictably affected the meander width: the steeper the gradient, the larger the bends. When the stream was not given a load of sand at the head of the model channel, meanders developed only after the stream had acquired

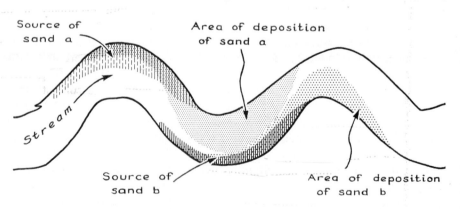

Figure 12-16.

Source of sand a

Area of deposition of sand a

Stream

Source of sand b

Area of deposition of sand b

Localization of erosion and deposition of marked sands in an experimental sinuous stream. (After J. F. Friedkin, U. S. Waterways Experiment Station, 1945.)

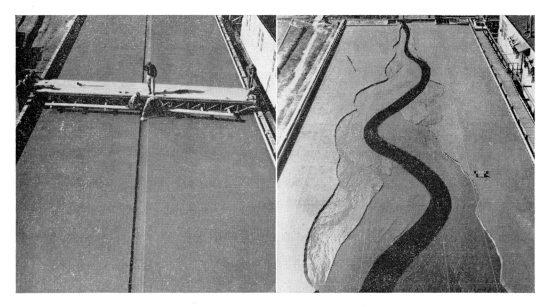

Figure 12-17.   Left: *Molding a straight channel in Mississippi River sand at the U. S. Waterways Experiment Station, Vicksburg, Mississippi.* Right: *Sinuous course produced after 72 hours of flow in an initially straight channel. (Photos from J. F. Friedkin; courtesy of the U. S. Waterways Experiment Station.)*

a load from its banks. In experiments with channels molded in partly cemented sand, the stream could gain no load from its banks, and did not meander. Easily erodible banks consequently seem to be one requisite for the formation of a truly meandering stream pattern. This generalization from the Vicksburg experiments is supported in nature by the common association of meandering streams with wide valleys underlain by loose and fine-grained alluvial deposits.

Nevertheless, even straight streams flowing on bedrock exhibit certain features that are hydrologically allied to meanders. Pools and riffles along a straight stream succeed one another in a definite periodic way, just as they do in a meandering stream (the riffles in a meandering stream are at the crossings between successive bends). Moreover, the **thalweg,** or line following the deepest part of a natural river channel, nearly always wanders from side to side of even a straight channel, coming close to one bank only to cross over to the other side like the bends of a meandering channel.

ORIGIN OF BRAIDED STREAM PATTERNS.   In braided streams the channel constantly subdivides around low alluvial islands that grew from bars in the stream bed. The bars develop in the center of the channel by the accumulation of material too coarse for the stream to move. This material traps finer debris, and by its roughness also diminishes the stream's velocity, causing still more deposition. The bar grows both in height and in length until eventually it becomes an island.

Braids are characteristic of heavily loaded rivers with easily erodible banks, such as those that flow from active glaciers, but they are not confined to such streams. They seem to form in any stream in which a considerable part of the load is too coarse for the stream to handle except during floods. Thus the smaller particles are winnowed out even more effectively than in meandering streams. Braids commonly form in intermittent streams, and in those whose discharge fluctuates so violently that the voluminous overbank flow during floods temporarily converts nearly the whole river plain into a vastly enlarged channel.

Summary: Stream Pattern, Gradient, and Channel Shape in Relation to the Concept of Grade

We have seen that close interrelations exist between changes in discharge, amount and character of sediment load, velocity, gradient, width and depth of channel, roughness of channel surface, and stream pattern. Change in any one affects the others, and a kind of balance must exist between all of them in the graded stream. Two streams of equal discharge but different gradients may both be graded—the difference is compensated for by such other factors as size of load or roughness of the channel. Channel patterns—meandering, straight, and braided—are merely another way in which a stream adjusts its gradient and cross section to the particular discharge and load imposed on it from upstream. By meandering, a river lengthens its course and thus decreases its gradient; by braiding, a stream can remove the smaller sized grains of sediment from its bed although it must leave the larger ones stranded as midchannel bars. Other changes in gradient and cross section, treated in early pages of this chapter, have been nicely summarized by an American geologist, W. W. Rubey:

> Cutting on the bottom increases the load of downstream parts of the stream and so eventually lowers the slope and decreases the velocity. Cutting at the sides widens the cross section, thereby decreasing the relative depth, and so reduces the efficiency of the stream. In either case, the load increases and the capacity decreases until an approximate balance is struck between the two. Conversely, an excessive load causes deposition on the bottom or at the margins of a stream or at both places. Deposition on the bottom, being greater upstream than down, tends to steepen the slope and thus to increase the velocity. Deposition at the side of the channel . . . narrows the cross section, thereby increasing the relative depth, and so increases the efficiency of the stream. . . .

It is true that [the] factors [leading to the stream's adjustment] may vary seasonally or even daily and, therefore, the stream may never actually attain complete adjustment. Nevertheless, with changing conditions, the stream is constantly cutting or filling and modifying its slope, velocity and cross section so as eventually to accomplish the imposed work with the least expenditure of energy. The recurrent floods of each season carve out or build up a channel that the stream is unable to destroy at lower stages . . . In short, the stream constantly approaches, even though it rarely attains and even then is unable to maintain, a condition of equilibrium in which the capacity for . . . cutting and filling are exactly equal. This equilibrium, which the stream constantly approaches, is one in which the imposed load is transported without either net gain or loss. . . . If discharge, load, grain size, and sorting are considered the controlling factors, then velocity, slope, and the depth of the channel are dependent variables that are affected not only by the independent variables but also by one another.

Departures from the Ideal Graded Profile

The smoothly concave curve of the ideal profile is closely approached but probably never attained by natural streams. Even in such rivers as the lower Mississippi, probably as well-graded a stream as could be found, the profile shows slight but abrupt changes of slope in many places (Fig. 12-18). This is quite normal; as we have seen, the inflow of most tributaries demands a change in gradient. Such changes in slope are not inconsistent with the concept of grade inasmuch as equilibrium may still exist in each segment of the stream's course. Such variations in slope, however, do result in a profile that is neither ideally smooth nor ideally concave.

One of the principal values of the concept of the ideal graded profile, however, is that great departures from it call attention to exceptional circumstances. Lava flows, landslides, or drifting sand dunes may upset the graded condition of a stream and make its profile strongly irregular. Glaciation in the recent geologic past has greatly modified the

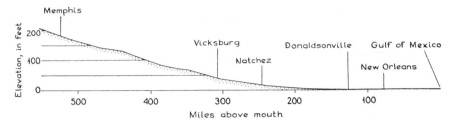

Figure 12-18.

Long profile of a part of the Lower Mississippi River at Low water. (After H. N. Fisk, Mississippi River Commission, 1947.)

slopes of nearly all the major streams of the northern United States. Earth movements are among the most important disturbing factors. Some of the anticlines in the south central part of the State of Washington (Chap. 8) have been uplifted rapidly and recently enough to destroy the former adjustment of the streams flowing down their flanks. The profiles in Figure 12-19 illustrate the local broad convexity (instead of concavity) of stream gradients on some of these folds.

Even streams long established in a stable region display distinct changes in slope caused by local outcrops of especially resistant rocks. Because considerable time is required for the concave profile to form in regions of resistant rocks, all kinds of structural or climatic "accidents" generally intervene before the graded profile can be formed. It is a tribute to the eroding power of running water that most large streams flow on grades that approximate the ideal profile.

Stream Deposits

Floodplains

Large trunk rivers commonly meander, or more rarely braid, within broad, smooth valleys sloping so gently seaward as to appear flat. The flat surface of such a valley is called a **floodplain**, for about once each year the river, at high water stage, overflows its channel and floods at least part of the flat valley floor. Some floodplains are little wider than the channel of the stream—the meanders impinge against bedrock at almost every bend. Most floodplains, however, are far wider than the meander belt, and their streams wind always through unconsolidated stream deposits.

Low indistinct ridges, called **natural levees**, border most river channels on floodplains. They are highest next to the stream bank, and slope outward away from the stream toward the edge of the flood plain. When a stream in flood spills over its floodplain, the immediate

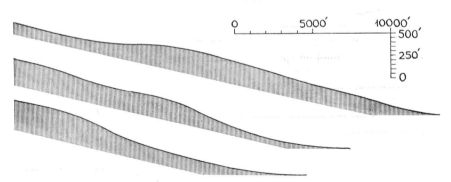

Figure 12-19.

Profiles of streams flowing down the flanks of anticlinal ridges in southern Washington. (From maps of the U. S. Geological Survey.)

decrease in velocity and turbulence as it overflows its channel causes rapid deposition of some of the suspended load. The coarsest and most voluminous part is dropped where the flood water first overtops the banks, and builds up the low natural levees. Finer silt and clay are carried farther and deposited on lower ground behind the natural levees. Since natural levees keep water from returning directly to the river, a flood plain such as that of the Mississippi is generally poorly drained and partly covered with shallow lakes and swamps.

The muddy deposits that build the natural levees are individually thin, and seldom pile up to any great total thicknesses, even over long periods of time. The role of the Nile floods in renewing the soils of lower Egypt is perhaps the most celebrated case of rapid overbank deposition, but although silt has risen as high as 15 feet above some ancient Egyptian structures, this indicates a deposi-

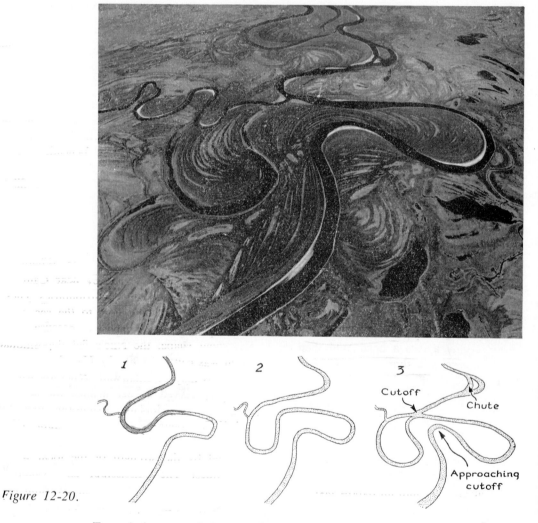

Figure 12-20.

Top: *A river meandering on a broad floodplain. Note the low-ridged deposits on insides of bends and the abandoned meander channels, including oxbow lakes.* Bottom: *Possible stages in the evolution of the meander cutoff that has recently taken place in the center of the view. (Photo by U. S. Air Force.)*

tional rate of only 4½ inches per century.

Migration of meanders constantly changes the sites of new deposition from later floods. The main deposits that constitute a floodplain are the channel deposits that are dropped on the inside of the bends of a meandering river, or that form the islands in the channels of a braided stream. Although the actual ratio of channel deposits to overbank deposits varies for different streams, the proportion of overbank material is very small for those streams on which reliable measurements have been made. Most floodplains show crescent-shaped lakes, and other scars of abandoned meanders, whose deposits have not been masked and healed by later overbank deposits. In the photograph in Figure 12-20, *top,* the low stripelike ridges that almost parallel the inside of the bends are sand bars left behind as the bends migrated. The **oxbow lakes** are former river bends. Meander loops are abandoned whenever a stream can cross the neck between bends and thus shorten its course and increase its slope. Such **cutoffs** may occur when one meander is slowed in its downstream migration, allowing the next bend upstream to catch up with it and cut through the narrowing neck between the two bends. The drawing in Figure 12-20, *bottom,* illustrates how this might have taken place on a bend in the river shown in the photograph. Another kind of cutoff, called a **chute cutoff,** forms when a river in flood simply overtops its banks and flows directly across a bend, and then continues to use this shortcut. The new chute channel is more efficient than the old channel, because, since it is shorter, the gradient is steeper and the velocity correspondingly higher. Velocity and turbulence in the bend that was cut off become so low that sand is quickly deposited at both ends of the old bend, damming it off from the new channel and converting it into an oxbow lake.

THE FORMATION OF FLOODPLAINS. A few broad floodplains have apparently been formed by the lateral plantation of the bedrock by shifting meanders during long-continued stream erosion, but wells drilled in most extensive floodplains penetrate great thicknesses of stream deposits instead of thin alluvial veneers overlying bedrock. Meandering or braided channels of such deeply alluviated streams carry more than three-fourths of the total runoff of the United States.

The Mississippi River Commission used data obtained from several hundred drill holes and water wells in studying the deposits underlying the lower Mississippi floodplain. These show that the plain is built up of alluvial debris from 100 to over 400 feet thick. Near Natchez, this debris is 260 feet thick, with its base 215 feet below sea level. Drill holes made on the present floodplain indicate that the buried surface—the valley of a prehistoric Mississippi—is not a smooth plain but a steep-sided though shallow valley with many tributaries. Drill holes also show that the Santa Ana River in southern California has buried its former channel beneath stream deposits 140 feet thick at the river mouth. Most other large rivers show similar filled channels.

Deltas

Any stream must drop its load when it enters quiet water such as a lake or sea. Where the Nile emerges from its valley near Cairo, it splits into channels called distributaries. These further subdivide and flow to the sea on a broad plain of river deposits. Because of its triangular shape, the Nile's flat depositional plain was called a **delta** by Herodotus.

Deltas may be triangular, generally with a convexly curved border against the sea, or irregular, with lobelike extensions like the "birdfoot" delta of the Mississippi (Fig. 12-21). The shapes and sizes of deltas are affected by the strength of the local waves and tides. The Mississippi and Colorado rivers, which empty into relatively calm and tideless gulfs, have prominent deltas, but the Columbia and Congo rivers have no deltas at all. The Columbia's load is scattered by ocean waves and currents for hundreds of miles along the sea coast; the Congo's is

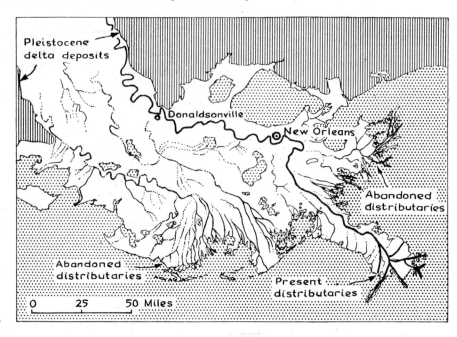

Figure 12-21.

The delta (white) of the Mississippi River. Note the old meander courses, the numerous lakes, the positions of abandoned distributaries, and the "bird's-foot" pattern of the present distributaries. (After H. N. Fisk, Mississippi River Commission, 1945.)

washed down a long, deep submarine canyon into the depths of the Atlantic.

Where sand-laden streams flow into a deep, still body of water, the layers of deltaic sediment are not simply parallel to the lake or sea bottom, but show a characteristically discordant arrangement (Fig. 12-22). The stream deposits formed on the top surface of the delta are called **topset beds** and most of them are thin, because the distributaries into which the stream divides must maintain certain minimum gradients across the delta. Thicker deposits, called **foreset beds**, are built on the frontal slope of the delta over which most of the debris is dumped. The finest part of the load is kept in suspension for a long time by weak currents moving down the frontal slope and is spread over the lake or sea bottom in front of the advancing foreset layers to form **bottomset beds.**

Most large deltas are much more complex than this. The Mississippi delta, like that of most other large rivers, shows little or no discordance between topset, foreset, and bottomset beds except at the front of rapidly advancing lobes. Large compound deltas

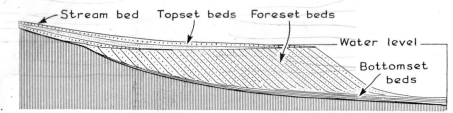

Figure 12-22.

Diagrammatic cross section of a simple delta.

formed by the filling of a structural basin by many streams are discussed in Chapter 17.

Alluvial Fans

A stream emerging from a steep, narrow valley onto a broader lowland may build up a gently sloping conical deposit with an apex at the mouth of the narrow valley. Such a deposit is called an alluvial fan (Figs. 12-23 and 12-28). These fans are especially common in arid and semiarid regions, particularly at the borders of steep-sided structural depressions such as downfaulted or sharply downfolded basins.

Deposition on an alluvial fan is like that on a small delta. After debouching from a canyon the flow is no longer confined; both the depth and the gradient may be lowered abruptly and the stream can no longer carry its load. In arid regions deposition is also hastened because most of the water is promptly lost by infiltration.

The slopes of fans differ with the size of the stream and the grain size of its load. Small streams transporting coarse particles may construct fans with slopes as steep as 15 degrees (as in Figs. 12-23 and 12-28). Bedding is generally indistinct in such accumulations. The slopes of many larger fans (Figs. 15-3 and 15-4) decrease from between 3 and 5 degrees at their apices to less than 1 degree near their bases. A decrease in the average grain size of the fan deposits goes hand in hand with this decrease in slope.

Sculpture of the Land

Land forms result from the interplay between opposing forces. On the one hand, earth movements and volcanism raise certain parts of the crust; on the other, erosional forces constantly work to level them.

Erosion in the steep headwater tributaries of a stream system not only deepens the valleys but also extends them by **headward erosion,** that is, by growth of the channel farther and farther upstream. Stream systems thus tend to grow in length as they reduce the land. If the underlying rock offers uniform resistance to weathering and erosion, tributaries subdivide headward like the limbs of a tree, producing a **dendritic pattern** (Fig. 12-24, *left*). Headward extension of streams,

Figure 12-23.

Small alluvial fans formed when leaks in a high-level canal caused rapid gullying, near Leadville, Colorado. (Photo by M. R. Campbell, U. S. Geological Survey.)

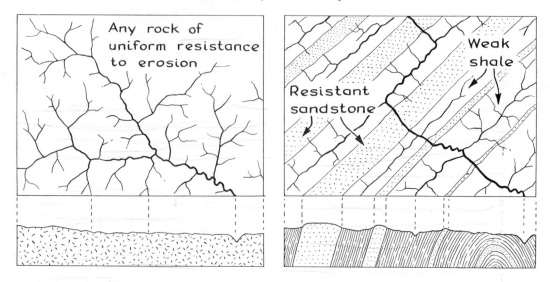

Figure 12-24.   *Structural control of stream patterns*. Left: *Dendritic pattern*. Right: *Trellis pattern*.

however, is closely guided by differences in the erodibility of the rocks. Therefore the stream pattern closely reflects the rock structure and the rock is said to exercise **structural control.** If the rocks are of unequal resistance, the tributaries lengthen and cut down most rapidly in the weaker rocks, wearing out valleys or lowlands between ridges or uplands of resistant rocks (Fig. 5-14). In a region of steeply dipping parallel beds, this headward growth along the weak rocks forms a rectangular or **trellis pattern** (Figs. 12-24, *right,* and 8-15). Other examples of the structural control of drainage are the concentric patterns on eroded domes and basins (Figs. 9-5, and 9-6) and the strikingly

Figure 12-25.   *Structural control of land forms, subdued by soil creep, San Jose Hills, Los Angeles County, California. (Photo by Robert C. Frampton, Claremont, California.)*

Figure 12-26. *A broad structural plain along the Colorado River, Arizona, formed where soft shale overlies a more resistant rock. The shale is overlain by a massive sandstone bed, remnants of which form cliffed buttes in the center of the view. (Photo by J. S. Shelton and Robert C. Frampton, Claremont, California.)*

linear stream courses along some faults (Fig. 9-15). Even though a stream system may constantly change because of earth movements or other interruptions it still keeps accentuating differences in rock resistance.

In temperate regions where soil creep is active, the structural control of land forms is much more subtle than in the desert examples shown in Figures 5-14 and 9-6. In the area shown in Figure 12-25, for example, the major ridges are underlain by resistant rocks and the larger valleys by easily erodible rocks. Yet the drainage pattern gives only slight clues to this underlying structure. Even when we are actually in such an area, it is difficult to tell what resistant rock underlies a given ridge, because downslope creep of a layer of grass and soil has masked the rock contacts, forming smoothly rounded hills.

Structural Terraces and Plains

The etching-out of the less resistant rocks by stream erosion produces striking effects even in areas where the rocks lie flat. In horizontal strata of unequal resistance, streams cut through weak beds quickly but are arrested by a resistant layer. Thus, a widespread temporary base level is formed, and headward erosion by tributaries may strip the weak layer from a large area overlying the resistant bed to form a **structural plain** (Fig. 12-26). In an arid or semiarid climate, the retreating edge of the layer that is being stripped rises in a steep embayed slope or cliff. Small detached segments of the layer, called **mesas** and **buttes,** are commonly left behind, as shown in Figure 12-26, to attest to the former extension of the layer over the entire plain. If a stream cuts its valley in a sequence of alternating weak and resistant beds, the eroded edge of each resistant bed forms a cliff, and the top of the bed forms a step, or **structural terrace,** along the side of the valley. Such terraces are common in the Grand Canyon of the Colorado (Fig. 5-13) where resistant sandstones and limestones form cliffs and the softer shales are worn back into gentle slopes and nearly flat surfaces called benches.

Stream Terraces

Not all terraces are structural terraces. Many are made up entirely of river deposits, others are cut in bedrock but have veneers, channel fillings, or residual patches of river gravel on their flat surfaces. Obviously these terraces are remnants of old floodplains, now incised by the streams that once made them. A stream may entrench its floodplain for any of several reasons: uplift by earth movements, lowering of sea level, increase in stream volume, or any event that increases the stream's ability to down cut.

The 12-foot offset along the front of the Sonoma Range (Fig. 8-2) that was formed at the time of the Pleasant Valley earthquake of 1915 produced a waterfall on a stream crossing the fault. Headward erosion at this step was rapid, so that by 1930 the waterfall had retreated far upstream, leaving the old floodplain as a pair of matched terraces on either side of the newly entrenched channel (Fig. 12-27). Because this stream has started to sidecut at its new graded level 12 feet below the old floodplain surface, the terraces will be slowly cut away, though probably parts of them that are protected by ridge spurs of resistant rock will remain for a very long time.

Another example of terraces caused by faulting occurs on the west side of the Panamint Mountains in California (Fig. 12-28). After faulting formed a series of small cliffs across the large alluvial fans bordering the range, streams cut trenches in the uplifted portions of the fans and formed steep new alluvial fans below the scarps.

Careful mapping of terraces along the Mississippi suggests that they result from more complex earth movements. Several terraces extend from Cairo, Illinois, to Natchez, Mississippi; these are approximately parallel to the present river profile, and stand a few tens to a few hundred feet above the river. South of the Mississippi-Louisiana line the terraces converge downward, and lie on Pleistocene alluvium instead of on older rock. Near Baton Rouge they disappear beneath the present floodplain. This pattern of warped terraces gives striking evidence of slow earth move-

Figure 12-27.

Newly entrenched channel formed after relative uplift of the Sonoma Mountain block, Nevada, at the time of an earthquake in 1915. The former valley floor now forms paired terraces. (Photo by Ben Page.)

*Figure 12-28.   Faulted and entrenched fans at the mouth of Tuber Canyon, Panamint Range,
California. Note the new fans growing on the down-dropped block and their rela-
tion to the newly entrenched channels on the upthrown block. (Photo by John
Shelton.)*

ments; the delta region has subsided while the upstream area has progressively risen.

Many stream terraces are not formed by earth movements, but by other causes such as a climatic change, a diminution in total load, or anything else that increases a stream's transporting power.

Extensive Erosion Surfaces of Low Relief

Under ideal conditions of crustal stability, a stream might cut a wide floodplain across even resistant bedrocks. Theoretically such a floodplain might coalesce with those in neighboring valleys to produce an extensive erosion surface of low relief. Because of the long time needed to cut such erosional floodplains, however, it is most likely that some geologic change will occur before such floodplains can become very extensive. Simple, laterally eroded floodplains are rare: most present-day

streams have been sufficiently affected by crustal movements, sea-level changes, or climatic changes to produce far more complex valleys.

Most widespread erosion surfaces of low relief seem to result from downcutting by both large rivers and small rills, aided by downslope movements, all of which have operated over great lengths of time and despite constant interruptions by warping or other causes. An example of such an undulating surface of low relief—really a complex series of coalescing surfaces—parts of which are now being destroyed by erosion, is the "Harrisburg surface" in the central and southern Appalachian Mountains. This smooth-to-hilly surface is well developed in the vicinity of Harrisburg, Pennsylvania—whence its name (Fig. 12-29). In some areas near the base of the mountains, the surface is many miles wide. The Susque-

Figure 12-29.   *The erosion surface at Harrisburg, Pennsylvania (foreground and middle distance). The level summits of the distant ridges are remnants of an older, more thoroughly dissected erosion surface called the Schooley surface. (Photo by George H. Ashley, courtesy of Pennsylvania Department of Internal Affairs.)*

hanna and other rivers have cut 200- to 300-foot gorges into the surface, and many lesser streams have partly dissected it. Deep residual soils mask its surface, and have been formed on all of the varied rocks that underlie it. The surface cuts across flat and tilted beds almost irrespective of their structure, though the more resistant rocks do underlie low hills and undulations. In those parts of the Appalachians that are dominated by ridges of resistant sandstone, the Harrisburg surface, if it can be recognized at all, exists only as valley terraces (Fig. 12-30). The terraces are 200 to 300 feet above the streams in their lower courses, but the terrace gradients are commonly less steep than those of the present streams, so that upstream the terraces are not as high above the streams. Most river valleys in the southern Applachians have terraces that can be approximately correlated with the Harrisburg surface, though such correlations are not without doubt. In some places there are broad passes between drainage systems, followed by roads and railways, on the Harrisburg surface, though it is of interest to note that the surface may be at quite different elevations in the valleys on either side of such passes.

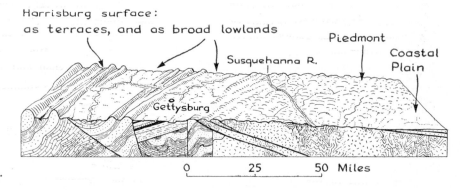

Figure 12-30.

Relief diagram showing the distribution of the Harrisburg surface in a strip across southern Pennsylvania, just south of Harrisburg. The underlying structure is generalized. (After maps and folios of the U. S. Geological Survey.)

Remnants of erosion surfaces of even greater extent, commonly called **peneplains** (from Latin *paene,* meaning "almost") occur in many parts of the world. Some, as in the central part of the United States, from Missouri and Kansas south, lie near but do not coincide with the graded level of the streams that flow through them. Others, as will be seen in Chapter 19, have been uplifted and so deeply eroded that only scattered remnants are left as flat mountain summits. How are such extensive, nearly flat surfaces formed? Study of the better preserved ones indicates that many are the result of erosion by many streams flowing very near their base levels, and constantly aided by rillwash and downslope movements. Evidence for such an origin lies in the facts: (1) that all but the hardest rocks—in all attitudes—are truncated by the surfaces, (2) residual stream channels and stream deposits are common upon them, and (3) surficial marine deposits are absent. It should be recognized that such widespread erosion surfaces are irregular and undulating, they are not truly flat featureless plains formed by the lateral cutting of meandering streams. Although small parts of such surfaces may be floodplains formed by the sidecutting of individual streams, the entire area of a peneplain is not looked upon simply as a vast floodplain. Peneplains are the result of long-continued erosion of a large land area by downslope movements and by numerous streams operating over vast periods of time, and despite numerous geologic interruptions caused by warping and other changes. Because of their complex history peneplains are not flat, but undulating, their low ridges and rounded crests being the last remnants of former much higher drainage divides underlain by resistant rock.

Though it is tempting to suggest that such extensive plains are the end product of erosion, the present status of the earth's landscapes does not bear this out. All such surfaces that have been found by careful study to result from stream erosion are, like the Harrisburg surface, variously uplifted, warped, dissected, or otherwise imperfect. There is no assurance that different areas on them reached their present stage of erosional development at the same time, and most parts of them, even today, are being actively eroded because they are out of adjustment with the streams that drain them. Nevertheless, these remnants of widespread erosion surfaces of low relief do record former local conditions more stable than those of the present, and, like stream terraces, they help us to estimate the nature and amount of crustal change in the relatively recent geologic past.

We conclude our discussion of peneplains and other widespread surfaces of erosion by some queries based on Figure 10-4, p. 151. This graph summarizes the total areas of the land (both above and below the sea) that lie between various altitude limits, and brings out the existence of two especially prominent altitude ranges.

What are the reasons for these two dominant levels in the architecture of the earth? Does the upper level, embracing areas from 200 meters below sea level to 500 meters above, represent the constant effort of streams to erode the landmasses to peneplains near sea level, and to pile the detritus worn from them upon the continental shelves? What isostatic effects are to be expected from the constant unloading of the landmasses by erosion and the loading of the continental shelves by deposition? Why is the boundary between continental shelf and ocean floor so marked? Is this to be explained in isostatic terms as a fundamental difference in density between continental and oceanic blocks? These questions are not easily answered— indeed, only partial answers are as yet possible. We will return to them in Chapter 16 after we have discussed other processes of erosion and deposition.

FACTS, CONCEPTS, TERMS

FACTORS THAT DETERMINE THE AVERAGE VELOC-
ITY OF A STREAM
DISTRIBUTION OF VELOCITY AND TURBULENCE IN
A STREAM'S CROSS SECTION
HOW STREAMS ACQUIRE AND CARRY THEIR LOAD
Suspended load; bed load; dissolved load
Abrasion of channel bottom and banks
COMPETENCE AND CAPACITY OF STREAMS
BASE LEVELS: ULTIMATE AND TEMPORARY
LONG PROFILES OF STREAMS
CONCEPT OF THE GRADED RIVER
Adjustment of gradient
Adjustment of channel shape

Adjustment of stream pattern
STREAM PATTERNS: MEANDERING AND BRAIDED
MEANDERS, CUTOFFS, OX-BOW LAKES
NATURAL LEVEES; CHANNEL DEPOSITS; RIVER BARS
SCALE MODELS OF STREAMS
STREAM DEPOSITS
Floodplain deposits, deltas, alluvial fans
SCULPTURE OF THE LAND BY STREAMS
Dendritic and trellis patterns; headward ero-
sion
Stream terraces
Floodplains
Peneplains

QUESTIONS

1. Would you expect the dissolved load per cubic foot of water to be higher in the Columbia (high rainfall) or in the Colorado River (low rainfall)? Why?

2. At most stream junctions the bed of the tributary and of the main channel are identical in elevation at the point where they join. Why?

3. Engineers have made many *artificial cutoffs* (Figure 12-14) in the lower Mississippi and other meandering rivers. Considering the nature of meandering streams, can you suggest reasons for these projects?

4. List several criteria for distinguishing between floodplain, delta, and alluvial-fan deposits in ancient sedimentary rocks.

5. Suggest how a change in climate might produce stream terraces in areas with which you are familiar.

6. The St. Lawrence, one of the great rivers of the continent, has no delta, even though it runs into a landlocked estuary. Can you suggest why?

7. The longitudinal profile of most large rivers resembles the land portion of the graph in Figure 10-4, page 151. Can you offer any explanation of this?

8. At what point on an alluvial fan is the sediment coarsest? Why?

SUGGESTED READINGS

Fisk, H. N. *Fine-Grained Alluvial Deposits and Their Effects on Mississippi River Activity.* Vicksburg, Mississippi, Waterways Experiment Station, 1947.

Gilbert, G. K. *Geology of the Henry Mountains,* section on "Land Sculpture," pp. 99-150. (U. S. Geographical and Geological Survey of the Rocky Mountains Region, 1877) (A classic paper, outlining the principles of stream erosion and applying them to the origin of the land forms of central Utah. Its publication marks a milestone in the study of physiography.)

Leopold, L. B., and M. G. Wolman. *River Channel Patterns: Braided, Meandering and Straight.* (U. S. Geological Survey, Prof. Paper 282-B) Washington, D. C., 1957.

Rubey, W. W. *Geology and Mineral Resources of the Hardin and Brussels Quadrangles in Illinois*. (U. S. Geological Survey, Prof. Paper 218) Washington, D. C., Government Printing Office, 1952. (Section on "Physiography," pp. 101-137. Pages 129-136 give a clear concise account of the adjustments a stream makes in its effort to attain grade.)

Sundborg, Ake. "The River Klarälven, a study of Fluvial Processes," *Geografiska Annaler*, Vol. 38 (1956), pp. 127-316. (A good description of the hydraulics of river channels and their relation to the morphology of a particular river.)

GLACIERS AND GLACIATION

SLOW-MOVING, thick masses of ice are called **glaciers. Snowfields** are thinner, almost motionless masses of permanent snow (Figs. 13-1 and 13-5).

Tide records prove that sea level has risen several inches within the last century. During the same period glaciers in both hemispheres have been slowly shrinking. These facts emphasize that snowfields and glaciers are savings banks in the water economy of the earth. Each year, some of the water evaporated from the seas and lands falls as snow. Most of this melts in summer, but on high mountains and in the polar regions some is stored in glaciers and snowfields. If melting and evaporation exceed snowfall, the snowfields and glaciers shrink and the bank balance diminishes; if precipitation exceeds withdrawals, the glacier grows and spreads.

The Snowline

The lowest limit of an area of permanent snow is called the **snowline.** The altitude of the snowline varies from place to place, depending on latitude, snowfall, temperature, wind direction (which controls drifting of the snow), and topography (which controls both snowsliding and shading from the sun).

Mean annual temperature decreases at higher altitudes and latitudes; therefore the snowline stands highest near the equator and lowers both to the north and to the south. Total snowfall strongly affects its position. The snowline lies at 8,000 to 9,000 feet altitude on the dry eastern side of the St. Elias Mountains at the Alaska-Yukon border but at 2,500 to 3,000 feet, 5,000 feet lower, on the wet western side. It is lower in well-watered Norway than in the far colder but dry Taimyr peninsula of Siberia. There are no permanent snowfields and glaciers in much of Siberia, Northern Alaska, and Canada. The mean annual temperature is low enough to support permanent masses of ice but the snowfall is too scanty. In such areas, the moisture in the pores of soil and rock remains frozen throughout the year, forming a great sheet of permanently frozen ground, or permafrost, that may be several hundred feet thick.

Snowfields

Permanent snowfields cover all but the steepest and windiest slopes above the snowline (Figs. 13-1 and 5-2). Excavations in snowfields show that the beautiful geometric patterns of new-fallen snowflakes (Fig. 13-2) do not persist at depth. Instead the snowfield consists largely of small granules of ice about the size of birdshot. This material, called **firn,** grows by compaction of the feathery snowflakes and by thawing and refreezing of their edges. This melting and freezing is not due entirely to variations of air temperature above the snow. Water expands 9 per cent when it freezes, hence pressure will lower the melting point of ice. This is why a snowball sticks together when squeezed and released. Even at temperatures slightly below the normal freezing point (0° Centigrade or 32° Farenheit) the snowflakes deep in a snowbank may be so tightly squeezed that a thin film of water forms where their edges are pressed together. This water flows to a point of lower pressure and there freezes, even though the temperature has remained constant.

Granular firn absorbs rain and summer meltwater like a blotter. This water freezes, perhaps the next night, helping to compact the firn by excluding air. Thus, deep in the snowfield, the firn changes gradually to interlocking granules of solid ice, with some entrapped air and dust. The walls of a glacial crevasse commonly show all stages in the transformation: snowflakes to firn to solid ice with depth. Thus we can trace all steps in the metamorphism of snow, a sediment, into ice, a metamorphic rock.

Glacier Motion

If ice were as strong as granite, even the highest mountains above the snowline would be eventually buried in accumulated ice, firn,

Figure 13-1.   *Snowfields above the head of a valley glacier, Alaska. Clearest relations are at right foreground and left background: much of the flat in mid-distance is a snowfield but it merges into moving ice—becoming a glacier below the crevasses that mark the head of a steep slope.*

Figure 13-2.

Forms of fresh snowflakes. (After A. E. H. Tutton, 1927.)

and snow. But ice is a weak rock, it begins to flow downhill and spread out under its own weight when only a few tens of feet of solid ice have formed beneath a thick cover of firn and snow. Glacier motion is too slow to be seen, but it is easily proved to exist by driving a straight row of stakes across a glacier. In a few days or months, the straight line is visibly bent in the direction of the glacier's flow; the displacement, and hence the speed of flow, is greatest in the middle of the glacier where friction against the walls is least. The speed varies in different glaciers, and also with the season. Speeds of more than 150 feet per day have been measured in a few Alaskan and Greenland glaciers, but these are exceptionally high. Figure 13-3 shows a

pattern of movement common in the Alps. Some Alaskan coastal glaciers are so nearly stagnant that their debris-covered margins are overgrown by forests.

The rocks resting upon glaciers also prove that they flow. Most glaciers carry many boulders that differ from nearby bedrocks but can be matched with rock ledges bordering the glacier upstream. The bodies of two climbers who plunged to their deaths in the treacherous crevasses of the Bossons glacier in the Alps were released 41 years later at the end of the glacier several miles below.

Nature of Glacier Flow

Ice appears to be hard and brittle; the surfaces of glaciers are riven by crevasses, and a

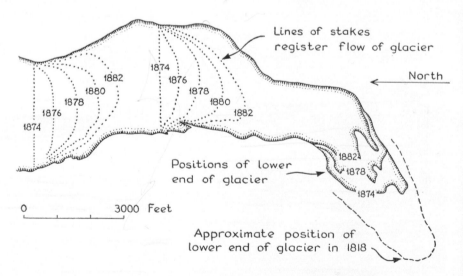

Figure 13-3.

Records of flow and frontal shrinkage of the Rhone glacier, Switzerland. (After A. Heim.)

piece of ice will shatter like glass under a blow. In the upper part of a glacier, ice yields almost entirely by fracture; flow is negligible. Deep within a glacier, on the other hand, deformation is chiefly by flow. Glaciers are perfect examples of the effect of size and time on strength (Chapter 10). In small masses and under quickly applied loads, such as a hammer-blow, ice is rigid and brittle, but in glacial masses under continual load it flows slowly under its own weight. The brittle, crevassed surface ice is rafted along on the flowing mass below.

The mechanism of flow is complex. Microscopic studies show that some ice crystals bend, others glide along the sheets of atoms parallel to the base of the hexagonal crystals, still others granulate and shear. Thus, though the mass as a whole flows, some crystals break, as in many other examples of flowage during metamorphism. As in other foliated metamorphic rocks, many crystals are strung out in parallel planes, suggesting that they recrystallized during movement. The recrystallization is proved by the coarseness of the crystals: those in the firn of Alpine snowfields average less than a quarter of an inch in diameter but those at the glacial front average about an inch. Crystals 6 to 8 inches in diameter have been collected at the edge of the Malaspina glacier in Alaska; thousands of smaller ones must have recrystallized to form them.

Ice at the glacial snout or deep within crevasses generally shows layering that superficially resembles stratification. The layers lie roughly parallel with the floor and curve upward along the glacial walls. Measurements show that adjacent layers move at slightly different speeds; each successive layer inward from the wall flows slightly faster than its neighbor. This proves that the layer boundaries are really not bedding, but surfaces of shear caused by friction against the floor and walls of the glacier. This shear banding of glaciers is commonly emphasized by streaks of dust and other rock debris dragged into the glacial mass. The shear banding—so like the foliation of many gneisses and schists—proves that the ice is no longer brittle but reacts to differential pressure by flowage and recrystallization.

Kinds of Glaciers

The topography over which a glacier flows largely controls its form. **Valley glaciers** are ice streams flowing down steep-walled mountain valleys. Fed by large snowfields above, such glaciers may extend far below the snowline. All glaciers end where the ice melts at the front as fast as it is replenished by flowage.

Figure 13-4. *Small cliff glaciers, Sierra Nevada, California. Note how the rock in the foreground has been shattered by frost action. (Photo by Francois Matthes, U. S. Geological Survey.)*

Glaciers occupy lofty mountain valleys the world over—even in the tropics, as in the Carstenz Range in New Guinea, Kilimanjaro in Kenya, and Cotopoxi in the Ecuadorean Andes. The valley glaciers of the United States, except for those of Mount Rainier, are short ice streams only a few hundred feet thick. Many are hardly distinguishable from snowfields; indeed all gradations occur from snowfields to glaciers. The Rocky Mountains, the Cascade Range, and the high Sierra hold hundreds of small irregular ice masses, called **cliff glaciers** or **hanging glaciers,** that lie in well-shaded clefts opening out over steep cliffs (Fig. 13-4).

In contrast to these puny ice streams, many valley glaciers in the Himalayas and Alaska are 30 to 70 miles long and over 3,000 feet thick. In such areas many tributary glaciers merge into an integrated system (Fig. 13-5) draining hundreds of square miles. At the foot of the St. Elias Mountains in Alaska several of these long systems of valley glaciers emerge, spread over the plain below, and join to form Malaspina glacier, a lobate ice mass covering 800 square miles (Fig. 13-6). Such glaciers are called **piedmont glaciers** (compare with bahada slopes, p. 273). The great Ice Barrier of the Ross Sea in Antarctica is also formed partly by coalescence of valley glaciers at the mountain front, but here most of the ice mass is floating, rather than lying on a coastal plain (Fig. 13-7).

Small masses of radially spreading ice are

Figure 13-5.   Valley glacier with numerous tributary glaciers, Alaska. (Photo by U. S. Air Force.)

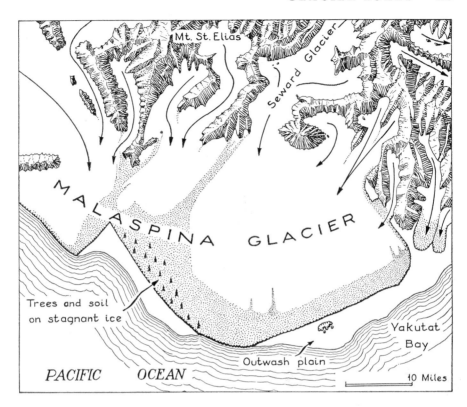

Figure 13-6.

Map of the Malaspina glacier, Alaska. The arrows indicate the flow of the valley glaciers that feed the Malaspina. (After R. S. Tarr and L. Martin, 1914.)

found on Iceland, Spitzbergen, parts of Scandinavia, and the islands north of Canada (Figure 13-8). These are called **ice caps.**

The largest of all glaciers are huge ice sheets, called **continental glaciers** found today only in high latitudes, though as we shall see, they were formerly much more widespread. All of interior Greenland—about 637,000 square miles—is covered with ice, leaving only a fringe of land along the coast. The Greenland glacier spreads outward in all directions from two high points in the interior. Parts of the coast are bordered by lofty mountains through which the glacier spills, splitting up between the peaks into valley glaciers that flow down the coastal valleys to the sea. Soundings by geophysical means (see Chapter 21) show that much of this ice mass is several thousand feet thick.

Antarctica supports a much larger continental glacier, estimated to cover 5,000,000 square miles—an area larger than the United States and Mexico. The Antarctic glacier overrides the coast and projects into the shelf ice formed by the freezing of the sea. In places it is held back by mountains through which the ice escapes in huge valley glaciers. The famous Beardmore glacier, ascended by several of the early explorers in their quest for the South Pole, is one of these. The Beardmore glacier is 300 miles long and 12 miles wide; it extends from the interior plateau at more than 10,000 feet altitude far out into the shelf ice of the Ross Sea.

Glacier Loads

Frost Weathering and Avalanching

Glaciers acquire rock debris in several ways. Valley glaciers generally cover only small

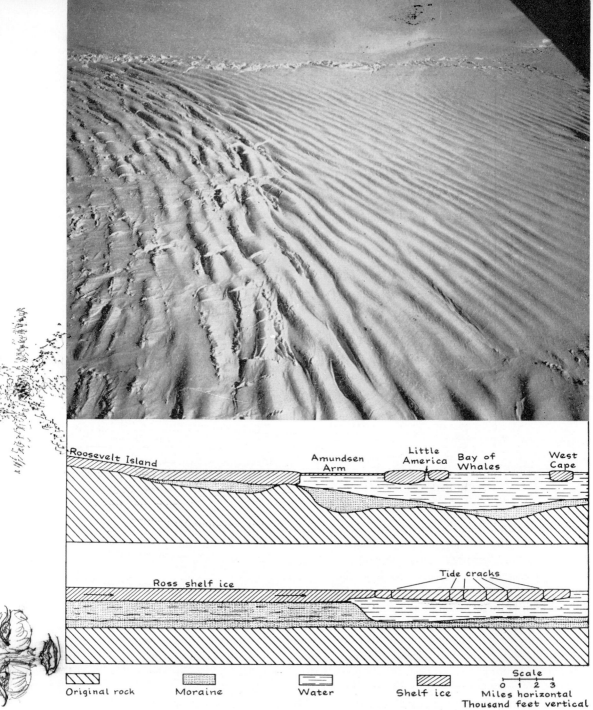

Figure 13-7.　Top: *Ice in the Bay of Whales, Antarctic. The Bay of Whales is a reentrant in the Ross Shelf Ice, protected in part by islands. The bay ice, 30 to 50 feet thick, is folded by the pressure of the advance of the much thicker shelf ice around the protecting islands. The individual folds are several tens of feet high. Similar folds nearby are caused by the drag of the shelf ice over its own morainal deposits. (Airplane Photo by T. C. Poulter.) Bottom: Sections through the Ross Shelf Ice and Bay of Whales. The thickness of the ice has been determined by seismic methods, described in Chapter 21. (After T. C. Poulter, Stanford Research Institute.)*

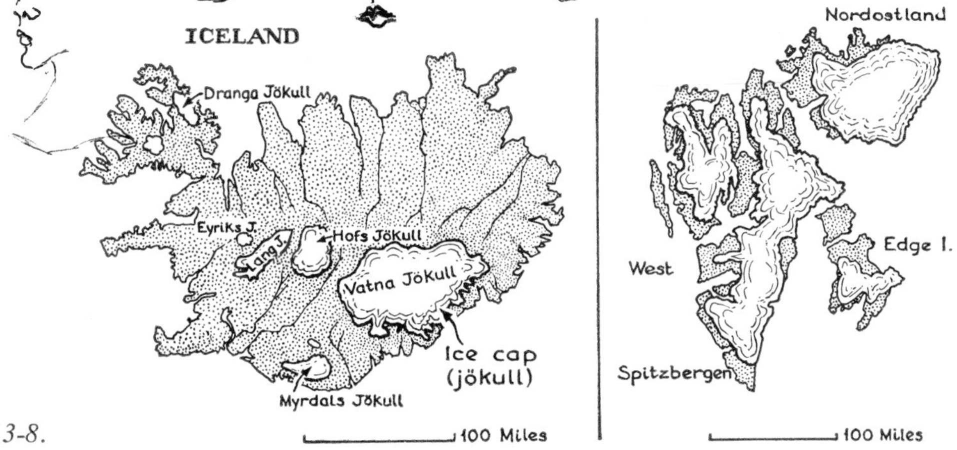

ICELAND

Dranga Jökull

Eyriks J.

Lang J.

Hofs Jökull

Vatna Jökull

Ice cap
(jökull)

Myrdals Jökull

Nordostland

West

Edge I.

Spitzbergen

100 Miles

100 Miles

Figure 13-8.

Ice caps of Iceland and Spitzbergen. (After Stieler's Atlas.)

parts of the mountains from which they flow. Gentle slopes above them hold extensive snowfields, but snow is unable to cling to steep windswept slopes so that great expanses of craggy ridges, peaks, and cliffs also rise above the glaciers (Figs. 13-4 and 13-5). Frost action strongly shatters these bare rocks (Fig. 13-4): during the day, meltwater from snowbanks seeps into the crevices; that same night it may freeze and loosen blocks from their parent ledges. Small grains, loose chips, and even great blocks of rock thus freed tumble down the slopes and accumulate in talus piles along the edge of the glacier. Landslides and rockfalls from cliffs undermined by the glacier crash down upon it. Much debris also tumbles down in **avalanches** (snowslides) during the spring thaw, and still more washes down in freshets from melting snow and summer rains (see Fig. 5-2).

Thus the ice, especially along its edges, becomes charged with rock material which forms conspicuous dark streaks along the edges of the glacier. These stripes of dirty ice and loose rock are **lateral moraines.** If two valley glaciers join, the inner lateral moraines unite to form a **medial moraine** along the center of the glacier below the junction. If tributaries are many, several medial moraines may streak the surface of the trunk glacier (Figs. 13-5 and 13-13). The moraines are

not merely surface features; they extend deep into the glacier. Glaciers also carry a great deal of rock debris scattered through the ice, particularly near their floors. Much is loose rock and soil scooped up from the floor as the glacier moves over it: some is plucked bodily from the bedrock by pressure of the moving ice, some is rasped from the floor by boulders frozen into the ice and dragged along with it. But material from the top of the glacier also becomes embedded in the ice: some falls into crevasses opened by glacial motion, much is buried under new falls of snow or beneath avalanches, and some doubtless sinks into the ice because of its higher density.

Meltwater Shattering

At the head of most valley glaciers is a deep arcuate crevasse, or a series of closely spaced crevasses, called the **bergschrund** (Fig. 5-2, and Fig. 13-9). The crevasses are formed by the downstream flow of ice in the lower part of the glacier, which breaks the brittle ice above and pulls it away from the rock wall. The bergschrund yawns open in summer but is generally filled or bridged with snow in winter.

Adventurous observers have descended into bergschrunds on ropes and found that the lower parts have a rocky wall on the upstream

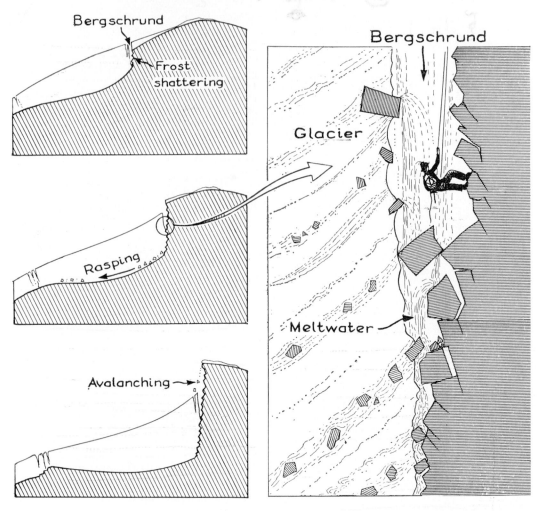

Figure 13-9.   Progressive stages of erosion at the head of a valley glacier (left), *with a detail of the bergschrund* (right). (*In part after W. V. Lewis, 1938.*)

side and an ice wall on the other. The rock wall is shattered and riven with joints, some of which gape open, disclosing slight displacements of the angular blocks of rock that they outline. Many blocks are broken free but have moved only slightly; others lean out against the ice in precarious imbalance; the rest, entirely free from their parent ledges, are now incorporated in the glacier (Fig. 13-9).

During the day, water from melting snow pours over the face of the bergschrund, filling the joints in the rock. The almost nightly frost loosens new blocks. Here, obviously, is a zone of active erosion, sapping the headwall

by the plucking of frost-riven blocks, steepening the cliffs behind, and gradually extending the glacier headward. (Figs. 5-2 and 13-9).

A crevasse, however, cannot long remain open after it has reached a depth of more than about 200 feet. Experiments on ice under pressure show that at loads corresponding to such depths ice flows plastically and slowly closes deeper openings. Glacier heads nevertheless show features indicating that shattering somehow extends deeper. For one thing, meltwater opens its own channels in the ice at the bottom of the bergschrund. On hot summer days much meltwater cascades into

the bergschrund, and a warm wind or a warm summer rain may greatly increase the amount. Despite the volume of meltwater, the bergschrund never fills with water to the point where streams emerge and overflow the ice. The inpouring water evidently melts its way down between the rock face and the glacier, far below the bottom of the bergschrund, possibly to the very base of the glacier. Also such melting of the deep ice should be expected from physical principles; the compressed ice at depth melts at a slightly lower temperature than the ice at the surface. Meltwater pouring into the crevasse thus carries heat downward to melt some of the ice deep within the glacier. Plastic flow of ice tends to close the tubes opened by meltwater, but as long as heat is continuously transferred downward, melting along the wall may offset the constriction by flowage. Moreover, the water in the tubes is under hydrostatic pressure, which also opposes closing by plastic flow. It must be remembered, however, that meltwater deep within a glacier is protected from daily temperature changes, so that meltwater shattering must be much less effective at depth than it is at the surface.

Cirques

The glacier motion removes the shattered rock at the bergschrund and exposes new rock surfaces to attack. Where valley glaciers have melted completely away, exposing their headwalls, the glaciated valley generally ends in a semicircle of high cliffs that bound a rock basin holding a beautiful mountain lake. Such cliffed valley heads are called **cirques.** (Figures 13-4 and 13-18). The curving cliffs at the head of the cirque are shattered clear to their bases, and generally meet the smoothed and polished floor of the valley at a sharp angle. The jagged and shattered cliff face, the product of frost erosion and meltwater shattering in bergschrunds, contrasts strikingly with the smooth valley floor, the product of rasping by the glacial ice.

The Glacial Rasp

We have seen that the head of a valley glacier is a zone of rapid accumulation of snow and ice that is heavily charged with rock debris. If accumulation has been rapid enough to produce a steep downstream gradient of the glacier surface, outward movement may occur along strongly curved shear surfaces, as it sometimes does in a landslide (Fig. 11-11). As the average block of debris incorporated in the ice at the bergschrund is much larger than those acquired downstream, and as most rocks are about three times as dense as ice, these large blocks sink slowly through the glacier and reach the bottom within a few

Figure 13-10.   *Rock surface showing glacial grooving, polishing, and, at the left, plucking, near Mount Baker, Washington. The ice flowed diagonally from the upper left to the lower right. (Photo by H. A. Coombs.)*

score yards of their parent ledges. Smaller blocks tumble down the bergschrund and through the meltwater tubes. Thus, at and near the bergschrund the bottom of the glacier is charged with unusual amounts of debris. As this debris-laden ice moves along the bedrock floor, the sharp blocks of rock are dragged across the glacier bed, abrading the bedrock (Figs. 13-9, 13-10) like a gigantic rasp—gouging into and scraping off irregularities on its bed and smoothing and grooving the rock beneath.

DEBRIS IN CONTINENTAL GLACIERS. A continental glacier covers nearly all of a landmass with ice, so that frost shattering and talus accumulation can take place only around islands of rock that rise above such a glacier. Less debris is also loosened by meltwater shattering of its rock floor than at the bergschrund of a valley glacier. Yet the ice at the margins of the Greenland glacier is heavily charged with rock debris, just as in valley glaciers.

One source of debris is the soil and loose rock that formerly covered the land over which a glacier flows. Where continental glaciers have recently melted back, the rock floor laid bare is nearly always free of soil and such unconsolidated material as stream gravels and floodplain deposits, except where the glacier has packed it into canyons or depressions in the surface as it rode over. Most loose material has been dragged off bodily by the moving ice. Any preglacial soil should

long ago have been eroded in this way from beneath the Greenland glacier which has surely existed far longer than the glaciers that stripped the soil from Labrador. Somehow the present load of the Greenland ice must therefore be derived from present-day plucking and rasping of the floor; perhaps meltwater shattering, though weaker than in valley glaciers, is also important in providing debris to the Greenland glacier. This problem is still very poorly understood by glaciologists.

EROSION BY GLACIERS. Rock floors exposed by the melting of continental glaciers, like those under large valley glaciers, are smoothed and polished. On these polished floors are numerous scratches, even deep grooves (Figs. 13-10 and 4-5). Obviously, the glacier has gouged and abraded material from its bed. Continental glaciers are thicker and heavier than most valley glaciers and hence make more effective rasps.

The rapidity with which a glacier abrades its bed depends on four factors: (1) the resistance to abrasion of the local bedrock, (2) the abundance of the cutting tools (rock fragments) frozen into the bottom of the ice, (3) the speed of flow, and (4) the weight (thickness) of the ice. Thick continental glaciers flowing over weak or shattered rock are powerful erosional agents; abrasion by valley glaciers is generally most vigorous on a cirque floor because there the ice is likely to be thickest and most heavily armed with cutting tools.

Till deposited by a valley glacier, West Walker River, Nevada. The largest boulders are 1½ feet in diameter. (Photo by Eliot Blackwelder.)

Figure 13-11.

Debris Released by Glaciers

TILL. That glaciers are effective eroding agents is well shown by the vast amount of debris released at the glacier front by melting. Piled in hummocky ridges along the ice front are heaps of boulders, sand and silt, mixed without appreciable sorting or stratification. Such unsorted debris (Figure 13-11), deposited directly by the ice, is called till. The proportion of boulders to fine material in till varies widely. Some till consists largely of coarse boulders, but that from thin ice caps eroding shale, limestone, or older glacial deposits may be chiefly clay and silt, with only scattered boulders.

Rock fragments in till are not shaped like those in stream and beach deposits. Most pebbles of streams and beaches are rounded, but those in till are mainly subrounded or sharply angular. Some have been cracked and broken by the crushing weight of the overriding glacier; many, especially in valley glaciers, are joint blocks loosened by frost action and only slightly modified by abrasion during transport. A few fragments have one or more nearly flat, grooved, and polished surfaces, called facets, formed as the boulder was dragged against the bedrock floor.

ROCK FLOUR. The effectiveness of the glacial rasp is made especially obvious by the large amount of rock flour (silt and fine sand)

released at the glacial front. Turbulent streams of milky water gush from tunnels in the front of a glacier (Fig. 13-12). If we collect a beaker of the roily water and let it stand, most of the suspended matter promptly settles to form a layer of fine sand and silt, but a little clay may remain suspended for hours or days. The silt, when examined with a microscope, is seen to differ strikingly from mud brought down by freshets in an unglaciated region. The minerals of the glacial silt are not the ordinary soil minerals that result from chemical weathering. Instead, small sparkling cleavage fragments of unweathered feldspar and other undecomposed minerals are abundant, and there is an almost complete absence of the yellow iron stain, the black and gray colors of humus, and the slimy clays so characteristic of soils. Most of the material is clearly not ancient soil, but rock flour from rock fragments that have been crushed against each other and against the bedrock.

Glaciers release an amazing quantity of rock flour and fine sand. Glacial streams are invariably overloaded; they quickly deposit the rubble and coarse sand they carry, building up a sloping gravel plain (Fig. 13-13) over which they spread in braided courses. Most of the rock flour is carried farther and builds floodplain deposits or is spread into lakes as extensive delta and bottom deposits. Such rock flour derived from granodiorite

Silt-laden stream emerging from an ice tunnel in the front of a glacier, Tanana district, Alaska. (Photo by S. R. Capps, U. S. Geological Survey.)

Figure 13-12.

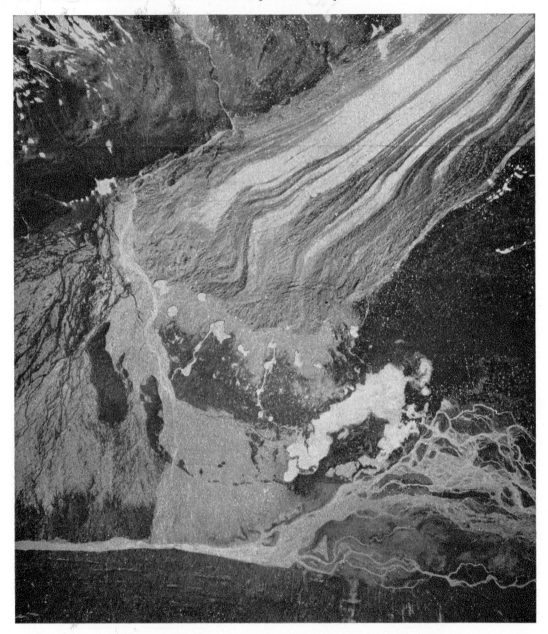

*Figure 13-13.   Vertical airplane photo and explanatory sketch of deposits at the foot of a valley
glacier, Alaska. Note how the recessional moraine (black in sketch) has been
partly buried by later outwash fans. Note also how the course of the through-going
stream becomes braided where the glacial outwash enters it.*

forms great terraces of white silt along the rivers of British Columbia and Alaska.

The ground-up rock is also widely scattered by the winds. Extensive unstratified deposits of **loess** (a loam consisting chiefly of silt particles carried by the wind) are found in and near many glaciated areas (Fig. 13-14). Loess generally contains innumerable roughly

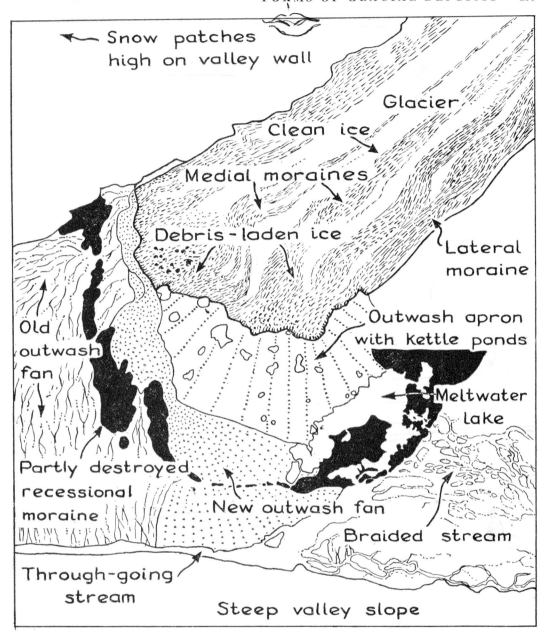

Snow patches high on valley wall

Glacier

Clean ice

Medial moraines

Debris-laden ice

Lateral moraine

Old outwash fan

Outwash apron with kettle ponds

Meltwater lake

Partly destroyed recessional moraine

New outwash fan

Braided stream

Through-going stream

Steep valley slope

vertical tubules left by the rotting of grass stems and roots. Because of the vertical tubules and a characteristic columnar jointing loess stands well in nearly vertical banks, although it is only feebly consolidated.

Forms of Glacial Deposits

The debris dumped by glaciers or by streams and lakes directly associated with them is called **glacial drift.** The unstratified material dropped directly by the ice forms **moraines;** that reworked by streams or lakes is called **stratified drift.**

Moraines

Till occurs chiefly in moraines. The term moraine is used both for the hills or other topographic forms of a till mass deposited by the ice, and also for debris upon or within an active glacier. The largest and best-developed moraines are generally at the front of a glacier. If the rate of ice flow and the rate of melting are both steady, so that the ice front remains in nearly the same place for a long time, the debris released from the melting ice may accumulate in great hummocky morainal ridges. Since the ice front fluctuates with mild climatic changes, however, more than one morainal ridge is likely to form. The furthest advanced is called the **terminal moraine;** those formed at stages of halt during glacial retreat are called **recessional moraines.** Terminal and recessional moraines of valley glaciers are generally high crescent-shaped ridges that curve around the glacier snout and extend up the sides as lateral moraines (Fig.

13-13). Small recessional moraines may be almost buried by outwash as shown in the same figure.

Most terminal and recessional moraines of continental glaciers are broadly lobate in plan and can be followed for many miles except where they are breached by outwash (Figs. 13-13 and 13-20). Some englacial (ice-enclosed) debris freed as the ice retreats is strewn as patches of till over the glaciated area (Fig. 13-19). This irregularly scattered **ground moraine** is not aligned in definite ridges: some is packed into such depressions as preglacial stream channels, some is plastered around low hills of bedrock. Ground moraine is the most widespread deposit of a continental ice sheet. In most places it is spotty and thin, but near the margin of a

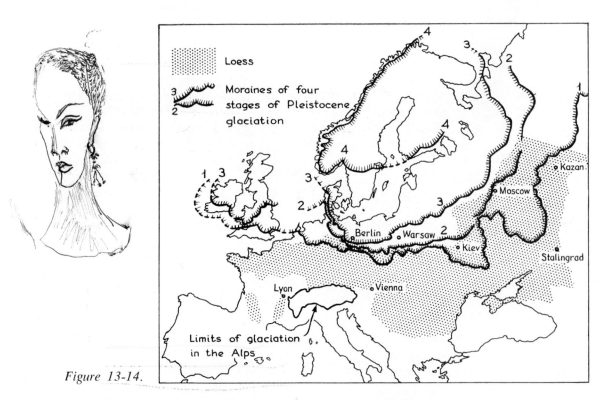

Figure 13-14.

Relation of loess-covered areas to the terminal moraines of four glacial advances in Europe. (Adapted from R. F. Flint, Glacial Geology and the Pleistocene Epoch, *John Wiley & Sons, 1947; and R. A. Daly,* The Changing World of the Ice Age, *Yale University Press, 1934.)*

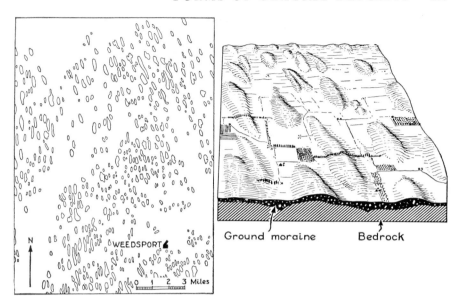

Figure 13-15.

Map of drumlins near Weedsport, New York, and sketch showing the low, elongate forms. (From Weedsport quadrangle, U. S. Geological Survey.)

glaciated area it may form an almost continuous veneer covering hundreds of square miles.

In many places ground moraine has been overridden by the ice and molded into clusters of closely spaced hills, each shaped like half of an egg cut lengthwise. These streamlined hills are **drumlins.** They range widely in size but many are more than a thousand feet long, three or four hundred feet wide, and 50 to 150 feet high. They occur in clusters of scores or hundreds, with each drumlin axis roughly parallel to the direction of glacial flow (Fig. 13-15). The form and composition of drumlins makes it clear that they are masses of subglacial debris molded into streamlined forms by active ice flow. Excavations show that they are chiefly composed of till, in most places a sticky variety containing much clay. Some have cores of bedrock; others are entirely till.

Stratified Drift

Glacial meltwater carries off large quantities of gravel, sand, and rock flour. Much of this

is deposited on the beds of overloaded streams (**glacio-fluvial deposits**) or in lakes (**glacio-lacustrine** deposits); some is carried to the sea. Alluvial fans deposited by the overloaded meltwater streams generally extend downstream from valley glaciers (Fig. 13-13). **Outwash plains**—of coalescing alluvial fans across which braided streams strew sand and gravel—spread from the margins of continental glaciers.

Pitted outwash is an outwash apron dimpled by countless undrained holes from a few feet to more than a hundred feet across; it may also contain depressions as much as a mile long and more than a hundred feet deep. Such holes are called **kettles.** Each marks a place where a block of ice left by the retreating glacier was surrounded or even buried beneath glacio-fluvial gravels. When the ice block melted the kettle was left (Fig. 13-16).

Streams emerging from valley glaciers immediately aggrade their valley floors and form long floodplains of stratified drift. Later, after the glacier has melted, these deposits are cut into by the no longer overloaded river

Figure 13-16.

Small kettle lake in outwash gravels of the Baird glacier, Alaska. (Photo by A. F. Buddington, U. S. Geological Survey.)

and are left as terraces clinging to the valley walls.

Long winding ridges of stratified sand and gravel called **eskers** traverse some areas formerly covered by continental glaciers. Most are less than a hundred feet high and a few hundred feet wide, but may be several miles long. Some of them merge downstream into outwash fans or deltas. Aggrading streams that flowed in tunnels beneath the ice or along crevasses probably built the eskers—presumably after the ice became almost stagnant during its wasting, for the thrust of an active glacier would surely close the tunnels or crevasses and scatter the esker into ground moraine.

Glacier-fed streams build deltas in lakes; these grow rapidly and may convert the lakes into swampy plains. Glacial deltas are composed of coarse material, generally gravel and sand, much of which shows characteristic foreset bedding.

Many glacial lakes are dammed on one side by the ice itself, and the water extends into crevasses and irregular holes in the wasting glacier. Such lakes are, of course, unstable; they fluctuate in level as advance or retreat of the glacier changes their outlets. Their sediments are thus generally interlayered with stream deposits and till. When the glacier melts, patches of these sediments that filled former crevasses and holes in the ice or that were laid down by streams flowing along

the ice margin, are left as terraces and flat-topped hills called **kames** and **kame terraces.**

Modification of Topography by Glaciers

It is evident that glaciers differ greatly from rivers in the mechanism of their flow and in their erosional and depositional features. Topography shaped by them differs sharply from that shaped by running water. The differences are conspicuous in areas recently uncovered by glacial recession.

The polished and grooved bedrock floor found in glaciated areas does not occur in normal stream channels. Glaciated areas contain swarms of lakes, ponds, and marshes that fill shallow rock basins scooped out by the ice, depressions dammed by moraines and outwash, and hollows left by the melting of blocks left stranded by glacial retreat. Streams connecting these lakes are generally ungraded, and have numerous waterfalls and rapids.

The upstream sides of most hills and small rock knobs overridden by ice are rounded, polished, and grooved; the downstream sides are irregularly jagged. The glacial rasp has worn the upstream side smooth but the lee side has been roughened by the quarrying and dragging out of joint blocks by the overriding ice. The pressure differences on upstream and downstream sides may contribute to the sculpture: the higher pressure on the upstream side melts the ice and the water freezes in the low-pressure area, causing plucking. Rock knobs sculptured in this way are called **roches moutonnées** (sheep rocks).

Most valleys of mountain streams are V shaped in cross profile, but those from which glaciers have melted are characteristically U shaped because their floors and walls have been scoured out by the glacial rasp. Remnants of the former V shape may be preserved on canyon walls higher than the top of the vanished glacier. Glacial valleys are also straighter and smoother than the usual V shaped valley; irregularities on their walls and the spurs between tributary valleys have been worn and quarried away by the ice (Fig. 13-17). A viscous glacier cannot turn sharp curves as readily as water; because of its mass and stiffness it planes off the irregularities in its channel and facets the ends of the spurs. Thus the valley floor is deepened and widened by the glacial rasp, transforming the original narrow V profile to a wide U. Many valley glaciers have deepened their channels far below sea level—not only in the coastal fjords of Norway, New Zealand, Chile, and Alaska, but also in such mountain valleys as that of Lake Chelan, Washington, and Lake Como, Italy. The long profile of a glaciated valley is commonly interrupted by abrupt steps, above and below which the smooth U-shaped valley may continue with flat gradients. Several such "cyclopean steps" may appear in a single glaciated valley, alternating with polished rock floors and lake-filled basins.

Unlike stream valleys, most glaciated valleys head in cirques. Abandoned cirques (Fig. 13-18) are conspicuous in recently deglaciated mountains; some of these huge semicircular basins may be so closely spaced that the divides between them are reduced to knife-edged "combs" (Fig. 13-5), or to triangular "horns" (Fig. 13-18).

Stream valleys and glaciated valleys also differ in the relation of the tributaries to the main stream. The upper surface of a tributary glacier generally accords with that of the main glacier—though because of the rigidity of a thin ice mass this is not always so—but the floors beneath the main glacier and the tributary are generally cut to different depths, depending on the volume and speed of the respective ice streams. A thin tributary glacier, unless favored by less-resistant bedrock, cannot keep pace with the scouring and plucking by the larger glacier. When the ice melts away, therefore, the floor of the tributary valley is left hanging high above the floor of

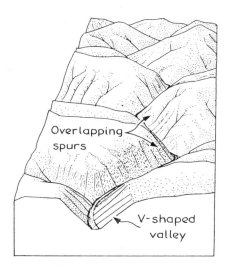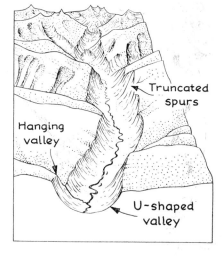

Figure 13-17.

A hypothetical stream valley and its associated forms before and after being modified by a valley glacier.

the main valley, and its stream plunges in waterfalls or steep rapids to the main valley.

Unquestionably, glaciers leave clear marks of their former presence upon a landscape; we shall see that such features testify to widespread former glaciation in areas that today have temperate or even tropical climates.

Former Periods of Glaciation

The Iowa farmer, sweltering under the August sun, may doubt that "the present is the key to the past" if he is told that the soil on which his corn grows came from deposits left by an ice sheet that formerly covered most of northern North America. Similarly, the native of the Talchirs in India, who pauses to rest from the steaming tropical heat on a polished and striated rock ledge, would doubtless think the idea fantastic, though alluring, if told that his perch is the floor of an ancient glacier that once spread over much of India.

Inferences such as these so tax the imagination that, despite clear-cut evidence, they were not accepted even by geologists until every possible alternative—from the Biblical flood to some mysterious kind of volcanic activity —had been tested and found inadequate to explain the facts that were so clearly recorded in the rocks and in the drainage patterns upon them.

Development of the Glacial Theory

In most of Scandinavia, southern Canada and Labrador, and in parts of the northern United States, the normal soil profile is either poorly developed or missing. Instead, rounded hilltops expose smoothly polished rock ledges like those beneath existing glaciers. In places the polish and smaller striations have been weathered off, but where protected by even a thin veneer of till or peat, they may be as fresh and clear as beneath a modern ice sheet (Fig. 4-5).

Figure 13-18   Mount Assiniboine, a glacial horn, near Banff, Alberta. Note the many cirques, some with hanging glaciers. (Photo by Alberta Department of Mines and Resources.)

Figure 13-19. *Glacial boulders resting on a surface polished by a Pleistocene valley glacier, Sierra Nevada, California. (Photo by Eliot Blackwelder.)*

Boulders—many of them huge—are randomly strewn over the polished surface (Fig. 13-19). Most of these boulders (called erratics) differ from the local bedrock: many in the Iowa fields are of gneiss and granite, though the bedrock beneath is limestone or shale. No gneiss or granite is exposed in the headwaters of local streams, so the boulders could not have been swept in by floods. In parts of Iowa, chunks of copper ore are occasionally found that are like the ore mined only from rock ledges on the Keeweenaw Peninsula in Michigan or on Isle Royale in Lake Superior. Boulders of an unusual variety of granite called "rapikivi," found in place only north of the Gulf of Finland, are scattered widely over Estonia and even far into Poland. The basalt plateau of eastern Washington is strewn with huge boulders of granitic rocks of kinds whose nearest outcrops are on the opposite side of Columbia River, many miles to the north. To reach their present positions, these boulders must have been transported directly across the Columbia River Canyon, at places where it is now 1,500 to 2,000 feet deep. A large nickel deposit was found in northern Finland by tracing scattered fragments of ore northward to their source near Petsamo.

The implications of such relations seem obvious to us now. Yet, in the period from 1821 to 1835, when two European geologists, Venetz and Charpentier, showed that boulders of rocks found in place only in the central Alps are widely scattered across the broad Swiss plain and correctly inferred that they must have been carried there by former extensions of the present Alpine glaciers, their ideas were generally rejected.

In 1836, however, Charpentier induced one of the skeptics, a young Swiss naturalist named J. L. R. Agassiz (1807-1873), to join him on a visit both to the active glaciers of the Rhone Valley and to the huge abandoned moraines lower in the same valley. Convinced on this excursion that the evidence for former more extensive glaciers was even stronger than Charpentier had claimed, Agassiz set to work on the problem. He promptly saw and correctly interpreted the association of the transported blocks with the polished and grooved bedrock over which the glacier had moved. He showed that this association could not have been produced by water. But Agassiz, too, was not believed. As his biographer relates: "Men shut their eyes to the meaning of the unquestionable fact that . . . the former track of the glaciers could be followed, mile after mile, by the rocks they had scored and the blocks they had dropped."

But Agassiz was not easily discouraged. In 1840, he visited Scotland and Ireland and there found glacial phenomena identical with those on the Swiss plain. He announced that glaciers not only had once existed in Britain, but had formerly covered most of the country. This conclusion raised a furore of objections, but it also caused geologists to observe and analyze the evidence more carefully. When the facts so easily gathered over the British countryside were squarely faced, Agassiz's views prevailed.

The Pleistocene Glaciations

Agassiz emigrated to America and began the studies of glaciation in New England that have

been followed so fruitfully by many investigators. Modern maps, summarizing these studies, portray in detail the erosional and depositional forms and deposits of the ancient ice sheets. Both in North America and in Europe, many abandoned moraines have been mapped, lobe by lobe, so that their distribution is now well known (Figs. 13-14 and 13-20). Most of the moraines are conspicuous ridges of till that are readily traced for miles. Behind them, like signposts pointing the way, lie striated rock floors strewn with till and erratic boulders. Innumerable lakes and marshes mark places where the vanished glacier gouged its floor, or blocked older drainage with debris, or left a stagnant ice block half buried in an outwash apron. Fans of outwash spread from gaps in the moraine;

Figure 13-20.   The distribution of the Pleistocene glaciers in the United States. (After map by a Committee of the Geological Society of America.)

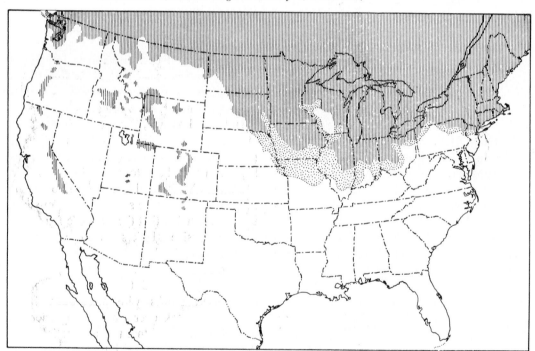

Unglaciated

Glaciated during
Wisconsin
glacial stage

Glaciated during older
Pleistocene stages but not
covered during Wisconsin

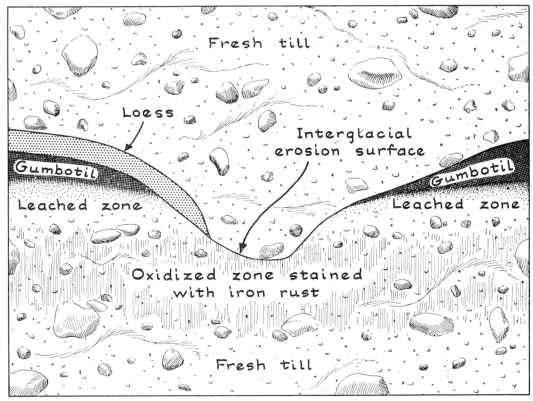

Figure 13-21. *Superposed tills, southwestern Minnesota. In the upper part of the lower till all boulders of granite and gneiss are thoroughly rotted, and only weathering-resistant quartzite is still undecomposed; the upper till contains abundant fresh boulders of granite and gneiss.*

beyond the fans are sheets of loess or terraces of silt. All these features serve to locate the position of the vanished glacier. The landscapes of New York, New England, the Great Lakes country, and the Pacific Northwest are unmistakably stamped with glacial imprints.

In mountainous areas, such as Yosemite National Park, the Cascade Mountains, or the Northern Rockies, the former existence of valley glaciers is recorded by innumerable cirques and U-shaped valleys, by fresh moraines, by superb waterfalls tumbling from hanging valleys, by clear mountain lakes nestled in rock-scoured basins, and by terraces of outwash gravel, sand, and silt extending downstream from the moraines.

ADVANCE AND RECESSION OF PLEISTO-CENE ICE SHEETS. At many places in North America and Europe, roadcuts reveal two or more different layers of till, one above the other (Fig. 13-21). The upper layer may contain boulders of almost fresh granite and gneiss, some with polished facets and striae. Beneath this is a layer of thoroughly weathered material showing a mature soil profile and grading downward into the lower layer of till. In this lower layer of till the outlines of boulders can still be recognized but the rocks can be cut with a knife—the feldspars are rotted to clay, and the ferromagnesian minerals are completely decomposed. Only chemically resistant rocks such as quartzite are found intact in this layer (Fig. 13-21). Such exposures prove that the lower till weathered for a long period of time before the younger till covered it. In places the B-horizon of the weathered till is so rich in clay that it forms a tough sticky mass. Such tough, clayey subsoils, whether of glacial origin or not, are popularly called "gumbo." **Gumbotil** is the technical term used to designate clay-rich weathered tills.

Moraines mantled by gumbotil, in contrast to younger unweathered moraines, have generally been greatly eroded since they were deposited; they enclose few, if any, undrained depressions.

Careful study of the superposition and degree of weathering of different glacial deposits permits discrimination of four main stages of ice advance. Between the ice advances, the climate appears to have been mild and warm, as shown by the fossils from stream and marsh deposits between the tills.

DATING PLEISTOCENE DEPOSITS BY VARVED LAKE SEDIMENTS.   Lake deposits abound in glaciated regions. Torrents of turbid meltwater pouring into glacial lakes build deltas quickly. The coarser sand and silt drops quickly on the delta or forms a bottom layer continuous with the foreset beds of the delta; the finest silt and mud settles slowly and spreads throughout the lake. Many glacial lakes are deep green, owing to the dispersion of light by the abundant particles of suspended clay.

In winter, the lakes freeze over and small tributary streams may freeze solid. During this quiet period, the suspended clay particles beneath the ice, along with fine algal matter that has accumulated during the summer, settle slowly to the bottom as a dark, fine-grained layer. By spring, most glacial lakes are nearly clear. Thus, the summer layer of deposits is coarser and consists of rock waste only, whereas the winter layer is finer and richer in organic matter. Such cycles can be observed in many existing lakes, and cores from holes bored in their bottoms show the characteristic two-fold layering.

These thin laminae of alternating fine and coarse material, each pair representing the deposit of a single year, are called **varves,** from a Swedish word meaning "seasonal de-

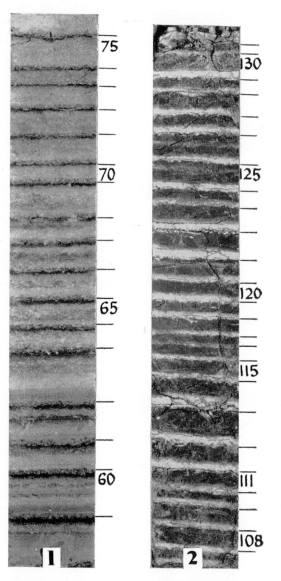

Figure 13-22.   Varved glacial clay from Steep Rock Lake, Ontario. The two samples are from two drill cores, each 12 inches long. The lines at the edge of the photo show the boundaries of each varve, and some of the varves are numbered. The light colored laminae are summer deposits; the dark, winter. (Photo by Ernst Antevs.)

posit." The double band representing a full year is, on the average, only a small fraction of an inch thick (Fig. 13-22), but some pairs are several times this thickness.

If we find glacial lake sediments exposed in a roadcut, or penetrated by a drill core, and count the varves, we can determine the number of years represented by the deposit. Furthermore, as the varves record climatic variations (for example, an exceptionally warm year yields an unusually thick and coarse summer layer), it is often possible, by matching sequences of comparable variations in thickness, to correlate the upper layers in a southern lake with those near the bottom of a more northerly, younger lake that lay along the line of ice recession.

By such methods, it has been determined that the last ice sheet retreated from the site of Stockholm, Sweden, about 9,000 years ago, that southern Ontario lay under ice 13,500 years ago, and that about 4,300 years elapsed while the ice retreated from a front near Hartford, Connecticut, to a front at St. Johnsbury, Vermont, a distance of 190 miles.

As mentioned in Chapter 7, radiocarbon (C^{14}) gives us another method of measuring ages during the past 35,000 years. Ages determined by this method for pieces of wood from forests overridden by glacial advances, are in many places consistent with those from varved sediments, but there are discrepancies also. Doubtless, some of these discrepancies are due to errors in stratigraphic assignments, others to errors in radiocarbon dating because of contamination by modern plant rootlets or the reworking of the fossil wood by bacteria, both of which introduce younger carbon into the material analyzed. Unquestionably, if a way is found to eliminate such sources of confusion, radiocarbon methods should allow us to trace the latest glacial episodes with still greater accuracy.

DRAINAGE CHANGES BEYOND THE LIMITS OF GLACIATION. The drastic climatic changes that buried so much of northern Europe and North America under glacial ice wrought striking changes at lower latitudes also, some of which we shall now describe.

Lake Bonneville.—In Pleistocene time, Nevada and Western Utah were not barren semideserts as they are today. Thin bedded clays that contain leaf imprints and fossils of fresh-water animals show that many of the intermontane valleys contained fresh-water lakes rimmed by trees and luxuriant grass. The highest wave-cut shoreline of the largest of these vanished lakes, called Lake Bonneville, makes a well-defined horizontal terrace on the cliffs and steep slopes fronting the Wasatch Mountains more than 1,000 feet above Great Salt Lake. Lake Bonneville, when filled to this level, overflowed into the Snake River and thence, by way of the Columbia, to the sea. The outlet was over unconsolidated alluvium into which the torrent quickly eroded a canyon to bedrock, 350 feet below the original divide. This resistant bedrock held the lake at this nearly constant lower level for a long time and great deltas and terraces were built along the shores. These are much more conspicuous than those at the higher overflow level. Moraines from valley glaciers in the Wasatch extend to the old shorelines. Some rest on lake sediments and are themselves cut by beaches. The glaciers were, therefore, about contemporaneous with the expansion of

Figure 13-23. Map showing the extent of the great Pleistocene lakes in the western United States. Present lakes, in part ephemeral, are in black. (After G. K. Gilbert and O. E. Meinzer.)

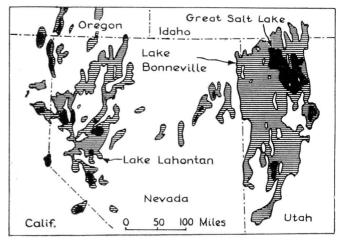

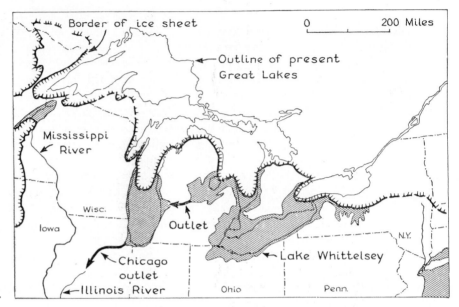

Figure 13-24.

Meltwater lakes formed during a recessional stage of the Pleistocene ice sheet in the Great Lakes region. The outline of the present lakes and State lines are shown for reference. (After F. Leverett and F. B. Taylor, 1915; F. Leverett and F. W. Sardeson, 1932; and W. S. Cooper, 1935.)

the lake—perhaps a little older than the maximum expansion.

As the climate became drier, the glaciers waned, the streams dwindled, and evaporation from the lake began to exceed inflow. The lake gradually evaporated to lower and lower levels, recorded in a series of shoreline features carved on the delta fronts and into the beach deposits of higher lake stands. Great Salt Lake and the Bonneville salt flats remain today as the last desiccation pools of this once-vast inland sea (Fig. 13-23).

Great Lakes and Missouri Valley Area.— In the north central United States, the continental glaciers overrode a stream-carved landscape, damming some of the pre-existing stream courses between the ice front and higher land to the south, and forming many ephemeral glacial lakes that were destroyed with further advance of the ice to the divides. The record of such lakes has been nearly obliterated by the overriding glacier. But the present channels of the Missouri and Ohio, which for many miles follow the approximate

edge of the vanished glacier, record the glacial blocking of northward-flowing stream courses with diversion of their waters to a position along the margin of the glaciers. The Milk and Yellowstone rivers were not always tributary to the Missouri. They formerly drained to Hudson's Bay, as shown by till-filled channels. The present course of the upper Missouri is the channel cut by the waters as they were diverted across low divides along the margin of the glacial ice. Similar ice-marginal drainage largely determined the present course of the Ohio River.

As the ice retreated, a new set of glacial lakes were impounded between the ice front and the higher ground to the south, as shore features and sediments still preserved clearly record. The drainage changes were many and complex. Several large glacial lakes and interconnected river systems were formed in succession as the retreating glacial front uncovered lower and lower outlets. The present Great Lakes are the last in a long series of such lakes whose history has been worked out

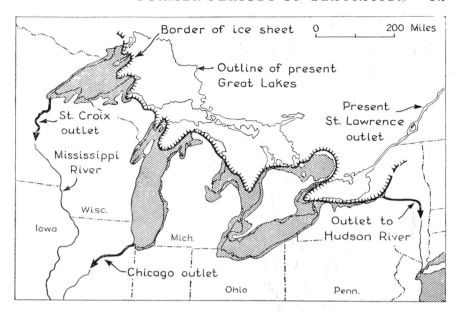

Figure 13-25.

Same as Figure 13-24 at a somewhat later stage. (After F. Leverett and F. B. Taylor, 1915.)

by glacial geologists. The evidence of the drainage changes and abandoned lakes is extensive and convincing. It consists of abandoned shorelines high above existing lakes, marked by beach ridges, wave-cut cliffs, deltas, spits, and bars. These features can be traced for miles, but when followed northward, they generally end abruptly against a moraine or apron of outwash that marked the glacial front against which the lake was dammed. Vast areas enclosed by the old shorelines are covered with varved silts and clays—the deep-water deposits of former glacial lakes.

As shown in Figures 13-24 and 13-25, a series of temporary glacial lakes occupied the southern end of what is now Lake Michigan. Their outlet was a short stream flowing from the present site of Chicago to the Illinois River and thence to the Mississippi. Simultaneously, a larger glacial lake, called Lake Whittlesey, occupied the expanded basins of Lake Erie and southern Lake Huron. Lake Whittlesey drained westward across central Michigan into ancestral Lake Michigan. Later the ice shrank northward, uncovering a lower

outlet across New York via the Mohawk and Hudson rivers (Fig. 13-25). Thereupon Lake Whittlesey shrank greatly, the cross-Michigan outlet dried up, and huge volumes of meltwater that had formerly flowed to the Gulf of Mexico now entered the Atlantic through the Hudson. Still later the ice retreated north of the St. Lawrence; both the Chicago and Mohawk-Hudson outlets were then abandoned and the present outlines of the Great Lakes were established.

As the ice withdrew still farther, an enormous glacial lake—larger than all the Great Lakes combined—developed in the Red River Valley of Manitoba, Minnesota, and North Dakota. This lake has been named Lake Agassiz, after the famous Swiss glaciologist. Its water spilled southward into the Minnesota River, ultimately entering the Mississippi at the present site of St. Paul. With further glacial retreat, Lake Agassiz was drained northward to what is now Lake Winnipeg. Its lake sediments form the fertile wheat lands of the Red River Valley.

Grand Coulee.—The great Columbia River was diverted by ice in eastern Washington, with striking effects (Figs. 13-26 and 13-27). A huge lobe of the ice sheet advanced at right angles upon the westward-flowing river, filled its 2,000-foot canyon, blocked the stream, and spread southward upon the Columbia Plateau. The huge river, diverted across the plateau, which here slopes southward several feet per mile, cascaded across the landscape and quickly carved a network of canyons into the plateau. The streams shifted with the changing ice front; a slight advance might block the head of a just-formed channel, or a retreat expose a lower one. Some of these shifts of the ice front released enormous volumes of water from Lake Missoula—a huge glacially dammed lake that lay in the mountain valleys of the northern Rockies a hundred miles east of Spokane. The outlet of the lake was a narrow but deep canyon whose mouth was periodically blocked by the ice front. Huge floods released by the bursting of the ice dam across this narrow outlet spilled in violent torrents across the plateau, scouring its surface into a weird complex of interconnected canyons draining southward toward the Snake River. For much of the time between these great floods the drainage was concentrated into a single channel now called the Grand Coulee. Here the river carved a great canyon 500 to 1,000 feet deep and 1 to 15 miles wide in the basalt flows of the Columbia Plateau. Midway was a gigantic waterfall 400 feet high and nearly 3 miles wide, which during the Pleistocene must have thundered with

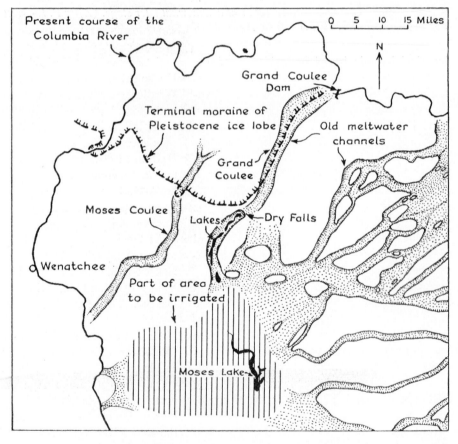

Figure 13-26.

Map of central Washington, showing Grand Coulee and other features formed by the glacial diversion of the Columbia River. (In part after J. H. Bretz.)

Figure 13-27. Dry Falls, a former huge waterfall in the glacially diverted Columbia River. (Courtesy of State of Washington Department of Conservation and Development.)

the roar of a thousand Niagaras (Fig. 13-27). Today, no water tumbles from its brink (it has been named Dry Falls): the waning of the glacier uncovered the preglacial canyon and allowed the river to resume its former course.

Recently, man has restored a part of the waterflow through Grand Coulee. Across the Columbia at the head of Grand Coulee stands Grand Coulee Dam, part of whose hydro-electric power is used to pump water from the lake behind the dam into the Coulee, whence it flows southward to irrigate millions of acres of rich but arid land. Grand Coulee Dam is the largest engineering project built by man, yet how puny it appears compared with the ice dam thrust across the river in the same position some 15,000 years ago!

Pre-Pleistocene Glaciations

Many ancient sedimentary formations show all the characteristics of till except that they are tightly cemented. They are composed of unsorted debris, contain striated and faceted stones, and are associated with varved shales and slates or with sandstones and conglomerates showing typical features of outwash deposits. Some show polished and grooved rock floors beneath them. Such features, in close association, can only mean that the deposits are glacial. Cemented tills are called **tillites.**

Although small bodies of tillite have been found in rocks of many different ages, two periods of earth history before the Pleistocene are particularly characterized by widespread glacial deposits. During the late Paleozoic, ice sheets spread widely over India, South Africa, Argentina and southern Brazil, and South Australia. In India, Australia, and South Africa, grooved rock floors beneath the hard tillite may be seen in hundreds of places. Their preservation is a result of their burial under a succession of younger sediments. These sediments protected them from weathering and erosion, and the unconsolidated glacial deposits were slowly cemented into rock. Recent erosion of the overlying deposits has now exposed them to view.

In the late Precambrian, also, glaciers seem to have been widespread. Ancient tillites that are considered to be of this age have been found on every continent except South America.

Causes of Glacial Climates

Geologists and climatologists have tried for more than a century to explain the recurrence of continental glaciation. Theory after theory has been suggested, but all seem to explain too little or too much. None can be considered satisfactory, yet they have an interest that justifies brief mention.

Facts to Be Explained

1. Continental glaciers in Greenland and Antarctica occupy about 10 per cent of the land surface today. In four different epochs of Pleistocene time they covered an area three times as great.

2. During the Pleistocene climatic zones were about parallel to their present positions but they were displaced southward during the periods of greatest glaciation and northward during interglacial epochs. In low latitudes, heavy rainfall was contemporaneous with glacial climates at higher latitudes.

3. Estimates of the duration of the several glacial and interglacial stages of Pleistocene time do not suggest strictly periodic recurrence; the climatic fluctuations seem to have been irregular.

4. Evidence of continental glaciation that was nearly as extensive as that of the Pleistocene is also found in Late Paleozoic rocks (about 200 million years old) and in Precambrian rocks (at least 500 million years old), but not in intermediate strata.

Suggested Explanations

The many theories suggested may be grouped roughly into two categories: geologic and astronomic. Some combine elements of both.

GEOLOGIC THEORIES. Several theories attempt to account for glaciation by climatic changes brought about by changes in continental elevations, or by changes in oceanic and atmospheric circulation caused by changes in the shape of ocean basins or of mountain uplifts. Such explanations are inadequate: there is no evidence whatever that since Pliocene time either the distribution or altitudes of the major land masses have changed significantly, and, under these theories, the average size and height of the continents would have had to fluctuate rapidly during Pleistocene time, for we have a clear record of at least four major glaciations in that period, and at least some of the interglacial climates were much milder than that of the present.

Changes in the amount of carbon dioxide and volcanic dust in the atmosphere might bring about climatic variation, and some theories are based on this. Carbon dioxide absorbs—blankets in—some of the heat radiated from the earth's surface. If the air contained more of it, the temperature should rise; if it contained less, the temperature should fall. Quantitatively, however, such changes would be inadequate to produce great climatic variation especially because simultaneous changes in the amount of water vapor held in the air would practically compensate for any variations in its carbon dioxide content. Volcanic dust undoubtedly screens out some of the sun's radiation, but there is no evidence that volcanoes were more active in glacial times than in interglacial. Changes in the salinity of sea water, with consequent modification of the ocean currents and their climatic influences, are likely results of glaciation, but they can hardly have brought it about, although it has been suggested that they did.

Geophysical theories, which attribute glaciation to shifts in the position of the continents, obviously give no explanation of either the warmer Pleistocene interglacial times or the cooler pluvial and glacial times. A theory of this sort has recently been advanced by the American geophysicists Ewing and Donn, who suggest that the crust is able to slide slowly over the interior of the earth. Glaciation, they say, is only possible when the configuration of land masses is such that there is both an unfrozen ocean at high northern latitudes, which supplies water for precipitation in middle latitudes, and a broad connection of northern and southern oceans that allows exchange of water between them. An objection to this theory is that the present massive ice cap of Antarctica proves that ice may accumulate to glacial thicknesses in high latitudes despite the lack of a polar ocean. It is also difficult to see how a special configuration of the northern continents can account for simultaneous glaciations in both hemispheres, and how a relatively slight interchange of Arctic and Atlantic water could produce so great a climatic effect when the far greater cooling effect of the sinking Antarctic waters now going on in all the oceans does not have a comparable influence. (See Fig. 16-6.)

ASTRONOMIC THEORIES. These are of three kinds: (1) that the solar system from time to time encounters clouds of cosmic dust, (2) that the earth varies periodically in its distance from the sun and hence in the amount of heat it receives, and (3) that the sun varies in the amount of heat it radiates.

Dark nebulae are known to be partly cosmic dust. If the solar system were to enter such a nebula it might either screen out the sun's radiation or blanket in the earth's radiation to outer space, depending on the size of the particles. Since there is no way of testing this hypothesis it is not seriously considered, in general, for the scientific method can work only with those hypotheses susceptible of some sort of test, however indirect. The other two suggestions are more amenable to testing.

Three known astronomic factors periodically affect the earth's relation to the sun: (a) changes in the eccentricity of the earth's orbit, with a period of 92,000 years, (b) changes in the angle between the earth's axis and its path, with a period of about 40,000 years, and (c), changes in the positions of the equinoxes,

with a period of about 22,000 years. The simultaneous effect of these variables is to produce periodic changes in the distance between every point on the earth's surface and the sun, and hence in the amount of solar radiation each point receives. If such changes had brought about glaciation, the effects on northern and southern hemispheres, though not exactly opposite, would certainly not have been parallel. Yet we are sure that glaciers have been simultaneously retreating in both hemispheres for some decades, and oceanic sediments from both hemispheres prove that the Pleistocene glaciation was simultaneous in both. Moreover, as these astronomic cycles are continuous, glaciation should have been regularly repeated every few hundred thousand years throughout geologic time, whereas we must go back to the Permian—almost 200 million years—to find anything comparable with the Pleistocene. These geologic arguments seem conclusively to negate such theories; some meteorologists further contend that temperature changes produced in this way would be far too small to cause glaciation.

Astronomers have shown that the sun's radiation fluctuates, and with it the amount of heat received by the earth. Short-term variations of as much as 3 per cent seem well established, and the American astronomer, Charles Abbot believes that still larger changes may have taken place in the past. A British meteorologist, Sir George Simpson, has built an ingenious hypothesis on this idea.

Simpson reasoned that, if solar radiation increased, the air temperature would rise and cloudiness and precipitation would increase all over the earth. More snow would fall, the ice caps in both hemispheres would expand, and the greater cloudiness would lessen summer melting. But the rising temperature would ultimately be so great that the ice and snow would melt faster than they were replenished. The glaciers would disappear. At the high point on the radiation curve (Fig. 13-28) the world climate would be milder and wetter than it is today. When radiation began to decrease, the sequence would reverse, ice would first

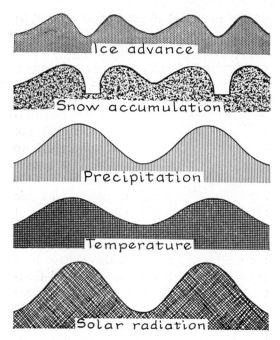

Figure 13-28. Simpson's theory of glaciation based on variation in the sun's radiation and its climatic effects.

advance, then, as heat became inadequate to supply precipitation, retreat, and finally, when radiation fell to its present value, we would be back to present conditions. Thus, somewhat paradoxically, a rise in the general temperature of the air would lead to continental glaciation. On this theory, one rise and fall of radiation would produce two glaciations, separated by a warm, wet, interglacial period. The climate following the second glaciation would be cold and dry, like that of the present. In low latitudes, beyond the limits of the ice, there would be a single long rainy epoch that would endure through both the glacial epochs and the interglacial state. The four Pleistocene glaciations recognized in Europe and North America would, on this hypothesis, require two cycles of increased solar radiation, separated by a time during which the climate would have been much as it is today.

Simpson's hypothesis appeals to meteorologists since it accounts for the increased precipitation that seems necessary to produce the huge ice sheets. The present line at which the mean annual temperature is at the freezing point lies much nearer the equator than do present ice sheets; this shows that low temperature alone cannot produce glaciation but that increased precipitation, or a different seasonal pattern of precipitation, is needed. With the present configuration of land and sea—essentially like that of the Pleistocene—increased precipitation requires greater evaporation from the sea.

Geologists, however, do not find the theory convincing, because the sediments, even in the equatorial ocean, show that the water was cooler during the Pleistocene. Both the kinds of fossils and the relative proportions of the several isotopes of oxygen found in their shells (which proportions are known to vary with the water temperature) point to cooler Pleistocene seas in both hemispheres and at the equator as well—not to the warmer equatorial seas Simpson's theory requires.

There is no hypothesis that satisfactorily accounts for the continental glaciation of the Pleistocene, nor can we say whether the present is simply another interglacial epoch. During the past several decades, glaciers have been receding in both hemispheres and the water released to the sea has raised sea level a few inches. If this retreat continued until all land ice was melted, sea level would rise more than a hundred feet. May we then expect, on the one hand, that our coastal cities and low-lying coastal plains will be drowned beneath a shallow sea, or, on the other, that some centuries hence the sites of Chicago, Copenhagen, and Warsaw may again be overrun by glaciers? From past geologic changes, it seems quite unlikely that the climate will remain as it is at present for many thousands of years, but much more work will have to be done before we will be able to make a prophecy based on sound reasons.

The Effect of Glacial Loads on the Earth's Crust

As we saw in Chapter 10, there is strong evidence from deflections of the plumb line and from measurements of gravity that large segments of the earth's crust are essentially in isostatic balance. The great weight of continental ice sheets might be expected to disturb this balance, and, as mentioned in Chapter 8, there is evidence that it did.

Wherever glaciers spilled over or around mountains, it is possible to get some measure of their thickness. In New England, for example, the ice must have been more than 4,000 feet thick, for the highest peaks were overridden. In southern Canada, nearer the source, the ice was certainly much thicker.

Although the density of ice is only about a third that of ordinary rocks, a load of ice 3,000 feet thick over an area as large as the Great Lakes and southern Canada would be equivalent to a load of more than 1,000 feet of rock and should have bent the crust downward. Though the high viscosity of subcrustal material might make the response sluggish, if isostasy is really general the lowering should have been great enough to be measurable.

Fortunately, the shorelines of ancient glacial lakes and of former extensions of the sea, as in the Baltic, give us a way of testing the idea. The shores were level when formed. After the ice load melted away, the crust should have tilted in response to the unloading and the shore lines should now rise toward the north. This is exactly what is found, not only in the Great Lakes region, but in the

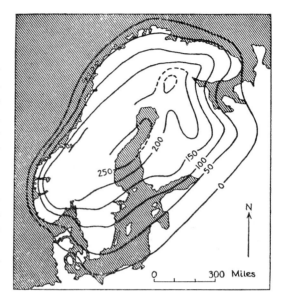

Figure 13-29. Post-glacial uplift in Scandinavia. The heavy lines connect points of equal uplift, in meters, of the highest strand line of the sea which flooded the area just after the melting of the glacier. (After R. A. Daly, The Changing World of the Ice Age, Yale University Press, 1934.)

Baltic (Figure 13-29), in Labrador, and even in the basin of Lake Bonneville, where the load was only 1,000 feet of water, covering an area much smaller than that of the great continental glaciers.

We will return to this geologic evidence of isostasy when we discuss the origin of mountains in Chapter 21. Suffice it to say here that the testing of the isostatic principle by glaciers is in full agreement with the geodetic evidence on which the theory was based.

FACTS, CONCEPTS, TERMS

SNOWFIELDS AND GLACIERS
  Transformation: snow → firn → ice
  Nature of glacier flow

  Concurrent brittleness and plasticity of glaciers
VALLEY GLACIERS; PIEDMONT GLACIERS; CONTINENTAL GLACIERS

ACQUISITION OF ROCK DEBRIS BY GLACIERS
    Frost weathering; avalanching; meltwater shattering; plucking; rasping
    Till; rock flour
DEPOSITS ASSOCIATED WITH GLACIERS
    Moraines: lateral; medial; terminal; recessional; ground
    Stratified drift: outwash aprons; kames and eskers; valley trains and silt terraces; deltas; varved clays
    Loess
TOPOGRAPHIC FORMS ASSOCIATED WITH GLACIERS
    Cirques; horns; U-shaped valleys; hanging valleys
    Smoothed and grooved rock surfaces
    Lakes and swamps; immature drainage patterns

Pitted outwash; terraces of silt
Morainal ridges; drumlin clusters
THE PLEISTOCENE GLACIATIONS
    Development of the glacial theory
    Evidence of advance and recession
    Evidence of multiple glaciation
        Weathered tills; superposed tills; interbedded interglacial deposits.
        Drainage changes
        Evidence of climatic changes from fossils
PRE-PLEISTOCENE PERIODS OF GLACIATION
CAUSE OF GLACIAL CLIMATES
SEA LEVEL CHANGES DUE TO GLACIATION
ISOSTATIC RESPONSE TO GLACIAL LOADING AND UNLOADING

QUESTIONS

1. What is the evidence that recrystallization takes place in the transformation of snow to firn and ice?

2. Why are glacial crevasses less than 200 feet deep?

3. Explain the processes by which the head of a valley glacier acquires (a) new snow and ice, (b) rock debris.

4. Explain the processes by which a continental glacier acquires its rock load.

5. Draw a longitudinal profile through a valley glacier and label the following features: cirque, terminal moraine, meltwater tubes, bergschrund, shear banding in ice, snowfield, rasped bedrock, plucked and shattered bedrock.

6. How does rock flour released from a glacier differ from the fine-grained materials formed during weathering?

7. Draw a hypothetical sketch map showing the location of all the following: (a) a lobate terminal moraine; (b) a recessional moraine; (c) pitted outwash; (d) ground moraine; (e) a drumlin cluster; (f) a plain underlain by varved clay; (g) an esker; (h) kame terraces; (i) an abandoned stream course; (j) spits and bars formed in a glacial lake dammed by the ice.

8. Outline the evidence that established the former existence of Lake Bonneville in northwestern Utah.

9. Outline briefly and illustrate by sketches the kind of field evidence indicating more than one period of Pleistocene ice advance.

10. Ice floats on water. How, then, is it possible for a glacier entering the sea to erode its bed below sea level? How deep below sea level is it theoretically possible for a glacier 1 mile thick to erode its bed?

SUGGESTED READINGS

Ahlmann, H. W., *Glacialogical Research on the North Atlantic Coasts,* Royal Geographical Society, Research Series No. 1. London, 1948.

Charlesworth, J. K. *The Quaternary Era with Special Reference to its Glaciation.* New York, St. Martins Press, 1957. 2 vols.

Coleman, A. P. *Ice Ages, Recent and Ancient.* New York, Macmillan Company, 1926.

Daly, R. A. *The Changing World of the Ice Age*. New Haven, Yale University Press, 1934.

Flint, R. F. *Glacial Geology and the Pleistocene Epoch*. New York, John Wiley and Sons, 1947.

Gilbert, G. K. *Lake Bonneville*. (U. S. Geological Survey, Monograph 1) Washington D. C., 1890.

Matthes, F. E. *Geologic History of Yosemite Valley*. (U. S. Geological Survey, Prof. Paper 160) Washington, D. C., 1930.

Zeuner, F. E. *The Pleistocene Period, Its Climate, Chronology and Faunal Succession*. London, Ray Society, 1945.

14 | GROUND WATER

WHERE DOES the water in wells come from? Why is water found only a few feet beneath the dry surface soil in many places but not even at several thousand feet in others? When air conditioning was introduced on Long Island and many new wells were drilled to obtain the cooling water, some of the wells soon became salty, and only salt water was found in many of the new ones. Where did the salt come from when the water had always been fresh before? The great limestone caverns of the Cumberland area extend for miles—so far that many are still unexplored. What made them? All of these questions have ultimately to do with underground water; water that geologists call **ground water.** It fills pores and cracks in soil and rock beneath the land surface. It comes to the surface in springs, and swells the volume of streams by seeping into them from their beds and banks. It can also be obtained by sinking wells.

Source of Ground Water

Water on the earth's surface has one obvious source—rain and snow—and, as Perrault showed long ago (Chap. 5) there are good reasons for considering this to be practically the only source. Rain and snow are also the ultimate source of nearly all water beneath the surface. Most soils and rocks contain voids and openings into which water can seep: tiny pores occur between the mineral grains; small tubules are left by the decay of grass roots, larger openings are formed by burrowing animals, and cracks are formed by the shrinkage of drying clays. Even well-consolidated rocks are riven by faults, joints, and intergranular openings into which water can penetrate. Some of the water that enters these openings after a rain remains near the surface, absorbed by the soil colloids, or held in the smaller voids by surface tension, or capillarity, the force that pulls water up a very slender tube and holds it there against the action of gravity. At least a part of the rain water, however, percolates deeper and deeper until it ultimately reaches a zone where all the pores in the rock are completely filled with water. Above this lies a zone where the openings in rock and soil are filled with air. At great depths there is a floor below which water cannot penetrate—where the openings in the rock are closed by compaction or are filled with minerals.

The Water Table

The name **water table** is given to the upper surface of the zone whose pores are filled with water. Above the water table the pores contain air, although discontinuous films and

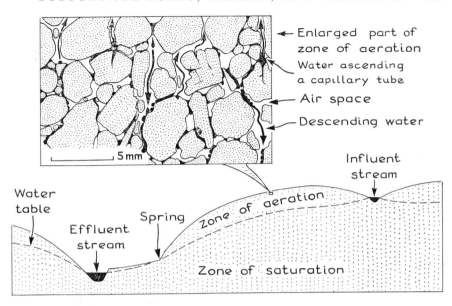

← Enlarged part of
zone of aeration
Water ascending
a capillary tube
Air space
Descending water

Figure 14-1.

Cross section showing the water table and its relationship to streams and a spring. The greatly enlarged inset shows the movement of water (black) in the zone of aeration.

irregular masses of water held by capillarity may cling to their walls (Fig. 14-1, *top*). This zone between the water table and the surface is called the **zone of aeration.** Here weathering and other chemical changes take place. Below the water table is the **zone of saturation** (Fig. 14-1).

In most places the water table is only a few feet, or a few dozen feet, below the ground surface, but in arid regions it may be hundreds of feet underground. In marshes the water table practically coincides with the ground surface, as it does at the edge of surface-water bodies such as lakes and streams. If many water wells have been drilled in a given area we can readily find the form of the water table below the ground surface and draw accurate contour maps of it by determining its level in the various wells. Such maps show that, in most areas, the water table is a somewhat flattened replica of the surface topography; it rises under the hills and sinks beneath the valleys, but is smoother than the land surface.

Subsurface Pores, Cracks, and Channels

If there are many large pores in the rock or soil below the water table, much water can be pumped from wells, because the water from openings in the nearby rock flows rapidly into the well and replenishes the water that is being extracted. If the pores are small and widely spaced, only a little water can be recovered by pumping, because replenishment is slow. The number and size—the aggregate volume —of the open spaces thus primarily determine the amount, and the rate of movement of available ground water.

Porosity and Permeability

Porosity is the ratio of pore volume to total volume, expressed as a percentage. Porosities of most uncemented clastic sediments range between 12 and 45 per cent, depending on the *shapes* of the grains, their *sorting* and *packing,* and the *degree of cementation* (Fig. 14-2).

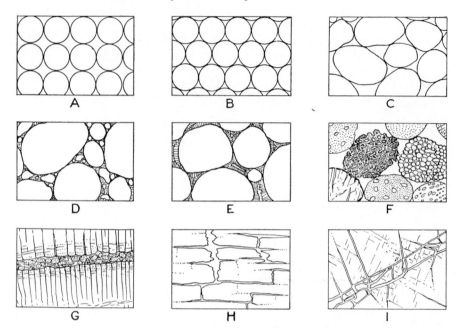

Figure 14-2.

Porosity in rocks. (A and B) The decrease in porosity due to compaction of spheres. (C) A natural sand with high porosity due to good sorting. (D) A second natural sand with low porosity due to poor sorting and a matrix of silt and clay. (E) Low porosity due to cementation. (F) Very high porosity produced by loose, well-sorted grains that are themselves porous. (G) Porous zones between lava flows. (H) Limestone rendered porous by solution along joints. (I) Massive rock rendered porous by fracturing.

Mineral and rock grains vary in shape from thin plates and irregular chips to nearly perfect spheres. The arrangement of the grains with respect to one another—the kind of packing, that is, whether they fit closely together or are stacked loosely—greatly affects the amount of pore space. As a rule, the packing is loose when a sediment is first deposited, and the pore space is relatively high. Compaction from the pressure of later deposited sediments then progressively reduces this space. Cementation (deposition of mineral matter in the pores) further reduces the pore space.

Spheres of uniform size in their closest packing have 26 per cent pore space. This is true whether the spheres are 1 millimeter in diameter, 5 feet in diameter, or any other size. Porosities greater than 26 per cent indicate irregular packing, or, more commonly,

that the grains are themselves porous. Shape, which of course strongly affects the tightness of packing, also affects porosity, but the presence of nonspherical grains may either raise or lower the porosity, depending on how tightly they pack with neighboring grains.

The total capacity of rock or soil to *hold* water is determined by the porosity, but the capacity to *yield* water to the pump depends on the size of the pores as well as on the total amount of pore space. Not all the water in the pores will flow toward a pumping well. Much is retained as water films stuck to the walls of the pores. In rocks with very small pores, practically all the water may be retained, even though the porosity is high. Laboratory measurements indicate that there is a fairly definite minimum size of pores—about 0.05 millimeter—through which water will move freely.

Sediments with smaller pores, such as clay, silt, and shale, are relatively impermeable even though their porosity may be high. **Permeability,** the capacity of a porous medium to transmit a liquid, and not porosity, is therefore the important physical property to be determined in estimating the yield of a water-bearing material. Permeability depends more on the size of the pore openings than on the percentage of pore space. A gravel with 20 per cent pore space is much more permeable to ground water than a clay with 35 per cent.

Aquifers

A body of rock or loose surface material that is permeable as well as porous, and so can yield water rapidly to wells, is called an **aquifer.** Most aquifers are sheets of sand or gravel, or beds of sandstone, limestone, or other permeable rock. Limestone, though granular, generally has very slight porosity; it transmits water not by intergranular flow but along fractures or along openings produced by weathering. A few aquifers are narrow sinuous bodies of gravel that fill former stream courses, but these are by no means as common as the popular expression "underground stream" indicates.

Perched Water

An aquifer may rest on an impermeable substratum that overlies unsaturated material above the normal water table. The water in such an aquifer is **perched.** It is prevented from percolating downward to the normal water table by the impermeable material beneath (Fig. 14-3).

Confined Water: Artesian Wells

A permeable sediment, such as a porous, coarse-grained, loosely compacted sandstone, may be overlain by an impermeable one, such as shale. If the rocks have been tilted and eroded, the permeable sediment may crop out in hills or mountains above the level of the surrounding country. Under these conditions, the ground water in the aquifer may be partly confined (some distance from the mountains, where it is overlain by shale) but easily replenished (in the mountains, where it appears at the surface). Such a situation is shown in Figure 14-4. Water enters the sandstone aquifer where it is exposed in the hills—at A, the intake area. The water table (t–t') within the aquifer of the intake area is higher than the ground surface at B, where the aquifer is confined beneath overlying shale. If a well (W_3)

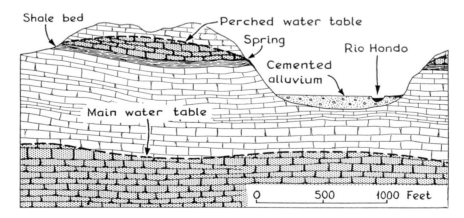

Figure 14-3.

Cross section of aquifers in porous limestone, perched on an impermeable shale bed, southeast New Mexico. Note that the Rio Hondo, also, is perched above the main water table. (After A. D. Fiedler and S. S. Nye, U. S. Geological Survey.)

is put down to this aquifer near B, the confined water will rise through the well under the pressure of the head of water from the intake area and flow out on the surface of the ground, making this an **artesian well.**

Artesian wells are often of great value, as they can furnish copious supplies of water even in very arid country. A dramatic example is furnished by the discovery of deep artesian water in the extremely dry southwestern part of South Dakota.

The early railroads crossing this arid region were large users of water. In 1905 N. H. Darton of the United States Geological Survey, who had just completed an investigation of ground water in the Great Plains region, recommended that the Burlington Railroad try for water in a deeply buried sandstone bed. The structure sections and geologic maps he had made indicated that by drilling at the town of Edgemont just south of the Black Hills, a Paleozoic aquifer that might be productive would be encountered at a depth of about 3,000 feet. After almost three years of old-fashioned churn drilling, a well flowing more than 400,000 gallons a day was developed at a depth within 31 feet of that predicted. Forty years later a new well, completed in the same aquifer after fifty days of rotary drilling, had an initial flow of almost 1,500,000 gallons per day, an unusually large yield from such an old and deeply buried sand, and very precious in this dry country.

The name "artesian" was originally restricted to flowing wells; it is now applied, however, to any well in which the water rises above the elevation of the aquifer penetrated, even if it does not reach the surface (see W_1 and W_2, Fig. 14-4).

Ground-Water Movement

The water that fills the pores below the water table is not stationary: like air masses of different height and density it moves slowly under the influence of gravity. The tendency is to lower the high points on the water table and either to raise the low points or else discharge water from them. If not replenished by rain, the water table would ultimately flatten out to a smooth surface.

Points of surface discharge, located where the water table intersects the ground surface, are called **springs** (Fig. 14-5). Most streams also mark *areas of discharge;* they lie in troughs on the water table toward which the ground water flows. Streams partly fed by ground water are called **effluent** (Fig. 14-1).

Streams that flow from mountains or other well-watered areas into deserts or semiarid regions, however, may lose water by percolation underground. Such **influent** streams leak water to the water table, and lie on ridges upon it (stream on the right in Fig. 14-1).

The rate and direction of movement of the water between two points on the water table

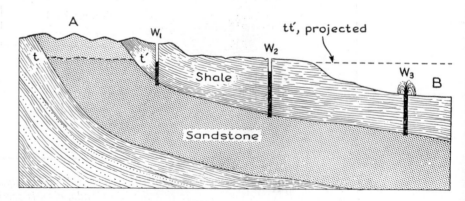

Figure 14-4.

Cross section showing a series of wells—W_1, W_2, W_3—penetrating a confined aquifer. The water table in the intake area is t–t'.

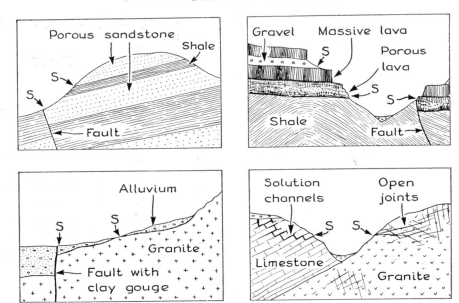

Figure 14-5.

Cross section showing likely locations for springs (S).

is determined by both the permeability of the rocks and the **hydraulic gradient,** which is the ratio between the difference of elevation, or head (H), and the horizontal distance between the two points (L). Ground-water gradients are usually low, such as a fall of 1 foot per 1,000 feet (0.001) or 10 feet per 1,000 (0.01).

Effect of Variations of Intake on Water Levels

For any given degree of permeability, the hydraulic gradient adjusts itself to the supply of water. If discharge into streams and other effluents is temporarily greater than the supply into the intake area, the water table flattens. In dry spells the water table sinks farther below the surface under the ground-water divides, reducing the hydraulic head and hence the discharge.

In arid western Texas, eastern New Mexico, and adjacent parts of old Mexico the water table is relatively flat, and in many places it lies 500 to 1,000 feet below the land surface. Large areas in that region lack permanent streams, though they may contain intermittent ones that flow upon perched bodies of ground water, or in natural flumes of cemented gravel formed where caliche has deposited from stream water as it evaporated under the desert sun.

Water Witching

Before the nineteenth century men thought that ground water flowed in definite underground streams just as surface water does. They reasoned that when one dug a well, if he were lucky, his well intersected one of these streams and produced a fine flow of water. A dry well, or one that produced only a little water, supposedly had failed to intercept any of the underground channels. Since one cannot see beneath the surface of the ground, the drilling of wells was always an uncertain operation, and in their doubt about where to dig for water, farmers often consulted "water witches" or "dowsers." Such people were supposedly endowed with supernatural powers that enabled them to discover the location of "underground streams." A belief in their ability to find water still persists in some localities. A dowser generally walks about with a forked stick (Fig. 14-6), tightly held, which dips violently when he crosses the channel of the supposed underground stream.

Figure 14-6.   Water witch or dowser of the sixteenth century. (Styled after old woodcuts.)

His success, if any, has no known scientific basis; but his probability of success is great because permeable rocks and soils that yield water are widespread.

Darcy's Law

The modern concepts of ground-water movement were discovered in the mid-nineteenth century. Almost all movements of ground water are so slow that they occur by laminar flow, whereas practically all surface streams are turbulent. Flow lines in laminar flow are smooth, continuous, and traceable. Investigation of the flow of water in pipes shows that for turbulent flow the velocity and discharge are approximately proportional to the square root of the hydraulic gradient, whereas in laminar flow the velocity and discharge vary directly as the hydraulic gradient. This fundamental law, as it applies to ground-water movement, was discovered and formulated in the 1850's by the French hydrologist Henry Darcy, during a study of the water supply of

the city of Dijon. Darcy's law may be stated as:

$$(1) \qquad\qquad V = PI$$

where

V = velocity of ground water.

P = coefficient of permeability—this is a measure of the ease with which water moves through a material and is determined by the character of the material through which the water moves. It is stated in terms of volume per unit of time passed by a unit cross-section under a hydraulic gradient of 1.

I = hydraulic gradient—the slope of the water table.

Geologists are usually more interested in the quantity of water in motion than in its velocity. Hence we usually replace the velocity in Darcy's law by a term that states the quantity of water moving per unit of time (Q) through a given cross-sectional area (A). Since $V = Q \div A$, we can write Darcy's law as $Q \div A = PI$, or

$$(2) \qquad\qquad Q = PIA$$

where

Q = quantity of water moving per unit of time (measured in gallons per day, cubic meters per day, etc.)

A = cross-sectional area through which water moves.

Darcy's Law, as thus stated, can also be used to determine the coefficient of permeability. If we measure the discharge of water from a well (Q) and know both the area of the holes in the casing through which the water enters the well (A) and the difference in elevation between the water in the well and the water at some higher point within the same water body (I), the coefficient of permeability is the only unknown in equation 2. By such measurements, we find that some aquifers have permeabilities several thousand times as great as those of others. Well yields show corresponding differences.

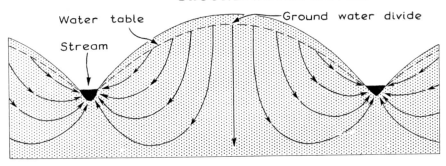

Figure 14-7.

Approximate flow pattern of ground water in uniformly permeable material. (After M. King Hubbert, Journal of Geology, *1940.)*

Rates of Ground-Water Movement

The movement of unconfined ground water through uniformly permeable material is shown diagrammatically in Figure 14-7, a section showing both ground-water divides and effluent stream levels. Some flow lines go deep, but little water follows these. The maximum velocities (and hence the greatest volumes of water transferred) are just below the water table, where the hydraulic gradients are steepest.

The actual velocities of ground-water movement, though almost everywhere low as compared to stream velocities, are highly variable. They even vary in different parts of a single body of water moving through rock of uniform permeability, as shown in Figure 14-7.

Mean or average rates of movement can be calculated from Darcy's Law, if the coefficient of permeability is known. Rate of flow can also be measured directly by introducing dyes or salts at one observation well and measuring the time elapsed until they appear at another. From such tests, O. E. Meinzer, an American authority on ground water motion, considered the flow of 50 feet per year in the Carrizo sandstone of Texas to be typical of many aquifers. Movements of 10 or 20 feet per day are sometimes attained in highly permeable materials, and velocities as high as 420 feet per day have been reported.

According to Darcy's equation, in materials of low permeability the gradient of the water table increases steeply as intake water is added locally to the mass of ground water. In materials of high permeability the water table is relatively flat, and hydraulic gradients may be only a few feet per mile.

Discharge of Ground Water into the Ocean

Along many coast lines, fresh ground water discharges directly onto the sea floor for some distance off the coast. Moreover, fresh ground water may also extend far below sea level beneath the shoreline (Fig. 14-8). The lighter, higher column of fresh water seems to be in static balance with the heavier sea water, like a foreign mass floating within it. A column of sea water 1,000 feet high can balance one of fresh water about 1,025 feet high. If, therefore, the surface of the water table near the ocean shore is 25 feet above sea level, fresh

Figure 14-8. Cross section showing fresh-water flow lines in relation to the contact with underground salt water. (After M. King Hubbert, Journal of Geology, *1940.)*

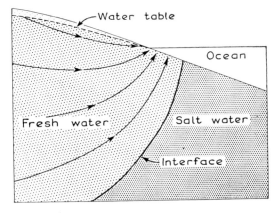

ground water might theoretically be recovered to a depth of 1,000 feet below sea level. But such a water body is not static; it is constantly discharging into the sea (Fig. 14-8). The friction of flow through the pores retards the spreading out of the fresh water, but if it were not constantly replenished from rainfall, the steep interface (see Fig. 14-8) separating salt and fresh water would soon flatten.

The body of fresh ground water under Oahu, one of the Hawaiian Islands, though hundreds of feet thick, is thinner than expected from the flotation hypothesis. Furthermore, the fresh water has no sharp interface but grades into salt water through a thick transition zone of brackish water. Perhaps the thinning of the fresh water body, and its mixing with salt water, has been caused by intermittent pumping from many large wells that exploit this large and valuable aquifer.

Drawdown by Pumping

A pumping well in an unconfined aquifer is a point of artificial discharge which disturbs the water table. We have already seen how the water table becomes adjusted to points and lines of natural discharge, such as springs and effluent streams. Similarly, removal of water through a well draws the water down adjacent to the well to produce a **cone of depression** in the water table (Fig. 14-9). This greatly increases the hydraulic gradient close to the well.

In the example shown in Figure 14-9, the pumping well removed water from moderately permeable alluvium in the valley of the Platte River. The undisturbed water table sloped eastward 6 or 7 feet per mile. The lowering of the water levels was determined in more than eighty observation wells drilled in eight radial lines extending to about 1,200 feet from the pumping well. Figure 14-9 is a section across the cone of depression produced by pumping. The lowering, or **drawdown,** at the well was 22 feet after 48 hours of pumping; this was accompanied by a lowering of 1 foot in the water table at a distance of 250 feet. Measurable lowering extended more than 1,200 feet from the pumping well. Flow lines toward the well must have extended at least this far laterally, and also some distance

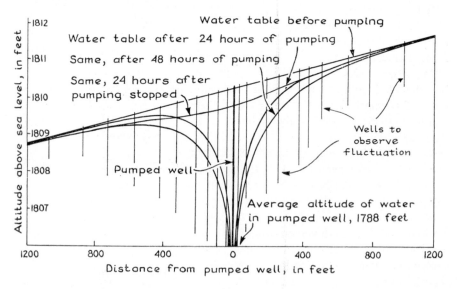

Figure 14-9.

Cross section (with vertical scale grossly exaggerated) showing the water table before, during, and after pumping from a well. Wells used to observe the fluctuations are indicated by vertical lines. (After L. K. Wenzel, in Hydrology, *courtesy of Dover Publications.)*

below the level of drawdown (compare with Fig. 14-7).

Effects analogous to the creation of a cone of depression are also observed in wells that tap a confined aquifer. If a group of artesian wells are capped so that no water escapes, the water in each well will exert a definite pressure against the top of the casing. If the cap of one well is opened so that the water begins to flow from it, a decline in pressure will soon be noted at nearby wells.

Composition of Ground Water

Ground water beneath swamps, peat bogs, and rain forests is always slightly acid because of the organic acids released into it from decaying vegetation. Where rain water passes slowly through limestone or even through decaying rocks that are only moderately calcium-rich, such as granite, it may dissolve enough calcium to become **hard water** ($CaCO_3 + H^+ \rightarrow Ca^+ + HCO_3^-$). The amount of calcium ion in hard waters in humid regions is only a small fraction of one per cent. Such water may also contain as much sodium ion as calcium ion, but the sodium ion is not easily precipitated and ordinarily goes unnoticed.

In arid regions, as we noted in Chapter 4, most of the water within a few feet of the earth's surface may be evaporated after each rain. Under such conditions, a large quantity of the relatively insoluble calcium carbonate is precipitated in the capillary fringe just above the water table as crusts of caliche. With more complete evaporation, even carbonates and sulfates of sodium may precipitate. Sodium-rich ground waters are toxic to plants, hence such "alkali soils" are nearly useless agriculturally. If such areas are drained, and the alkaline water flushed downward by heavy irrigation, they may be reclaimed for agricultural use.

Still other ground waters are salty. Such waters contain enough sodium chloride to make their taste unpleasant and to make them injurious to plants. Some salty ground waters are in whole or part sea water, infiltrated directly from the ocean. Salt water in deeply buried marine sedimentary rocks is presumably sea water entrapped at the time of deposition, and is called **connate water.** Connate waters rarely have exactly the same composition as the water in the present ocean. Most variations are probably due to dilution by ground water since burial, to concentration by evaporation before burial, to salt dissolved from salt beds in the rocks, and to chemical reactions with the enclosing rocks. In most areas, salinity increases with depth, probably because the more saline brines, however formed, are denser than the less saline and so seek the lowest possible level.

Ground Water in Carbonate Rocks

Solution Passages

Rain water, and especially the slightly acid ground water of humid regions, is so effective a solvent of limestone that it enlarges cracks and pores and dissolves tunnels, irregular passages, and even large caverns along joints or other openings in this rock. Carbonate rocks may dissolve so extensively that much of the surface drainage goes underground through vertical tubular passages called **sinks** (Fig. 14-10) and discharges through caves (Fig. 14-11). Sinks and caves, of course, develop very slowly. Water percolating down a crack in limestone enlarges the opening by dissolving the rock: weathering, rainwash, and gravitational collapse of the walls then widen the opening at the surface, enabling it to trap more and more surface water, which, in turn, causes more rapid solution of the limestone walls. The vertical sink thus formed may extend completely through the limestone bed, discharging at its base into horizontal openings and caverns formed where the limestone has been dissolved along its contact with the underlying rock. In time, the entire bed of limestone becomes honeycombed with interconnected sinks and caverns. A part of the dissolved calcium carbonate is redeposited

Figure 14-10.   *A large sink, with alluvial floor, in limestone, Karst region of Yugoslavia. (Photo from Th. Benzinger, Stuttgart.)*

within the caves as masses of **dripstone,** which may hang from the roof of the cave in bizarre icicle-like forms (Fig. 14-12).

The easy movement of water through a cavernous limestone aquifer and the flatness of its water table have often been demonstrated by pumping tests. At the Los Lamentos mine, in Mexico, about a hundred miles southeast of El Paso, Texas, two years of constant pumping did not lower the water table appreciably, and the rich ore body had to be abandoned when the water table was reached. Many other mines have found the same bar to successful operation.

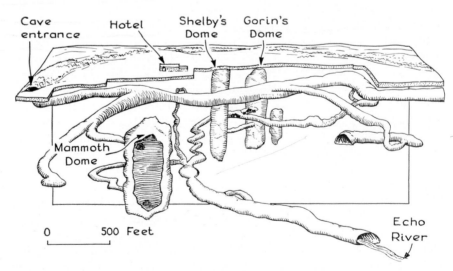

Figure 14-11.

Diagram showing part of the Mammoth Cave system, Kentucky. (After A. K. Lobeck, Geomorphology, *McGraw-Hill Book Co., 1939.)*

Karst Topography

Some limestone or dolomite regions have few or no surface streams. The rain seeps underground at once through sinks and joints, and flows through large and small caverns, cascading at intervals to still lower levels until it reaches the water table far below the surface. Water may reappear at the surface in giant springs where the walls or floors of deep valleys cut the water table. Such an area of sinks and underground drainage is called a **karst** region (from the Karst district of the Dinaric Alps in Yugoslavia). Other well-known karst regions are the Causses Plateau of southern France west of the Rhone River, and parts of the Cumberland Plateau in Kentucky and Tennessee.

The topography of a karst region differs from that of an area with normal surface drainage. Instead of a system of slopes closely adjusted to surface streams, a karst region is pock-marked by large and small depressions (Fig. 14-13). The smaller depressions are the upper ends of sinks, some of which have been enlarged at the surface by weathering, rainwash, and downslope movements (Fig. 14-10). Larger openings appear where the roofs of caverns have collapsed. The main rivers gain most of their water from numerous large springs. A stream may disappear underground in a sink in one valley, and then boil forth as a huge spring in a neighboring valley.

Karst drainage has influenced men's actions for ages. Crops are poor on the dry plateaus, lush in the well-watered valleys. In southern France, great springs that emerge at the edge of the Rhone Valley have determined the sites of towns, many of which have flourished since remote antiquity.

Figure 14-12.   Dripstone in an Indiana limestone cavern. (Photo by Arch Addington.)

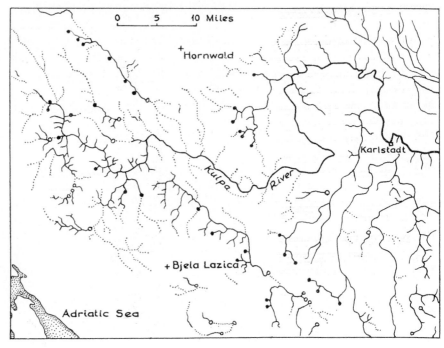

Figure 14-13. ⤙⤙ Stream ⋯⋯ Dry valley • Karst spring ○ Stream sink

> *Map of part of the Karst region in Yugoslavia. The drainage is partly underground, as shown by stream sinks in small, partly dry valleys, and great springs in larger, deeper valleys. (After N. Krebs, 1928.)*

Solution and Cementation by Ground Water

In general, solution is more important above the water table; deposition and cementation below. The extreme effects of solution in carbonate rocks have already been described. But carbonate rocks are not the only ones that dissolve; in the long lapse of geologic time even minerals that the chemist regards as highly insoluble are appreciably dissolved. Grains of garnet in sandstones may be pitted and etched by ground water, and pyroxene and amphibole may even be completely dissolved. Fossil shells composed of calcite are commonly leached out of shales and sandstones, leaving open cavities that may later be filled to form "casts" that faithfully preserve the fossil form. Casts of soluble crystals such as halite or pyrite also are common.

In Chapter 3 we described the cementa-tion of sand to form sandstone. Calcite cements many sandstones, but the reason it is deposited in the pores of a sandstone is somewhat obscure: certainly it is not possible for water to evaporate and deposit calcite far below the water table as it does in forming caliche and dripstone above it. One possible explanation is that the decreased pressure on bicarbonate-rich ground water as it rises near the surface, allows carbon dioxide to bubble out and escape, and calcite to precipitate. Some sandstones are locally cemented around shell fragments or other nuclei, the calcite grows out from these cores to form ball-like masses called **concretions.** Experiments show that slow precipitation of any material from solution generally results in deposition on existing crystals rather than development of new centers of crystallization.

Ground water also deposits many other substances. Silica (as opal, chalcedony, or quartz), and iron oxide (as limonite or hematite), may fill or coat cavities in rocks. Many other minerals, such as feldspar, mica, and chlorite, form in rocks at depths of two or three miles, where temperatures are close to the boiling point of water at the earth's surface.

Ground-Water Supplies in the United States

Water supply vitally concerns inhabitants of arid regions—indeed, even in the humid areas of western Europe and eastern North America industrial demands tax all available water supplies. The quantity of fresh ground water recoverable at any one place is a matter of economic importance. Estimates indicate that the amount of ground water is much less than the amount of water in the oceans, but greater than the amount in the atmosphere, or even than that which falls as rain and snow in a single year. In almost any area wells will yield some water, but rocks of low porosity yield little, and nonpermeable rocks, even if porous, yield negligible amounts.

Large yields of ground water come chiefly from unconsolidated surface formations, mostly of Pleistocene and Recent age, and secondarily from older, partly consolidated, but permeable, sediments or lavas. The principal unconsolidated aquifers are: (1) *alluvial gravels and sands that fill deep interior basins,* (2) *glacial outwash sands and gravels,* (3) *the coarser parts of deltaic and other coastal plain deposits, and* (4) *sands and silts beneath river floodplains.*

Interior basins filled with unconsolidated sediments are common in the western third of the United States. In much of this arid to semiarid region, the quantity of ground water sets definite limits on population growth. Interior basins normally supply about one-half the ground water used in the United States. In California alone, several large and productive basins yielded, in 1948, enough ground water to cover ten million acres to a depth of one foot—about 35 per cent of all the ground water used in the United States.

Glacial outwash sands and gravels lie slightly south of the relatively less permeable Pleistocene till sheets or are interbedded with them. Glacial gravels grade into river-floodplain and deltaic gravels and sands, notably along the Mississippi River. Large floodplain aquifers are also found on the Great Plains, and permeable coastal plain deposits extend from New Jersey to Texas.

Among older, more consolidated rocks, the chief aquifers are: (1) *permeable sandstones,* (2) *well-jointed volcanic rocks,* (3) *cavernous limestone or dolomite,* and, more rarely, (4) *fissured crystalline rocks* such as quartzite or shattered granite. Sandstone aquifers supply much ground water in the Dakotas and elsewhere in the northern Mississippi Valley and also in Texas and other regions. Basalt flows are important aquifers in the Pacific Northwest and in Hawaii. In New England, though the glaciofluvial gravels yield much water, even more is derived from fissures in the metamorphic gneisses and schists.

The numerous cracks and cavities in many volcanic rocks make them almost as permeable as cavernous limestone or dolomite. The most productive springs in the United States are in basalt flows along a fifty-mile stretch of the Snake River in Idaho. Into the Snake these springs discharge 5,000 cubic feet of water per second, two-thirds as much as the average flow of the Mississippi at St. Paul, Minnesota. Cavernous limestones yield abundantly in Florida, in parts of the Cumberland Plateau, and in the Great Valley of Virginia and West Virginia.

The aquifers of three highly productive areas will be described in the following pages.

Ground Water of Long Island

Long Island has no large streams, partly because it is small and partly because infiltration is so easy. It has been estimated that of the 40 to 50 inches of annual precipitation in west central Long Island, 20 per cent goes to surface runoff, 40 per cent to ground water, and 40 per cent to evaporation and transpiration. Lacking adequate local surface supplies, the 4,500,000 inhabitants of Long Island depend on ground water and on surface water brought to the Brooklyn and Queens sections of New York City from the mainland. About 300,000,000 gallons of ground water per day is pumped from wells—a quantity a little less than that imported from the mainland. Nearly three-fourths of the ground water comes from glacial outwash sands and gravels, and one-fourth from unconsolidated Cretaceous sands that lie at a greater depth.

Among the Cretaceous sands, the most productive is the basal bed, 100 to 250 feet thick. It is a clean quartz sand, practically uncemented, and is overlain by impermeable shale. The Cretaceous sands and shales are unconformably overlain by glacial sediments as much as 400 feet thick. Interbedded Pleistocene till, sand, and gravel form two ridges, one near the northwest shore and the other along the middle of the island. The outwash plains of sand and gravel that are the chief aquifers lie between and south of the ridges.

In a small area in Brooklyn, excessive pumping lowered the water table in the outwash sands until it was below sea level. The water table was from sea level to 15 feet above it (zero to 50 feet below the ground surface) in 1903, but by 1943 it had been drawn down to a maximum depth of 34 feet below sea level. This reversed the hydraulic gradient, and salt water from the sea invaded the margins of the aquifer. The State of New York now requires that water pumped for cooling and air-conditioning be returned after use to the aquifer from which it was withdrawn. By 1946 more than two hundred recharge wells were returning water underground in the urban portion of Long Island. In the rural areas, several large surface recharge basins, where storm and industrial waste water could be held until it seeped into the ground, had also been established. Total recharge in the summer of 1944 amounted to 60,000,000 gallons a day. The warmer recharge water raised the ground-water temperature a few degrees, making it less valuable for cooling, but the recharge wells and water basins served their main purpose—the water table no longer fell rapidly, and salt-water inflow was almost stopped.

Ground-Water Basin in Southern California

In semiarid southwestern California, several large interior basins contain alluvial deposits across which intermittent surface streams flow to the sea, charging the alluvium with ground water on the way. A section through one of them is shown in Figure 14-14. The basin is filled to a depth of 500 to 1,200 feet with alluvial fans that have grown southwestward from the San Gabriel mountains to form a compound apron extending almost entirely across the basin. The heads of the fans consist of gravels, and the slope of their surfaces and the initial dips of their strata are

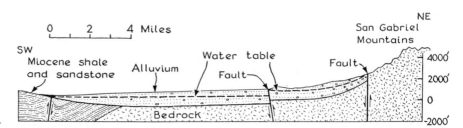

Figure 14-14.

Section across the Santa Ana ground-water basin, California, showing the water-bearing Pleistocene alluvium and the effect of a fault on the position of the water table. (After California Division of Water Resources, Bull. 45, 1934.)

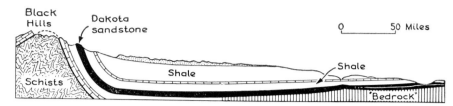

Figure 14-15.

Section through the Dakota artesian aquifer, from the intake area in the Black Hills of western South Dakota to northern Iowa. The vertical scale is tremendously exaggerated. (After N. H. Darton, U. S. Geological Survey.)

as great as 9 degrees. Farther out on the fans the gravels grade into, and are interbedded with, sands and silts, and the angle of slope decreases. Over parts of the deposits, relatively impermeable soils have formed, and in several places these have been buried by renewed upbuilding of the fans. The strata of permeable gravels and coarse sands between less permeable soils and silts make a rather complex set of aquifers. On the lower parts of the apron, some wells were originally artesian: the aquifers are confined by fine sediments or soil zones within the fans, and the initial dip is great enough to give a good hydraulic head.

Many basins in California are broken by faults so recent that they cut through the alluvium. Some of these are effective barriers to ground water movement because impermeable clay gouge is smeared along the fault planes. At the fault shown in Figure 14-14, the water table drops 400 feet—making a difference of many dollars in pumping costs to those who must obtain their water from wells on the side of the fault where the water table is deeper.

In this populous but arid region, the winter flood waters are diverted onto complex spreading grounds underlain by coarse gravel, thus giving the water a chance to infiltrate instead of flowing on to the sea. These man-made spreading grounds serve the same purpose as the recharge basins on Long Island.

It should be noted that lowering of the water level in a basin by pumping is not wholly a misfortune. Surface or subsurface outflow from the basin is decreased or even stopped

and the water that would have flowed by becomes available for use. Moreover, the partly emptied subsurface reservoir can also take in a larger recharge during the rainy season.

Dakota Sandstone Artesian Aquifer

The great Dakota sandstone basin is the largest and most important source of artesian water in the United States. It extends over much of North Dakota, South Dakota, Nebraska, and parts of adjacent states. At least 15,000 wells have been drilled into this Cretaceous sandstone, which is generally somewhat less than a hundred feet thick and is overlain by hundreds or even thousands of feet of other sediments, mostly impermeable shales. As shown in Figure 14-15, the principal intake areas are at the west, in the upturned zone along the edges of the Black Hills and Rocky Mountains. The sandstone is not a simple aquifer. It includes a widespread shale bed near its eastern margin, dividing the sandstone into upper and lower parts, and the compositions and pressures of the artesian waters vary in detail. Movement of ground water from the intake area also appears to be interrupted locally by relatively impervious parts of the formation. Because of heavy use, pressures in the aquifer have decreased progressively since the first well was drilled in 1882.

The Dakota sandstone is not the only productive aquifer in its area. We have already mentioned the deeper Paleozoic aquifer whose depth and productivity were so accurately foretold by Darton.

Economic and Legal Aspects of Ground-Water Use

Where there is not enough surface water and ground water to supply everyone's needs, disputes have arisen between individuals, communities, and states. Many such disputes have been carried to the courts. Applying and broadening the rule that the owner of the land surface also owns everything beneath the surface, the courts have held that all the owners of land above a ground-water basin are considered to have joint ownership of the basin. Water may not be exported beyond the basin's surface area without good reason. In addition, the principle of best use has been established, as in a dispute between cattlemen, who wish to preserve feeble springs, and truck gardeners, who wish to pump the abundant ground water of the same area and put it to more productive use. In some states —for example, New York and Maryland— the permission of state authorities is required for the drilling of large wells, and return of used water to the aquifer may be required. Ground water is an important public commodity, and its use now requires regulation by well-informed public officials.

FACTS, CONCEPTS, TERMS

GROUND WATER IS RAIN WATER THAT FILLS OPEN-
    INGS IN SOIL AND ROCK
THE WATER TABLE
    Zone of aeration
    Zone of saturation
RELATION OF WATER TABLE TO STREAMS, LAKES,
    AND MARSHES
POROSITY AND PERMEABILITY
PERCHED WATER; CONFINED WATER
GROUND WATER MOVES UNDER THE INFLUENCE
    OF GRAVITY
    Hydraulic gradient
    Darcy's Law: $Q = PIA$
NATURAL DISCHARGE OF GROUND WATER
    Springs
    Effluent and influent streams

    Discharge into the ocean
ARTIFICIAL DISCHARGE OF GROUND WATER
    Cone of depression around pumping wells
    Pressure drop in artesian wells analogous to
        cone of depression
SOLUTION AND PRECIPITATION BY GROUND WATER
    Solution channels, caves, and caverns in car-
        bonate rocks
        Karst topography
        Formation of dripstone
    Slow solution of relatively impermeable min-
        erals
    Cementation of sandstones
PRODUCTIVE AQUIFERS OF THE UNITED STATES
    In unconsolidated deposits
    In consolidated but permeable rocks

QUESTIONS

1. Draw sketches showing several geologic conditions that could result in the formation of a spring.

2. Draw one well-labeled cross section showing all of the features listed below:

    a. An area of rounded hills with two through-flowing streams: one with a floodplain, the other downcutting far above grade.

    b. Two deep but dry ravines.

    c. The position of the normal water table.

    d. A perched water table.

    e. A swamp

    f. Two wells of equal depth: one with water, the other dry.

3. A group of large fresh-water springs emerge on the sea floor about half a mile off the mountainous coast of Ecuador. Show by a well-labeled diagram how this is possible.

4. Amphibole and garnet grains are abundant

in well-cemented concretions from a sandstone, but the remaining, poorly cemented sandstone contains only a few etched grains of these minerals. How do you account for this?

5. Compare the drawdown at the test well near the Platte River (p. 262) with that at the Los Lamentos mine (p. 264) and account for the difference.

6. How can you tell an area of karst topography from the hummocky surface of a large landslide or debris flow?

7. Large springs are common in areas underlain by basalt, but almost nonexistent in areas of granite. Why?

8. How can ground-water basins be artificially recharged from waste water at the surface?

9. If water is neither moving through an aquifer, nor being discharged from it, can there be a hydraulic gradient? Explain, using a diagram.

SUGGESTED READINGS

Hubbert, M. King. *The Theory of Ground Water Motion,* Journal of Geology, Vol. 48 (1940), pp. 785-944.

Meinzer, O. E. *Ground Water in the United States: A Summary.* (U. S. Geological Survey, Water Supply Paper 836-D) Washington, D. C., 1939, pp. 157-229.

Meinzer, O. E., editor. *Hydrology. Physics of the Earth: No. 9.* (National Research Council) New York, Dover Publications, 1942.

Tolman, C. F. *Ground Water.* New York, McGraw-Hill, 1937.

Veatch, A. C., *et al. Underground Water Resources of Long Island, New York.* (U. S. Geological Survey, Prof. Paper 44) Washington, D. C., 1906.

15 | DESERTS

DESERT REGIONS are barren because there is not enough water available to support a continuous cover of vegetation. The rugged angular hills, cliffed canyons, and pebble- or sand-covered plains of the desert contrast sharply with the smoothly rounded hills and curving transitional slopes familiar in more humid country (compare Figs. 15-1 and 12-25). To a visitor from a well-watered region, the desert at first seems to have been molded by forces different from those of his homeland. The contrasts, however, are not a result of the operation of different agencies, they reflect only the differences in the results achieved by streams and downslope movements under different climatic conditions.

About one-sixth of the land area of the earth is desert. The greatest deserts lie in the subtropical belts of high atmospheric pressure where the winds are dry, clouds are few, precipitation is low, and evaporation high. Some great deserts, like those of central Asia and parts of western North America, lie in "rain shadows" behind high mountain ranges above which the clouds cannot rise without precipitating most of their rain.

Climatic Controls

In most great subtropic deserts such as the Sahara, the average rainfall is less than four inches per year. A year or more may pass without any rainfall at all. But the absolute amount of rainfall does not alone control the amount of vegetation. For example, the annual rainfall (5 or 6 inches) at Point Barrow on the Arctic coast of Alaska is nearly as low as that at Yuma, Arizona, yet the ground at Point Barrow is sodden with water and matted with vegetation, whereas at Yuma the soil is parched and the few plants are highly specialized in drought resistance. The contrast is largely due to the low rate of evaporation in the Arctic, though other factors, among them a high water table perched on permafrost, also aid plant growth.

Some writers divide arid regions into **steppes,** where scattered bushes and short-lived grasses furnish a scanty pasturage, and true deserts, where vegetation is sparse or absent. On this basis, most deserts of North America are steppes. There are, of course, continuous transitions from extreme deserts, through steppes, to humid regions.

Interior Drainage

Only the greatest rivers, like the Nile, Indus, Colorado, and Niger, are able to persist through deserts to the sea. Most desert streams dwindle by evaporation until the remaining water sinks into the ground or collects in a series of stagnant pools, a salt lake, or an alkali mud flat (Fig. 15-2). The drainage system of the desert is consequently not integrated into larger and larger tributaries that feed one or more trunk rivers, as in humid regions. Instead, it generally consists of many small stream systems, each of which ends in a closed basin or disappears on a desert plain. Such unintegrated **interior drainage** is characteristic of deserts.

The water table generally lies far deeper in deserts than in humid regions. Rainfall in the deserts, as in most humid areas, is greater at high elevations than at low. After a rain, rills and even rushing torrents rise in the desert mountains, but quickly shrink and disappear on the plains below. Yet, although most stream courses are dry except for a few hours or at most a few days a year, deserts show unmistakable evidence that stream action is the most important element in molding the landscape. Barren mountains scarred by stream gullies and plains built by stream deposits are the characteristic features of deserts.

Stream deposits are especially conspicuous in deserts (Fig. 15-1). Most desert storms are local, and the streams they generate run for only a few hours. Therefore most of the sediment is not transported to the sea, as in a humid area, but is carried only a short distance and then dumped in alluvial cones at the mouth of mountain canyons. The cones grow until they merge with those of adjacent canyons to form great alluvial aprons along the mountain bases (Figs. 12-28 and 15-3). These compound alluvial aprons, or **bahadas,** flatten gradually toward the center of the valley and merge imperceptibly with the valley floor, to which the streams, decreased by evaporation and infiltration into the permeable ground, can carry only the finer material.

Closed depressions on the desert surface are generally not filled to overflowing with water as are the lake basins in a humid country. The water that gathers in them after periods of heavy rain forms only temporary lakes, which evaporate during the dry season, leaving a sun-baked floor of clay, silt, and salt called a **playa** (Fig. 15-2). A few playa lakes may persist for several years after an unusually wet season. Typical playas are the Black Rock Desert of northwest Nevada and the floor of Death Valley. Although Great Salt Lake is perennial and thus not strictly a playa, it fluctuates widely with wet and dry

Figure 15-1.   *Broad alluvial plains between desert mountains, Salton Desert, California. Belt of small sand dunes in foreground. The straight black line is a railroad. (Airplane photo by Robert O. Frampton and John Shelton, Claremont, California.)*

Figure 15-2. *North Alvord playa, southeastern Oregon. The irregular dark patches on the white playa surface are wet ground. The straight mountain fronts to the upper left are fault scarps. (Airplane photo by Richard E. Fuller.)*

seasons, so that the flat western part of its bed—the Bonneville Salt Flat—has all the features of a true playa. When a playa lake dries up, the material dissolved in the water is, of course, deposited as crystallized salts, among which halite and various carbonates and sulfates of sodium are most abundant. The "alkali flats" of many arid regions are coated with such deposits.

Geologic Processes in Deserts

Geologic processes in deserts differ from those in humid regions primarily because of (1) the lack of vegetation, which greatly influences erosion, especially minor details of land sculpture, and (2) the intermittent stream flow and general lack of integrated drainage to the sea.

Weathering

Rocks disintegrate and decompose in the desert, though more slowly than in humid regions because of the paucity of moisture and of organic acids in the soil. We have already seen that an Egyptian obelisk moved to New York weathered more in 50 years than it had in 3,500 years in Egypt (Chap. 4).

Because of the slowness of weathering and the exposure of the barren ground to rain-wash and wind, fine-grained residual soils are rare. The fine rich soil of lower Egypt, flooded annually by the Nile, and that of Iraq, where the alluvium of the Tigris and Euphrates have supported civilization for centuries, is transported. Most of the weathering that produced the soil minerals took place in the humid headwater regions. Limestone, which dissolves readily and generally forms lowlands in humid climates, makes bold ridges in deserts. This may be partly because joint blocks spalled from its outcrops dissolve slowly and therefore protect the slopes, and partly because percolating ground water evaporates near the surface and redeposits its dissolved calcite, thus sealing the openings in the limestone.

Rainsplash and Rillwash

Besides the few permanent or intermittent streams, the principal mechanisms of rock transport in the desert are rainsplash, rillwash, and sheetfloods.

Desert plants are so scattered that their roots bind together only a small part of the surface material. Rain drops strike the ground directly, their impact unbroken by leaves and twigs. They splash fine fragments of rock and soil into the air and these dislodged particles fall and roll downhill. Anyone who has noticed mud and sand splashed onto a board resting on a garden plot after a light rain can readily imagine the effects of rainsplash during a heavy rainstorm in a barren desert. Silt, sand, and even small chips of rock are knocked downhill. During a heavy rain, small rills soon form. Rainwash coursing down them carries mud, silt, sand, and, as the rills enlarge, even gravel and boulders. These streams carry much more material than corresponding rills in a humid region where plant roots protect the soil from erosion. In the desert this material is not swept out to sea, but is generally left stranded after only a short journey, helping to fill previously eroded channels. Newly exposed bedrock is made accessible to weathering by cutting of the gullies, and it sheds new chips and grains into the rill courses. Little effluent water is available to keep the channel clear. If no rain heavy enough to produce a running stream falls for some years, the channel may lose its identity by being blocked with boulders and filled with fine debris that rolls down from the walls.

Mudflows and Sheetfloods

From time to time—perhaps only once in a decade, or even a century—intense rains pour down in deserts. There are the so-called "cloudbursts," during which several inches of rain may fall in an hour. Most of them cover only a small area; although over a few square miles a tremendous downpour may take place, little or no rain falls only a few miles away. The torrent from a cloudburst quickly digs gullies in the long-stable slopes, strips off the loose debris, and carries away all the sediment stranded in former rill channels. Rapidly gaining both volume and load, it races down the canyon as a wall of debris-laden water so charged with mud and sand that it forms a turbid fluid far denser than water alone—a viscous muddy sludge capable of buoying up huge blocks and boulders as it rolls downstream. Such a flash flood, pouring down Cajon Pass, California, after a cloudburst, overwhelmed a freight train, carried the engine more than a mile down the canyon, and buried it so deeply beneath mud and boulders that it could be found only by using a sensitive magnet. Such viscous mudflows may travel completely out of an area of heavy rains before they reach the alluvial fans at the foot of a mountain. There the water sinks into the fan and the mudflow grinds to a halt, sometimes with a steep frontal scarp several feet high. Excavations show such deposits to be heterogeneous piles of rock, sand, and clay, almost unsorted by size or shape. They greatly resemble unstratified glacial drift.

Loose silt, sand, and rock fragments are so abundant on desert fans that water flowing over them is soon loaded to capacity. As was pointed out in Chapter 12, it is therefore unable to cut deeply into the surface. Diverted by cobbles and boulders and by jams of floating plant fragments and scattered clumps of vegetation, the water spreads widely in a plexus of small braided channels, or it may cover the whole surface in a film a few inches deep, forming a **sheetflood.** When it sinks in or evaporates, the sheetflood leaves a coating of mud and silt to dry in the desert sun.

Downslope Movements

Downslope movements produce somewhat different results in deserts than in humid areas. Although weathering is relatively slow, many joint blocks have weathered so long that they are rotten and fall apart when they tumble from cliffs. Talus piles therefore form only beneath steep cliffs of rock that is not easily weathered, such as quarzite, chert, or limestone. Both steep and gentle slopes may be mantled with fallen boulders and chips, but most of these are only "one boulder thick," with the bedrock visible beneath them. The boulders are ultimately swept away by cloudbursts or reduced by slow weathering to grains small enough to be carried away by rills.

Every desert occasionally undergoes violent downpours during which runoff is rapid and great. Nevertheless, because such downpours are soon over, great masses of water-soaked soil and rock like those responsible for the Gros Ventre slide (Chap. 11) rarely develop in deserts. In fact, the presence of large ancient landslides and debris flows in Arizona is considered strong evidence of a former more humid climate.

Relation of Slopes to Structure

The lack of soil and vegetation affects downslope movement and other kinds of desert erosion in still another way. As the loose surface material is not effectively bound by roots, it does not creep as a mass and consequently does not soften contrasts in steepness and roughness of the surface slopes as it does in moist climates. The steepness of the slopes is apparently determined by the size of the joint blocks yielded by the bedrock—slopes are steep where blocks are large, gentle where they are small. Sandstones and shales that break down into small grains have gentle slopes unless masked by boulders that have rolled upon them from above. Basalt and quartzite stand in cliffs whose bases are hidden under large talus blocks. Even minor differences in particle size are accurately reflected by the changes in slope developed on different rocks (see Figs. 5-13 and 9-6). Abrupt changes in slope at the boundaries of different rock masses are the rule in desert hills and mountains, in marked contrast to the blurred and transitional slope changes characteristic of regions where soil creep is active (compare Figs. 9-5 and 12-25). In the

deserts no curving transitional slopes link hillsides with valley floors and round off the summits. Steep slopes remain steep, and even on the wide desert plains isolated buttes left after erosion of great volumes of rock rise with characteristic abruptness, their slopes adjusted to the size of the coarse particles weathered from them (Figs. 15-3, *bottom*, and 12-26).

Evolution of Desert Land Forms

The deformation of the earth's crust may disrupt pre-existing drainage courses in deserts just as in other regions; so, also, may rapidly growing alluvial fans, mudflows, volcanic eruptions, or even roof-collapse of limestone caverns. Basins thus formed range from enormous areas like the Caspian depression, the Dead Sea trough, or the basin of Great Salt Lake, down to wind-carved hollows a few feet across. Because of high evaporation the basins do not fill with water but they do become centers of interior drainage.

Every such closed basin is a local base level for the tributary area. Sediment brought to it cannot escape and slowly builds up the basin floor, gradually raising the base level. This, and the dwindling of the streams by evaporation and infiltration, causes the stream courses near the center of the basin to acquire flatter gradients, and as a result the streams can carry less sediment. They therefore tend to steepen their gradients by depositing material upstream, on the lower and middle parts of their fans. But while sedimentation is filling the basins, erosion continues in the mountains, lowering the headward portions of the stream courses, until the streams begin to cut down into the heads of their fans.

Governed by these conditions, the topography of desert areas where crustal deformation has been fairly recent geologically (as shown by deformation of late Tertiary or Pleistocene deposits) comprises three main kinds of land forms: (1) relatively steep mountain slopes of bare rock and loose chips, (2) bahada slopes made up of coalescing alluvial fans along the mountain bases, and (3) playa floors covered with fine silts, clays, and various salts left behind by evaporation of the water upon them (Fig. 15-3, *top,* and Fig. 15-4, *top*). These three land forms abound in Utah, Nevada, and southeastern Oregon.

As we have noted, slopes in desert mountains are little modified by soil creep—each segment of a slope is adjusted to the size of the joint blocks or other particles loosened by weathering. The foot of a slope slowly retreats as the bedrock weathers down to sizes that can be moved by streams on the bahada below. Thus the base of the mountain gradually moves back from its original position and the whole slope above retreats but maintains a fairly uniform front. The sharp break between bahada and mountain slope remains; it is not rounded off, as in humid regions, by soil creep.

As the base level rises, sheetfloods and braiding streams build up the lower parts of the fans while rainwash and rills slowly lower their upper parts. Lateral swings of the streams emerging from the mountain canyons wear away the spurs of the interstream ridges and the higher parts of the fans are planed off as the streams meander across them. The lower ends of the interstream ridges are also reduced by rillwash as the mountain front retreats, and are slowly regraded to slopes almost identical with those of the frontal fans. A broad, gently sloping surface, called a **pediment,** is thus carved on the bedrock at the foot of the mountain slope. This surface is covered with a thin and discontinuous veneer of gravel in slow transit toward the valley. At such a stage the desert landscape is composed of four main elements: (1) the mountains, whose slopes are about as steep as in the earlier stage described above, (2) the pediment, or planed-off surface of bedrock, at whose junction with the mountains there is an abrupt break in slope, (3) the

bahada, composed of the old fan deposits regraded to a lower surface which blends imperceptibly upslope into the pediment and downslope into (4) the playa (Fig. 15-3, *middle,* and Fig. 15-4, *middle*). This stage of development of the desert landscape is widely represented in southeastern Arizona and southern New Mexico, areas in which geologically recent crustal disturbances have been mild.

The ephemeral streams may eventually fill the basin with their deposits and flow over the rim into an adjoining basin, thereby integrating two small drainage systems. As erosion continues, streams draining to lower closed basins or to the sea continue to grow headward, just as they do in humid regions. Such streams successively capture higher basins and ultimately regrade them to lower levels. The main streams thus grow longer and longer, and in time their long profiles become graded throughout, even though no single storm may produce enough rain to cause them to flow along their full lengths at any one time. It is clear that this process of drainage integration and regrading of higher basins to lower levels must result in the scouring out of old deposits from the higher basins. As the base level lowers, such materials, like the bedrocks of the original topography, are eroded into slopes appropriate to the size of their component particles. Because these deposits are poorly consolidated and readily eroded, pediments generally develop rapidly across them and spread widely at the expense of older bahada slopes. In this stage of desert erosion, playas are absent (if the drainage is external) or sparse (if trunk streams have not succeeded in extending through the region to the sea); bahadas are relatively much less extensive; mountains have shrunk; and pediments cover most of the area (see Fig. 15-3, *bottom,* and Fig. 15-4 *bottom*). This is the stage represented in the United States by large parts of southwestern Arizona, where the Gila and Colorado rivers form a slowly lowering base level for the local streams, and where

Figure 15-3. *Three stages in the erosion of desert mountains.* Top: *Panamint Range, California, showing alluvial fans at the foot of only moderately eroded fault block.* Center: *Ibex Mountains, California, showing broad pediment embaying deeply eroded range.* Bottom: *Cima Dome, California, showing a broad graded surface above which rise a few residuals of former larger mountains. See Figure 15-4. (Photos by Eliot Blackwelder.)*

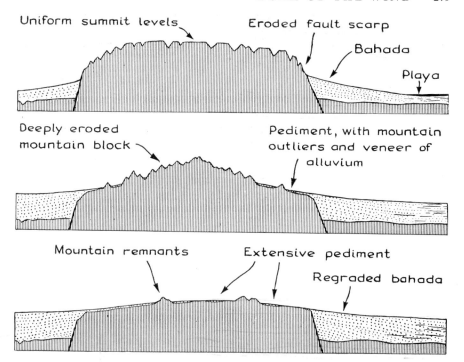

Uniform summit levels

Eroded fault scarp

Bahada

Playa

Deeply eroded
mountain block

Pediment, with mountain
outliers and veneer of
alluvium

Mountain remnants

Extensive pediment

Regraded bahada

Figure 15-4.

Diagrammatic cross sections of the three stages of erosion shown in Figure 15-3.

there are no present-day playas (cf. Fig. 15-1). Nevertheless, as shown by wells drilled for water, large parts of this area are underlain by thick alluvial fans and playa clays deposited in former interior basins. Pediment surfaces growing across these easily eroded deposits blend indistinguishably into other areas of pediment where only a thin veneer of gravel masks hard bedrock. In the bedrock areas small mountain masses rise abruptly from the smooth desert surface.

In a still later stage, the mountains, though they retain their steep slopes, have shrunk to small isolated hills that rise abruptly above a rock floor like islands from the sea. Such mountain remnants are called **inselbergs** (from German word for "island mountains"). Presumably, if no structural or climatic change intervened, continued erosion would eventually produce a wide rock plain whose flat surface would be subject primarily to wind erosion. Parts of the Kalahari Desert approach this condition, but no large area has

been recognized as representing such a final stage in desert landscape evolution.

Work of the Wind

The desert land forms just described indicate the dominance of water-molded surfaces in the landscape. Many people have the impression, perhaps fostered by movies and fictional romances, that deserts are chiefly great wastes of sand dunes. These, they suppose, furnish the chief contrast to a humid landscape. For most deserts this is not true. Yet, because vegetation is sparse or absent in deserts, wind erosion is much more prominent there than in humid regions, and locally its effects may be very noticeable.

Every gust of wind wafts dirt along a city street. In the country, on hot summer days, dust devils (small whirlwinds) swirl fine debris high above plowed fields. Occasionally tornadoes uproot trees, lift the soil, and destroy houses. Dust is in the air everywhere;

even in humid regions it accumulates within a few days in every closed room.

Sorting by the Wind

Anyone who allows dry soil to dribble slowly from his hand during a wind notices that some of the material falls almost vertically, but much of it strings out downwind. Fine particles of dust are carried away completely. By repeated trials, the coarse grains can be rather cleanly winnowed from the fine, even by a gentle breeze.

This example illustrates a general condition. If any object is dropped through a fluid, such as air or water, it falls at a speed that increases at first but eventually becomes constant—the so-called "terminal velocity" of fall for the object. Two forces are acting on the body: (1) the downward pull of gravity, and (2) the resistance of the fluid to the passage of the object. The pull of gravity depends directly on the difference between the mass of the body and that of the volume of fluid it displaces. But the resistance of the fluid to the movement depends on the viscosity of the fluid, on the diameter of the

body, and on its speed through the fluid. Resistance increases with increasing speed. Thus, gravity, which in a vacuum would produce constant acceleration, is ultimately balanced by the increasing resistance of the fluid. There is then no further downward acceleration of the body—its speed is constant at the terminal velocity.

Experiments show that the terminal velocities of different-sized spheres falling in any fluid vary tremendously. When the particles are smaller than about 0.01 mm., their terminal velocities in air vary almost exactly with the square of their diameters, a relationship, or "law," deduced by Sir G. G. Stokes in 1851. The speed of fall of such particles is slow enough to let the air accommodate their passage by laminar flow. The velocities of larger spheres are not so simply related to their diameters, for their greater volumes displace more air, so that the inertia of the air displaced in their passage becomes important. The displaced air, especially behind them, becomes turbulent as they fall through it. Figure 15-5 shows in a general way the relations between size and terminal velocities of particles in air, though flakes and other irregular

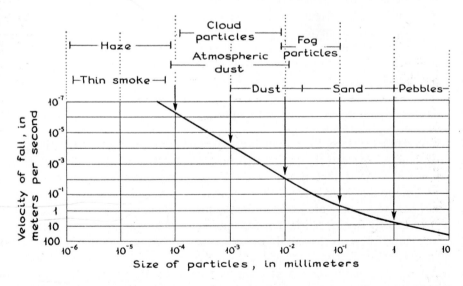

Figure 15-5.

Graph showing the variation of terminal velocity of fall with grain size of falling particles. (After R. A. Bagnold, The Physics of Blown Sand and Desert Dunes, *William Morrow and Co., 1942.)*

grains do not have terminal velocities quite as high as spherical grains of the same mean diameter. From the figure we see that the fine particles in our handful of soil were blown farther by the wind before sinking to the ground than were the coarse particles because they fell more slowly.

This helps us to understand the transporting power of the wind. Winds are always turbulent; gusts and eddies that swirl in every conceivable direction are superposed on their general motion. Close to the ground the ratio of the speed of upward gusts to the average forward velocity of the wind is extremely variable but averages about 1 to 5. Hence, if there are particles in the air whose terminal velocities are lower than one-fifth of the wind speed, some of them will be carried upward by gusts and remain suspended in the air until they are either caught in a compensating downdraft or sink with their ordinary terminal velocity to earth. While they are in suspension they will, of course, travel along with the wind. Particles with terminal velocities greater than one-fifth of the wind speed are not wafted aloft. Measurements of wind speed in dune areas indicate that sand begins to move when the average velocity reaches about 5 meters per second (11 miles per hour). If the maximum updrafts have one-fifth of this speed, or 1 meter per second, we see from the curve of Figure 15-5 that grains smaller than about 0.2 mm. diameter should be winnowed out of surface dunes.

This deduction from the curve is amply confirmed by observation of actual dunes. When dune sands are shaken through sieves graded in size, it is found that grains 0.3 mm. to 0.15 mm. in diameter greatly predominate. Even the finest dune sands contain almost no grains smaller than 0.08 mm.

Wind-blown sand rarely rises more than six feet, even in a severe storm, and most of it moves within a few inches of the ground, as shown by abrasion of the bases of telegraph poles. The great clouds that blacken the sun in areas like the floodplain of the Nile and the Dust Bowl of Oklahoma, Kansas, and Texas, are clouds of dust, not sand. In sandy deserts away from floodplains the air is generally clear, during even high winds, above a carpet of moving sand only a few feet thick.

Motion of Particles with the Wind

Sand grains momentarily carried forward by gusts strike the ground at a low angle, and if the surface is rocky they bounce into the air and travel along in a series of hops. If the surface consists of loose sand, such a falling grain may eject others as it "splashes" into the surface so that, even though a particular grain makes only one jump, it may cause one or more other grains to jump. Even grains too large to be caromed into the air may be

Figure 15-6.   Desert pavement in Death Valley, California. Note how several of the pebbles have been faceted by sandblast. (Photo by Eliot Blackwelder.)

pushed along slowly by the successive impacts of many smaller grains. The thickness of this layer of sand that creeps downwind depends on wind speed and grain size. If the sand is pebbly, the wind may winnow the sand grains away and leave the pebbles behind so that they accumulate over the desert surface as a residual layer, one pebble thick, to form a so-called **desert pavement** (Fig. 15-6). The more exposed pebbles generally have smooth surfaces cut by the sandblast. Pebbles are undermined as the sand blows away from around them; the pebble may then be rolled over by the wind, exposing new sand behind it. When this is blown away, neighboring pebbles are also undermined and overturned, and sandblasted surfaces develop on the new upper sides of the pebbles. In this way pebbles may ultimately acquire several flat facets that meet at sharp angles like those of a Brazil nut, as shown by several pebbles in Figure 15-6.

The surface of a sand dune is so rough that the wind directly in contact with it is made turbulent, and the most exposed grains are whipped aloft in momentary whirls. Where, however, the average diameter of grains is less than about 0.03 mm. (much below sand size) the result is different: even the most exposed grain projects so slightly above the general surface that it fails to swirl the air into turbulent eddies except at very high wind speeds. Dunes never form on a surface composed exclusively of grains as fine as this, and only a high wind can set the grains into motion.

In a wind-tunnel experiment, a British military engineer, R. A. Bagnold, showed that a surface of loose, dry Portland cement was stable, and the air above it dustless, even though the wind was strong enough to move pebbles $\frac{1}{6}$ inch in diameter. This stability of even-surfaced fine material accounts for the general lack of dust storms on large playas whose surface material is both fine grained and well sorted. Such material is stabilized by the small size of its grains and their strong cohesion when capillary water is present. Only when a playa surface has recently dried up and is covered with curled flakes of dried mud does it yield much dust, even to a strong wind. After these flakes have been blown away (to accumulate as dunes of clay chips to leeward) the playa surface is nearly dust-free unless disturbed by animals or wheels.

Measurements made while sand is drifting show that the wind near the ground moves much less swiftly over loose sand than over a rock floor, even though the wind velocity at a height of six feet is identical in the two localities. A study of grain movements suggest why this is so. Momentarily suspended grains that bounce along the rocky floor are so highly elastic that relatively little energy is needed to keep them rebounding. But more energy is needed to keep similar grains moving over a surface of loose sand because they lose momentum on splashing into it and disturbing other grains. Hence, grains that will bounce over a rocky floor slow down or stop when they strike an accumulation of sand. This explains the peculiar ability of sand dunes to collect grains from intervening barren areas instead of permitting the sand to spread evenly over the entire surface between dunes. This is how dunes grow.

Wind Erosion

Unlike streams and glaciers, winds are not confined between banks but blow freely over the whole surface of the earth. Dust clouds raised by the wind may be blown far away before they settle. This process is called **deflation** (from the Latin, "to blow away"). The only base level for wind erosion is the local water table, and even this may be slowly lowered by evaporation as wider areas are eroded down to the capillary fringe.

Most of the large undrained depressions on the deserts of North America and Asia—those of Death Valley and the Dead Sea, for example—have been formed by crustal movements rather than erosion. However, in Wyoming, Texas, New Mexico, and Colorado, there are wind-carved hollows hundreds of feet deep and several square miles in area. In the Kalahari Desert of South Africa many

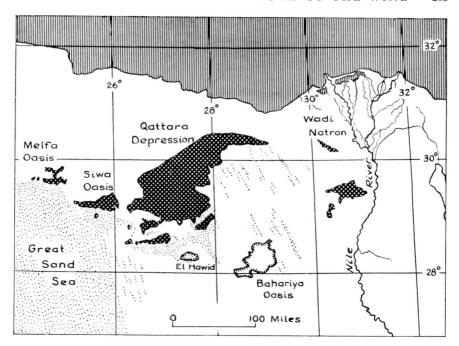

Figure 15-7.

The large depressions and sand dune areas (dotted) of Egypt and Libya. The dark-patterned depressions are below sea level. (After AAF Aeronautical Charts.)

shallow "pans" lie below the general surface of the granite bedrock. These are undrained and hence could not have been formed entirely by running water.

Perhaps the most striking depressions in whose formation wind erosion must have played a major part form a chain of oases extending about 400 miles westward from the Nile Delta into the Libyan Desert (Fig. 15-7). Although the depressions may have been started by some other process (ground-water solution, for example), there is strong evidence that they have been enlarged and deepened by the wind.

The northern margins of these depressions are steep escarpments, greatly dissected by stream-carved ravines. The bottoms of some depressions are well below sea level; others are a few hundred feet above. Their floors rise gradually toward the southeast and merge with the general level of the desert plain, a few hundred feet above the sea. Long chains of sand dunes cover the southeast slopes and string out beyond the depressions for hun-

dreds of miles. They were built in part from the material excavated in forming the basins. Flat-lying sandstone underlies the desert, and there is no evidence that the basins are fault troughs. The dunes piled up to leeward from these depressions are strong evidence that the wind has been a major factor in excavating them, but the water-scoured slopes that drain into the depressions show that the wind need have done little actual wearing away of rock. Sand, of about the right size to be transported by the wind, had already been carried into the basins by rainsplash and rills. Wind probably enlarged the basins only a little by abrasion; in the main it removed material already prepared for transport by weathering and running water.

When such basins as these are lowered to the local water table, moist ground and vegetation prevent further downcutting by wind, unless the water table itself is simultaneously lowered by evaporation. Many of the Egyptian oases have springs of fresh water around a central depression filled by a salt marsh or

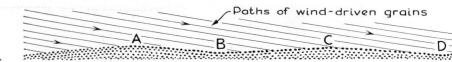

Figure 15-8.

The beginning of rippling on a sand surface. (After R. A. Bagnold, The Physics of Blown Sand and Desert Dunes, *William Morrow and Co., 1942.)*

playa whose floor is sealed from the main body of ground water by clay.

Although these large depressions are impressive, they are rare. Most deserts afford little direct evidence of deep wind erosion, although, in some places, grooves a few feet deep and a few hundred feet long have been carved from poorly consolidated sediments. In topographic gaps through which wind armed with sand is funneled, even hard bedrock may be smoothed and polished or etched by shallow grooves, testifying to the ability of the wind actually to abrade strong rocks. The main role of the wind, however, is to remove unconsolidated material from the sandy and silty surfaces of fans and other stream deposits, whose very presence testifies to the dominance of running water in the making of the desert landscape.

Surface Forms of Moving Sands

Small-Scale Features

As soon as the wind rises to the speed at which sand grains begin to jump, the surface of a dune is bombarded by grains that splash into it and eject some of the grains they hit. Though the leaping grains differ widely in range and trajectory, most grains, being approximately the same size, will strike a flat surface at roughly the same angle and with the same momentum.

A surface of sand which is not quite flat is shown in Figure 15-8. A small hollow has developed at B. The paths of the leaping grains are represented by the equally spaced parallel lines. The forward drift of the sand along the surface, the aggregate movement of both jumping grains and those hit by others, should be roughly proportional to the number of grains striking a given area. On the upwind side of the hollow (AB) there are fewer impacts per unit area than on an equal area of the downwind side (BC). More grains will be driven up the slope BC than down the slope AB, and the hollow will get deeper. There are also more impacts per unit area on the slope BC than on a level area of equal size. Grains carried up the slope will, therefore, accumulate at C, on the lip of the hollow. A second slope (CD) is thus formed.

Wind ripples on the surface of a sand dune near Newport, Oregon. (Photo by Parke D. Snavely, U. S. Geological Survey.)

Figure 15-9.

On it, as on AB, the grain motion is at a minimum; a second hollow must form farther to the right. In this way the originally flat surface of the sand becomes rippled (Fig. 15-9).

Once rippling begins, more grains will be ejected from slopes facing the wind than from the sheltered slopes, as shown in Figure 15-10. The ripples thus tend to become identical in size and spacing. Furthermore, as their crests rise they enter streams of stronger wind, and only the larger and heavier grains can remain on them, for the lighter are more readily moved by impact and by gusts. This concentration of coarser grains on the crests is the exact opposite of the way grains are concentrated in water-formed ripples: when preserved in consolidated rocks, it helps dis-

of accumulations are obviously related to topography: **climbing dunes,** which form where the wind must rise over a sharp topographic break (an example is the sea of sand banked against the northeast wall of Panamint Valley, California), and **falling dunes,** which form where sand is swept over a cliff and falls into a hollow protected from the wind. Almost as clearly related to structural configuration are the dunes and sand sheets formed where the wind, after sweeping sand through a topographic gap, enters a wide plain and diverges, with consequent slackening of speed.

Sand also accumulates on wide, flat plains and forms great persistent dunes that travel slowly across the country for scores or even hundreds of miles. Although the mechanism of dune advance is complex, we may gain

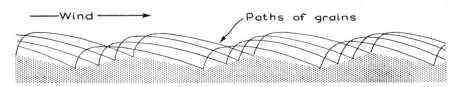

Figure 15-10.

Uniform transfer of grains and wind-formed ripples. (After R. A. Bagnold, The Physics of Blown Sand and Desert Dunes, *William Morrow and Co., 1942.)*

tinguish rocks deposited by wind from those deposited by water.

Rippling takes place during gentle winds; when wind speed rises (in wind-tunnel experiments, to about three times that needed to start grains moving) the ripples are destroyed, apparently because the difference between the speed of the wind over the crests and in the hollows becomes negligible. Moreover, if the wind dies away gradually, the hollows tend to fill, because the wind in these protected places is too feeble to maintain them. Hence, winds that slacken slowly may leave a nearly flat, though mildly rippled surface.

Large Accumulations of Sand

When sand travels across country and enters an area where either the nature or configuration of the ground or the vegetation interferes with the wind, it accumulates. Two kinds

some understanding of it if we consider briefly a few of the factors involved. Among these, vegetation is of paramount importance: other important elements are the effect of sand accumulation itself on the pattern of wind currents over it, and the relation between sand supply and the prevailing winds.

DUNES IN BARREN DESERTS. Although no desert is entirely without vegetation, the plants are generally so small and widely scattered as to exert only trivial influence on wind speed. When an accumulation of sand grows high enough to create a wind shadow behind it the wind speed is obviously greater on the windward than on the leeward side (Fig. 15-11). Sand will thus be selectively removed from windward and deposited on the leeward side. When the difference in speed becomes great enough so that the average path of grains in momentary suspension does not carry them all the way to the foot of the leeward slope, the sand tends to accumulate in the wind shadow high on the leeward slope. Eventually, the grains pile so high that they become unstable. The loose pile then slides down to form a **slip face,** building an even more efficient wind shadow than before (Fig. 15-11).

Dune accumulations a few feet high rise into air streams that are speedier than those near their bases, and therefore become increasingly unstable. The wind is funneled through any gaps along their crests, counteracting the tendency of grains to roll sidewise into the gaps, and in this way a large dune of irregular height that lies at a right angle to the wind may be split in two. In deserts of extremely sparse vegetation and constant

wind direction many dunes are of the crescentic variety called **barchans** (Fig. 15-12). The points of the crescent (wings) point downwind, the curving bow faces the wind. The middle of the lee face is a slip face. Even when the wind is blowing, there is relative quiet in the lee of the dune, so that all the sand swept over the top of the slip face accumulates there. At the ends of the dunes, on the other hand, sand streams away to leeward in great quantities. The slip face is at right angles to the wind and extends about two-thirds of the length of the dune. Since no sand escapes from the bottom of the slip face, additional sand arriving from upwind must either be deflected around the wings or the dune will grow larger. If the barchan remains the same size, the sand streams released from its tips must carry away nearly all the sand that

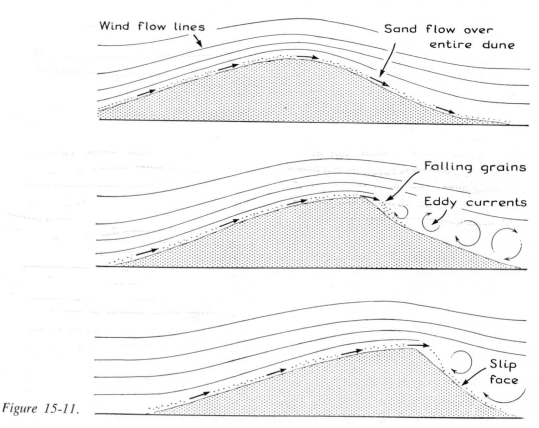

Wind flow lines ———————————   Sand flow over
                                       entire dune

                                  Falling grains

                                  Eddy currents

Figure 15-11.   Slip
                                                      face

Evolution of a sand dune with a slip face. (After R. A. Bagnold, The Physics of Blown Sand and Desert Dunes, *William Morrow and Co., 1942.)*

Figure 15-12.   Barchan dunes near Laguna, New Mexico. The dunes are several hundred feet long. (Airplane photo by Robert O. Frampton and John Shelton, Claremont, California.)

reaches the dune from upwind. Consequently the sand streaming from the tips of a barchan often starts new dunes farther to leeward. Field observations indicate that barchans form where the direction of the wind is almost uniform throughout the year.

In general, the larger a barchan the slower it migrates. A small dune will therefore overtake a larger one downwind; and its wings will enclose a hollow between its slip face and the larger dune. This alters the course of the wind and hence the shape of the dune. Barchan fields can become very complex, especially where their advance is modified by vegetation or topography.

Where wind direction varies considerably the barchan form is unstable. If the sand comes mainly from one source, so that winds from its direction supply nearly all the sand, but winds from another direction are more powerful, the movement of the sand may be highly irregular, and the dunes may be strung out in long chains at an angle to the winds (Fig. 15-13). For these dune chains the name **seif** (from the Arabic word for "sword") has been suggested. Seifs can grow to great size: some in Iran rise more than 700 feet above their bases and are three-fourths of a mile wide. Individual seif ridges as much as sixty miles long are known, and groups of seifs extend for more than two hundred miles in western Egypt.

DUNES IN CONFLICT WITH VEGETATION. Even an open vegetative cover greatly influences dune forms. Plants establish themselves more readily in sags in the dunes than on the more active crests, for there they are abraded less by moving sand, and their roots are more likely to reach ground water. Hence **transverse dunes,** at right angles to the wind, do not split up into barchans if plants in the low spots gather and stabilize the sand that would otherwise drift through the sags and form the barchan's wings. Transverse dunes often attain lengths of half a mile or more and reach heights of 10 or 15 feet before breaking up. Where vegetation is able to establish itself widely over the sand, however, long transverse dunes do not form; instead, two other varieties of dunes predominate; parabolic, or "blowout," dunes and longitudinal dunes. The relations between the three forms are shown in Figure 15-14.

Figure 15-13. Seif ridges of the Sahara, Africa. (Photo by U. S. Air Force.)

Parabolic dunes, some of which have elongate "hairpin" shapes, with the points facing
upwind, in contrast to the downwind points of
barchans, may form either by blowouts of
older stabilized sand or by accumulation of
sand downwind from patchy sources. Such a
dune may form where sand from a dry stream
bed is swept up a gully in a bordering slope
and onto a brushy terrace, overwhelming the
plants in the line of maximum supply. The
gully funnels both wind and sand grains so
that the center of the dune advances faster
than its sides (Fig. 15-14). The wings may
lag enough so that vegetation develops over
their outer slopes and ultimately anchors them
completely. In extreme cases the lengthening
is so great that the dune may be shaped like a
hairpin, or even break up into a longitudinal
ridge extending directly downwind. Parabolic

dunes also form where excessive cultivation,
or trampling by animals, destroys the plant
cover and exposes the sand beneath to the
action of the wind.

Where the sand supply is spottily distributed or comparatively scanty, and the
wind's direction is constant, a common form
of dune is a long ridge parallel to the wind.
These **longitudinal dunes** also form where
climbing dunes reach the top of a cliff and the
sand is channeled from notches in the crest
(Fig. 15-15). Their formation requires an
extremely constant wind direction and is evidently favored by a rather small sand supply
and a climate so dry that only a little sand
motion is needed to overwhelm the sparse
vegetation. Such ridges are the dominant dune
forms in the Navajo country of northeast
Arizona, where many of them are several

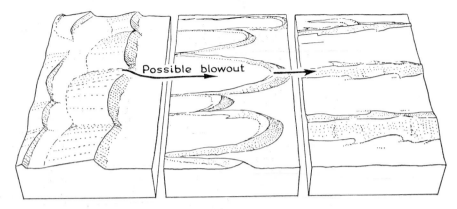

Figure 15-14.

From left to right: *Transverse, parabolic, and longitudinal dunes; the arrows indicate a possible transition between the three forms. (After J. T. Hack, 1941.)*

miles long and as much as thirty feet high. Their pattern is remarkably constant over hundreds of square miles.

SUMMARY OF FACTORS INFLUENCING DUNE SHAPES. We have suggested some of the many factors that influence the formation and shapes of dunes. Others are doubtless involved and much remains to be learned, but it seems clear that three factors are highly important: wind speed, sand supply, and vegetation. Abundant sand and strong winds produce transverse dunes in both barren and brushy deserts; where there is less sand and weaker vegetation, barchans and longitudinal dunes predominate. Moderate winds may produce parabolic dunes where vegetation grows rapidly enough partly to anchor the slowest moving parts.

Characteristics of Ancient Dune Sands

Highway and railroad cuts through dunes show that they differ from other accumulations of sand in several ways. One of the most

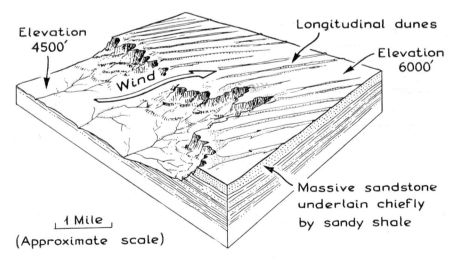

Figure 15-15.

Longitudinal dunes on the Moenkopi Plateau, Arizona, formed where sand released by weathering of sandstone cliffs is drifted across the plateau by the wind. (After photo of the U. S. Soil Conservation Service.)

Figure 15-16.

Cross-bedding in the Navajo sandstone, Kane County, Utah. (Photo by H. E. Gregory, U. S. Geological Survey.)

conspicuous is the type of cross-bedding they exhibit. The internal stratification of dunes is extremely complex, as suggested by their diverse forms, their slip faces, and their complicated progress as they move downwind. A well-cemented sandstone that contains these complex cross-bedded patterns is illustrated in Figure 15-16. This particular sandstone, a part of the Navajo formation of Jurassic age, contains other features that suggest its dune origin. Among these are the excellent sorting, the occurrence of wind-carved pebbles, and the frosted, or sandblasted, surfaces of the grains. Frosted surfaces on sand grains are common in wind-blown but are rare in water-laid sands, both because small grains move faster in wind than in streams and because their effective mass is far higher, since the density of the fluid in which they are suspended is much lower. Hence, the impact of wind-blown grains on one another though not strong enough to shatter them completely, does tend to pit, or frost, their surfaces, in contrast to those of waterborne sands of the same size. Such features have made it possible to recognize ancient dune sands in many geologic formations from Precambrian age onward.

Loess

Great areas of southern Germany, Russia, Turkestan, and China in the Old World (see Fig. 13-14), and of the Mississippi Valley and Columbia River plateau in the New, are blanketed with fine-grained, loosely coherent material called **loess.** Despite its lack of cohesion, loess stands in nearly vertical walls because it contains vertical tubules (left by rotting out of grass roots) and joints. These also make it highly permeable to ground water. Many of the loess-covered areas are very fertile farm lands—for example, the Palouse country of eastern Washington. Some loess deposits are hundreds of feet thick, as in western China, but most are only a few feet thick.

Microscopic studies show that loess is composed of angular particles—mainly less than 0.05 mm. in diameter—of quartz, feldspar, hornblende, and mica, pieces of fine-grained rocks, and some clay. Most of the grains are fresh or only slightly weathered.

All these features suggest that loess is a deposit of dust and silt that settled from the air in grassy country. Most loess lies downwind from areas that were glaciated during the

Pleistocene period (see Chap. 13), but some deposits are in the lee of deserts. The great loess deposits of China, for example, lie downwind from the Gobi and other deserts, and are probably being added to at the present time, just as dust from the Dust Bowl must, in the middle 1930's, have added to the soil of the more humid lands of the eastern United States.

FACTS, CONCEPTS, TERMS

INTERRELATIONS BETWEEN CLIMATE, SOILS, AND
    LAND SLOPES
INTERIOR DRAINAGE; BAHADAS; PLAYAS
PEDIMENTS
SHEETFLOODS AND MUDFLOWS
RELATION OF GRAIN SIZE OF WEATHERED PARTI-
    CLES TO DESERT SLOPES
EVOLUTION OF DESERT LANDSCAPES

SETTLING VELOCITY AND WIND SORTING
ORIGIN OF RIPPLES ON SAND SURFACES
BARCHANS, SEIFS; DESERT PAVEMENT; WIND-
    CARVED PEBBLES
DUNES IN CONFLICT WITH VEGETATION; PARA-
    BOLIC AND LONGITUDINAL DUNES
ANCIENT DUNE SANDS
LOESS

QUESTIONS

1. Why are the southwestern slopes of the Hawaiian Islands arid, whereas the northeastern sides receive heavy rainfall?

2. Why do dune sands vary so little in grain size? Why are they generally free from clay?

3. Why does sparse sand on a rock floor accumulate into dunes instead of spreading out uniformly over the whole surface?

4. Draw a cross section through the area shown in Figure 15-1 and label the following features on the section: (a) area that is being reduced in height by rainwash and gullying, (b) pediment, (c) area of stream deposition and braided streams, (d) area of active sand dunes, (e) area where wind-carved pebbles and desert pavement might be found, (f) area from which water might be obtained from wells.

5. Why are pediments not formed in humid regions?

6. Why are wind-borne sands more likely to be frosted than stream sands?

7. What differences can you find between pediments and stream-cut terraces?

8. The so-called cloudbursts rarely exceed 3 or 4 inches in total rainfall over a period of an hour or two. Heavy rains that last for much longer periods of time are common in humid regions. Explain the cause of the generally more drastic results associated with the desert cloudbursts.

9. Rainfall is higher along the recently uplifted shores of the Baltic Sea than it is along the Italian coast. Why, then, are sand dunes so much more abundant on the North German and Polish coasts than near Naples?

10. The walls of many stream canyons in the steppes of southeastern Oregon are draped with the remains of ancient debris flows and landslides which are no longer in motion, but are being actively gullied by rillwash from cloudbursts. What does this imply about climatic changes in the area? What additional features would you look for to prove the point?

SUGGESTED READINGS

Bagnold, R. A. *The Physics of Blown Sand and Desert Dunes*. New York, William Morrow and Co., 1942.

Bryan, Kirk. *Erosion and Sedimentation in the Papago Country, Arizona*. U. S. Geological Survey, Bulletin 730, Washington, D. C., 1932.

Gautier, E. F. *Sahara, the Great Desert*. (Tranlated by D. F. Mayjew.) New York, Columbia University Press, 1935.

Hack, J. T. *Dunes of the Western Navajo Country*. Geographical Review, Vol. 31 (1941), pp. 240-263.

Hume, W. F. *Geology of Egypt*, Vol. 1. Cairo, Government Press, 1925.

16 | THE OCEANS

Fossils of marine animals in the rocks of high mountains and inland deserts prove that even many of the continental heartlands were at one time or another drowned beneath the sea. Nearly three-fourths of all the land surface is underlain by marine rocks. To understand the record of these rocks, we must know something of the sea—of the processes that go on in it, the organisms it contains, and the varying environments of erosion and sedimentation that diversify its floor.

General Features of the Ocean

Most of the earth's surface is covered by the sea. Analysis of the best maps and charts available shows the following:

Area of the sea	361,059,000 sq. km.	70.8%
Area of the land	148,892,000 sq. km.	29.2%
Total	509,951,000 sq. km.	100.0%

Land and sea are very unevenly distributed: the earth can be divided into two hemispheres —one contains four-fifths of all the land and the other is nearly nine-tenths covered by water.

The outstanding relief features of the ocean floor are indicated in Figure 16-1. As outlined in Chapter 5, the grosser topographic forms include the shallowly submerged edges of the continents—the continental shelves, the much steeper continental slope, the abyssal plains which cover large parts of the ocean floor, and the submerged mountain ranges such as the Mid-Atlantic Ridge.

But the marine environment has many other typical topographic forms. The most striking features of Pacific Ocean topography are the great **island arcs** that festoon its northern and western sides. Among them are the Aleutian, Kurile, Japanese, Ryukyu, and Philippine archipelagoes. These island-crowned arcuate ridges separate comparatively shallow seas— the Bering, Okhotsk, Japan, Yellow, and East China seas—from the Pacific Basin proper. Several comparable arcs branch southward from Japan through the Bonin and Marianas islands. The seas that border these are not shallow; the Philippine Basin, on their concave side, is as deep as the main Pacific on their convex side.

The ocean floor itself has many different topographic forms: some elevated, others depressed. The depressions may be grouped into: more-or-less rounded **basins,** elongated **troughs** with gentle side slopes, and similar but steep-sided **trenches.** Depressions whose floors are more than 7,000 meters (23,000 feet) deep are called **deeps.** Most of the great deeps of the oceans are in the Pacific, near the shores of such island arcs as the Aleutian, the Japanese and the Philippines, but the Atlantic

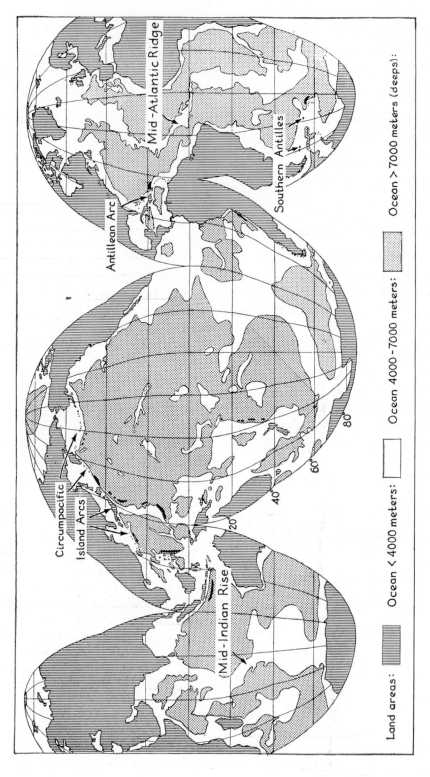

Figure 16-1. Map of the world showing the major relief features of the ocean floor. Note the Mid-Atlantic Ridge, the Mid-Indian Rise, and the Island arcs with their associated deeps. (From H. U. Sverdrup, M. W. Johnson and R. H. Fleming, The Oceans, Copyright 1942, by Prentice-Hall, Inc.; Goode Base Map used by permission of the University of Chicago.

has the Puerto Rico Trough and South Sandwich Trench, each more than 8,000 meters deep, and the Indian Ocean has the Sunda Trench, south of Java. Each of the great deeps, except one south of New Britain, lies on the convex oceanward side of an arcuate island chain or mainland range.

Among the elevated areas, long, relatively narrow tracts are called **ridges;** broader and larger ones, **rises.** Small flat-topped but steep-sided elevations are **sea mounts;** shallower and broader flat-topped elevations are **banks.**

Circulation of the Sea

Ocean water is about eight hundred times as dense as air, hence its movements, though complicated and difficult to predict, are sluggish compared to those of the atmosphere. Waves and wave currents may beat violently against an exposed coast, and some tidal currents travel at velocities of more than twelve miles an hour, but most of the moving water in the oceans is carried by huge currents that in only a few places move more than a mile or two per day.

Currents within the Surface Layer of the Ocean

The large oceanic currents at the surface of the ocean closely reflect the wind pattern. Indeed, wind drag is the chief motive force and steering mechanism of the currents in the upper layer of the ocean. In tropical areas, the trade winds cause the ocean water to drift slowly toward the equator and, at the same

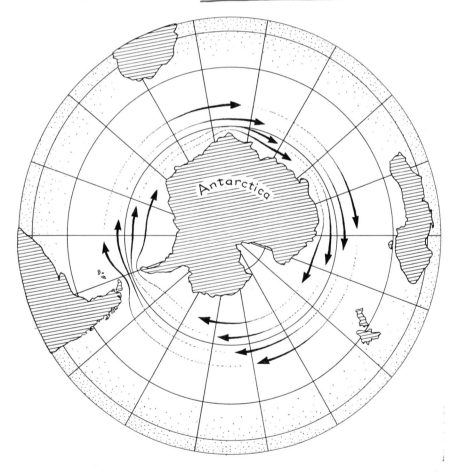

Figure 16-2.

The West Wind Drift in the Antarctic seas.

time, westward. Hence, there is a strong **equatorial drift** of westward moving water. The famous raft *Kon-Tiki* rode this drift in its journey from the Peruvian coast to the mid-Pacific islands.

In the middle latitudes of both hemispheres, westerly winds set up a similar drift of water eastward across the ocean. In the southern hemisphere, this eastward drift is not interrupted by continental land masses; hence a continuous "West-Wind Drift" rings the Antarctic continent (Fig. 16-2). In the northern hemisphere, a similar west-to-east drift is broken up by the continental masses, which deflect it both to north and south. The continents similarly divide and deflect the equatorial current. Thus, in the landlocked basin of the north Atlantic, a vast clockwise eddy of oceanic water is set up of which the well-known Gulf Stream is an important part. A similar whirl, directed counterclockwise, is found in the south Atlantic, and the other oceans also have such systems of currents.

THE GULF STREAM. "There is a river in the sea—the Gulf Stream," said Maury, the great American oceanographer of a century ago. Modern studies confirm his picture of a well-defined stream of warm water, with relatively sharp boundaries, that courses with the speed of a river across thousands of miles of ocean (Fig. 16-3).

The Gulf Stream system consists of three segments: The Florida Current, the Gulf Stream proper, and the North Atlantic Current. The Florida Current pours through the

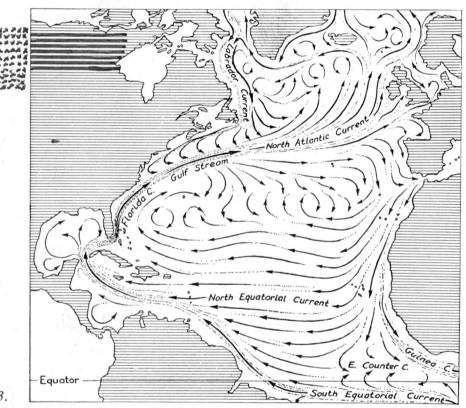

Figure 16-3.

The currents of the north and equatorial Atlantic Ocean in February and March. (After H. U. Sverdrup, M. W. Johnson and R. H. Fleming, The Oceans, *Copyright 1942, by Prentice-Hall, Inc.)*

strait between Cuba and Florida at an average speed of nearly 3 miles an hour, carrying as much water out of the Gulf of Mexico as fourteen Mississippi Rivers could bring into it. Precise leveling across Florida shows that the Gulf stands about 7 inches higher than the Atlantic—this is the immediate cause of the Florida Current. Water piles up in the Gulf because of inflow from the Equatorial Current as it is driven across the ocean by the Trade Winds and deflected northward by the South American landmass (Fig. 16-3).

As the Florida Current emerges from the Gulf of Mexico, it is joined by water flowing north along the east coast of Cuba. The combined stream sweeps north along the continental shelf, augmented by water from great eddies in the Atlantic. Until recently, it was considered to be a single stream moving leisurely northward at a speed of about 2 miles an hour, but detailed studies reveal that it consists of several narrow threads, some traveling at speeds of up to 6 miles an hour. Other studies show that the Gulf Stream does not always stay in the same position, but sometimes wanders a hundred miles or more off course in great wavelike meanders that occasionally break off completely to form large eddies that rapidly interchange large bodies of cold and warm water between the two sides of the Gulf Stream. The total amount of water transported varies with these fluctuations and with the seasons, but where it courses northeastward off the east coast of the United States the Gulf Stream transports as much water as a thousand Mississippis—roughly 70 million tons of water per second—in a current about 50 miles wide and 1,500 feet deep.

Inshore from the Gulf Stream, numerous counterclockwise eddies are thrown off; these give rise to the near-shore drift that shifts sand southward along Atlantic beaches.

As it sweeps past the Grand Banks near Newfoundland, the Gulf Stream spreads out to the northeast, subdivides, and becomes less definite. Here it is called the North Atlantic Current. Its northern branches spread far into the Norwegian Sea, and even into the Arctic Ocean: by transporting warm water far to the north, they notably affect the climate of the British Isles and Scandinavia. Its southern branches carry water southward along the European coast to the trade-wind belt, where it is pushed back across the Atlantic in the equatorial drift, completing the circulation.

The Deep Water Circulation

Oceanographers have found that the deep water of the oceans is stratified into several layers, superposed according to density. Differences in density arise in different parts of the sea through a variety of processes. Like the atmosphere, sea water differs in density because of variation in amount of solar heat received, warm water being less dense than cold. But differences in density of sea water also arise from differences in **salinity** (the concentration of dissolved salts): the greater the salinity the greater the density. Salinity is high near the Horse Latitudes, where dry winds pick up moisture from the ocean's surface, but leave most of the dissolved salts behind (Fig. 16-4). Salinity is low in areas of heavy rainfall, and where great inland rivers dump fresh water into the sea. When sea water

Figure 16-4. Graph showing the close correlation between changes of surface salinity and evaporation minus precipitation at different latitudes. Average for all oceans. (After Wust, from H. U. Sverdrup, M. W. Johnson and R. H. Fleming, The Oceans, Copyright 1942, by Prentice-Hall, Inc.)

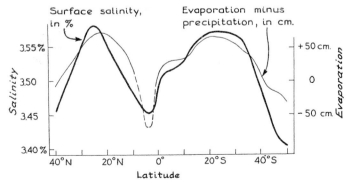

freezes, it excludes salt from the ice, and salinity is consequently high along the edges of the Antarctic continent, where the formation of shelf ice concentrates salt in the cold water beneath. These differences in density make the circulation of the sea quite complex because, of course, the denser water everywhere tends to sink and displace the less dense. Nevertheless, water masses of different density, and hence of different source areas can be traced fairly readily by measurements of their temperature, salinity, and oxygen content. As examples, we shall describe two density streams, one named the Mediterranean Water, the other the Antarctic Bottom Water.

THE MEDITERRANEAN DENSITY CURRENT. The Mediterranean Sea, because of its hot, dry climate, is a huge evaporating pan. Constant loss of water vapor to the atmosphere soon increases the salinity of surface water that enters the Mediterranean to about 3.86 per cent, 10 per cent higher than normal

sea water. Thus even though the surface water is relatively warm (about 13°C in winter) it sinks to the bottom because its density is increased. At the Strait of Gibraltar, this sheet of dense bottom water is out of equilibrium with the less dense, though cooler, water of the adjacent Atlantic. Hence it pours across the rock sill on the bottom of the Strait in a huge density current that delivers about two million cubic meters of water per second into the Atlantic—an amount equivalent to the flow of the Mississippi River. At the surface of the Strait, low-density water from the Atlantic flows into the Mediterranean to maintain balance. During World War II, German submarines, with engines turned off to avoid detection, rode into the Mediterranean in the upper current, and left by the lower one.

On emerging into the Atlantic, the Mediterranean current flows down the sea floor until it reaches a depth of about 6,000 feet. Here it finds water of approximately the same density (but of lower salinity and temperature) which it joins, spreading out in a great flat sheet over

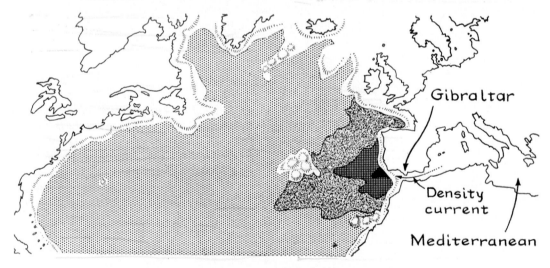

Figure 16-5.   Salinity in the North Atlantic at 6,000 feet. The map is drawn as if all the water above 6,000 feet below sea level were stripped away. Extremely salty water from the Mediterranean pours through the Straits of Gibraltar and flows down the slope of the sea bottom until it encounters water of higher density, upon which it spreads as a flat sheet. The successively lighter shades indicate the gradual dilution by mixing with adjacent water sheets as the Mediterranean water spreads outward. (After H. Stommel, Scientific American, 1955.)

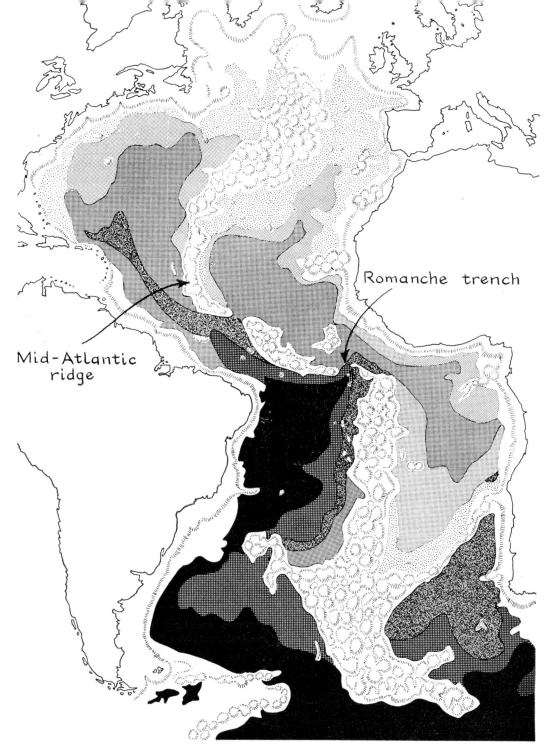

Romanche trench

Mid-Atlantic ridge

Figure 16-6.   *The Antarctic Bottom Water as it would appear if all the water lying above 12,000 feet below sea level were stripped away. Note how the cold saline water spreads northward, channeled into the western part of the South Atlantic by the Mid-Atlantic Ridge (which rises well above its surface) until the Romanche Trench provides a low pass through which it can spread into the eastern Atlantic. The darkest shade indicates the pure Bottom Water, and the lighter tones successive stages in its dilution.* (*After H. Stommel,* Scientific American, *1955.*)

most of the North Atlantic, and gradually mixing with adjacent layers of water that dilute and cool it (Fig. 16-5).

THE ANTARCTIC BOTTOM WATER. The water around the border of the Antarctic continent is also very dense, but for an entirely different reason. Freezing of the surface of the sea forms extensive masses of floe ice along the edges of the continent and increases the salinity of the remaining sea water, because little of the salt is taken into the ice. Thus, the shallow seas bordering the continent contain a very cold and highly saline water which has the highest density (1.0274) of any water in the oceans. This water sinks and slides along the bottom, spreading far to the north in each of the oceans. In the Atlantic, its upper surface is generally about 12,000 feet below sea level. Figure 16-6 shows this deep water mass as it would appear if the overlying water strata down to 12,000 feet were stripped off. Note how the Mid-Atlantic Ridge channels the Antarctic bottom water into the western half of the Atlantic basin until it finds a low pass—the Romanche Trench—near the equator through which it can spill over onto the floor of the eastern Atlantic.

Tides, Waves, and Currents

Moving water is a powerful erosional agent, both on land and in the sea. Nevertheless, although the major ocean currents move immensely greater volumes of water than all the rivers on earth, they perform little erosion. Their energy is largely dissipated in friction against other water masses instead of against the sea bottom. Only locally—as over the Blake submarine plateau off the east coast of Florida—does the Gulf Stream extend so deep that it scours the sea floor, so that in the area through which it flows there is little deposition, and even, perhaps, some erosion at depths of 6,000 feet or more. For the most part the only geologic effect of the great oceanic currents is climatic. It is the smaller but swifter currents caused by tides, storms or earthquakes, and the turbidity flows of sediment laden water, that are the efficient agents of erosion and transportation in the sea.

Tides

The ancients knew that the ebb and flow of the tides varied with the phases of the moon. So complex is the real earth as compared with the idealized earth assumed by the astronomers and physicists that we have as yet no general theory that permits tidal forecasts for any point on an ocean. Tides are, of course, predicted with great accuracy for all the principal ports; these are not computed from general theory, however, but from comparison of tidal records for a long period of years for the particular port concerned.

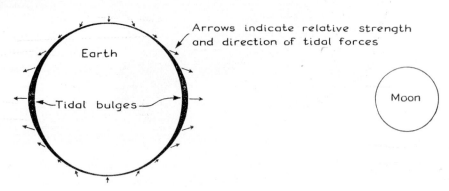

Figure 16-7.

The lunar tides. The distance between the moon and the earth should be much greater than shown in the diagram. The tidal bulges are greatly exaggerated. (In part, after, H. U. Sverdrup, M. W. Johnson and R. H. Fleming, The Oceans, *Copyright 1942, by Prentice-Hall, Inc.)*

Since Newton's time, the forces that produce the tides have been visualized much as shown in Figure 16-7. If D is the distance from the center of the earth to that of the moon, and M is the mass of the moon, and r the radius of the earth, the moon's attraction for a mass, m, at the earth's surface on the side nearest the moon is greater than its attraction for a like mass at the earth's center: $Mm \div (D - r)^2$ is greater than $Mm \div D^2$. Theoretically, if this surficial mass is water, it will bulge upward. Similarly, a mass on the earth's surface directly opposite the moon is attracted less than a like mass at the earth's center: $Mm \div D^2$ is greater than $Mm \div (D + r)^2$. Theoretically, a water mass is "left behind" in a corresponding bulge. At all other points on the earth's surface, there is also a difference in the moon's attraction for particles at the surface and for the "average" particles of the earth's body. Hence the earth's gravitation and the attraction of sun and moon causes a force which acts on each particle along a line inclined to that joining the centers of the earth and the moon, as illustrated in Figure 16-7. In general, this inclined force can be resolved into both vertical and horizontal components. Because the earth rotates with respect to the moon once in 24.84 hours (not 24, because the moon advances eastward in its orbit), two tidal bulges pass over any given point on the earth's surface during this time.

The sun's attraction acts like that of the moon, but it is so much farther away that despite its far greater mass its maximum tide-producing force is only 0.46 that of the moon. Twice during the lunar month, at new and full moon, both sun and moon lie on a straight line passing through the earth and their influence is additive. These are times of extreme tides (spring tides); at all other times their tide-producing forces tend in some degree to neutralize each other. At the moon's first and third quarters their influences are directly opposed and the tides are smallest (neap tides). Of course, the tidal forces affect all parts of the earth, not merely the water bodies. The

tides in the rocky crust are so infinitesimal, however, because of the rigidity of the rocks, that they can be detected only by extremely sensitive instruments.

Although the simple diagram of Figure 16-7 illustrates the tide-producing forces, it certainly fails to explain the vagaries of local tides. For example, many ports have but one tide in a lunar day, in others the high tide lags many hours behind the time the moon passes overhead, in still others the two daily tides are of greatly different heights. Tides also vary with the seasons. These and many other facts make it clear that the tides are not a simple direct response to the vertical component of the moon's gravitational pull, which is really far too small for effective lifting of the huge water masses involved. It is mainly the horizontal component of the tide-producing force which induces these horizontal motions of water masses that are the effective tides. The configuration of the ocean's bottom so strongly influences the tidal currents that they vary greatly in strength and direction at different points and, because of seasonal density currents, even at the same point during different seasons.

To the geologist, the principal interest of the tides is in the erosional power of their currents. Some tidal currents are prodigious, particularly those in estuaries with converging shores. In the Bay of Fundy, between New Brunswick and Nova Scotia, the vertical tidal range is sometimes as much as 70 feet, and the possibility of harnessing the power of the huge water masses that rush into and out of the bay twice daily has been seriously studied. So far, the cost of the necessary dams and the hourly fluctuations in available power have made the project seem uneconomic. Yet these tidal currents attain speeds of 9 miles an hour during both rise and fall of the tide, and have scoured basins in the bottom more than 150 feet deep.

In St. Malo Bay, on the coast of Brittany, the tidal range is 40 feet, and currents reach speeds of 8 miles an hour. Between the Orkney and Shetland islands the tidal currents move at 12 miles an hour. In some rivers, the tide enters as a rushing wave of water called a bore. The bore of the Hangchow River, in China, is often as much as 16 feet high and may speed up the river at 16 miles an hour.

Experiments show that water moving half a mile an hour will transport medium-sized sand grains, and at 3 miles an hour will carry gravel an inch in diameter. Clearly, tidal currents are locally important agents for the transport of sediments. Dredgings off the Mull of Galloway, in Scotland, prove that coarse gravel is moved by tidal currents at depths of more than 800 feet.

Current meters lowered in the ocean indicate that even at great depths some tidal motion extends to the bottom. Such currents should be strongest near the edges of the shallow continental shelves, because there the volume of water flowing in and out is greater in proportion to depth than elsewhere. Perhaps this accounts for the fact that sediments near the outer edge of the shelf are in many places coarser than those nearer the land. The stronger currents should winnow out the finer sediment and drop it off the shelf onto the continental slope. On submarine ridges, regardless of depth, tidal currents must be perceptible where the ridge rises steeply from the bottom. Many ridges yield bare rock to the dredge, and nearly all show coarser sediments than adjoining basins or depressions.

We thus have reason to think that the winnowing action of tidal currents significantly affects the size, sorting, and distribution of sediment on the sea floor. But in only a few places are these currents important in shaping the shore itself, and their effects are in general subordinate to those of wave currents.

The great shallow-water waves that are the tides are caused by the gravitational pull of the sun and moon. Two wholly different kinds of waves, neither of them tidal, have unfortunately become popularly known as "tidal waves." One, the seismic sea wave, caused by earthquakes, is considered in Chapter 19; the other is a high-water wave caused by prolonged and unusually violent onshore winds.

It was such a hurricane-driven water mass that overwhelmed Galveston, Texas, in 1900, with great loss of life.

Waves

GEOLOGIC EFFECTIVENESS.   Waves and the currents they generate wash every shore on earth. Anyone who has watched the never-ending play of waves on the shore—whether the gentle ripples that carry grains of sand up and down the beach or the great rollers that pound against the cliffs—cannot help being impressed with the power the sea has to mold the shape of the coast and to move detritus. The sea is a great saw; armed with cobbles, pebbles, and sand, it works away at the beach, undercutting cliffs and wearing a notch in every rock exposed at this level. In relatively unconsolidated materials erosion is rapid: the sea has eaten back the cliffs of glacial gravels making up the Holderness coast of Yorkshire at a measured rate of 7 to 15 feet a year for more than a century. Repeated soundings and studies of bottom sediments in all parts of the world show that waves also have great effect on the movements of sediment at shallow depths.

The mechanism by which winds produce waves in water is complex. In theory, wind friction should not be great enough to cause waves until the wind speed over the water is 11 to 15 miles an hour, yet winds of only 2½ miles an hour produce waves on ponds. Wind motion is always turbulent: that is, some air particles move much faster than the current as a whole. These variations produce corresponding variations in surface pressures and friction against the water; it must be these that first ruffle the surface.

The motion of the water particles in a wave depends on the wave length—the distance from crest to crest of successive waves—the wave height, and the depth of the water (Fig. 16-8). Waves on water that is deep compared to the wave length (depth greater than one-fourth the wave length) are called deep-water waves. Their speed is not affected by

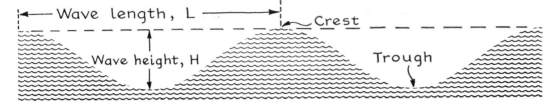

Figure 16-8.   *Schematic diagram of a progressive wave.*

the depth. It has been shown by watching floats that the water particles in such waves move up and down in roughly circular orbits but retain the same general position. Indeed, if the water masses actually moved forward with the speed of the waves no ocean would be navigable. The orbits through which the particles at the surface move have diameters about equal to the wave height (see Fig. 16-9), but the size of the orbits diminishes quickly with depth. For waves with a length of 330 feet and height of 16 feet, traveling about 28 miles an hour, the velocity of surface particles is about 4.4 miles an hour; at a depth of 65 feet the velocity is only about 1.2 miles an hour and at 330 feet it is negligible. Because of this quick falling-off of orbital velocity with depth, Vening-Meinesz's submarine (p. 155) was stable enough for gravity observations when it was submerged

less than a hundred feet in moderate seas. But in great swells 1,250 feet long and 33 feet high, traveling about 56 miles per hour, even though the particle velocity at the surface is again only about 4.4 miles an hour, at a depth of 330 feet the orbital motion is still nearly 1 mile an hour.

Under steady winds, the waves grow in size and speed up to a limit imposed by friction. The wind gives them energy in two ways: by its push against the wave crests and by the friction of the air against the water surface. The first depends on the difference between wind speed and wave speed: when wind speed is greater the waves are pushed, but when wave speed is greater than air speed the wave encounters air resistance, like a moving car. Frictional drag, on the other hand, depends not on the difference between the speed of the air and that of the wave itself,

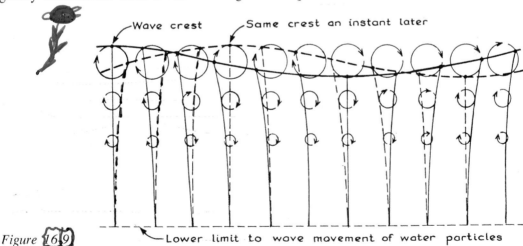

Figure 16-9

Circular movement of water particles in a deep-water wave of small height. Full lines indicate the position of the water particles at one instant, dashed lines the same particle, ¼ period later. (After U. S. Hydrographic Office, Publ. No. 11.)

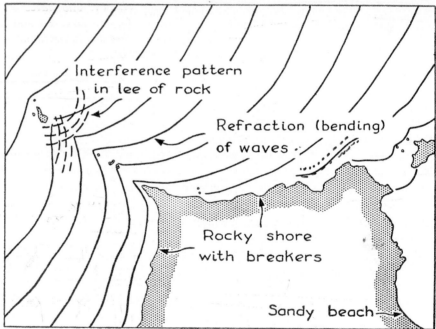

Interference pattern
in lee of rock

Refraction (bending)
of waves

Rocky shore
with breakers

Sandy beach

Figure 16-10.

Vertical airplane photo (top) *and diagram* (bottom) *showing bending of the waves (wave refraction), around a point of land.* (*After U. S. Hydrographic Office, Publ. No. 234.*)

but on the difference between the speed of the air and that of water particles. Wave size and speed thus depend on wind speed, wind duration, the fetch (the distance across which the wind blows with the same direction and speed) and, finally, the state of the sea at the time the wind began to blow.

WAVE REFRACTION. When deep-water waves enter shallow water, the bottom interferes with the orbital motion of the water particles and causes the wave to slow and steepen. Normally, this effect becomes notable when the depth is between ¼ and ½ of the wave length; where the water shallows to

½₀ the wave length, the wave speed no longer depends on wave length, as in deep-water waves, but becomes proportional to the square root of the depth. Most waves begin to "feel bottom" at depths of less than 500 feet, but during exceptionally heavy storms waves may extend to depths of 1,500 feet. The wave slows down, not because of friction, but because the water particles near the bottom can no longer move in circular orbits to fill the wave form; their paths become ellipses, and at the very bottom are reduced to straight lines, the particles moving to and fro in the direction of wave advance.

On a uniformly sloping bottom, the inshore end of a wave approaching the shore obliquely feels bottom sooner than the offshore parts and therefore slows down sooner. The wave crest then becomes bent, for the offshore part continues to advance as a deep-water wave, with its original speed, after the inshore end has begun to slow and change to a shallow-water wave. Along a straight, evenly sloping coast, no matter what the original angle of approach of the waves may have been, they tend to be bent (refracted), so that they approach the shore nearly straight on—that is, with their crests nearly parallel to the beach (Fig. 16-10).

Because the energy in the waves is carried in paths at right angles to the crest lines wave refraction modifies its distribution. The energy which was uniformly distributed along the wave length in the deep-water waves now tends to be concentrated against the sections of coast where shallow water extends farthest seaward, since the slowing of the waves where they first feel bottom tends to render the wave crests concave toward the shallows. Wave energy is thus concentrated on headlands rather than along equal segments of bay coasts (Fig. 16-11). The waves on headlands thus become more powerful and higher, those on bay shores less powerful and lower, than they would be on a straight coast. This differential attack tends to shorten and straighten the shoreline by eroding the headlands and filling the coves with transported debris.

BREAKERS.   When waves reach water so shallow that they can no longer find enough water to fill out their wave forms, they steepen

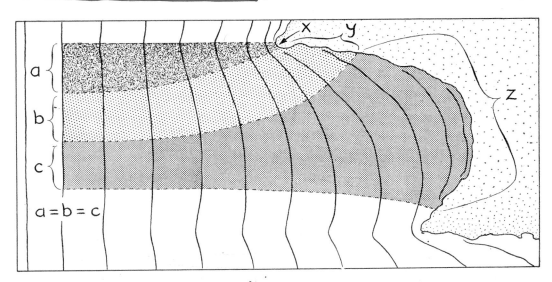

Figure 16-11.   The distribution of wave energy as conditioned by coastal shape. Each of the equal segments a, b, *and* c, *of the offshore wave has the same amount of energy. The refraction of the waves due to the coastal configuration leads to concentration of energy on the headlands and weakening in the re-entrants of the shore. The energy is carried in the direction at right angles to the wave front at all times. Thus the energy distributed over* a *is concentrated at* x, *that distributed over* c *is spread over* z.

and begin to break. They may continue, though, for hundreds of feet without curling over at the crest—the ideal wave for the surf-rider. Eventually, where the water is shallow enough, the wave curls over and breaks with a single great crash, tumbling its water forward onto the beach. This is the **breaker.** Breakers occur where the still-water depth is from one to two times the wave height.

The energy of the breaker is dissipated in collision with the bottom and in turbulence of the water. The bottom material in the breaker zone is thrown violently into suspension, as any surf swimmer can testify, and the concentrated turbulence often scours a trough in the bottom along the breaker line. Some of the material thrown into suspension is deposited to build bars both seaward and landward of the breaker zone, some is carried landward with the rush of water up the beach. As the water shallows and becomes less turbulent, the detritus is sorted according to its size, shape, and density.

Wave Erosion

Waves erode the shores in three ways: (1) by their impact and hydraulic pressure, (2) by corrasion—the sawing and grinding action of the sand, gravel, and cobbles hurled against the cliffs or rolled and dragged across the foreshore—and (3) by solution, which is a minor process, even along limestone shores.

Hydraulic Pressure

Waves contain astounding energy. If we calculate the pressure of even a moderate wave 10 feet high and 100 feet long, we find it capable of exerting a push of 1,675 pounds per square foot against an obstruction. Great storm waves, 42 feet high and 500 feet long, should exert a pressure of more than 3 tons per square foot.

At Wick, in northern Scotland, storm-wave pressures as great as this are common. There, as noted in Chapter 5, the waves have carried away masses of concrete weighing as much as 2,600 tons from the breakwater built to protect the harbor. The tremendous wave pressures not only act directly but also by compressing air driven into crevices in the rocks. Such compression creates pressure great enough to pry huge blocks from cliffs exposed to full-wave attack. At Ymuiden, Holland, a seven-ton block in the breakwater was seen to move a few feet toward the sea, presumably because of compression of air in crevices behind it.

Storm waves seek out weak strata or joint cracks in a cliff and dislodge the blocks between them. Along the jointed rock they tunnel out sea caves, scores or even hundreds of feet long; some caves penetrate entirely through small promontories and produce spectacular arches. The roofs of others collapse, leaving isolated **stacks** in front of the cliff line (Fig. 16-12).

Figure 16-12.   Sea caves and sea stack at low tide, near Santa Cruz, California. (Photo by Eliot Blackwelder.)

Corrasion

We have seen that great storm waves can tear huge blocks from the cliffs and hurl them against the shore. Even moderate waves move boulders and cobbles, and feeble ones sand. In a Cornish mine that extends beneath the sea, the grinding of boulders against the shore overhead is easily heard through a nine-foot roof of rock. The shore zone is a veritable grinding mill. At Cape Ann, Massachusetts, angular fragments from granite quarries have become rounded on the beach within a single year. Shakespeare's Cliff, several hundred feet high, a part of the "Chalk Cliffs of Dover," is so rapidly undercut as to produce frequent large landslides. One of these, in 1810, was so great that the vibrations were felt as a strong earthquake at Dover, several miles away. These are spectacular examples of wave erosion in soft rocks, but even rocks as resistant as the rhyolite shown in Figure 16-13 are impressively notched.

Although the greatest part of the waves' energy is spent between the breaker line and the shore, corrasion is not confined to the water's edge. If the wave length is great, particles of sediment move vigorously at greater depths. Great waves 500 feet long and 22 feet high should theoretically produce speeds of 10 inches per second in water particles at a depth of 300 feet: this is enough to move fine sand. When account is taken of tidal and other currents, it would seem that the bottom water should be agitated enough to keep clay particles in motion to depths of 600 feet—on some coasts to more than 900 feet. These theoretical conclusions are partly confirmed by the character of the sediments found by dredging. The depth to which movement of sediment by waves is perceptible is called the **wave base.**

Now, it is true that outside the breaker zone the particles moved by the waves reverse their direction with every wave. But most of the shallow sea floor slopes seaward and accordingly a particle moving to and fro on the bottom is moving downhill seaward and uphill landward; outside the breaker zone, where

Figure 16-13. Cliff in rhyolite, undercut by waves. Kindall Head, Moore Island, Maine. (Photo by E. S. Bastin, U. S. Geological Survey.)

these oscillations are about equal, the sediment tends ultimately to progress downhill—seaward—in response to the pull of gravity. (It must not be forgotten that tidal currents also operate to maintain motion.) As the motion becomes less and less with greater depth, coarser particles eventually reach positions where the agitation is too feeble to keep them moving; there they come to rest. But finer particles can still be moved, and will continue to travel seaward until they, in turn, are sorted out in accordance with their size and density. During all this agitation, the particles of sediment rub against each other and against the bottom. They gradually become smaller

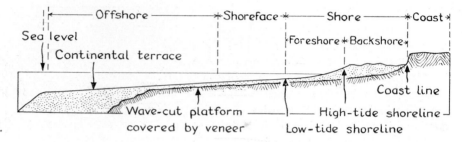

Figure 16-14.

Elements of the shore zone and profile of equilibrium. (After D. W. Johnson, Shoreline Processes, *John Wiley and Sons, 1919.*)

and smaller, until they can be moved by successively feebler oscillations. Dragged back and forth with each passing wave, they also wear away the bottom, so that not only the breaker zone, where the wear is much the greatest, but all the coastal zone, to the depth of wave base, is corraded to some degree.

Inshore from the breaker zone the situation is somewhat different. Here the shoreward-moving water masses may dash coarse fragments to heights from which the feebler backwash cannot carry them back, even though favored by a steep slope. Although as much water must flow away from the shore as toward it, the shoreward movement is generally concentrated in a shorter time, so that the velocity of a breaking wave is greater than that of the backwash. A **storm beach** of coarse pebbles may thus be built above the reach of the normal waves. Such a beach is steep, for coarse material can be moved seaward only on steep slopes. Eventually a beach develops a vertical profile at which onwash and backwash are about equally effective; the slope of the profile is determined by the size of the waves and the size and amount of detritus.

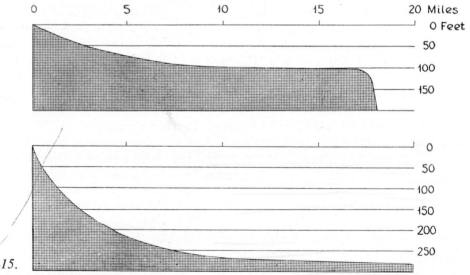

Figure 16-15.

Average profile of the sea floor off Madagascar. Note the striking difference between the profile of the protected west coast (top) and the exposed southeast coast (bottom). (Redrawn from D. W. Johnson, Shoreline Processes, *John Wiley and Sons, 1919.*)

The Profile of Equilibrium

Partly from wave theory, partly from observed motion of detritus in waves, partly from dredgings and soundings, and partly from study of large dried-up lakes (see Chapter 13, Lake Bonneville) or of uplifted sea-floors (see Fig. 16-16, Middleton Island), the concept of the **marine profile of equilibrium** has been developed (Fig. 16-14). This profile is a smooth, sweeping curve, concave upward. It is steep in the breaker zone and flattens seaward. Its slope is adjusted to the average particle size of the detritus moved by the waves at each particular place along it. The slope is just great enough to keep the material in slow transit toward deep water. As the waves fluctuate in size, the profile is constantly readjusted, flattening and shallowing with feeble waves, steepening and deepening with more powerful ones. But for any coast there should be, theoretically, a general average slope about which the profile fluctuates.

That such profiles are real and not merely hypothetical is shown by soundings which indicate that the sea floor near the coast is usually concave upward, despite the complications to be expected because of the world-wide changes in sea level that occurred during the Pleistocene. As in Figure 16-15, the slope and depth of the offshore profile is in most places closely adjusted to the fetch and power of the waves. Moreover, such a graded profile can actually be seen on former sea floors (Fig. 16-16), which, in many places, have been uplifted to form **marine terraces.** Though now above the reach of the waves, they show some or all of the features common to modern coasts: cliffs and cliff notches, stacks and caves, storm beaches, gravel and sand beaches, and a sedimentary veneer resting on a smoothly truncated surface of bedrock whose profile is gently concave upward but retains a general seaward slope. Yet it should be clearly understood that a perfect idealized profile is probably nowhere to be found. Continual changes in wave power, the effects of tidal and other currents, and perhaps most important, the fluctuations of sea level and slow movements of the earth's crust, constantly interrupt the development of every profile.

Wave Currents

Despite refraction, most waves approach the shore at a slight angle, so that the swash of

Figure 16-16.   Uplifted beaches on Middleton Island, Alaska. The lines of low bluffs are old sea cliffs. Note how the uplifted wave-cut platform truncates the inclined beds. (Photo by S. R. Capps, U. S. Geological Survey.)

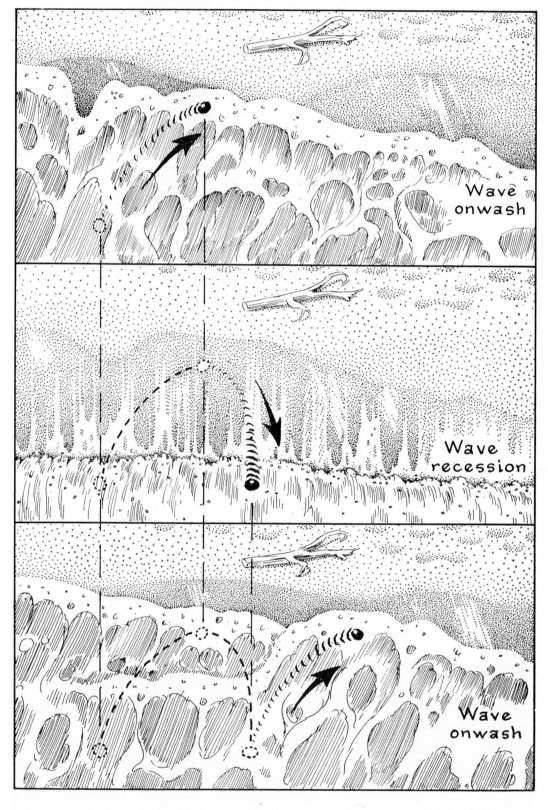

Wave
onwash

Wave
recession

Wave
onwash

Figure 16-17. (OPPOSITE) *Longshore drift (to the right) resulting from oblique wash of the waves. Each arcuate segment of the particle's path represents the movement due to one wave.*

the breaking wave has a component of motion parallel to the shore. This produces a current parallel to the beach called the **longshore drift,** which, depending on the exposure of the shore, may consistently flow in one direction or reverse with differences in the wind. Such a drift may become swift, especially if there is a longshore wind or if tidal currents reinforce it. The breaking wave carries sand and gravel obliquely up the beach—the sand particles farther than the gravel because they move with a feebler current—the backwash also retains a longshore component. Each particle thus moves in a series of sawtooth-like oscillations down the beach (Fig. 16-17). Marked pebbles made from bricks have been traced along a beach as much as half a mile in a single day; similar movements doubtless occur in the whole zone of the sea bottom that is agitated by the waves. Vast amounts of sand are transported parallel to the shore by

these longshore currents and their ability to smooth out irregularities in the shape of the shore is great.

Artificial Interference with Shore Processes

The nice adjustment of beach profiles and shore outlines to the average power of waves and currents acting on shore detritus is clearly shown almost anywhere that the shape of a beach has been artificially altered. Even a slight obstacle often causes drastic changes. Dredging of sand and gravel offshore has frequently been followed by erosion of the shore; the material between the excavation and the shore has been swept seaward to fill the hole and restore the slope to its original form. Even more striking effects have followed the building of groins on many bathing beaches. Groins are low walls extending sea-

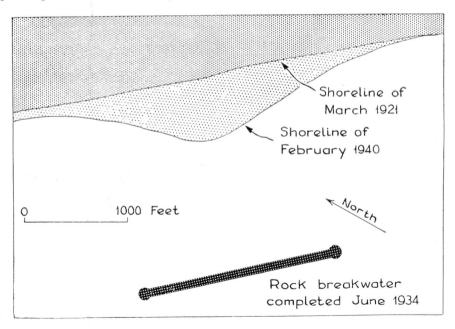

Shoreline of
March 1921

Shoreline of
February 1940

0   1000 Feet

North

Rock breakwater
completed June 1934

Figure 16-18.

Map of Santa Monica beach before and after building of breakwater. The beach has continued to advance since 1940, but no accurate surveys are available since then. The direction of longshore drift is from left to right.

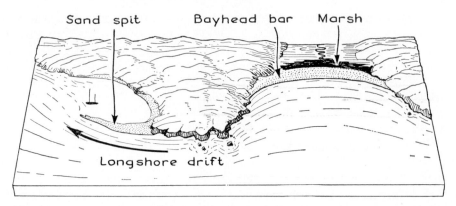

Sand spit   Bayhead bar   Marsh

Longshore drift

Figure 16-19.

Map and two common depositional features on an embayed coast: a sandspit springing from a headland and a bayhead bar.

ward from the high-tide line, built to prevent sand removal by longshore drift. Where they have been successful in holding the fine sand the beaches farther downdrift, being deprived of their normal supply of traveling sand, have often been severely scoured and have changed from sandy beaches to gravel or cobble ones. Many parts of the famous Waikiki Beach have been severely scoured because of artificial interference with the normal shore drift.

Breakwaters of rock or concrete, built to protect anchorages from storms, have often caused beach modification, as at Santa Monica, California (Fig. 16-18). Here a 2,000 foot breakwater was built parallel to the shore and about 2,000 feet from it, to make a small-boat anchorage. The longshore drift here is generally to the southeast. As the breakwater naturally reduced the power of the waves striking the shore behind it, thereby weakening their capacity to keep detritus in suspension, the beach in the lee of the breakwater began to build itself forward. In about six years it advanced more than 500 feet into the sea. The beaches to the southeast of the breakwater have not been greatly eroded, despite being starved of their normal quota of sand that drifted from the northwest; it is noteworthy, however, that great storms cause considerably more damage to the beach southeast of the breakwater than to other nearby parts of the shore.

Erosional and Depositional Features of Shores

The Shores of Mountainous Coasts

The shores of mountainous or hilly coasts are more varied than those of coastal plains. Waves attack exposed promontories, producing cliffs; the coarse and fine debris eroded from them is distributed by longshore drift, producing characteristic shore features—bayhead and bay-mouth bars, and land-tied islands, spits, and bars.

Wave refraction on bay shores produces currents that tend to sweep material toward the head of the bay, where it accumulates as a bay-head bar (Fig. 16-19). Material carried by longshore drift from eroding headlands tends to continue straight across coastal indentations; a smoothly curved spit may be formed by the debris from a cliffed point at whose base it begins. Toronto Harbor is protected by a long sand spit growing westward. As spits grow out into deep water, wave refraction and, in the sea, local tidal currents, cause their ends to become curved (Fig. 16-19). Where the outflow from a bay is small, such spits may grow completely across the opening to form a bay-mouth bar (Fig. 16-20). The lagoon behind may be brackish or fresh and may be slowly filled by silt from the land or by sand blown inland from the beach.

Islands near the shore, like breakwaters, protect the beach behind them from the full force of the sea, so that the longshore drift cannot effectively carry material behind them. A mainland beach protected by a nearby island therefore builds out in the same way as the beach at Santa Monica, diverting the long-shore currents toward the island. Eventually, a spit may extend to the island, tying it to the shore (Fig. 16-21). Many islands become joined to the coast by two spits that enclose a triangular lagoon between them.

Bottom irregularities may deflect the drift, even on straight coasts, and cause the beach to build seaward. The height of the beach thus formed is determined by the amount and coarseness of the detritus supplied, and the height of the storm waves. As the beach advances seaward, it leaves behind it a series of older beach ridges, some of them as much as twenty feet high, separated by swales. Perhaps the best known of these advancing beaches is that at the Dungeness, in southeastern England, which has grown more than a mile into the sea since the time of Elizabeth I—about 6 yards a year.

The Shores of Plains

Along low-lying coasts like those of the Gulf of Mexico and the southeastern Atlantic states, the wave attack is spread widely instead of being concentrated upon headlands. The sea deepens so gradually that the waves feel bottom far offshore and the material they stir up is built into an offshore bar, just inland from the zone of the greatest breakers (Fig. 16-22). As wave agitation continually erodes the sea bottom on the seaward side of a bar and slowly moves the detritus seaward, bars must constantly rebuild landward in order to survive if there is a stable sea level. In places offshore bars along plains have thus been driven landward until they touch the mainland. Where they do the waves directly attack the land and the shore may be undercut to produce low cliffs. Part of the material eroded is carried by longshore currents and added to the bar.

The lagoon behind an offshore bar is salty, but rivers may freshen it somewhat. A large river may raise the lagoon level to such a height above the sea—naturally the difference is greatest at low tide—that the bar is broken, forming an inlet through which tidal currents can sweep. Great storm waves also breach bars during hurricanes. Such tidal inlets across bars shift from time to time because of shore drift: some fill in, and new ones appear. Salt grass grows in the protected lagoon, and as plant debris and silt brought by streams, tidal

Figure 16-20.   Baymouth bar and lagoon, St. Mary's Lake, Glacier National Park. (Photo by E. Stebinger.)

Figure 16-21. *Land-tied island, Hancock County, Maine. (Photo by E. S. Bastin, U. S. Geological Survey.)*

currents, and winds accumulate, the lagoon gradually changes to a marsh.

The famous beaches of Florida and New Jersey are offshore bars. Another striking example is the long sand bar that fringes the southern coast of the Baltic from Danzig to Memel, enclosing an almost continuous brackish lagoon. Figure 16-23 illustrates a plains shoreline along which some offshore bars enclose lagoons, though others have advanced shoreward to crowd meandering rivers behind them. Magnificent examples of offshore bars fringe the Carolina coast. Their cuspate shape has been attributed to junction of eddies thrown off by the Gulf Stream (Fig. 16-3) but it may be partly a result of wave refraction from bottom irregularities.

Along plains coasts there is no coarse gravel and the beaches are almost wholly sand. Between tides the beaches dry out and winds may blow the sand inland to form dunes that overrun the country.

The Life Zones of the Sea

Life is everywhere in the sea. Even the greatest depths—far below levels to which light penetrates and where the water temperature is only a little above freezing—yield living organisms to the trawl. Although marine environments are less diverse than those on land, they do differ from place to place and so, consequently, do the organisms inhabiting them. A large proportion of all sedimentary rocks are marine; the fossils they contain enable us to infer something of the conditions of their deposition by analogy with associa-

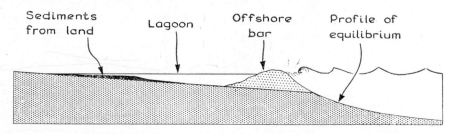

Figure 16-22.

Cross section showing the features of the shore zone of a low-lying coast. The vertical scale is exaggerated.

tions of similar organisms in the modern seas.

Marine biologists classify the different parts of the sea as shown in Figure 16-24. The two main divisions are the **benthic,** or sea-bottom environment, and the **pelagic,** or open-water environment. Both are divided, at a depth of 200 meters (about the depth of the edge of the continental shelf) into a littoral system landward and a deep-sea system seaward. The depth of 200 meters is critical because it is near the limit to which light can penetrate. On the deep-sea floor, there is neither light nor seasons and hence there is no photosynthesis by green plants. The bottom life is confined to scavengers that live on organisms sinking from above, and to a few bacteria, nearly all of which depend on organic compounds brought to the depths by currents or by sinking.

The life of the sea, both plant and animal, is classed in three large groups: the **benthos** (from Greek, "depth of the sea") or bottom dwellers; the **nekton** (Greek, "swimming") or swimming forms; and **plankton** (Greek, "wandering") or floating and drifting organisms. The benthos includes all the attached, creeping, or burrowing organisms of the bottom: seaweeds and grasses, sponges, barnacles, clams, oysters, corals, bryozoa, worms, lobsters, crabs, and many other animals, among them many species of the minute, single-celled Foraminifera, most of which secrete shells of calcium carbonate. The nekton includes the squids, fishes, seals, whales and many other animals that are economically important but of little geologic significance. The plankton includes all the surprisingly varied organisms, chiefly microscopic, that float with the ocean currents. Among them

Figure 16-23.   The west coast of Cape York Peninsula, Australia, showing features of a plains coast. The curved white stripe in the upper right is an offshore bar; the ridged beach in the foreground is probably an older offshore bar. (Photo by U. S. Air Force.)

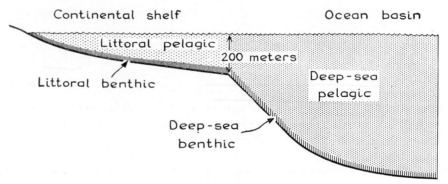

Figure 16-24.

Diagrammatic cross section showing the four major divisions of the life zone of the sea. (After H. U. Sverdrup, M. W. Johnson and R. H. Fleming, The Oceans, *Copyright 1942, by Prentice-Hall, Inc.)*

are several kinds of diatoms with opaline shells; a group of organisms, the Coccolithophores—of uncertain classification but usually considered algae—which secrete rounded shells made up of calcite in thin plates; many individual Foraminifera (though but few species); and the silica-secreting Radiolaria.

All living things, except for a few bacteria, ultimately depend on photosynthesis—the process by which plants utilize radiant energy from the sun to form organic compounds directly from carbon dioxide and water. Plants also require small amounts of many substances, among them phosphates, nitrogen, iron, and manganese. Variations in the abundance of these substances in different parts of the sea are partly reflected in different densities of plant population and in the corresponding variations in the abundance and kinds of animals that feed on the plants.

After a planktonic or nektonic organism dies, its body, unless it is eaten immediately, ultimately sinks, perhaps to feed some scavenger in the depths. During and after sinking, much of the organic matter of which the body consists is decomposed by bacteria. This decomposition both uses up oxygen dissolved in the water and releases carbon dioxide to it—results that, because of the effect of dissolved CO_2 on the solubility of calcite (see Chapter 4), have much to do with determining what

kinds of sediments are deposited in the deep sea. Decomposition at any depth returns phosphorus, nitrogen, and other nutrient elements to solution, making them once again available for plant growth if water drift brings them to the lighted zone. Deep-water masses ultimately return to the surface by slow mixing or by upwelling. Upwelling of deep water that contains nutrients accounts for the flourishing plant life and the resulting prolific fishing grounds in such parts of the ocean as off the Newfoundland Banks and the western coasts of North and South America and Africa.

The remains of marine organisms are valuable clues to the environment in which a fossiliferous sedimentary rock was deposited, no matter whether the organisms are found in their original habitat as a "life association," or whether their dead bodies have been transported from widely differing habitats, finally to be deposited together as a "death assemblage." Obviously the former is the better guide. This aspect of the life of the sea and its significance in geology will be discussed more fully in Chapter 17. Here we will consider only those organisms whose activities actually influence the shape of the sea floor and, indeed, the form of the coasts and islands of much of the world—the assemblages that make up the coral reefs.

Coral Reefs

Although some species of coral animals can live in cool water, the reef-building species require water at least as warm as 68° F. Not only must the water be warm, but it must also have normal salinity and be nearly free from mud. The coral animal, anchored in his limy case, depends on food brought by waves and currents, and therefore thrives best on the windward and offshore sides of reefs. Many species of coral live in reefs, but reef-builders do not grow below a depth of about 150 feet nor much above low-tide level. Because of their narrow depth range, coral reefs are delicate indices of crustal movement, as noted in Chapter 8.

Although corals—either living animals or broken fragments of their skeletons—form the conspicuous framework of the reefs, algal remains bind them together, and many other calcareous organisms—mollusks, worms, foraminifera, and a host of others—contribute to the formation of a reef and may constitute far more of its bulk than coral.

Coral reefs have three forms: fringing reefs, barrier reefs and atolls. **Fringing reefs** are confined to the very border of the land. A few are thousands of feet wide, but most are less than a hundred.

A **barrier reef** is separated from the shore by a lagoon; this may be shallow, but some are hundreds of feet deep. Many of the volcanic islands of the Pacific and Indian oceans are surrounded by such barriers, the white reefs forming a ring a short distance offshore (Fig. 16-25 and Fig. 8-8). The Great Barrier Reef of Australia roughly parallels the Queensland Coast at distances ranging from 25 to nearly 200 miles offshore and extends for 1,200 miles south from Torres Strait.

In an **atoll,** there is no central island, only a ringlike reef enclosing a central lagoon. The enclosed lagoon is dotted with isolated coral heads, and floored with algal mud and some sand that is derived from broken reef fragments hurled into the lagoon by waves.

The Origin of Atolls

The origin of barrier reefs and atolls has fascinated students ever since the publication of Darwin's *Voyage of the Beagle* more than a century ago. Darwin believed that fringing reefs, barrier reefs, and atolls form a sequence (Fig. 16-26): if an island with a fringing reef subsided slowly, the reef would subside with it but would also grow upward, keeping pace with the subsidence, to become a barrier reef, and later, if subsidence continued until it had drowned the central island, an atoll. In sup-

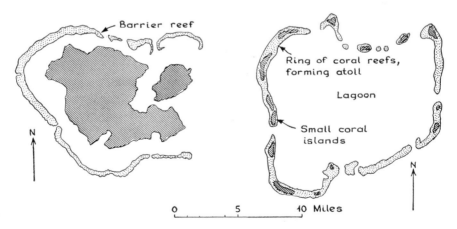

Figure 16-25.

Left: *The barrier reef of Vanikoro Island, Caroline Archipelago.* Right: *Peros Banhos Atoll, Chagos Archipelago. (After Charles Darwin, 1842.)*

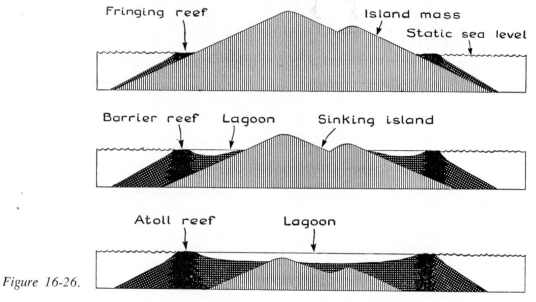

Figure 16-26.

Cross section showing three stages in the origin of an atoll, according to the sinking-island hypothesis. (After Charles Darwin, 1839.)

port of this, it has been pointed out that the shores of many of the islands within fringing reefs have identations like those that might be produced if a stream-dissected mountain sank slightly. Moreover, the outer slopes of many atolls and reefs descend steeply to great depths, and borings on several reefs, or geophysical tests by seismic means (Chapter 21), show that the reef structure extends many hundred feet below the ocean's surface, and, in some atolls, rests on volcanic rocks.

An alternate hypothesis was suggested by the American geologist R. A. Daly, in 1910. Daly noticed that charts showed that the lagoons of many barrier reefs and atolls have remarkable similar and uniform depths, ranging from about 150 to 250 feet. He also noted that some of the higher peaks of the Hawaiian Islands had been glaciated, presumably during the Pleistocene, and inferred that the water along the shore below must have been too cool for coral growth at that time. If so, the present fringing reefs of Hawaii must all date from postglacial time. He then computed the volume of sea water that must have been locked up in the ice sheets during their greatest expansion. From this he inferred that sea level was then 300 feet lower than now, and that the water in which the corals now flourish must have been not only colder but also siltier, because the waves would be working on unconsolidated sediments newly exposed to wave attack. Daly concluded that the reefs that then existed would not have been able to withstand the attack of the sea but would have been planed off at a level appropriate to the lowered sea of the time. When the ice sheets melted and sea level gradually rose, the surviving corals would find smoothly planed banks to colonize, and would build atolls and barrier reefs on them. It is not necessary, in Daly's theory, to assume subsidence of the land in order to explain the lagoons: they now vary in depth because of sedimentation, the smaller being shallower than the larger because their areas are relatively smaller in relation to the reefs over which sediment is washed during storms. Banks and sea mounts not colonized by reef-builders since the rise of sea level are simply the planed-off islands of preglacial time (Fig. 16-27).

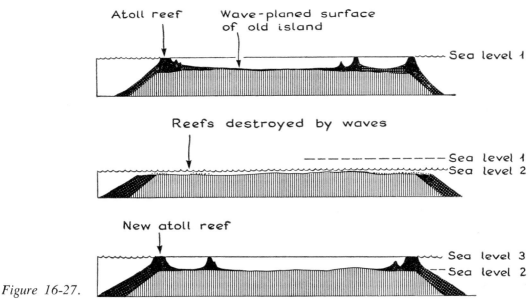

Atoll reef   Wave-planed surface
of old island
— Sea level 1

Reefs destroyed by waves
— — — — — — — — — — Sea level 1
Sea level 2

New atoll reef
Sea level 3
Sea level 2

Figure 16-27.

Cross section showing three stages in the origin of an atoll, according to the glacier-control hypothesis. (After R. A. Daly, The Floor of the Ocean, *University of North Carolina Press, 1942.)*

Daly's theory fails to explain the indented shores of many islands within barrier reefs, for the relief of the valleys and ridges is far greater than can be explained by a mere 300-foot drop in sea level. On the other hand, it does explain the uniform depth of the lagoons. Probably both Darwin's and Daly's explanations of the origin of fringing reefs and atolls are partly correct, for certainly not all parts of the ocean floor have had the same history, even since the Pleistocene. For instance, we know of both drowned reefs with perfectly preserved atoll shapes near the Philippines and of greatly elevated reefs in Indonesia, Fiji, and Samoa.

Submarine Canyons

It was long thought that, except in some small areas of concentrated current action, erosional processes did not operate below wave base to any noteworthy extent. Beginning about 1890, and especially since about 1920, when sonic sounding began to multiply our data on the topography of the ocean floor, it has become evident that most of the continental shelves are dissected by steep-sided canyons and extensive submarine valleys. Figure 16-28 shows many such canyons indenting the margin of the shelf off the northeastern United States. Note that the only river mouth clearly connected with a submarine canyon is that of the Hudson. This exceptional trench extends from the estuary of the Hudson almost across the shelf, and then, fading out on the shelf, reappears as a deep trench in the continental slope, extending clear to the floor of the Atlantic.

Other stretches of continental shelf, notably those bordering California, Alaska, and southwestern Europe, are cut by similar gorges. Most submarine canyons are on the continental slope; short and steep, they begin far from shore except where the shelf is very narrow or interrupted by deep basins, as off southern California. A few canyons are 70 to 150 miles long and 3,000 to 5,000 feet deeper than the adjacent sea floor, being comparable to the Grand Canyon in size. Among the great submarine canyons are: the

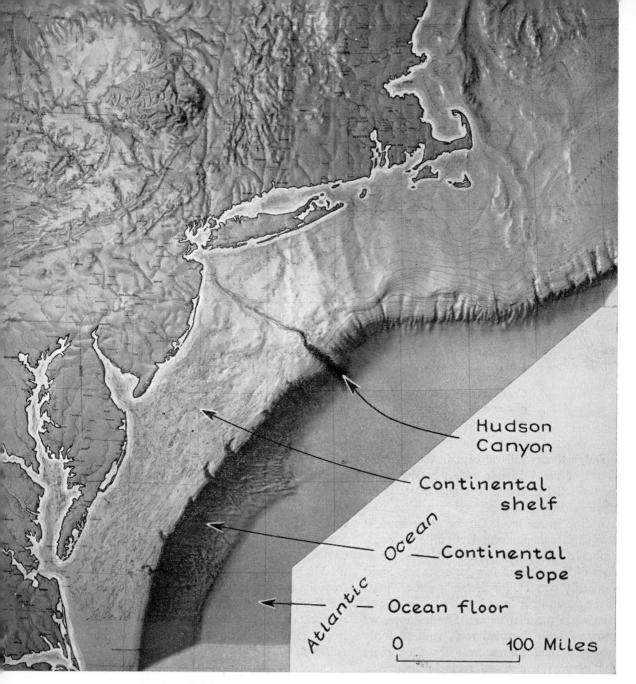

Hudson
Canyon

Continental
shelf

Ocean

Atlantic

Continental
slope

Ocean floor

0   100 Miles

Figure 16-28.   *Relief model showing the land and submarine topography of the northeastern United States. Submarine canyons are abundant on the steep continental slope (partly in shadow). The irregularly ridged submarine topography in the upper right corner is submerged glacial topography. (Courtesy of the Aero Service Corporation, Philadelphia.)*

Monterey Canyon off California, which heads near (but not at) the mouth of the Salinas River; the Congo Canyon, which extends into the Atlantic from the mouth of the Congo River; and the Nazare Canyon off Portugal, which heads far from any existing river mouth. A smaller, but well-studied example, the La Jolla Canyon, off California, heads close to the Scripps Institution of Oceanography, which has examined it intensively.

Monterey Canyon's long profile is shown in Figure 16-29, together with that of the Salinas River. Some of the irregularities in the submarine profile may represent errors in soundings, but the general form is trustworthy. The average grade of the Canyon bottom is almost 4 degrees for the first 40 miles from shore, while that of the lower Salinas River is less than 0.1 degree. The submarine canyon is probably cut almost entirely in Miocene, Pliocene, and Pleistocene sediments, though near the middle of its course, granite has been dredged from one wall. The tributary Carmel Canyon seems to be excavated chiefly in sheared granite. The head of Monterey Canyon is just outside the beach zone, and is apparently cut into late Pleistocene or even Recent marine and river deposits.

In general, submarine canyons are marked by steep gradients, roughly concave long profiles, few tributaries, and heads at depths of a few hundred feet. The relatively small number of canyons whose heads are near the mouths of land rivers include most of the largest ones. Few canyon mouths have been adequately surveyed. Some canyons end in small basins, at various depths below 1,200 feet, some at the base of the steep continental slope, 7,000 to 11,000 feet below sea level; the Hudson Canyon extends to the very base of the continental slope at an even greater depth. The walls are composed chiefly of young sedimentary rocks, in part fairly well

Figure 16-29. Map and profile of Salinas River, Monterey submarine canyon, and its tributary, Carmel Canyon. The vertical scale is exaggerated 20 times.

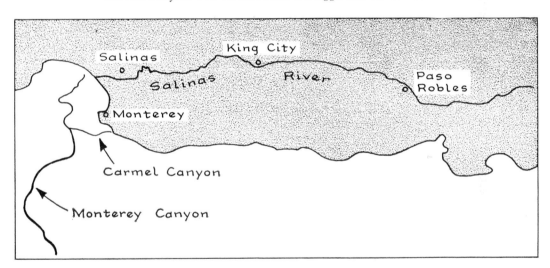

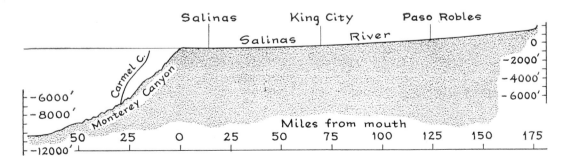

consolidated, as shown by specimens and fossils raised by the dredge.

Hypotheses of Origin

The many hypotheses advanced to account for submarine canyons belong to two groups, the subaerial and the submarine. The principal subaerial hypothesis is based on the lowering of sea level during the Pleistocene glacial epochs, discussed in Chapter 13. Its validity depends on how much water was removed from the oceans and locked up in glacial ice. Although we are fairly certain of the extent of the Pleistocene glaciers, we are not certain of their thickness, so estimates of the volume of ice vary. As we noted in discussing atolls, Daly estimated that sea level was lowered three hundred feet; borings from which fossils have been obtained in the Mississippi Delta suggest a lowering of about four hundred feet there. Surely no conceivable glacial lowering could account for the Hudson Canyon, with its mouth at the very foot of the continental slope, for even though one were to accept the idea of the formation of the huge volume of ice necessary to lower the sea to that level, the corollary increase in salinity of the oceans would have left unmistakable records by extinction of numerous species. But only a few species of shellfish became extinct in the Pleistocene; the number is about what one would expect for an epoch of that length, and does not suggest an extreme change in the salt content of the sea. Furthermore, if glacial lowering had been so great, one would surely expect to find systematic terraces carved in the sediments of the continental slopes at many places throughout the world. Submarine terraces are believed to exist off west Central Africa, but they are surely not widespread or they would have been detected in sounding. If the sea level had indeed been lowered many thousands of feet, surely all the great rivers would have cut deep canyons at the present shore. Every river of the world should end in an estuary formed by drowning of its valley. The Mississippi Valley was indeed about four hundred

feet deeper during the Pleistocene, but not several thousand feet deeper, as it would have had to be to account for the depth of the Hudson or Monterey canyons. The head of the La Jolla Canyon shows unmistakable signs of subaerial cutting, but only to a depth of two hundred or three hundred feet below sea level. None of the expected corollaries of a subaerial origin of the deeper parts of any submarine canyon seem to have been found.

The alternative to subaerial origin is obviously that the canyons have been cut under conditions not very different from those of the present—and, in fact, may be forming now. On this hypothesis the canyons were formed by the erosive action of turbidity currents, to which we will now turn.

The cable breaks connected with the Grand Banks earthquake (Chapter 5) seem clearly to point to the action of a huge turbidity current or submarine mudflow acting over a wide segment of the continental slope. The motive power of such a current is, of course, gravity, and its force depends on the difference in density between the muddy water and clear sea water at each point along the path. Since this difference in density is always much less than the difference between the densities of water and air, a greater slope is needed to produce a given velocity in a submarine channel than is needed to produce it in a surface channel of the same size. On the other hand, owing to the incoherence of most marine sediments, large quantities of material may be stirred up at one time and the great volume may more than compensate for the smaller drive of the individual particles. The speed attained may thus be many times greater (as it was off the Grand Banks) than in any known river flood. As mentioned in Chapter 15, desert mudflows carry large boulders in suspension; some marine sedimentary rocks contain similar boulders in a poorly sorted matrix—perhaps they, too, were carried in suspension. It is important, of course, to find whether a turbidity current such as seems to have been created by the Grand Banks earthquake could occur in the constricted area of a submarine canyon and thus continue to deepen it once it had started.

The best historical evidence of subaqueous channeling by turbidity currents comes from Swiss lakes. The flow of 1887 in the Lake of Zug has been described in Chapter 11. The mean gradient of that flow, 4 degrees, is similar to that of many submarine canyons, and is much higher than most stream gradients on land. The largest trench in a Swiss lake is that cutting the delta of the upper Rhone, in Lake Geneva. It is a few tens of feet deep and clearly the product of a turbidity flow like that of the Lake of Zug.

In a fresh-water lake, a turbidity current sinks to the bottom if its density exceeds 1. In the sea, the density must exceed 1.025, the density of clear sea water. Bottom density currents in the sea are obviously hard to discover. Neither the Grand Banks current or slide, nor the one in Tokyo Bay at the time of the Tokyo earthquake (Chapter 8) seem to have cut channels. There are, nevertheless, suggestions that sediments do travel down submarine canyons, and it seems reasonable to conclude that once started they should continue and erode effectively. The La Jolla Canyon, for example, has been shown by soundings to deepen suddenly after some storms and to become shallow during quiet weather. This suggests that storm turbulence starts accumulated sediment down the canyon as a turbid stream. It is also known that hundreds of thousands of cubic yards of gravel and sand are carried along the shore of Santa Monica Bay from both directions toward the submarine canyon off Redondo. Yet the canyon does not fill up and the shore is not advancing. The sediment must disappear down the canyon somehow—and it can hardly do so except as a turbidity flow.

Should we accept the hypothesis that turbidity currents are responsible for most undersea canyons, we would expect to find several of the features that actually exist: steep gradients, canyon heads in water shallow enough to be turbulent, mouths at various levels but mostly at the foot of the continental slope, canyons situated where they can be supplied with unusual amounts of sediment. A large muddy river would be one good source of sediment, the meeting place of two longshore currents another, the outer edge of the continental shelf a third—especially during the Pleistocene times of lowered sea level when abundant debris from melting glaciers was available and storm waves could stir up the unconsolidated sea bottom. Once erosion was started, the canyons themselves would furnish additional sediment.

If turbidity currents cut deep submarine canyons, they must deposit submarine deltas or fans, and there are suggestions that they do. At the mouth of the Hudson Canyon, a broad flat cone extends out onto the floor of the ocean and cores taken here show alternating layers of clay and coarser material—sand, silt, and shells. Many of the fossils are of benthic Foraminifera known to live at shallow depths. The coarse layers show coarser material at their bases, grading up to finer at the tops—graded bedding (Chapter 17)—which suggests sedimentation from a turbidity current. The alternation of these coarse layers with the fine clay that is usual at this depth (nearly three miles) suggests that the processes responsible for them are sporadic, rather than continuous. Identical graded bedding, some in deposits that contain coarse boulders in a contorted and tumbled sandy and silty matrix, has been found in Cenozoic strata of Italy and California, and is less certainly represented in many other formations of all eras, including the Precambrian.

Although many facts seem to fit the turbidity-current hypothesis of the origin of submarine canyons, we cannot yet feel completely satisfied. More information is needed. Can hard rocks be eroded by density currents, as we know unconsolidated sediments can? How thick is the sedimentary layer on the deep-sea floor, and what kind of stratification and what alternations in kind of sediment does it show? Do debris fans extend out from all submarine canyons as one does from the

Hudson? Some of these questions have been partly answered, but many more sonic and seismic surveys (Chapter 21) are needed, as are many more long cores from the deep-sea sediments.

We may, however, conclude this review of oceanic processes with an additional comment on the questions raised by Figure 10-4. Of the two dominant levels of the earth's relief, the higher seems reasonably to be explained by the fact that it is the level at which streams drop their loads in deltas and where most of the land-derived sediments of today and of the recent geologic past have accumulated. We do not know enough about the lower of the two great levels, that of the oceanic floor, to be sure of its origin. Perhaps it is accounted for by the average difference between the densities of the continental and oceanic blocks, in accordance with the Pratt scheme of isostasy. Perhaps, also, part of its remarkable extent is due to the filling of irregularities in an originally irregular oceanic bottom by sedimentation from turbidity currents and by slow sinking of volcanic ash and of terrigenous (land-derived) clay.

FACTS, CONCEPTS, TERMS

RELATIVE AREAS OF OCEAN AND LAND

CONTINENTAL SHELF; CONTINENTAL SLOPE

ISLAND ARCS; RIDGES AND RISES

TROUGHS; DEEPS; BANKS; SEAMOUNTS

CURRENTS IN THE SURFACE LAYER OF THE OCEAN
  Effects of wind drag
  Equatorial Drift; West-wind Drift
  The Gulf Stream

DEEP-WATER CIRCULATION
  Effects of temperature and salinity on density
  Density currents
  The Antarctic bottom water

TIDES: TIDAL CURRENTS; NEAP TIDES; SPRING TIDES

WAVES: DEEP-WATER WAVES; SHALLOW-WATER WAVES; PARTICLE MOTION

WAVE GROWTH AND SPEED

WAVE REFRACTION; ENERGY DISTRIBUTION IN WAVES

BREAKERS; TURBULENCE IN THE BREAKER ZONE

WAVE EROSION: HYDRAULIC PRESSURE; CORRASION; WAVE BASE; MOTION OF SEDIMENTS

STORM BEACHES, PROFILE OF EQUILIBRIUM

WAVE CURRENTS; LONGSHORE DRIFT

COASTAL TOPOGRAPHY: BAY-HEAD AND BAY-MOUTH BARS; LAND-TIED ISLANDS; SPITS; OFF-SHORE BARS

MARINE LIFE ZONES: BENTHIC; PELAGIC; LITTORAL; DEEP-SEA; PLANKTON; NEKTON

CORAL REEFS: FRINGING REEFS; BARRIER REEFS; ATOLLS

ORIGIN OF ATOLLS: DARWIN THEORY; DALY THEORY

SUBMARINE CANYONS: DISTRIBUTION, SLOPES, FORMS

SUBAERIAL ORIGIN OF CANYONS AND COROLLARIES THERETO

SUBMARINE ORIGIN OF CANYONS AND COROLLARIES THERETO

EFFECT OF GLACIAL LOWERING OF SEA LEVEL

TURBIDITY CURRENTS

QUESTIONS

1. Why are tides in the Mediterranean Sea smaller than those in San Francisco Bay, which also has a narrow connection with the ocean?

2. If the effect of wave refraction is to concentrate attack on headlands, why is a cuspate form of sand spit such as those off Cape Hatteras not destroyed?

3. If a wave 400 feet long has a period of 8 seconds, what is its velocity in feet per second? in miles per hour?

4. Roughly estimate the ratio between the velocity of a storm wave far from land and that of the swiftest ocean current.

5. What would be a reasonable difference in elevation between seaward and landward edges of the rock floor of an erosional marine terrace 2,000 feet wide? What is your basis of estimate?

6. The Congo submarine canyon heads in the Congo estuary, which is studded with alluvial islands. The depth of sedimentary fill in the estuary is not known. Draw two long profiles of the base of this fill: (1) assuming that the estuary is the slightly emergent head of a canyon formed beneath the sea, and (2) assuming that the whole submarine canyon was formed sub-aerially, but has since been warped below sea level. Explain.

7. At the equator, water on the bottom of both the Pacific and Atlantic is only a few degrees above freezing. What is the source of this cold water and why does it not mix quickly with the warm water at the surface?

8. What probable effects did the waxing and waning of the Pleistocene ice sheets have upon:

a) the salinity of the ocean?

b) the number of turbidity currents coursing down the continental slopes?

c) the circulation through the Straits of Gibraltar?

SUGGESTED READINGS

Darwin, C. R., in K. F. Mather and S. L. Mason. *Source Book in Geology*. New York, McGraw-Hill, 1939, pp. 354-357.

Davis, W. M. *The Coral Reef Problem*. American Geographical Society Special Publication 9. New York, 1928.

Fisher, Robert L., Roger Revelle, and Walter H. Munk. *The Planet Earth*. Scientific American Book. New York, Simon and Schuster, 1957.

Kuenen, P. H. *Marine Geology*. New York, John Wiley and Sons, 1950.

Ommanney, F. D. *The Ocean*. New York, Oxford University Press, 1949.

SEDIMENTARY ROCKS AND THE ENVIRONMENTS OF DEPOSITION

BECAUSE OF their predominance at the earth's surface the sedimentary rocks supply the chief record of earth history, and because fossils are essentially restricted to them, the fullest chronology. In earlier chapters we have considered many geologic processes. It is the aim of this chapter to show how the record of these processes has been used to reconstruct past geographies—and thereby as clues to the evolution of the earth. But first we will review some of the general features of sedimentary rocks.

The Volume of Sedimentary Rocks

Though stratified rocks probably make up only between 10 per cent and 20 per cent by volume of the earth's crust down to a depth of ten miles, they cover nearly three-fourths of the land and are undoubtedly even more widespread on the ocean floor. Although generally thin, they are in places as much as eight or perhaps even ten miles thick. Volcanic rocks are also common, but by far the most abundant of the stratified rocks are sedimentary.

Though many sedimentary rocks are reworked from older sediments, inevitably all must originally have been derived from igneous rock. The American chemist F. W. Clarke computed that a layer of igneous rock about a half a mile thick has been weathered and eroded to yield sediments during the course of geologic time. He based this estimate on the amount of sodium in the seas and in sedimentary rocks, assuming that the sodium had been released from igneous rocks by weathering. Owing to the swelling of feldspars as they weather to clay, and to the notable porosity of most sedimentary rocks, the volume of sediment is surely larger than that of the parental igneous rocks. Clarke guessed that there were 90 million cubic miles of sedimentary rocks; this is less than 5 per cent of the volume of the earth's crust to a depth of ten miles. Other estimates, based on other data and taking account of other corrections (many sedimentary rocks contain much unweathered feldspar, for example), are as much as forty times as large as Clarke's. A recent one, by the Dutch geologist P. Kuenen, is based on a better estimate of the average composition of igneous rocks than was available to Clarke, and also takes into consideration the sediments of the deep sea: Kuenen's results indicate that the sedimentary rocks make up about 15 per cent of the outer ten-mile shell.

Abundance of Different Rock Varieties

Scores of different kinds of sedimentary rocks have been described, but fully 99 per cent of the total volume is made up of only three: shale, sandstone, and limestone (including dolomite). Different geologists have computed the relative proportions of these varieties as reported in measured stratigraphic sections. Taking average chemical compositions of each, the relative proportions to be expected from the weathering of the "average igneous rock" can be computed. Since the data for these measurements and computations are inadequate, the proportions of each kind as computed by the different geologists are quite variable (see Table 17-1). Undoubtedly, if the data were better, the figures would not differ so greatly, but it is nevertheless nearly certain that shale is really far less abundant than one would expect. A much higher proportion of clay should be produced during weathering of the average igneous rock. The difference may be explained if we assume that much of the clay released by weathering has been swept into the oceanic depths and thus is not proportionately represented among the rocks available for study. In other words, the accessible sedimentary rocks do not represent all weathering products in the proportions in which they were formed because the deep sea sediments are not represented. As we shall see, intrinsic characteristics of the rocks now exposed to view on the lands testify to the accumulation of most of them in shallow water, thereby supporting this explanation of the discrepancy.

Factors Influencing Diversity of Sedimentary Rocks

In earlier chapters we touched upon many factors that influence the diversity of sedimentary rocks. These are of three main kinds, operating respectively (1) in the source area, (2) during transportation, and (3) at the place of deposition.

In the source area.—Source rock is obviously important. On weathering, most rocks produce some clay, but no amount of weathering can release clay from a pure quartz sand. Climate and relief are also pertinent factors. Climate exerts a major influence on weathering, as strikingly shown by the contrast between, say, the frost-riven fragments of fresh granite on an Arctic mountain, the clay-rich soil derived from granite in Virginia, and the high-aluminum laterite, also derived from granite, on a lowland in British Guiana. Vegetative cover is of course climatically controlled and influences strongly both the breakup of the rocks and the speed—even the mechanism—of erosion. Relief is a major determinant of the agency of erosion—for example, almost unaided downslope movement on a steep mountain slope, but almost unaided solution on a low plain of coral limestone. Relief also influences the maturity of the weathering profile, and thus the completeness of chemical decomposition of the source rock. Many sedimentary rocks have characteristics that enable us to infer much about the source area from which they were derived.

During transportation.—The fragments on a mountain talus pile—angular, and unsorted by either size or shape—exemplify material moved wholly by gravity. Such material is

ROCK	AS MEASURED IN ROCK OUTCROPS	THEORETICALLY TO BE EXPECTED, AS COMPUTED FROM ANALYSES
Shale	42 to 56	70 to 83
Sandstone	14 to 40	8 to 16
Limestone	18 to 29	5 to 14

TABLE 17-1

Percentage Proportions of Sedimentary Rocks Computed by Different Geologists.

only exceptionally preserved as consolidated rock, but where it has been, as along the buried mountain slope that underlies the Titus Canyon formation in the Death Valley region, its characteristic random sorting, angularity of fragments, and obvious derivation from adjacent bedrock leaves no doubt as to its origin. Contrast this with the well-winnowed dune sand that has been cemented to form the Navajo sandstone (Fig. 15-16). The Navajo is free from clay and other weathering minerals, is composed of well-rounded, uniformly sized grains of quartz without either pebbles or silt, and is much richer in quartz than any nearby source rock. Or contrast the mixture of rock flour, sand, and boulders at a glacier's snout, with the mud of a tidal flat, or the sand and gravel, ground round by the waves, of a coastal spit. These examples, among scores that could be given, show how the agency of transport clearly places its stamp upon many sedimentary deposits.

At the place of deposition.—Though source area and transport agency may leave their record, and many later processes such as cementation or partial solution by ground water and deformation during crustal disturbances are all commonly recorded, it is the depositional environment that generally gives sedimentary rocks their primary character. It was the similarity between the structures and compositions of ancient sedimentary rocks and those of modern deposits whose accumulation could be observed that gave rise to the doctrine of Uniformitarianism.

We have earlier given many illustrations of how depositional environment affects particular sedimentary rocks. It would take several books the size of this to discuss thoroughly each of the many environments and its characteristic sediments: talus cone, moraine, alluvial fan, floodplain, river bar, marsh, reef, dune, grassland, lake, estuary, sandspit, protected bay, exposed coast, offshore bottom, and scores of other geographic settings. We must content ourselves with outlining briefly a few of the more significant sedimentary features and suggest how they may be used as clues to the interpretation of the geographies of the geologic past.

Stratification

The most striking feature of most sedimentary rocks, and a common clue to their manner of origin, is stratification or layering. Layers may be microscopically thin or many scores of feet thick. In coarse clastic rocks grains of varying size lie in layers parallel or nearly parallel to the base of the stratum. Slight variations in the size and color of the grains in each of the layers usually emphasize the stratification. In fine clastic rocks, there may be no obvious difference in grain size from one layer to another—perhaps only a color-banding, brought out by slight differences in the content of organic matter, of carbonate, of magnetite, mica, or some other mineral, or of clay and silt. Many carbonate rocks show stratification only by broadly spaced surfaces of ready parting; others by thin layers of clay or shale between the beds of carbonates. Among the clastic rocks, four varieties of stratification deserve especial consideration because they record significant differences in depositional processes. They are: parallel lamination, current bedding, graded bedding and massive bedding (Fig. 17-1).

Origin of Stratification

The word sediment implies that a particle has settled from a fluid, and when applied to rocks it implies further that currents have transported the particle. Even if the particle has grown in place, currents must have carried in the materials composing it. As we saw in Chapter 12, most currents are turbulent, with a wide range of velocities for different threads of current in both time and place. Particles carried by a turbulent current are thus subject to widely fluctuating forces, although over a period of a few minutes or hours these fluctuations should average out. In Chapter 12, we considered the forces of friction and of impact that are exerted on a sedimentary particle in a moving fluid and we also noticed that almost any natural water current is turbulent enough to retain very fine particles in suspension almost indefinitely.

PARALLEL LAMINATION. Grains larger than about .1 mm. in diameter are not all carried by a feeble current, even though the current may be turbulent; the size of grain that can be either kept in suspension or dragged along the bottom depends on the current speed. A mountain freshet may be able to roll great boulders along its bottom, but as its velocity decreases, the size of the particles it can carry also decreases; part of the material that has been rolling along the bottom comes to rest and smaller particles become part of the rolling, rather than suspended, load of the current. Thus a layer of sediment is laid down. If the current continues to lose speed a considerable thickness of finer and finer material may be deposited. This deposition generally alters the bottom configuration, so that the turbulence pattern of the next rapid current will differ from that of the old. The new current may pick up some of the finer material previously deposited but leaves the coarser grains as a thin uniform bed. Of course, if it is swifter than the old current, it may re-entrain all the sediment laid down by the declining current and even scour the bottom below it. However, the settling of fine particles into the interstices between the coarser grains already stranded on the bottom smooths the surface and compacts the sediment so that it is less easily eroded at a particular current velocity than it would have been during the declining cycle. Thus a current even faster than the one from which grains of a given size were deposited may not suffice to pick them up again and move them along the bottom. The resistance to re-entrainment of silt-sized and clay-sized particles is particularly great, as has been proved many times in irrigation canals and in other controlled channels (see Fig. 12-7). Perhaps for this reason parallel lamination is especially common in shales and fine grained sands.

To summarize, almost any current that

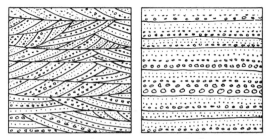

1. Current bedding   2. Graded bedding

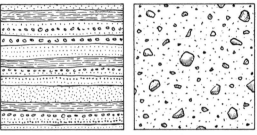

3. Parallel lamination   4. Massive bedding

Figure 17-1.   Several varieties of stratification of clastic rocks. 1, current bedding, in which the minor laminae lie at a notable angle with the major bedding planes; 2, graded bedding, in which the gross lamination parallels the major bedding planes, but each individual lamina grades from coarse at the base to fine at the top; 3, parallel lamination, in which thin layers of differing grain size lie essentially parallel to the major stratification and to each other; and 4, massive bedding, in which no systematic arrangement by grain size is recognizable within individual thick strata.

reaches bottom can deposit a sequence of alternating fine and coarse parallel laminae. The moving water sorts out and drops grains of a particular size with each change of current velocity. Thus is produced the common **parallel lamination** shown in Figures 17-1, *3* and 17-2, *a.*

CURRENT BEDDING. When a sand-laden current slows on entering slack water, as on the inside of a river bend, the sand grains rolling along the bottom are deposited and the larger grains in suspension also sink rapidly. The deposition soon constricts the channel, and much of the entrained sand is

a

Figure 17-2. Features of sedimentary rocks. (a) Thinly laminated sandstone interbedded with a few thicker beds: Coaledo formation, Washington (Photo by P. D. Snavely, U. S. Geological Survey). (b) Slump bedding and intraformational disturbances due to sliding of soft sediments. Mudstone in Miocene rocks north of Dos Pueblos Creek, Santa Barbara County, California (Photo by M. N. Bramlette, U. S. Geological Survey). (c) Massive bedding in two-foot mudflow on beach at Cape Thompson, Alaska (Photo by R. Kachadoorian, U. S. Geological Survey). (d) Ripple marks on Silurian siltstone: west shore of Moose Island, Washington County, Maine (Photo by E. S. Bastin, U. S. Geological Survey).

b

c

d

then swept past the constriction and dumped over the edge of the earlier deposit. It builds forward with a sloping front down which the grains tumble and roll to the bottom. Grains accumulated at the bottom decrease the slope of the embankment, and some of the succeeding grains therefore are retained on the slope, building it forward parallel to itself but at an angle to the surface of the water. (See Figs. 12-22 and 17-1, *1.*) Succeeding increments continue to extend the embankment forward into the slack water, forming a layer of sediment with foreset bedding, perhaps only a fraction of an inch thick if the current is weak, but perhaps a score or even more feet thick if the current is strong and well loaded with sand. Each increment added to the end of the deposit, though, is sloping forward at the angle of sliding friction, which may be only a few degrees or as much as 40. A trench cut through such a deposit shows lamination at an angle to the horizon—that is, to the bedding proper. This lamination is called **cross-bedding, cross-lamination,** or **current bedding.**

The process just described is the one common in shallow streams. But cross-bedding is also very common in deeper waters and in marine environments, and there the process is like that by which sand dunes are formed (Fig. 15-11). The sand ripples create a current shadow like that in the lee of a dune, and grains falling on the upcurrent side are rolled over the top to accumulate at the angle of sliding friction. Whether formed in deep or shallow water, however, any deposit showing cross-bedding has obviously been laid down from a fluid whose motion extended to the then-existing bottom. In Chapter 15 we described how distinctive curving cross-bedding is formed in sand dunes (see Fig. 15-16). Similar bedding is commonly found in water-laid sands but nowhere so consistently or over so wide an area as in dune sands. Most cross-bedding in water-laid deposits is in beds a fraction of an inch to a few feet thick, whereas in dune sands the curved cross-bedding may extend through scores of feet across the bedding.

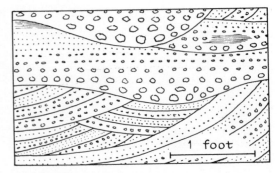

Figure 17-3. Scour-and-fill structures and accompanying features of fluviatile bedding.

Cross-bedding, then, is often a clue to the sedimentary environment of a deposit displaying it: the current that formed the cross-beds must have extended down to the surface of the bed. Fluctuations in current speed and volume cause scouring of the upper surface, forming depressions to be filled by later deposits. Thus **scour-and-fill** structures are commonly associated with cross-bedding (see Fig. 17-3).

GRADED BEDDING. Another variety of bedding, called **graded bedding,** consists of layers, each with a sharply marked base on which lie the coarsest grains in the deposit (Fig. 17-1, *2*). In each layer the coarse bottom material grades up without a break or sudden change in grade size to fine material at the top of the layer, there to be succeeded abruptly by the coarse base of another layer. Such a graded bed can be easily produced by stirring up sediments of widely varying grain size in a beaker and allowing it to stand. The coarse fragments fall through the water quickly but the finest may remain in suspension for hours. Much finely laminated material is laid down from such pulses of sediment-laden water, and each lamina may then show graded bedding. The varves of glacial lakes (Chapter 13) furnish excellent examples of graded bedding; it is also found in stream backwaters into which freshets overflow; in sheltered bays, where storm waves that have entrained much sediment are driven; and in the ocean, where turbidity flows deposit sand covered with finer silt. Graded beds are commonly interbedded with others having even parallel lamination or showing current bedding. This association is reasonably to be expected.

Graded bedding is also commonly associated with submarine landslides because these are likely to generate turbidity currents. Sliding of little-consolidated material may be accompanied by much gouging and plowing into the sediments below the slide. Twisted and rolled chunks of mud—mudgalls—are formed, thin beds are broken and crumpled (Fig. 17-2, *b*) and sandstone dikes may be injected into the soft sediments beneath because of the sudden loading. At the same time the landslide sets up strong currents which sort unconsolidated material and produce current bedding. As these currents die away the sediment in the overlying turbid water settles to produce good graded bedding. Graded bedding is thus in many places associated with evidence of subaqueous slumping, and because of this some geologists regard graded bedding as a criterion of deep-water deposition. But varved lake sediments and overbank deposits on floodplains are also truly graded, and submarine landslides can form at any depth, as shown by the sliding masses in the Lake of Zug, in Sagami Bay at the time of the Tokyo Earthquake, on the slope below the Grand Banks, or at the mouth of the Hudson submarine canyon (Chapter 16). Graded bedding indicates only that, unlike current bedding, it was formed under conditions such that bottom currents were not active enough to sort the sinking sediment by grain size. Active currents may have operated at that site just before the bed in question was laid down, and may recur later.

MASSIVE BEDDING.   In the coarser clastic sediments, **massive bedding,** that is, thick bedding with no internal lamination, may be formed by sedimentation so sudden that there is no sorting either by grain size or density. Desert mudflows whose internal structure can be seen in stream banks or roadcuts, exhibit no bedding; neither do volcanic mudflows. Mudflows are sufficiently saturated with water to flow, but too viscous to undergo much sorting (Figs. 17-1, *4*, and 17-2, *c*). Some pyroclastic deposits are also without notable bedding, doubtless because the rapidly erupted clouds of ash glided downslope like an avalanche, with such turbulence as to give no opportunity for sorting.

Some well-sorted sediments also form massive beds. Presumably some of these result from redeposition of material already well-sorted in an older sediment, but in many of the finer muds burrowing organisms may so thoroughly mix the material as to destroy all sign of bedding, thus producing a massive deposit.

TEXTURES.   The word **textures** refers to those aspects of a rock that are determined by the size, shape, sorting, and mutual space relations of the component particles (see Appendix III). A moment's consideration of the helter-skelter arrangement of angular fragments on a cinder cone or talus pile, of the coarse, poorly sorted and poorly rounded bouldery deposits of a mountain stream bed or beneath a wave-cut headland, of the well-sorted and rounded sands of a desert dune or an ancient beach, or of the impalpable mud dredged from a stagnant pond or the deep sea, is enough to show that textural features may be clues to the environment of deposition of a rock.

Even the degree of rounding of the component material tells much. Boulders, even of hard rock, may become rounded within a few hundred yards of the place where they fell as angular fragments into a mountain stream, but sand grains, with their relatively greater surface per unit volume, are much less quickly rounded. Even long wear on a beach may fail to round sand-sized material well—in fact, many geologists think that highly rounded quartz grains are never formed in a single cycle of erosion and deposition, but testify to the reworking of sand from one sandstone to another, or even to repeated reworkings. As the weight of a sand grain is greater in air than in water, mutual collisions during transport by the wind entail relatively more abrasion than during water transport. Hence sand in dunes is commonly better rounded than that in stream or beach deposits.

Terrestrial Sediments

The distinguishing features of many terrestrial sediments have already been described: flood plains, stream gravels, deltaic deposits (Chapter 12); moraines, varved clays, outwash gravels, loess (Chapter 13); dunes, mudflows (Chapter 15). Still others are treated in later sections of this book: ash flows (Chapter 18), and coal (Chapter 21). Here we examine some terrestrial deposits with a view to recognizing their ancient analogs among the sedimentary rocks.

Stream Deposits

As we saw in Chapter 12, nearly all rivers fluctuate widely in volume through the year and thus range widely in their capacity to move detritus. Streams of high velocity transport great boulders and, in receding flood stages, may leave a layer of coarse pebbles strewn over a surface of more heterogeneous but crudely sorted gravel. The wide fluctuations in current speed are reflected in alternate scouring of older sediments or of the bedrock, and deposition of gravel, sand, and silt, either in backwaters during high floods or over the whole stream bed during flood recessions. The features characteristic of coarse stream deposits thus include scour-and-fill structures, current bedding, local graded bedding, and poorly sorted material, generally with many angular or subangular pebbles and cobbles interspersed with well-rounded ones. These are readily examined in the walls of many stream terraces. Another feature common on alluvial plains is channel fillings of coarser sediments separated by wider areas of finer as overbank deposits. All these features are present in the Arikaree formation, of Late Ter-

tiary age, in eastern Colorado, Nebraska, and Kansas, and strongly imply that this formation represents the deposits of an aggrading floodplain: an idea that finds support in the fossils of the Arikaree—bones of antelope, camels, and horses, shells of land snails, and pollen of grasses—all of which might be found on an open floodplain.

Such streams as the lower Mississippi and the Nile carry little coarse sediment. Their flood deposits are chiefly silts and fine sands, with the sands forming the channel fillings, and the silts and clays the overbank deposits in natural levees or in backwaters. Sporadic lenses of fine gravel and coarse sand form in the main channel. Similar deposits, with sinuous lenses of coarse silt, sand, and fine gravel between broad expanses of fine clays and silts are recognizable in the cores recovered from wells drilled into the Pleistocene deposits of the lower Mississippi. They contain freshwater mollusks and plant remains comparable to those along the present river. Some excavations show local current bedding and scour-and-fill phenomena, others the even lamination of flood-plain lake deposits. These features allow only one interpretation: the deposits are fluvial, undoubtedly those of the ancestral Mississippi. Studies of excavations and drill cuttings, from which a sequence of former levee and channel deposits may be reconstructed, have enabled Harold Fisk and other geologists of the Mississippi River Commission to recognize a long succession of shifting delta distributaries (Fig. 17-4). Similar features that remain recognizable in cemented and consolidated rocks from many geological systems and on every continent have been interpreted in the same way.

Marine Sediments

Sources of Marine Sediments

Except for a trivial amount of meteorite dust, the much greater but unmeasurable increment from submarine volcanoes, and an uncertain but probably small addition from tidal scour and downslope movements off submarine

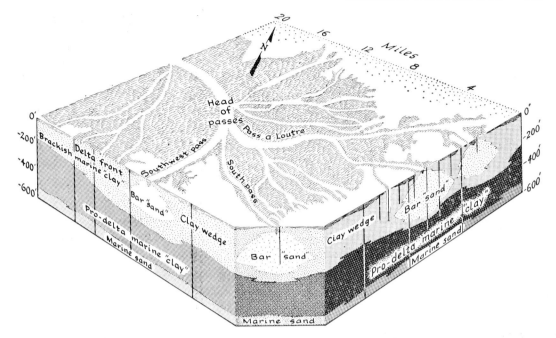

Figure 17-4.   The sedimentation pattern of the Mississippi delta. (After H. N. Fisk, E. Mc-Farlan, Jr., C. R. Kolb and L. J. Wilbert, Journal of Sedimentary Petrology, 1954.)

ridges, the marine sediments are derived ultimately from the land. Even the material of the marine shells, which contribute significantly to the bulk of marine sediments, was originally leached from terrestrial rocks. Rivers and rills, sluggish or swift, sweep the land waste seaward. Detritus from downslope movement, glacial plucking, and abrasion, windblown volcanic ash and desert dust, all are carried to the sea, there to mingle with the debris won by the ocean itself in its attack on the shores.

The rivers bring about twenty billion tons of rock waste to the oceans every year. More than four-fifths of this is clastic material carried in suspension or rolled along stream bottoms; the rest is dissolved. The fate of the clastic material is clear: waves can be seen to sort it out almost as soon as it reaches the sea. Samples dredged from the sea floor show partly consolidated sediments identical in grain size and mineral content with the detritus supplied by nearby rivers. Because of the continual wave agitation, good stratification

and sorting are more common in ocean deposits than in river sediments.

The fate of the dissolved material is not so obvious. We know that some of it is deposited, for there are great marine beds of limestone, dolomite, salt, and anhydrite—even though the sediments of the modern seas do not seem to include so high a proportion of these deposits as is recorded in the geologic past (Table 17-1). Present-day river waters hold a much higher proportion of silica and calcium than does sea water—so much higher that the composition of the sea would change greatly in a geologically short time if these substances were not somehow withdrawn from solution. This withdrawal is chiefly a result of life processes: much of the calcium and silica brought to the sea in solution is incorporated into the limy and siliceous shells of various organisms. Some geologists think that part of the difference in the proportion of ancient and modern limestones to their respective contemporary clastic sediments is due to the relatively greater number of organisms that float freely in the modern seas. Materials they extract from the sea are thereby widely distributed over the sea floor, rather than being restricted mainly to the continental shelves as in earlier geologic time, before these abundant pelagic forms had evolved.

Realms of Marine Sedimentation

By far the most abundant strata in the geologic column are marine, so that ascertaining the conditions of the origin of these rocks is a most important problem in stratigraphy.

The *Challenger* expedition in 1873-1876 proved that sediments are being deposited virtually everywhere in the sea except where currents scour the bottom, or where the submarine slopes are too steep to retain them. But even where depth, exposure, distance to shore, submarine slope, and other obvious factors appear identical, the local sediments vary. Despite much careful work, we are far from understanding all the reasons for this variation, though we can recognize the characteristic sediments formed in many different realms of sedimentation.

Sediments of the Strand Zone

The **strand zone** is that along the shore. Its widely variable sediments include those of beaches, deltas, and tide flats.

BEACHES.   Beaches are wave-worked deposits of cobbles, gravels, and sands on and near the shore. During great storms, much or all of this material is moved about or even stripped away by the waves, but between storms only the surface layer is agitated. Beaches vary greatly in length: some in narrow coves are only a few feet long, others on low-lying coasts stretch uninterruptedly for hundreds of miles.

The waves wear down and round the grains and sort them by size. Thus a beach develops a stratification whose perfection depends on the size, range, and amount of the available material. Stratification is generally poorer

along coasts of high relief, where steep streams and downslope movement supply heterogeneous unsorted material, than it is along low-lying coasts, where the source material is generally an old sediment or sedimentary rock that has already been sorted during its first cycle of deposition.

Beach sands may be largely of quartz, especially if they come from deeply weathered granitic regions or from disintegration of older sandstones. If an older sediment is the source, any feldspar in it will have had at least its second chance to weather to clay. But in regions of rapid erosion or of ineffective chemical weathering, feldspar may abound in beach sands. In Hawaii, whole beaches are made up of grains of olivine—a mineral that weathers readily—derived from the easily eroded piles of cinders formed where lava streams entered the sea. Some beaches, particularly in the tropics, are composed largely of shell fragments. Along the Brazilian coast these are being cemented almost as quickly as they form; the spray dissolves a little calcite from the shells at the surface and deposits it below as a cement. Many sand beaches (like other current and stream deposits) contain concentrations of heavy minerals—"black sand"—such as magnetite, chromite, and garnet, that have been sorted out by the wash because their density is higher than that of other associated minerals. At Nome, Alaska, black sands have long been worked for gold, both on the modern beaches and in ancient raised beaches some miles inland.

Relatively few beach deposits have been recognized among the consolidated rocks, although there are many recently uplifted beaches (Figs. 8-7 and 16-16). The reason is that beach deposits are readily destroyed: uplift exposes them to subaerial erosion, and submergence to any depth less than wave base subjects them to reworking by waves and tidal currents. Cambrian beaches, however, with associated cliffs and tumbled stacks, have been recognized in the Montana Rockies, and Carboniferous and Jurassic beaches in Great Britain.

DELTAS. Where a stream enters the sea, the surface slope that gives it a current vanishes. If wave action is strong, river and sea water quickly mix, but along quiet coasts the fresh water may float for awhile above the salt water. The powerful flood of the Amazon spreads widely over the Atlantic near its mouth, and fresh water may be dipped from the surface many miles at sea.

Sediment suspended in river water is thus distributed widely over the sea floor. Rivers vary tremendously in the grain size of their sediments, and all carry coarser material when in flood than during low water. Some, like the Colorado, carry much sand, some of it coarse; others, like the Amazon, Mississippi and Rhine, carry little but clay, silt, and fine sand. At the river mouth the coarsest material settles out first, followed by progressively finer and finer material, as can be seen in the Mississippi delta (Fig. 17-4).

Streams generally form deltas where they enter the sea, but if the stream load is small, the coast exposed to strong waves, or the tidal range large, the detritus may be so widely scattered by waves and currents that no delta forms—even so great a stream as the Columbia has none. And where deltas do form, longshore currents carry much sediment away from them. In fact, the greater part of beach material, including that in spits and longshore bars, is derived from streams or by reworking of unconsolidated sediments rather than from direct wave and current attack on coastal bedrock.

Rivers generally subdivide into distributaries to form deltas. Such distributaries as enter shallow waters commonly build deltas characterized by foreset, bottomset and topset bedding (Fig. 12-22). But the great bird-foot delta of the Mississippi, built into the deep water of the Gulf of Mexico, consists of such fine sediment that the slopes of all bedding are extremely low, so that "foreset bedding" is a meaningless term. Coarse silt and fine sand extend on either side of the distributary channels far out into the Gulf as underwater natural levees. When traced landward these underwater levees are found to be continuous with the natural levees of the flood plain and delta. Like all natural levees, they are made of coarser sediment near the channel (Fig. 17-4). The activity of a delta varies with river discharge and with shifts in flow from one distributary to another. Some segments may advance into the sea while others are being destroyed by the waves. The shore processes are like those along a plains coast. Offshore bars sheltering tidal lagoons are common; the waves may push the bars inland to the delta front and then rework the stream-laid beds, concentrating the coarser material on the beach and strewing the finer over the sea floor. Deltas furnish an excellent example of the difficulty of geologic classification, for all ocean deltas contain some beds that are truly marine, others that are brackish lagoonal deposits, and still others that are truly fluviatile —all complexly interfingering.

To summarize: the coarsest material comes to rest chiefly on the stream bed or on beaches; finer material forms natural levees and their submarine extensions; the finest sediment is deposited on the outer side of the levees or is swept out to sea.

Delta subsidence.—Some deltas, like that of the Mississippi, are known from surveys to be sinking, in places as much as eight feet per century. It has been suggested that this is isostatic sinking due to the load of sediments locally added to the earth's crust. As with glacial loads, some sinking seems to be a necessary consequence of isostasy, although the sinking of the Mississippi delta seems far too great to be explained in this way alone. The new, unconsolidated sediments are much less dense than any deeper lying rocks, and their floor should, therefore, sink far less than the thickness of added sediment. (A canoe will float lower in the water if it is filled to the top with sawdust, but it will not sink.) Perhaps, instead of sinking wholly isostatically, the sediment is also compacting and consolidating under the weight of newly added material, thereby causing part of the subsidence. Moreover, there may be a slow mass flowage of the unconsolidated material seaward; or possibly the river is being deflected toward an area that is subsiding at a rate that compensates for the added sedimentary thickness. No one knows the relative importance of these possible factors.

Whatever the cause, parts of the subaerial delta are being slowly submerged to form tidal lagoons or even open channels in which fine brackish or marine sediments accumulate. It may be this submergence of all the outer surface except the natural levees that gives the Mississippi delta its peculiar bird-foot form. As distributaries shift, deltaic marine beds may be buried by river deposits. If subsidence continues, the delta may remain nearly in place and not advance into the sea in proportion to the amount of detritus added to it. Interlayered marine, fluviatile, and brackish-water deposits may accumulate to great thickness, thinning into completely fluviatile beds landward and into completely marine beds seaward.

Many deltas can be clearly recognized among the ancient sediments from such an intimate association of varied deposits. In New York and Pennsylvania, a Devonian delta shows strata more than 8,000 feet thick, and borings for petroleum indicate that the ancestral Mississippi delta was comparably thick along the Louisiana coast. The structures revealed in outcrops or well cores show that each bed formed in relatively shallow water, despite these great aggregate thicknesses. Clearly, therefore, sinking concurrent with delta formation is real, whether it is partly isostatic or whether the sinking *only localized the delta* by providing a hole toward which the river ran.

The clay particles in river water have very large surface areas relative to their weight. They are dispersed as tiny individual particles, largely because each has a positive electrical charge and thus repels its neighbors. The unsatisfied electrical charges of the surface ions in the crystals of clay attract negatively charged ions such as OH^- from the water so that each clay particle acquires a

shell of negatively charged ions. On entering the sea, the negatively charged ions in the surface shells unite with the abundant ions of Na^+ and Mg^{++} in the sea. With their surface charges thus neutralized, the clay particles can then stick to each other—flocculate—instead of being mutually repelled, and thus form clots, or aggregates, that can sink faster than the individual clay particles composing them.

Much clay, therefore, may settle quickly on entering the sea. Actually, few careful studies of this process have been made in natural environments, though the idea outlined above conforms with laboratory tests. In one study, Revelle and Shepard (1938) found that off the California coast, despite thorough mixing of stream and ocean water, much clay was carried by eddies and currents as far as 150 miles from shore before settling to the bottom, though most was deposited nearer the coast. As is discussed later in this chapter, even this distance is less than fine clay might be expected to travel before sinking through several thousand feet of water.

TIDAL-FLAT DEPOSITS. Tidal-flat deposits accumulate in estuaries of sluggish streams or behind offshore bars. Many are deposited rapidly; at Wilhelmshaven and Cuxhaven, both on the North Sea coast of Germany, 8 to 10 feet of mud may accumulate locally in a single year, rapidly filling the lagoons behind offshore bars. Much of this mud and silt is brought in by rivers but much is also swept in by the tide. The mud is full of bottom-dwelling organisms which pass the sediment through their digestive tracts, disturbing or even obliterating its stratification. Some of the mud contains so much organic matter that it is used as agricultural fertilizer. Shallow parts of many tidal lagoons support a luxuriant growth of brackish water plants, which, by filtering out the sediment, speed up the silting of the lagoon.

Lagoonal deposits, like beaches, are rarely preserved among older rocks. Some Devonian shales of Germany, however, have many features in common with modern lagoonal deposits and may have formed in a similar environment.

Sediments of the Shelf Zone

The discussion of shore processes in Chapter 16 emphasized that the marine profile of equilibrium is merely an ideal concept. It applies as a sound generalization in such areas as the northern Gulf of Mexico, the Gulf of Paria, and many other places whose bottom topography and modern sediments have been well studied. In these areas, as one would expect, we pass from near-shore deposits of sand outward to deep water with a mud bottom—a sequence conforming to the theory. Perhaps it is significant that these areas are abundantly supplied with river-borne sediments and are in places that were not occupied by the Pleistocene glaciers. At any rate, this simple arrangement is not found everywhere, although it does appear that near shore the bottom is generally concave upward and flattens seaward. Offshore, however, the bottom deviates considerably from a smooth ideal profile and the sediments in transit across the shelf do not everywhere diminish regularly in grain size. The deviations from regularity may be partly explained by the rise of sea level—perhaps 300 feet—since the melting of the Pleistocene glaciers. This occurred so recently that the sea has possibly not had time completely to adjust its profile and sediments to the new level except in areas abundantly supplied with sediment: or perhaps crustal movements have similarly interfered with the development of a smooth slope and effective sorting. An example of such a complex pattern of both bottom topography and modern sediments is that of the Atlantic Coastal Shelf of the United States.

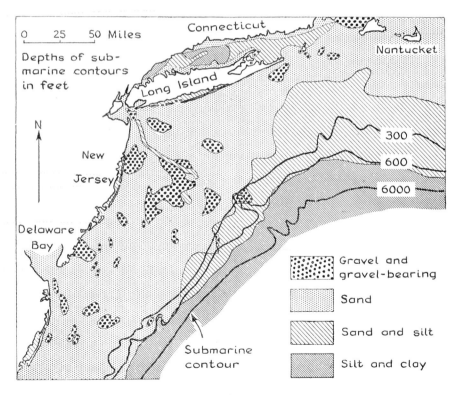

Figure 17-5.

The size distribution of sediments on the continental shelf of the eastern United States. (After F. P. Shepard and G. V. Cohee, 1936.)

SEDIMENTS OF THE ATLANTIC CONTINENTAL SHELF. Figure 17-5 shows the distribution of bottom sediments on the continental shelf off the Mid-Atlantic states, as reported in the hydrographic charts of the United States Coast and Geodetic Survey. The material reported is that which adhered to the tallow on a sounding lead. The charts show that rather than simply grading from coarse to fine seaward, the sediments are very irregularly distributed. There is actually more sand near shore and more gravel in deep water. Moreover, the sediments of the outer edge of the shelf are coarser than those inshore. Silt and clay, however, are rare at depths less than 600 feet and widespread below these depths.

Figure 17-6 shows the profiles along three lines surveyed across the shelf off the eastern United States. Above the bottom profile is plotted the median diameter of the grains of sediment obtained from cores. Profile A, off

Cape Cod, shows a rather regular bottom slope except near the shelf edge; it also shows finer sediments—largely silty—offshore, except near the shelf edge. The coarser materials within 20 miles of the shore are very irregularly arranged. This profile has been developed on an area glaciated during the Pleistocene, and the advancing sea has therefore had to sort material of all sizes, from boulders to rock flour. Profile B, off New Jersey, where the floor was not glaciated, shows finer material inshore but considerably coarser material at the same depth as that at which Profile A shows silt. Here, too, grain sizes of sediment are irregularly distributed, but beyond a line 25 miles from the coast the material tends to be finer seaward except near the edge of the continental shelf, where it again coarsens. Perhaps silt is scarce along this profile because the sea is here working on old coastal plain sediments which contain little except

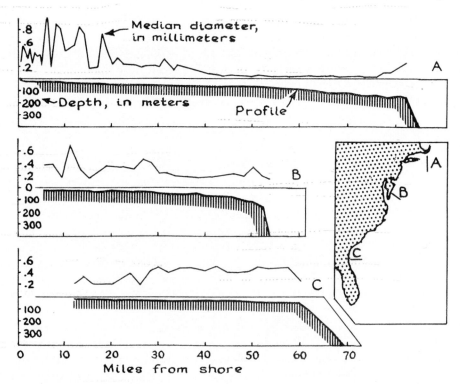

Figure 17-6.

The distribution of sediment sizes along three profiles of the Atlantic shelf of the United States. (After H. C. Stetson, redrawn from H. U. Sverdrup, M. W. Johnson, and R. H. Fleming, The Oceans, *Copyright 1942, by Prentice-Hall, Inc.*

sand. Profile C, off northern Florida, slopes regularly, but even here the material outside the 25-mile limit is consistently coarser than that inshore. The coarseness of sediment clearly shows that the Gulf Stream, whose currents sweep the outer shelf, is here swift enough to carry fine sediment right across the shelf, down the slope, and even across the Blake plateau whose edge is 6,500 feet below the surface. Here coarse sand is probably being swept to depths greater than 6,500 feet.

Another region with unusual sediments is Indonesia—an area of unusual interest because, as we noted in Chapter 8, many geologists regard it as one of incipient mountain-making.

SEDIMENTS OF THE INDONESIAN SEAS. The submarine topography of the Indonesian area is highly irregular, with deep basins, shallow marine plains, and submerged mountain ridges. Some basins, such as the Sulu, Celebes, and Banda Seas, are more than three miles deep and are separated from the ocean basins by ridges and saddles. The region contains many volcanoes, more than fifty of which have been active at some time since 1600. Although only a few hundred samples of the sediments of this great region of more than a million square miles were studied, the Netherlands *Snellius* Expedition of 1929-1930 obtained some extremely interesting information.

When Tamboro, east of Java, erupted violently in 1815 (p. 365), the ash was thrown high in the air and great quantities were spread by the winds—10 inches fell at a distance of 240 miles. This ash is readily recognized by its distinctive minerals and textures. The effect of benthic organisms in mixing sediments is shown by the fact that this characteristic ash was found, more than a century later, at the surface of the bottom mud not only in areas of slow deposition, but also near the mouths of mud-laden rivers, where the annual influx of mud should have buried it beneath many feet of younger material. Here it is mixed with terrestrial clays through several feet of sediment.

Rock bottom was found on the tops of many ridges between basins, even at depths of several thousand feet, yet fine muds occur at far shallower depths in places less-exposed to currents. Terrigenous mud was cored fully 300 miles from the nearest land and at depths of 16,000 feet; volcanic muds were dredged from still greater depths even farther from shore. In the Philippine Trench, 50 miles east of Mindanao, silty and clayey sediments were dredged from depths of 33,000 feet. These contain little sand but many larger fragments of metamorphic rock like that exposed on Mindanao. The travel of these coarse sediments to such great depths suggests submarine sliding and also strong currents that sweep across even the deep ridges and saddles, thereby winnowing out the fine material as it settles and wafting it into quiet basins and off the continental slope. Current speeds ranging as high as 1 mile an hour at 600 feet, and to $\frac{1}{14}$ mile an hour at 6,500 feet were measured by the *Snellius* on the divide between two of the basins.

Some of the coarse sediments now at great depth have undoubtedly slid from steep submarine slopes, exposing the underlying rock high on the slopes and bringing coarse debris to rest where the normal sediment is much finer. Effects of submarine slides are well shown in some consolidated rocks by contorted and dislocated bedding between otherwise undisturbed rocks and by exposures of the actual sliding surfaces. Such features, as well as mud-galls, load-casts, plastic overfolds, grooves in bedding, and sandstone dikes —all suggesting submarine slides—have been observed in the Silurian rocks of parts of Wales, in Tertiary rocks of Peru, Ecuador, the Alps, southern California (Fig. 17-2, *b*), and in many other places.

Experiments show that particles of quartz of various sizes settle in water at speeds indicated in Table 17-2. Grains of clay—with more surface area for a particle of the same weight—settle more slowly. Miss Neeb, a Dutch geologist who studied the *Snellius* collections, computed the distance a current of

DIAMETER OF PARTICLE (mm.)	RATE OF SETTLING IN WATER OF 27° C (cm/hr.)	DISTANCE TRANSPORTED WHILE SINKING 1,000 METERS (current speed 1 cm/sec.)
0.100 (fine sand)	2,000	1.8 km (1.1 miles)
0.030 (coarse silt)	180	20 km (12 miles)
0.005 (fine silt)	5	720 km (430 miles)
0.001 (clay)	0.2	18,000 km (11,000 miles)

TABLE 17-2

Theoretical Dispersal of Sedimentary Particles by Currents. (After Neeb)

only 1 centimeter per second ($\frac{1}{44}$ mile per hour) would carry quartz grains of different sizes during the time required for them to settle 1,000 meters (3,300 feet). (See third column of Table 17-2.) She assumed quiet water (laminar flow) as the particle sinks, but of course turbulence would further prolong the sinking time, as would the greater viscosity and density of the water in the cold oceanic depths.

Even though these computations neglect the flocculation of clay, which should speed the sinking somewhat, we see that fine silts and clays could be carried almost any distance by currents as strong as those actually measured in the Indonesian area. Clay particles settling to the bottom of a deep marine basin may thus have sources far different from those of the coarser grains of the same deposit. Cores from the deep eastern Pacific Basin, collected by the Swedish Deep Sea Expedition of 1947-1948 contain much clay, though the area is more than 2,000 miles from the nearest land. Several students have pointed out that, if the clays are settling far from their source, they should be doing so almost uniformly all over the sea floor in areas of equal depth. Both silica and calcium carbonate are organic deposits that vary with latitude and other geographic factors, but the amount of clay in a deep sea core should be a measure of the time during which it has been accumulating. By comparing measures of clay accumulation against radiocarbon dates of material at different depths, it appears that this is at least roughly true. We may thus have here a tool for correlating the sediments of deep oceanic basins with one another.

Still another result of the Indonesian studies is noteworthy. The drowned river plain of the Sunda Shelf (Fig. 8-11) hardly exceeds 200 feet in depth. Bottom muds near Java are largely volcanic debris from the nearby island, but farther north they consist mainly of coarse quartz sand, undoubtedly derived from the deeply weathered granite of Borneo and other islands to the north. These coarse sands are, however, separated from these islands by a belt of much finer, and presumably younger, quartzose sands, and hence must be either isolated deposits of river sand or else residual sands that were once on the land surface, and have remained little disturbed by the sea, which submerged them when the Pleistocene glaciers melted.

Comparison of Ancient and Modern Offshore Sediments

As only a few thousand samples of modern marine sediments have been carefully studied, probably less than one sample for each 100,-000 square miles of ocean, any general conclusions about them must be tentative. The data do, however, suggest that relatively little silt and clay are now being deposited on the continental shelves except in areas of heavy sedimentation, like those near such rivers as the Mississippi, the Orinoco, and the Nile. Elsewhere clay seems to remain suspended in the sea until it drops into a quiet basin or over the shelf edge. In many places even sand is swept along by currents until it, too, reaches a deep basin. Beyond the immediate beach zone, at least in areas of slow deposition, the grain size of the sediment may or may not diminish regularly with distance from shore; it seems to be most closely related to the local submarine topography and current pattern.

The most widespread ancient sediments are marine shales, clays, and mudstones, which generally contain fossils of shallow-water organisms. Many of these rocks can be traced laterally into sandstones in one direction and into limestones in the other, and these rocks also contain shallow-water fossils. Local gradations of this sort are known in present seas off the coast of northern Australia, in the Gulf of Mexico, the southern Caribbean Sea, the Yellow Sea, and elsewhere. But we know of relatively few marine environments where muds and clays are accumulating in shallow water over areas of thousands of square miles, although geologic mapping shows inescapably that they did so accumulate at many times in the geologic past. Perhaps this is because we have fewer shallow seas now than were generally present during the geologic past—nothing today, for example, resembles the huge expanse of shallow-water, muddy bottom that must in Cretaceous time have covered the interior of North America from the Arctic to the Gulf of Mexico and from the present Mississippi-Hudson Bay embayments to the interior of the Rockies. Pending further studies of marine sediments now forming, therefore, our inferences about the conditions under which such huge shale bodies as the North American Cretaceous were formed must rest in large part on the intrinsic character of these rocks and their fossils, rather than upon close comparison with any possibly analogous deposits forming today.

A few dominantly shaly formations, notably the Repetto formation (Pliocene) of California, and some others in Timor, Cuba, and elsewhere, contain fossils that indicate that the deposits were laid down in deep water. The Repetto seems to have been deposited in a basin several thousand feet deep, like some of these off the present California coast and in Indonesia. The basin ultimately filled completely with clay, silt, and winnowed sand dumped into it from nearby high topography. Deposits of the organic oozes and red clay characteristic of the really deep sea, which are described in the next section, seem to be exceedingly rare or missing from the continents.

Pelagic Sediments

Pelagic sediments cover nearly three quarters of the ocean bottom, as the *Challenger* discovered. Deep-sea deposits are of three main types: calcareous ooze, the most widespread, covering nearly 48 per cent of the sea floor; red clay, covering 38 per cent, and siliceous oozes, 14 per cent (Figure 17-7). These sediments are not found near land, even in extremely deep water, because their characteristic materials are masked by a deluge of terrigenous debris, as we noted for even the extreme deep of the Mindanao Trough. According to recent compilations, calcareous oozes (812 samples) have been dredged from depths of 2,300 to nearly 20,000 feet, with the average less than 12,000 feet, siliceous oozes (only 37 samples) from depths between 3,400 and 26,500 feet (average about 14,000), while red clay (126 samples) has nowhere been found at depths less than 13,000 feet.

Calcareous ooze covers most of the floor of the Atlantic and Indian oceans and of the equatorial and southern Pacific, as far as latitude 50°S. It consists largely of calcium-carbonate shells of planktonic organisms. Shells of Foraminifera and plates of calcareous algae are most abundant (Fig. 17-8). Minute particles of clay and less abundant siliceous shells are present. Calcareous ooze, the shallowest of the pelagic sediments, is believed to be forming where skeletons of calcareous plankton rain down on the ocean floor so abundantly as to mask the terrigenous clay that is also settling, and also faster than the cold deep water can dissolve the minute shells.

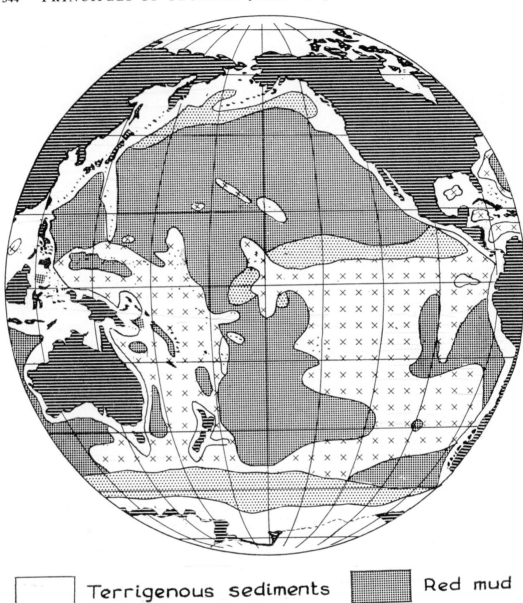

Terrigenous sediments   Red mud

Figure 17-7.   The distribution of terrigenous and pelagic sediments. (After H. U. Sverdrup, M. W. Johnson, and R. H. Fleming, The Oceans, *Copyright 1942, by Prentice-Hall, Inc.*

Red clay covers most of the very deep ocean floor. Most is too fine-grained to be identified microscopically, but X-ray study has shown that the chief minerals are quartz, mica, and several kinds of clay minerals, all generally strained red by iron rust. Because, in the truly oceanic islands, quartz-bearing rocks are absent or very rare, and because the clay minerals of the red clay are like those found in soils formed on land, it is thought that most of the material has been derived from the continents—a conclusion conforming with

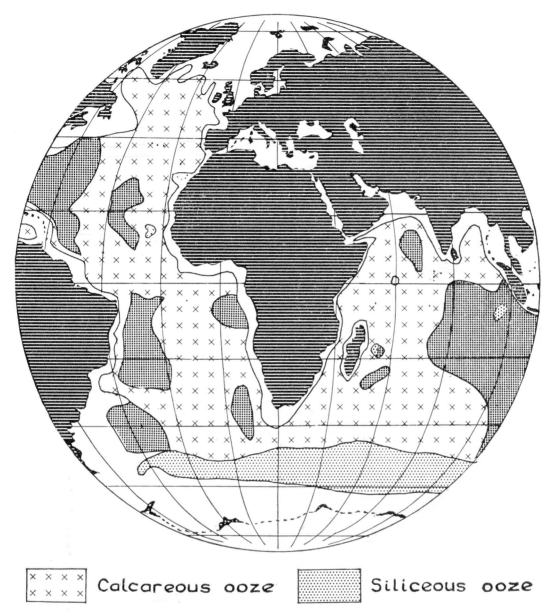

 × × × ×
× × × ×   Calcareous ooze   Siliceous ooze
× × × ×

what is known of settling velocities. Volcanic ash was once considered to be the chief source of red clay. It contributes, of course, but although occasional world-circling dust-falls of volcanic ash follow strong eruptions from siliceous or andesitic volcanoes, even the gigantic eruptions of Krakatoa and Tamboro yielded infinitesimally small amounts of material compared with the great bulk of red clay. The slow settling velocities of fine parti-

cles can account for the presence of the quartzose red clays even thousands of miles from land.

The red clays contain a few organisms like those in both the calcareous and siliceous oozes. In fact, all three varieties of pelagic deposits intergrade. Red clay predominates either where calcareous plankton is sparse (in high latitudes) or where the shells of such organisms must sink through vast depths to

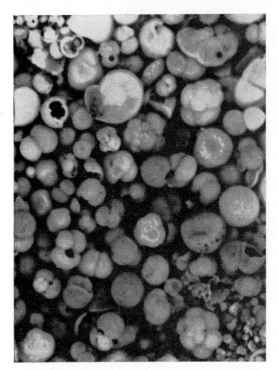

Figure 17-8.   Foraminiferal ooze dredged from a depth of 9,900 feet in the Gulf of Mexico. Enlarged about 15 times. (Courtesy of the Humble Oil and Refining Company.)

reach bottom and in so doing are dissolved by the cold, deep, carbon-dioxide-rich waters. Calcareous ooze may accumulate locally even at great depth if the sinking shells are so abundant as to bury themselves before solution is complete. On the sea floor itself solution must go on only slowly and the interstitial water in the ooze must diffuse so sluggishly that it soon becomes saturated. At great depths there is so little organic matter that the oxygen in the water combines with iron to give the characteristic red hue to the red clay.

Siliceous oozes carpet much of the polar seas and an equatorial strip across most of the eastern Pacific. There are two varieties. The equatorial ooze is composed largely of shells of radiolaria—minute single-celled animals: the ooze in high latitudes consists chiefly of shells of single-celled plants, the diatoms.

Radiolaria flourish in the nutritious water of the equatorial drift. In high latitudes, the mixing of deep water with cold surface water and the excessively deep turbulence caused by the prevailing westerly currents furnish abundant food for plankton. These waters are also cold and rich in carbon dioxide, so that most limy shells dissolve before reaching bottom. Diatoms thus accumulate here so abundantly as to mask other constituents of the ooze.

PELAGIC SEDIMENTS IN THE GEOLOGIC RECORD.   Claystones so similar to pelagic red clays (fine-grained, iron-rich, containing manganese nodules and fragmental foraminifera) that some geologists regard them as true deep-sea deposits, have been found in the Alps, in Barbados (West Indies), and in Timor (Indonesia). These rocks are, however, so intimately associated with coarser clastics generally considered to be of shallow-water origin that a deep-sea origin has been questioned. But because the coarse clastics may have been carried to great depths by turbidity currents, their present close association with material that might have come from a deep-sea environment does not necessarily disprove a deep-sea origin for the entire assemblage.

The Cretaceous chalk of England and France was once thought to be a consolidated deep-sea ooze, but its fossils are chiefly forms that are believed to have lived in littoral waters and it is now considered likely that the chalk was deposited in clear water not more than a few hundred feet deep. The Cretaceous rocks of the Caspian region include thick chalks that contain algal plates (coccoliths) like those of some calcareous oozes. These are associated with narrow zones of terrigenous (blue-mud) shales not unlike some deep-sea muds. Shallow-water fossils appear to be lacking. But whether or not these particular beds represent a fossil deep sea ooze—and there are strong geophysical arguments opposed to the possibility (Chapters 19 and 20)—it seems certain that rocks of truly deep-sea origin are extremely rare on the continents.

Deposition of Limestone and Dolomite

Limestones and dolomites make up about 20 per cent of the sedimentary rocks. Today, as we have just noted, calcareous ooze covers nearly half the ocean bottom. The pelagic oozes, however, do not at all resemble the limestones found on land: most limestones have been formed in shallow water, as is shown by their fossils. Among modern shallow-water sediments we find many analogs to these limestones, but not to the abundant dolomites.

Chemical Conditions Affecting Carbonate Deposition

Calcite is among the most soluble of the common minerals. Though only slowly soluble in pure water, it dissolves readily in the presence of carbon dioxide (Chapter 4). The solubility of calcite in natural sea water is difficult to determine because of the interference of so many other dissolved ions, and there is considerable difference among chemists who have worked on the problem as to whether normal sea water is or is not nearly saturated with calcium carbonate at a temperature of 68°F. Despite the complexity of the problem, all chemists agree that if sea water is warmed, thereby decreasing its carbon dioxide content and usually increasing its salinity, precipitation of calcite is favored, whereas decomposition of organic matter yields carbon dioxide and thereby increases the solubility of calcite. Since, as we have seen, calcite shells in some deep-sea oozes are dissolved, deep cold oceanic water seems clearly to be undersaturated.

Life processes modify the carbon dioxide content of the water and so affect deposition and solution of calcite. Many organisms secrete shells of calcite and aragonite (a mineral composed of calcium carbonate of crystal form different from that of calcite). Photosynthesis by marine plants extracts carbon dioxide from the water, so diminishing the solubility of calcite that, in the littoral zone of the warm tropical seas, the water is practically saturated. Over the shallow Bahama Banks, several processes unite to lower the solubility of calcite: as water flows over the banks to replenish that evaporated, it is warmed; flourishing plants withdraw much carbon dioxide; and the abundant bacteria in these shallow muds include species that turn nitrogen into ammonia, which, being weakly alkaline, neutralizes some of the free hydrogen ions in the water and thereby favors precipitation of calcium carbonate. (Calcium carbonate is much more soluble in acid water than in water that is neutral or alkaline.) As a result of these processes the water becomes saturated with calcium carbonate and fine needles separate out and settle to the bottom, there to accumulate as limy muds. It seems likely that some of the fine-grained limestones of the geologic past were formed similarly.

Many lime-secreting plants and animals flourish in the littoral zone of tropical seas. Shells and their broken fragments in many places make up whole beaches, and also pile up in shallow off-shore waters where they are slowly cemented to limestone. Microscopic studies of ancient limestones show that many are composed of grains of calcite broken from fragments of fossil shells. Calcite recrystallizes so readily in warm water that many microscopic textural features are partly destroyed. It is probable that many limestones that have been formed from fragments and grains of shells give no demonstrable evidence of such formation.

Dolomites

Dolomite, the carbonate of both calcium and magnesium, offers one of the greatest geological puzzles. Very few organisms secrete shells with an appreciable content of magnesium carbonate, and in the few that do, the ratio of magnesium carbonate to calcium carbonate falls far short of that in dolomite. We know of no inorganic dolomite being deposited in the present seas. Yet dolomites, though practically unknown among the Tertiary rocks, are both abundant and widespread among Mesozoic and older strata. Does the principle of Uniformitarianism fail us here?

Around certain igneous intrusions, large quantities of limestone have been altered to dolomite. This dolomite shows, however, a definite association with faults and fissures and is clearly a product of metamorphism by ascending hot solutions. No such origin is possible for the great sheets of early Paleozoic dolomite that can be traced for scores or even hundreds of miles, some of them everywhere interbedded with layers of unaltered limestone and shale.

A possible clue to the origin of dolomites comes from a boring on the atoll of Funafuti, in the Ellice Islands, not far from Tarawa, of World War II fame. In this boring, about 1,100 feet deep, all the material greatly resembled the rock of the coral atoll—that is, it contained coral heads, algal deposits, and shells of many different animals. Although the structures of these organic remains were well-preserved, the composition of the material at depth differed notably from that at the surface. The content of magnesium carbonate increased irregularly with depth and there was much dolomite near the bottom (Fig. 17-9). It was inferred that part of the calcium in the calcite shells had been replaced by magnesium ions from the sea water, which, of course, thoroughly soaks the porous atolls. This hypothesis may be correct, but, if so, there must be other, unknown factors that prevent dolomite from being formed under what seem to be identical conditions, for a hole drilled to a depth of 2,200 feet on another South Pacific atoll, Bikini, found neither dolomite nor any significant downward increase in magnesium content, even though the lowest beds contain fossils as old as Miocene and thus must have remained in virtually continuous contact with sea water for more than fifteen million years. How the many cubic miles of dolomite found in the rocks of Mesozoic and earlier ages were formed remains one of the great unsolved problems of geology.

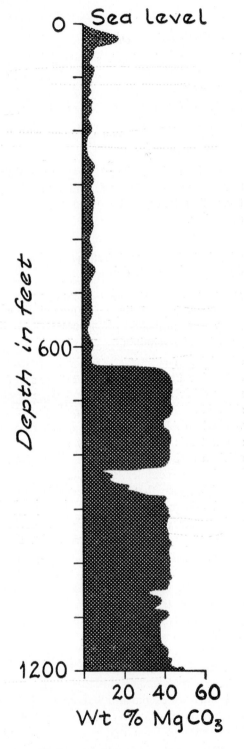

Figure 17-9. Average magnesium carbonate content of the Funafuti core.

Stratigraphic Syntheses

The Principle of Uniformitarianism is the key to the understanding of the geologic past. If we were successful in interpreting the environmental conditions in which a particular formation or part of a formation had developed and could make similar interpretations for all nearby rock bodies that correlate with it, we would be able to reconstruct a segment of ancient geography. The tracing of successive ancient geographies makes up the special study of **historical geology,** most of which is beyond the scope of this book, but we will illustrate the reasoning used in that study by applying some of the data given in this and earlier chapters to a few sedimentary rock assemblages. Many economic deposits are found only in specific geologic settings. An understanding of the environment in which they were formed is often necessary for their intelligent exploitation—the Key to the Past may unlock the door not only to scientific knowledge but to wealth as well.

Devonian Geography of Western Europe

Prominent in the history of the development of geology is the analysis and interpretation of the Old Red Sandstone of northern England and Scotland. The British geologist Hugh Miller, in mid-nineteenth century, interested thousands of amateurs in geology by his reconstructions of the past as revealed in the rocks of this formation. As the name implies, the chief component of the "Old Red" is sandstone, stained red with iron rust. The sandstone is composed of quartz and much relatively fresh feldspar, whose cleavage faces sparkle on fresh fracture. Sorting is poor and lenses of both coarse- and fine-grained material—from conglomerates and breccias with boulders several feet in diameter to fine clayey and silty partings—interfinger with the dominant sandstone. Some of the finer-grained beds contain cubical casts that resemble salt crystals in form. In the same or nearby beds, skeletons of many fossil fish are found. These fish possessed internal breathing organs that

were like lungs, and it is inferred that they resembled some of the so-called lungfish of modern Australia, which can live through periods of drought by burying themselves in moist mud. Locally, too, there are layers of sandstone with complex cross-bedding and sparse layers of faceted pebbles that are like those of modern dune sands with desert pavements. All in all, the current bedding of the coarser layers, the record of dominantly mechanical instead of chemical weathering, the evidence of the work of wind and of the existence of intermittent lakes and playas in which salt crystals precipitated and redissolved, seem to compel the conclusion that we have here a desert deposit on an old continent. The conditions indicated are much like those of the present day in the Mohave Desert or in Western China.

Southward, in northern Devonshire, a few beds of this typical red sandstone are interlayered with coarse sandstone, shale, and thin limestone that contain marine fossils. Still farther south the red sandstone disappears, interlensing into a stratigraphic succession composed of marine shale and thick fossiliferous limestone. Here is the type area of the Devonian System, and one of the early triumphs of systematic stratigraphic studies was the recognition that these marine rocks correlate with the very different Old Red Sandstone so widely exposed farther north. Clearly, between the semiarid continent in the north and the marine area in southern Devonshire there must have been a shoreline; the lenses of interfingering red terrestrial sandstone and gray marine rocks show that its position fluctuated from time to time across a belt some scores of miles wide.

Rocks like the Old Red Sandstone, and containing the same kinds of fish and primitive plant fossils, are found in the Hebrides and in Norway. In the Ardennes of Belgium, in Czechoslovakia, and in Poland, interfingering marine and continental Devonian rocks like those of north Devonshire and south Wales are also well known, and they extend across the Leningrad region to the White Sea. To

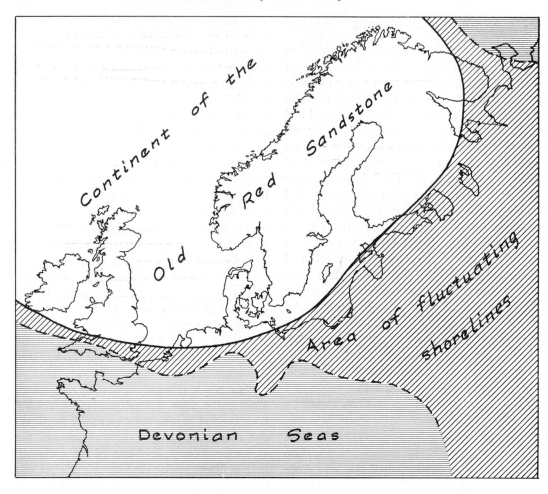

Figure 17-10.   The Old Red Continent and its borderlands. (After M. Gignoux, 1955.)

the south, in the Alps, the Devonian beds are wholly marine (Fig. 17-10). Across the Atlantic, the Devonian beds of New Brunswick strongly resemble the Old Red Sandstone; to the northwest they interfinger with marine beds just south of the St. Lawrence estuary. The Catskill formation of New York (Upper Devonian), several thousand feet thick, consists of similar red sandstones and shales with primitive amphibian, fish, and plant fossils. Toward the west, in New York, the terrestrial beds interfinger with black marine shales and eventually disappear in a thick marine section. Rocks resembling the Old Red and with a similar fish fauna are also present in parts of Greenland. Many

geologists believe that these relations mean that a former continent extended from the White Sea to Greenland and New Brunswick, across the present site of the North Atlantic, but the same evidence may be taken to show a general aridity of all the near-shore lands throughout this vast area. So much of the pertinent record is lost either by erosion or by burial beneath younger beds or the sea that absolute proof of either hypothesis cannot be obtained.

**The Permian Basin of Texas
and New Mexico**

Another example of synthesis of the rock record into an ancient geography is given by

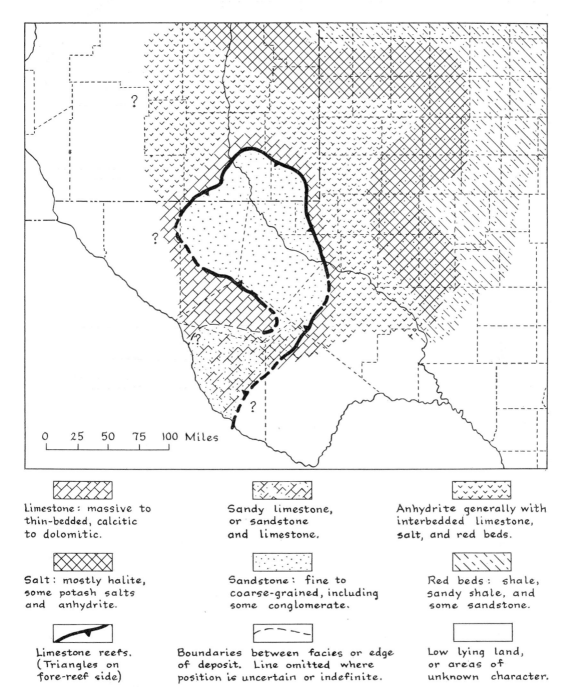

Limestone: massive to
thin-bedded, calcitic
to dolomitic.

Sandy limestone,
or sandstone
and limestone.

Anhydrite generally with
interbedded limestone,
salt, and red beds.

Salt: mostly halite,
some potash salts
and anhydrite.

Sandstone: fine to
coarse-grained, including
some conglomerate.

Red beds: shale,
sandy shale, and
some sandstone.

Limestone reefs.
(Triangles on
fore-reef side)

Boundaries between facies or edge
of deposit. Line omitted where
position is uncertain or indefinite.

Low lying land,
or areas of
unknown character.

Figure 17-11.   The paleogeography of part of Middle Permian time in the area of western Texas
and New Mexico. (After P. B. King, 1942, with permission of the American Association of Petroleum Geologists.)

studies of the Permian Basin of western Texas and southeastern New Mexico. This huge area, rich in oil, gas, and potash salts, has been explored by literally hundreds of geologists in the past forty years. Accurate reconstruction of the former geography is aided by many thousands of wells and by the widespread exposures of rock in this barren region. The results of these studies, as they relate to a part of the geography of the Permian, are illustrated in Figure 17-11.

The weakly stippled area is approximately the site of the present Delaware Mountains and the Delaware Basin to their east. The rocks of Late Permian age to which the map refers are not exposed in this area, except in the mountains. They are, however, cut by many wells and are known to be fine-grained sandstones with thin interbeds of very dense gray limestone. The even lamination of both rocks suggests deposition in quiet water. To the west, northwest, north, east and southeast, this area of sandstone is almost surrounded by thick, massive beds of limestone into which the thin limestone of the basin area can be seen to interfinger. Near the zone of interfingering, there are huge breccia beds, composed of the same kind of organic limestone that constitutes the thick massive beds. These breccias lie at the foot of long sloping layers

Figure 17-12. The relation between reef, back-reef, and basin deposits as interpreted for the Middle Permian rocks of western Texas and New Mexico. (After P. B. King, 1942, with permission of the American Association of Petroleum Geologists.)

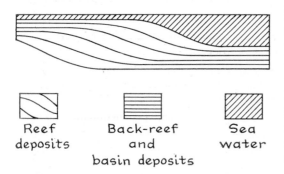

| Reef deposits | Back-reef and basin deposits | Sea water |

that rise at angles of 10 to 30 degrees from the plane of the thin-bedded limestones for hundreds of feet and then flatten out and change quickly into thin-bedded, well-laminated limestones. The massive beds are highly organic, and extend as much as 2,500 feet below the topmost layers of gray limestone and sandstone. The thin-bedded limestones, into which the massive beds abruptly change outside the basin, lie nearly flat and show no curvature into the massive beds. These relations are interpreted as indications that the thick, massive beds constitute a fossil reef that grew on a gently sloping bottom. The breccias comprise storm-broken fragments that rolled down the reef front into the basin, the basin deposits represent deep-water deposits, and the upper thin-bedded limestone was the back-reef, quiet-water, lagoonal deposit (Fig. 17-12). Thus the high sloping curve of the massive reef limestones is considered an original feature of the growing reef and the amount of rise a rough measure of the difference in depth of the basin and the back-reef lagoon. If this hypothesis is correct, the difference was more than 1,200 feet, so that the basin deposits were laid down at depths of at least 200 fathoms. Many corollary features that support this idea can be found. If we consider the reef (whose most conspicuous outcrop is Guadalupe Peak, Figure 17-13) to have been a fringing reef bordering the ancient land that nearly surrounded the basin, it coordinates many other features. To the northwest, north, and northeast, the back-reef limestones at both surface and subsurface (from well cores) are known to become poorer and poorer in fossils, and to interfinger with beds of anhydrite, salt, and red shale, as might be expected on a low-lying plains coast in an arid to semiarid climate. Still farther north, in both New Mexico and the Texas and Oklahoma panhandles, the limestones give way to clastic beds. These red sandstones and shales have yielded sparse reptilian fossil faunas and are clearly fluviatile deposits formed in a semiarid climate. To the south, relations are obscured by overlying

Figure 17-13. *The great reef deposit of Guadalupe Peak, Texas. Oblique aerial view of El Capi-*
tan and Guadalupe Peak from the south. Southern Guadalupe Mountains, Culber-
son County, Texas. (Photo by U. S. Army Air Force, 1938.)

Cretaceous rocks, but possibly some of the sand that forms the basin deposits within the reef perimeter was derived from land in what is now the Big Bend country of Trans-Pecos Texas.

The interpretation of this former geography is of the highest economic importance. The reef limestones form highly porous bodies and, under some conditions, are prolific reservoirs for petroleum; the salt deposits are locally rich in potash salts, valuable for fertilizer and chemical uses. The understanding of the relations and geographic trends of the various sedimentary formations is the objective of a fascinating detective game whose prizes have been wealth as well as knowledge.

A Miocene Geography in California

Another example of reconstruction of an ancient geography is given by an area in the San Joaquin Hills, southeast of Los Angeles, California. Here a considerable area is underlain by a thick diatomaceous shale called the Monterey shale, containing, besides a myriad of diatoms, many foraminifera and, in sandy interbeds, some mollusks that prove its marine origin. The very thin and even laminations testify either to deep water or a sheltered position, for the well-laminated shale shows no sign of bottom disturbance. Along the northeast part of the area are thick, rather poorly sorted coarse sandstones and shales. These contain fragments that could have come from older granitic rocks within a few miles to the north, northeast, and east. A few beds of these coarser clastics extend well out into the area of diatomaceous shale, and suggest, by their molluskan fossils and cross-bedding, that they are beach deposits. Some interfinger near the center of the area with a very different kind of rock, to which the formation name, San Onofre breccia, has been given. The San Onofre breccia is made up almost exclusively of the debris of glaucophane schist and related metamorphic rocks. (Glaucophane is an amphibole of very distinctive optical properties, readily recognized under the microscope.)

In the breccia are great boulders and angular blocks many feet across (Fig. 17-14). Nearly all fragments above sand size are of glaucophane schist, as is most of the abundant finer material, some of which has been shredded down to a kind of glaucophane-rich silt. Although toward its northeastern limits the San Onofre breccia interfingers with the Monterey shale and with the coarse marine sandstones that extend as lenses from the northeast, it does not itself contain marine or other fossils. It is poorly sorted, and, though locally bedded, is for the most part almost massive. Most of it seems to be a mudflow breccia, perhaps a gigantic debris flow that glided out into a protected seaway.

Perhaps the most significant thing about the San Onofre breccia is the composition of its materials. To the east or northeast no glaucophane schist has been found closer than Wales, Corsica, or the Alps, but it is well exposed on Catalina Island and on Palos Verdes Peninsula to the southwest, across what is now an arm of the Pacific. The San Onofre breccia unquestionably came from an area to the southwest that is now almost buried beneath the Pacific. The strata and their mutual relations show that in the San

Figure 17-14.   An exposure of an old mudflow, part of the San Onofre breccia. (Photo by Wright M. Pierce.)

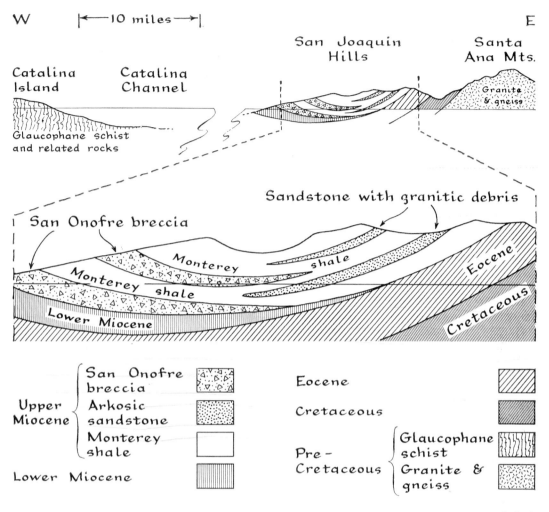

W |←—10 miles—→| E

San Joaquin Hills   Santa Ana Mts.

Catalina Island   Catalina Channel

Granite & gneiss

Glaucophane schist and related rocks

Sandstone with granitic debris

San Onofre breccia

Monterey   shale

Eocene

Monterey shale

Cretaceous

Lower Miocene

Upper Miocene
- San Onofre breccia
- Arkosic sandstone
- Monterey shale

Lower Miocene

Eocene

Cretaceous

Pre-Cretaceous
- Glaucophane schist
- Granite & gneiss

Figure 17-15. Sections showing the relations of the San Onofre breccia to the Monterey shale in southern California. (After A. O. Woodford.)

Joaquin Hills we see the deposits of a north-westerly-trending depositional trough to which sediments were supplied from both northeast and southwest. This trough was an arm of the sea bordered on the southwest by a former high land from which coarse sediments could be shed as mudflows. Perhaps the climate was semiarid: not only do the mudflows in the San Onofre breccia indicate this, but we find almost no clay in the diatomaceous sediment of the Monterey. Did the paucity of streams in a semiarid landscape hamper the sorting of debris in the area northeast of the basin as well as in that to the southwest? Critical ex-

posures are lacking to demonstrate this, so the matter is unproven.

The former highlands on the southwest are all but buried beneath the Pacific, with only local remnants rising above the waters. Here we are not dealing merely with a Miocene flooding of the continental margin but with a series of earth movements so complex that some particular spots rose high above sea level and then sank far below—as shown by present day soundings—while other spots not far away were going through the opposite movements.

FACTS, CONCEPTS, TERMS

VOLUME, SOURCE, AND DISTRIBUTION OF SEDI-
MENTARY ROCKS
FACTORS AFFECTING DIVERSITY OF SEDIMENTS
In source area; during transport; during deposi-
tion
STRATIFICATION
Origin
Factors affecting suspension of sediments in
water
Foreset bedding; current or cross-bedding
Graded bedding: association with turbidity
currents
TEXTURES
Rounding of sand grains
TERRESTRIAL SEDIMENT
Gravel-filled channels; scour-and-fill; current
bedding; sorting
Association of features of aggrading streams
Alluvial sediments of fine grain
MARINE SEDIMENTS
Sources; clastic and dissolved materials
Organic sediments
REALMS OF MARINE SEDIMENTATION
Strand zone: components of strand deposits
Beach deposits and their recognition
Deltas: arrangement of sediments in; subsid-
ence of

Clay deposition
Tidal-flat deposits
Shelf deposits
In areas of abundant sedimentation
In areas of slow sedimentation and of
Pleistocene glacial deposits
Sediments of Indonesia
Basins and ridges and their deposits
Submarine slides
Settling of fine particles
Deep-water shales
PELAGIC SEDIMENTS
Calcareous ooze
Red clay
Siliceous ooze
In the geologic record
LIMESTONE AND DOLOMITE
Chemical conditions affecting carbonate de-
position
Metamorphic dolomite
Dolomite in Funafuti Atoll
STRATIGRAPHIC SYNTHESIS AND ANCIENT GEOG-
RAPHIES
Old Red Sandstone
Permian Basin of Texas and New Mexico
Miocene of Southern California

QUESTIONS

1. Why is the systematic distribution of sediments in lakes not paralleled by that in the
oceans?

2. Assuming that turbidity currents build
delta-like deposits on the ocean floor at the
mouths of submarine canyons, how would you
expect the form of such a deposit to differ from
that of a normal delta? How would its composition and internal structure differ?

3. Why are dune sands generally better sorted
than water-laid sediments of the same average
grain size?

4. If relief in the source area is an important

factor in sedimentation, how would you expect
the marine sediments off California to compare
with those off Texas?

5. How would you expect first-cycle sandstones to differ from reworked sandstones?

6. The St. Lawrence carries much more water
to the sea than the Colorado. Why does it end
in an almost unsedimented estuary whereas the
Colorado has been building a huge delta since
Pleistocene time?

7. Aside from the temperature control of the
life cycle of reef corals, would you expect
greater, less, or similar proportions of calcium-

carbonate deposits to noncarbonate deposits in arctic or tropical waters? Why?

8. How would you expect graded bedding formed by a steadily weakening current to differ from that formed by settling of a turbid flow?

SUGGESTED READINGS

Gignoux, Maurice. *Stratigraphic Geology.* San Francisco, W. H. Freeman & Co., 1955, Chapter 1.

Kuenen, P. H. *Marine Geology.* New York, John Wiley and Sons, 1950.

Marr, J. E. *Deposition of the Sedimentary Rocks.* Cambridge, Cambridge University Press, 1929.

Shepard, F. P. *Submarine Geology.* New York, Harper and Bros., 1948.

18 IGNEOUS ACTIVITY AND METAMORPHISM

IGNEOUS ROCKS, as we explained in Chapter 3, congeal from molten magmas generated within the earth. Some, the volcanic rocks, have been erupted to the surface; others, the plutonic rocks, solidify underground and are revealed only where unroofed by erosion or penetrated by wells and mines. Metamorphic rocks result from the transformation of other solid rocks by heat, pressure, and chemically active fluids acting upon them during their deep burial in the earth's crust.

Igneous and metamorphic rocks affect our lives. Spectacular eruptions from Vesuvius, Etna, and other Mediterranean volcanoes strongly impressed the ancients, and the destruction they caused was considered evidence of the wrath of the gods. Today the ores of gold, silver, copper, uranium, and many other metals that geologists have found to be concentrated near the borders of plutonic igneous masses are the foundation of our industrial civilization. From metamorphic rocks come the ores that supply our steel industry, the marble and slate in our buildings, and most of the gem stones with which we adorn ourselves.

Entirely aside from economic considerations, the igneous and metamorphic rocks arouse interest because of their wonderful diversity. Microscopic study reveals thousands of different varieties, and even at a

glance many different textures, minerals, and other physical variations are apparent. Moreover, each combination of minerals and textures is a record of past events capable of revealing a fascinating chapter in earth history if we can learn to read it aright. Despite this diversity, two varieties of igneous rocks are much more abundant than any others. These are the dark-colored, quartz-free volcanic rock called basalt, and the light-colored, quartz-bearing intrusive rock called granite. Why should this be? No geologist can give a final answer to this query, but some of the progress made toward an answer is reviewed here.

We begin our study with volcanoes. Geologists recognize several kinds, based on the kind of eruptive activity that has built them.

Volcanoes

Volcanoes are mountains or hills made by materials erupted from the earth's interior through a central vent, or, more commonly, a group of vents. The material flows from the vents as liquid *lava,* or else is violently ejected as fragments of partly or completely solidified rock (*pyroclastic debris*). Every active volcano also gives off *gas,* chiefly water vapor, often in astounding amounts. During one phase of the 1906 eruption of Vesuvius in

358

1906, vast quantities of steam blew from the crater as from a gigantic safety valve, eroding the walls and greatly enlarging the crater.

Shield Volcanoes.

Low, flat cones composed almost entirely of coalescing and overlapping lava streams are called **shield volcanoes.** The hot lava wells out in part from the central conduit, but chiefly from numerous fissures on the flanks of the cone. It pours down the cone (Fig. 18-1) in thin interlacing streams. Because the lava is of low viscosity, and pyroclastic material is scarce or absent, shield volcanoes have gentle slopes and are shaped like an inverted dinner plate, in contrast to steep-sided volcanoes built largely of pyroclastic debris (Fig. 18-2). Most shield volcanoes are composed of basalt, though a few are of andesite. (For rock names see Appendix III.) Many contain a few small bodies of rhyolite or obsidian, either as intrusive masses or as flows and pyroclastics.

At the summit of most shield volcanoes is

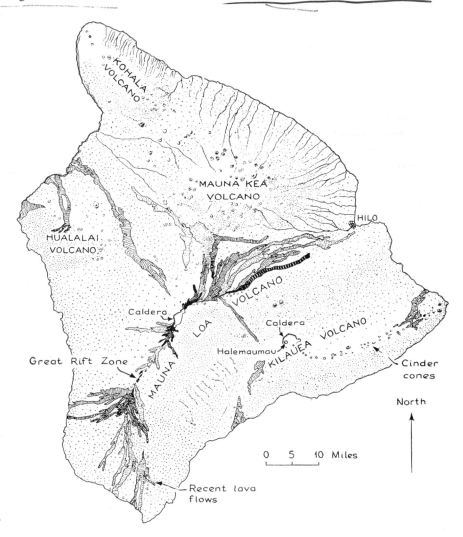

Figure 18-1a.

Generalized map of Hawaii. Note the alignment of cinder cones and lava flows on the fissure zones of Mauna Loa and Kilauea. (After H. T. Stearns and G. A. Macdonald, Hawaii Div. of Hydrography, 1946.)

Figure 18-1b.

Cross section through Hawaii, showing the concentrations of dike feeders that make up the rift zones. (Same source as Fig. 18-1a.)

a cone-shaped **crater;** some contain a much larger basin called a caldera. **Calderas** are large volcanic depressions, steep-sided and more or less circular. They are commonly from three to nine miles in diameter, whereas volcanic craters are much smaller, generally less than 2,000 feet across. Although some calderas have been interpreted as pits made by gigantic explosions, it is now believed that nearly all were formed by subsidence of the top of the volcano into the space below as it was emptied of magma by voluminous eruptions. The area of subsidence is generally bounded by a roughly circular fault. The rocks on the floors of some calderas can be matched with rocks hundreds of feet higher on the walls, thereby proving central subsidence. A few calderas have collapsed so recently that concentric faults are still visible along their margins, but most of the rim faults are hidden by talus, or by younger lavas and pyroclastics that have welled up along the faults.

Other characteristics of shield volcanoes may be illustrated by examples from the typical shields of the Hawaiian Islands.

MAUNA LOA AND KILAUEA. Despite their gentle slopes, shield volcanoes are the world's highest and bulkiest volcanoes. The Hawaiian Islands are composed of overlap-

Figure 18-2.   Cotopaxi volcano, Ecuador. (Photo courtesy of E. Lewis.)

ping volcanoes, some rising more than 13,000 feet above the sea. As the nearby Pacific Ocean is more than 15,000 feet deep, some of the volcanoes must be more than 28,000 feet high (Fig. 18-3).

Mauna Loa (Fig. 18-1), on the island of Hawaii, rises nearly 14,000 feet above sea level. At the summit is a caldera 2 miles wide and about 1,000 feet deep. On the caldera floor, a pit contains a lava pool that fluctuates in size and in height and occasionally spills thin lava flows over the caldera floor.

FISSURE ERUPTIONS ON THE FLANKS OF MAUNA LOA. Within historic times several lava flows have been added to Mauna Loa (Fig. 18-1). These have emerged, not from the Halemaumau and Mauna Loa "fire pits," as must sometimes have happened, but from fissures that opened lower on the shield. Many came from a northeast-trending zone of roughly parallel cracks—the Great Rift Zone —that crosses the top of the shield (Fig. 18-1). Some flows are very small; others, such as that of 1855, contain several billion

Figure 18-3.

Profile of Hawaii. (*After H. T. Stearns and G. A. MacDonald, Hawaii Div. of Hydrography, 1946.*)

On the southeastern slope of Mauna Loa, about 20 miles from the summit and nearly 9,000 feet lower, is a second volcano, Kilauea, with a caldera about 1½ miles in diameter. It contains a lava lake that has been crusted over during most of historic time, but in a pit in this crust lies a pool of molten lava, called Halemaumau. Surface crusts form on the lava pool but are soon broken up and engulfed by slow convection currents. Gases, largely water vapor, emerge continuously, and in places escape so violently that the molten rock boils up in "lava fountains." Small amounts of sulfur and hydrogen are present in these gases, and they may burn on reaching the surface. From time to time the lava in Halemaumau rises and floods the crater of Kilauea. In 1924 it withdrew deep into the pit, and ground water poured into the hole, causing a violent steam explosion. Later the lava lake reappeared. It has been alternately active and quiescent through most of historic time.

As the lava in Mauna Loa stands nearly 9,000 feet higher than that in Halemaumau, the two lava columns cannot now be directly connected; if they were the lava in Mauna Loa would drain down to the level of Kilauea.

cubic feet of rock. Thousands of such lava streams must have slowly built up the massive piles of the shield volcanoes, although only the most recent fissure flows can be traced easily to visible sources. These younger flows evidently conceal the hundreds of dikes that must have fed the older flows that make up the deeper parts of the cone. Confirming this inference, deeply eroded shield volcanoes such as those on nearby Oahu expose innumerable dike feeders.

PARASITIC CONES. Small **cinder cones** (Fig. 18-4), which are steep-sided accumulations of pyroclastic debris (chiefly bombs and lapilli, see Appendix III) heaped around a central vent, form on the surface of many shield volcanoes. These **parasitic cones** are generally less than a mile across and 50 to 500 feet high. Mauna Loa has several, and Mount Newberry, a shield volcano in central Oregon, is embellished with over 150. In places, several cones are arranged along a definite line, indicating that they formed above a fissure, perhaps while the dike occupying the fissure was congealing.

Much larger parasitic cones—of lava, of

Figure 18-4. *Cinder cone with lava flow pouring from its base, Lava Butte, Oregon. (Photo by H. A. Coombs.)*

pyroclastic products, or of mixtures of both —may also form near the summit of a shield volcano, particularly along the rim or on the floor of a caldera.

As the top of a volcano slowly subsides to form a caldera, magma from the underground chamber may rise along the circular bounding fracture and solidify as an arcuate or circular dike called a **ring dike** (Fig. 18-5). Lava from a ring dike also may well out and flood

the caldera floor, but more often it reaches the surface through several parasitic volcanoes spaced at intervals along the caldera rim. At Askja volcano, in Iceland, a caldera about 4½ miles in diameter was formed by the sinking of the top of the volcano, following which several rim volcanoes were built along the ring fracture at the margin of the caldera. Basalt flows and scoria erupted from them have partly buried the caldera floor and

Figure 18-5.

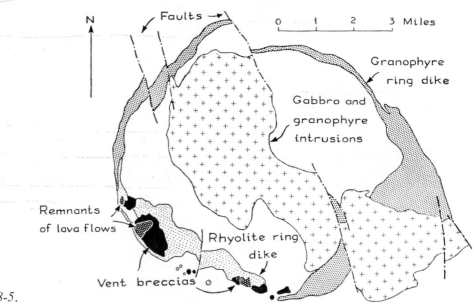

Geologic map of an eroded volcanic complex, Slieve Gullion, Ireland. (After J. E. Richey, 1932.)

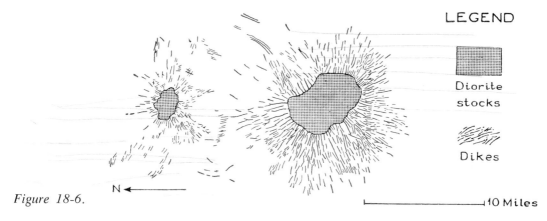

LEGEND

Diorite stocks

Dikes

Figure 18-6.

N ← ———————— ⊢———————————10 Miles

Geologic map of stocks and dikes, Crazy Mountains, Montana. (After W. H. Weed, U. S. Geological Survey.)

walls. Another example is the Medicine Lake volcano of northeastern California. Here a great andesitic shield volcano is capped by nine steep-sided lava cones arranged in an ellipse. This ellipse presumably outlines an old caldera whose rim has been completely buried under lava and ash from the nine rim volcanoes.

DIKE SWARMS IN ERODED VOLCANOES. Deeply eroded volcanic centers tell us still more about ring dikes, calderas, and the swarms of dikes that fed most of the surface flows. The eroded volcanic center of Slieve Gullion in northern Ireland (Fig. 18-5) was probably once surmounted by a volcano very similar to that at Medicine Lake. At Slieve Gullion only a few patches of surface lava have survived erosion, and these only because they collapsed into the depths of the volcano to become part of the floor of a caldera. Today the most obvious feature is a huge ring dike of granophyre (a fine-grained variety of granite), which encircles a down-dropped block of basement rocks about 7 miles in diameter. Large irregular intrusions of gabbro riddle the down-dropped block. These are probably congealed parts of a body of underground magma that once fed the long-vanished volcano. A second dike of aphanitic rhyolite clings closely to the first ring dike for about

one-fifth of its circumference. Perhaps the most interesting feature disclosed by geologic mapping, however, is that in several places along one side of the complex the main ring dike grades into or is cut across by pipelike masses of explosion breccia. These are obviously roots of explosive parasitic volcanoes built along the caldera rim, as at Medicine Lake.

In many eroded volcanoes, such as those on Oahu, hundreds of dikes radiate outward through the pile of overlapping lava flows. How would the roots of such a volcano look if erosion had removed all the lavas, exposing the floor beneath? In many regions geologists have mapped isolated, rudely circular masses of igneous rock from which swarms of dikes radiate. Figure 18-6 is a geologic map of two such masses in central Montana which might have fed volcanoes that have long since been eroded. In other areas, swarms of roughly parallel dikes cluster near intrusive masses, recalling the fissures of the Mauna Loa rift zone.

Composite Volcanoes

Composite volcanoes differ from shield volcanoes chiefly in their strong explosive activity. The beautiful steep-sided cones of snow-capped Fujiyama in Japan, Mount Hood in Oregon, Vesuvius in Italy, and Cotopaxi (Fig.

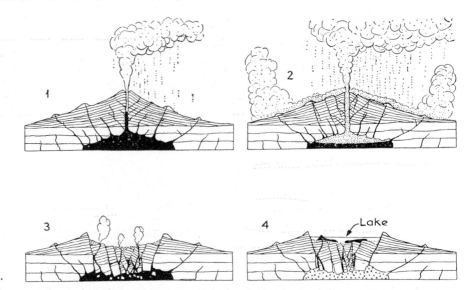

Figure 18-7.

The evolution of the caldera at Crater Lake, Oregon. (1) Early eruption cloud. (2) Great pumice eruptions, with mountain beginning to founder. (3) Caldera resulting from collapse into magma chamber. (4) Crystallization of magma after minor eruptions. (After Howel Williams, 1942.)

18-2) in Ecuador have been built by a combination of relatively quiet outpourings of lava and violent explosions that heaped pyroclastic fragments about the vent. In most composite volcanoes, layers of pyroclastic debris alternate fairly regularly with lava flows: a few are great chaotic piles of pyroclastic rock with relatively little interbedded lava.

A graceful steep-sided cone such as Cotopaxi or Fujiyama appears at first to have little in common with a low flat-topped lava shield like Mauna Loa. Yet there are close similarities. Most of the lava may come from fissures low on the flank of the cone, though the pyroclastic debris is exploded chiefly from the crater at the summit. Subsidence of the top to form a large caldera is common (Fig. 18-7). Such subsidence may take place along ring fractures as in shield volcanoes, or it may be caused by the piecemeal crumbling and sinking of a chaotic jumble of huge blocks into the magma chamber immediately after violent eruptions of pumice lapilli (frothy bits of glassy lava, see Appendix III). Large parasitic cones may appear, but small cinder

cones like those on shield volcanoes are not common. Furthermore, if the activity changes from quiet lava outflow to strong explosions, a composite volcano may grow directly on top of an old shield volcano.

VARIETIES OF EXPLOSIVE ACTIVITY. Explosive activity may take many forms. Five volcanoes that have erupted violently in recent centuries illustrate the general range of activity.

Stromboli.—At Stromboli, called the "Lighthouse of the Mediterranean," the characteristic activity consists of mild explosions spaced at intervals of a few minutes. With each explosion, showers of glowing lava belch from the crater and rain down on the cone as red-hot pasty clots of bubble-filled basalt scoria. Many are shaped into spindle- or tear-like forms (bombs) during their flight. Rarely, during a quiet interval, the lava in the throat crusts over. Such a quiet period is ended by a stronger explosion that blasts the crust into fragments that fall, together with many clots of gas-charged lava, on the sides of the cone.

Few of the quiet periods last long enough, however, to allow much magma to congeal.

Strombolian explosions generally build huge cinder cones composed of lapilli, bombs, and angular blocks of broken lava; some also contain lava flows that have issued either from the crater or from fissures (Fig. 18-4). Paricutin, the celebrated new volcano that broke the surface of a Mexican corn field in 1943, is now a typical cinder cone over 1,000 feet high.

Vulcano.—The Italian mountain called Vulcano is another composite cone. Unlike the almost continuously active Stromboli, Vulcano has stronger and more irregularly spaced explosions. During the long quiet periods the top of the magma column solidifies to considerable depths, then is shattered and blown out by explosions to form great seething eruption clouds composed mainly of solid fragments of basalt and basalt scoria. These are mixed with clots of pasty, glowing lava from farther down in the throat. Tremendous masses of steam often follow the black eruption clouds and boil from the crater to hang as swirling white clouds above the cone. Some of the activity at Paricutin has been like that at Vulcano.

Katmai.—The strongest known volcanic explosions have occurred in long-dormant composite volcanoes. Many of these volcanoes appeared dead, not having erupted previously within historic times; the cones of several had even been largely destroyed by erosion. Most strongly explosive volcanoes are composed of andesite, though many contain basalt, rhyolite, and other kinds of volcanic rocks.

In 1912, Mount Katmai in Alaska, not previously active in historic time, exploded with great violence; its steep-sided but deeply eroded cone became a shattered irregular mountain containing a pumice-filled basin. Bits of pumice, broken lava, and tiny sharp-cornered particles of natural glass called shards (volcanic dust) rained from the eruption cloud in great quantities, burying forests on Kodiak Island, 60 miles away, to a depth of 10 feet or more. Even today automobiles in Anchorage wear out quickly because of the abrasive volcanic dust that gets into the engines.

Tamboro and Krakatoa.—In 1815 a tremendous explosion racked the volcano Tamboro on an island in the East Indies. It is estimated that more than 30—possibly as much as 50—cubic miles of molten and solid rock was shattered into fragments and blown into the air, scattering pyroclastic debris in a thick coating over an area with a radius of more than 200 miles.

Krakatoa, in Sunda Strait, between Java and Sumatra, exploded violently in 1883, blowing about a cubic mile of shattered rocks into the air. In prehistoric time a large composite volcano had been built up and, after great eruptions of pumice, had collapsed, leaving only an arc of islands to mark the caldera rim. (Compare with Crater Lake volcano, Fig. 18-7.) Later eruptions built several parasitic cones within the ring; the largest of these was Krakatoa, which grew to a height of more than 2,600 feet. Then, in 1883, after emission of some steam and dust, a violent steam explosion demolished the island and blasted a great hole 1,000 feet deep beneath the sea. The eruption cloud from this gigantic explosion rose 17 miles into the air and rained millions of tons of angular rock fragments, dust, and pumice lapilli over the sea. Fine ash was wafted all over the earth and remained suspended in the air for years, causing brilliant sunsets.

Few people lived within the killing range of Krakatoa's eruption cloud, but the sea waves generated—as high as 100 feet—overwhelmed the low-lying coasts of Java and Sumatra, killing thousands of persons and causing tremendous damage.

Mont Pelée.—In 1903, Mont Pelée, on the island of Martinique, was strongly active. Fortunately, many stages of this activity were observed by the great French geologist A. Lacroix. He described how, during the strongest explosions, immense clouds of dust, pumice lapilli, and fragments of red-hot rock shot to great heights, boiling, eddying, and swelling

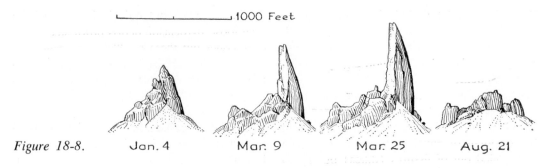

└────────┴────────┘ 1000 Feet

Figure 18-8.   Jan. 4   Mar. 9   Mar. 25   Aug. 21

Four stages in the evolution of the Mont Pelée spine. (After A. Lacroix, 1904.)

into a gigantic black mushroom of seething particles high above the volcano. Then, slowly, gravity overcame the upward force, the cloud of fragments fell back, hit the steep slopes of the volcano, shot out laterally, and rolled down the slope. Racing hot avalanches roared down the mountain side at more than 60 miles an hour, completely devastating everything in their path. Their great mobility is explained by the fact that each bit of pumice in a volcanic cloud continuously emits water vapor and other volatile substances; the pressure of these expanding gases buoys up the particles and makes the mixture so mobile that it flows at tremendous speeds. The town of St. Pierre, containing about 28,000 persons, was caught in the path of one of these glowing avalanches. Only one man, imprisoned in an underground dungeon, survived the searing blast.

SPINES AND DOMICAL PROTRUSIONS. Following steam explosions such as these almost solid lava may rise into the throat of the volcano. At Mont Pelée such a **domical protrusion** of glassy lava rose through the crater floor, and, being too viscous to spread laterally, punched up as a gigantic **spine** (Fig. 18-8), much like a cork in the neck of a bottle filled with a gas-charged liquid. At intervals steam exploded violently from the edge and base of the spine, spurting forth eruption clouds made up of gas-charged pumice fragments, ash, and even large blocks, that flowed turbulently down the sides of the cone.

Spines and domical protrusions seem char-

acteristic of waning activity at composite volcanoes. They may rise in the crater, as at Mont Pelée, or punch through the lower flanks of a volcano like the newly formed Showa Shin-zan protrusion at Usu-Yama volcano, Japan. This dome, in 1944, pushed up through wooded ground and a cultivated field, lifting and heaving the broken rock and soil aside, and finally emerging as a steaming blocky mass of practically solid lava.

Many domical protrusions are less viscous than these examples. On approaching the surface they swell into bulbous rounded masses or may even flow down the slopes as sticky steep-sided flows. Although such viscous masses of glassy lava are generally associated with composite volcanoes, they may appear in shield volcanoes, or even rise independently as isolated rounded piles of blocky lava like those that form the Mono "Craters" in California.

Most such domical protrusions are of obsidian, which swells into bulbs at the surface, breaking the chilled crust into great angular blocks that mantle the dome in talus.

ASH FLOWS. Glassy lava is generally so highly charged with gases that instead of rising as a dome or spine it froths violently into bits of pumice as it approaches the surface. If the frothing is violently explosive, seething eruption clouds like those of Mont Pelée are formed. During some eruptions, however, the gas-charged lava boils more quietly from the vent, bubbling with minor explosions into a pumiceous froth that breaks into small slivers of glass and particles of pumice. These broken bubbles of frothy lava pour over the lip of the vent and rush down the flanks of the volcano in hot, highly mobile **ash flows.** Some ash flows are still so hot when they come to rest that the particles weld together again, to form a rock, **welded tuff** (see Appendix III), that superficially resembles obsidian or rhyolite. Most welded tuffs have boiled out of fissures (dikes) but some come from large central vents. C. N. Fenner, an American geologist, who first comprehensively described this type of eruption, showed that the "sand flows" (his name for ash flows) which rolled down the Valley of Ten Thousand Smokes soon after the great Katmai eruption of 1912 were fed from fissures on the valley floor. Many rocks formerly mapped as flows of rhyolite or obsidian have since been recognized as similar welded tuffs, deposited as hot avalanches of pumice fragments and broken glass bubbles.

VOLCANIC MUDFLOWS. Volcanoes occasionally explode through a crater lake, as the Javanese volcano Klut did in 1919. Gas-charged avalanches of pumice may melt snow on the slopes of a volcano and pour down as a mudflow, as in the 1877 eruption of Cotapaxi in Ecuador, or ash flows may roll into a river and make a mixture of water and volcanic debris that rushes far down the valley, overwhelming all in its path. The resulting deposits are **volcanic mudflows.** Heavy rains also wash loose pyroclastic debris down steep volcanic cones but these mudflows are generally less destructive. Mudflows are common in volcanic assemblages of all ages.

Plateau Basalts

In some of the world's most extensive volcanic areas true volcanoes are rare or absent. Instead, great sheets of lava have welled out through fissures in no way connected with volcanic cones. Such **flood basalts,** or **plateau basalts,** cover vast areas in the northwestern United States, western India, the Parana basin of South America, and the part of the north Atlantic that includes Iceland, Northern Ireland, and the Hebrides. Old plateau basalts, now folded and metamorphosed, are found in many other areas.

Basalts of Miocene age cover approximately 150,000 square miles on the Columbia River plateau of eastern Washington (Fig. 18-9) and northern Oregon. The Eocene basalts of western Washington and Oregon are even more voluminous. Hundreds of dikes of basalt and dolerite, marking the fissures through which these lavas rose, are grouped in great dike swarms. Such floods of basaltic magma, piled up in flow after flow to thicknesses of thousands of feet, are the most extensive of all volcanic deposits.

Figure 18-9. *Plateau basalt flows, near Vantage, Washington. The cliff is 1,100 feet high. (Photo by courtesy of the Washington Department of Conservation and Development.)*

Figure 18-10. Pillow lavas of Miocene age near Ellensburg, Washington. The lava, flowing from the left, entered a shallow lake whose bottom was covered with light-colored mud that has squirted up between the pillows. Length of view is 12 feet. (Photo by A. C. Waters.)

Pillow Lavas

Basaltic flows in Samoa have been observed, on entering the sea, to subdivide into irregularly rounded and ellipsoidal masses from several inches to a few feet in diameter that resemble a stack of pillows with peculiar cavernous spaces between them (Fig. 18-10). Such **pillow lavas** are commonly interstratified with marine sedimentary rocks. Many flows of Eocene basalt in western Washington and Oregon are pillow lavas that were erupted into shallow seas. Many pillows have a thick rind of glass formed by chilling of their surfaces by water. Openings between pillows are partly filled with fragments of altered glass, or with mud squirted up by hot water and steam from the sea floor. The Miocene basalts of the Columbia River plateau also contain many pillow lavas, but the fossils in the associated sediments show that these flows entered shallow fresh-water lakes (Fig. 18-10).

Intrusive Igneous Masses

Volcanic phenomena depend on the presence of masses of magma underground to supply the lavas and pyroclastic products. We now turn to these root zones of the volcanoes, and also to other igneous masses, large and small, that have congealed within the upper part of the earth's crust.

Shallow Intrusive Masses

PLUGS AND STOCKS. Among the masses of igneous rock that solidify at shallow depths are the vertical pipelike conduits through which lava rose to feed volcanoes. These are called volcanic **plugs,** or **necks.** They are commonly round or elliptical, but may be quite irregular. Although they average only about 600 feet in diameter, some are well over a mile across.

Most plugs are composed of porphyritic rock, perhaps medium-grained in the center but chilled to glass or fine-grained rock at the borders. Some are entirely glassy; these may once have fed domical protrusions or seething ash flows. Many, particularly in their upper parts, are made of explosion breccia. As might be expected from observed volcanoes, many plugs are composite, consisting of several kinds of rock that differ in texture and perhaps in composition and were emplaced at slightly different times.

The walls of most plugs are nearly vertical, but some can be seen to flare outward with depth and to pass into larger igneous masses, called **stocks,** that are a few miles across. Not all stocks, however, show any connection with volcanoes; many may never have reached the surface.

Most plugs and stocks resist erosion better than the surrounding rock and are left as steep-sided buttes above the surrounding country. In some areas where there are few volcanic rocks today, thickly clustered plugs record the presence of a former volcanic landscape very different from the present one. Over 150 plugs, marking the sites of vanished volcanoes, rise above the plateaus of north-western New Mexico and nearby Arizona. An area of less than 150 square miles near Neuffen, Germany, contains over 100 plugs. Most steep-sided buttes in the Midland Valley of Scotland, along the Rhine in Germany, and in the John Day basin of Oregon, mark the feeders of former volcanoes.

LARGE DIKE SWARMS. Dikes are among the most common igneous forms. Many regions contain **dike swarms.** Some are obviously related to volcanoes; among these are the buried linear dike swarm that must be inferred from the rift zone of Mauna Loa (Fig. 18-1), and the radial swarms within the dissected volcanoes on Oahu. Some large dike swarms, such as those in northeastern Oregon and central Washington, fed plateau basalts; others fed sill complexes, or other igneous masses. Still others appear to be off-shoots of large plutonic masses deep beneath the surface.

The great series of dolerite dikes in western Scotland and northern Ireland (Fig. 18-11) cluster thickly near such major volcanic centers as Skye, Mull, and Arran. But many, like the 110-mile-long Cleveland dike of northern England, extend so far they cannot be considered "parasitic" dikes fed laterally

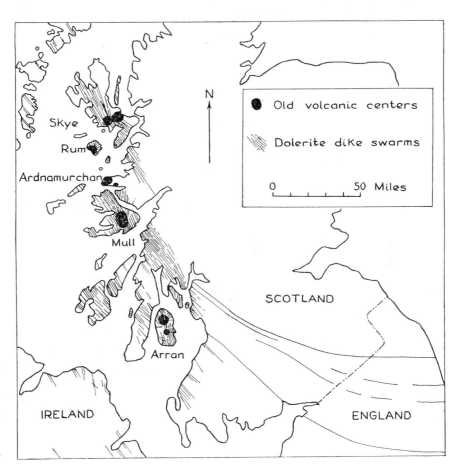

Figure 18-11.

The dolerite dike swarms and eroded volcanic centers of Scotland and adjacent parts of England and Ireland. (After J. E. Richey, H. H. Thomas, and others, Geological Survey of Great Britain.)

from the volcanic conduits. The map in Figure 18-11 has been greatly generalized from many detailed geologic maps. The reduced scale permits only a few of the largest dikes to be shown; for each line on this figure there are scores or even hundreds of dikes visible in the field.

Similar swarms of dolerite dikes cut rocks of widely diverse structures and ages, yet large areas of the earth's surface show none. Only in places have fissures riven the crust deeply enough to tap a source of basalt magma beneath, but through these fissures vast amounts of molten rock have risen to or near the surface.

SILL SWARMS. In many areas of flat-lying sedimentary rocks magma has been squirted between the strata to form flat pan-cake-like bodies called *sills* (see Chap. 3, especially Figs. 3-3 and 3-4). Sills, like dikes, differ greatly in size, in component rocks, and in associations with other igneous masses. Dolerite sills are the most common, and they may appear in great **sill swarms.**

A tremendous sill swarm in South Africa —the Karoo dolerites—consists of hundreds upon hundreds of dolerite sills, ranging from a few feet to over a thousand feet thick. The sills are injected into the relatively flat lying sedimentary rocks of the Karoo series in Basutoland and nearby Cape Province. The aggregate volume of these sills and related dikes nearly equals that of the Columbia River flood basalts.

LACCOLITHS. Magma may spread sill-like between sedimentary layers and concurrently lift the roof rock into a dome, thereby forming an underground magma body with a flat floor and an arched roof. When such a mass congeals it forms a **laccolith** (Fig. 18-12). Laccoliths are seldom more than a few miles across. Like sills, they tend to form

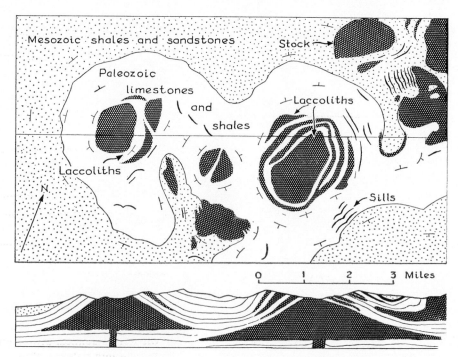

Figure 18-12.

Map and cross section of a group of laccoliths and stocks in the Judith Mountains, Montana. (After W. H. Weed and L. V. Pirsson, U. S. Geological Survey.)

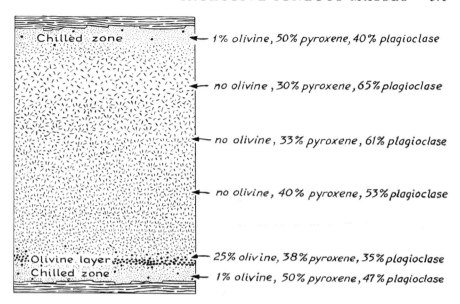

Figure 18-13.

← 1% olivine, 50% pyroxene, 40% plagioclase

← no olivine, 30% pyroxene, 65% plagioclase

← no olivine, 33% pyroxene, 61% plagioclase

← no olivine, 40% pyroxene, 53% plagioclase

← 25% olivine, 38% pyroxene, 35% plagioclase

← 1% olivine, 50% pyroxene, 47% plagioclase

Diagrammatic cross section of the Palisades sill, New Jersey, showing the vertical variation of texture and mineral composition. (After Frederick Walker, 1940.)

clusters, and they are generally associated with stocks, dikes, and sills. Many laccoliths, such as those of the Henry Mountains in Utah, are grouped radially about a central stock which evidently fed them.

DIFFERENTIATED SILLS AND LACCO-LITHS. The Palisades that confront New York City from across the Hudson River mark the eroded edge of a dolerite sill that is in places more than 900 feet thick. This large sill is not uniform dolerite from top to bottom, but consists of layers of differing composition. Along its base and in places at its top, olivine phenocrysts are scattered through a zone of fine-grained rock. The central part of the sill consists mainly of relatively uniform dolerite containing no olivine. Pyroxene is more abundant in the lower part than in the upper part of this central zone. Just above the fine-grained basal zone there is a layer 10 to 20 feet thick, about 25 per cent of which consists of olivine crystals (Fig. 18-13).

If the olivine in this olivine-rich layer were uniformly distributed throughout the much thicker central mass of olivine-free dolerite,

the entire sill would have the same composition as the fine-grained border zone. We infer from this that the fine-grained rock is a chilled zone representing the original composition of the magma when it was injected. Evidently, during the slow cooling, early-formed olivine crystals had time to settle through the magma and accumulate on the top of the basal chilled layer.

The Palisades sill illustrates the phenomenon of **differentiation,** which means the process whereby a once-uniform magma may yield rocks of differing compositions upon solidifying. The special kind of differentiation illustrated by the Palisades dolerite is *gravitative crystallization differentiation.* Many thick sills and laccoliths contain dense ferromagnesian-rich rocks at their bases; apparently a large proportion of their heavier minerals have sunk during crystallization. Gravitative differentiation doubtless occurs in some volcanic plugs and stocks as well, which may account for the rise of domical protrusions of obsidian or rhyolite into volcanic throats that formerly erupted much denser basalt and andesite. The obsidian may represent only the last liquid residue of a large volume of magma from which crystals typical of basalt had separated and sunk to lower levels.

Deep Intrusive Masses

Many sills, dikes, and particularly some of the very large intrusive masses called lopoliths and plutons, were doubtless intruded at much greater depths than the shallow forms just described. In general, intrusions that are coarse-grained and show little chilling at contacts are inferred to have cooled slowly against hot wall rocks and thus at considerable depth. When coarse-grained intrusions cut metamorphic or other deep-seated igneous rocks this conclusion is still more likely.

LOPOLITHS; STRATIFORM COM-PLEXES. Characteristic of the deep intrusive masses, though they also rise near the surface, are the highly differentiated igneous-rock complexes, called **lopoliths** (from the Greek words for "basin" and "stone"). These are shaped like a basin—both floor and roof of the chamber sag downward like a saucer (Fig. 18-14).

A huge mass of gabbro called the Duluth lopolith crops out along either side of Lake Superior and apparently continues beneath the western end of the lake like a thick saucer. It is about 150 miles across, perhaps 10 miles thick, and probably contains about 50,000 cubic miles of rock. Lopoliths differ from sills and laccoliths in their enormously greater size as well as in their form.

Most lopoliths, some large and deep sills, and even a few small intrusions are marvellously differentiated into many thin sheets and bands of contrasting mineral composition. In the Bushveld complex, a large lopolith in South Africa, this banding is so striking that when viewed from a distance outcrops of the igneous rock resemble thin-bedded sediments. How the layering in such **stratiform complexes** is formed has been debated. Since the heavier rocks are generally near the base and the lighter at the top, crystal settling by gravity probably plays a part, as it almost certainly did in the Palisades sill. But the hundreds of thin layers of alternating light and heavy minerals are not easily explained by crystal settling alone. Perhaps fluctuating convection currents within the slowly cooling

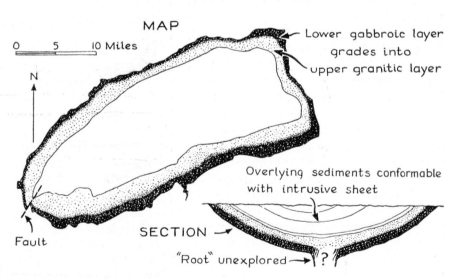

Figure 18-14.

The Sudbury lopolith, Ontario, Canada. (After A. P. Coleman, and E. S. Moore, 1929.)

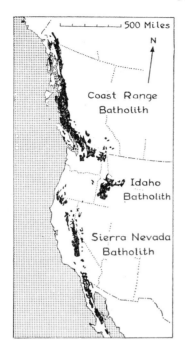 

Figure 18-15.

Large granitic intrusives (black) of western North America (left), and the Patagonian batholith (right). (After Geologic Maps of North and South America, Geological Society of America.)

magma helped sort the sinking crystals into layers, just as fluctuating water currents produce stratification in deposits of surface streams.

One small stratiform mass of gabbro, the Skaergaard intrusion of Greenland, forms a tilted cone with the apex downward. Its strikingly layered structure is well exposed on the walls of the deep Greenland fiords. The stratiform layers bank up against the wall-rock contacts, and in places show structures that resemble the cross-bedding and channeling of stream deposits. From these features, the English geologists Wager and Deer concluded that as the mass began to fill with crystals, convection currents sweeping slowly across the floor of accumulating crystals had sorted the crystallizing minerals into thin layers.

BATHOLITHS, OR PLUTONS. The largest igneous masses consist of great bodies of granite and granodiorite that extend along the cores of most major mountain ranges and underlie vast areas of the ancient shields. The body of granodiorite and related quartz-bearing plutonic rocks in the Coast Range of British Columbia (Fig. 18-15) is at least 1,000 miles long and 20 to 150 miles wide. Uniform granitic rocks extend as much as 7,000 feet down the canyon walls without revealing a bottom to the granite. Other huge granitic masses are exposed in the Sierra Nevada, in the Patagonian Andes (Fig. 18-15), and along the cores of most large mountain chains. Granitic masses of various sizes —some rounded in plan, some elongated, and some irregular—form intricate patterns with the metamorphic rocks that underlie most of eastern Canada, Scandinavia, and Brazil.

Masses of granitic rock having a surface area of more than 40 square miles are called **batholiths**; if their area is less, they are called **stocks.** In most definitions batholiths are said to flare outward with depth and to be "bottomless," in contrast to intrusions with a definite floor, such as lopoliths and laccoliths. Although anything resembling a floor can rarely be seen in the field, many students of batholiths have advanced indirect evidence that they taper downward—possibly like a tooth, perhaps like a tree with many short stubby roots, or even to a rounded or flat bottom—at depths of a few miles. Isostatic and seismic evidence for this conclusion is given in Chapters 19 and 20. From surface exposures alone it is impossible to infer the form of an igneous mass at depths of 10 or 20 miles. Because of the uncertainty regarding the shape of the lower parts of large granitic masses many geologists prefer to use the term pluton instead of batholith. A **pluton** is defined as any very large igneous mass, irrespective of form.

Contact Relations of Plutons.—Plutons show various relations to their roofs and walls. Some break across the bedding, folds, and other structures of the surrounding wall rocks (Fig. 18-16). Obviously these acted as liquids, engulfing numerous fragments of wall rock and penetrating their walls in large and small dikes (Fig. 3-6). In places the small injections so abound that the contact area becomes a transitional zone of "injection gneiss" consisting of intimately interpenetrating masses of granite and metamorphic rock in small layers, bands, dikes, or irregular masses.

In other areas the metamorphic wall rocks bend concordantly around the pluton instead of being cut off by it. The granite itself may also show a marked flow banding, or even a gneissic structure parallel with its walls, along which it may be streaked out, granulated, and even partly recrystallized. The structural pattern in many areas (Fig. 18-18) indicates that both pluton and wall rock have undergone slow laminar flow as pasty masses of only slightly different viscosity. Such structural relations seem best explained by the idea that the pluton was injected into wall rocks nearly as hot as the magma itself. Perhaps it moved into place as a pasty mass of almost completely crystallized magma, or perhaps it was a mixed mass of older metamorphic and new liquid material which had only partly melted into magma before it was forced upward.

Complex small-scale mixtures of granite and wall rocks (Fig. 18-17) are called **migmatites** ("mixed rocks"). Migmatites abound in many areas; in Finland they make up 26 per cent of the surface rocks (Fig. 18-18). Migmatites are very puzzling. Do they represent an intimate soaking of schists and other metamorphic rocks by granitic magma that was injected in small sills, tongues, and dikes? Or do they represent the selective melting of metamorphic rocks, the granitic parts being accumulations of the most easily fusible constituents that have melted and run

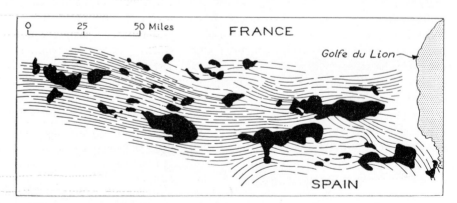

Figure 18-16.

Map of cross-cutting batholiths (black) in the Pyrenees. The lines are trends of folds. (After R. A. Daly, Igneous Rocks and the Depths of the Earth, McGraw-Hill Book Co., 1933.)

Figure 18-17.   *Migmatite, Clear Creek Canyon, Colorado. Note the complex folds, and the inti-mate interpenetration ("mixing") of light-colored granitic and dark-colored schis-tose rocks. (Photo by Warren Hamilton.)*

together into small masses, leaving the dark-colored, less fusible metamorphic parts of the migmatite unassimilated? Or is the granite a result of differential replacement, in the solid state, of parts of the original metamorphic rock by minerals characteristic of granite; just as we know fossils can be replaced by silica or garnet? Or do all these processes occur together when complex migmatites are formed? These are difficult questions, and clear-cut answers cannot always be given.

Some parts of a pluton may show no defi-nite contact with the wall rock; instead the granite fades gradually into metamorphic rocks. Although the metamorphic rock is

thoroughly recrystallized, it may show clear relics of undoubted sedimentary or volcanic structures. Metamorphosed sedimentary rocks, when traced toward some granitic masses, begin to lose their typical foliation and other structural features; feldspar and other minerals typical of granite begin to ap-pear within them, first in small isolated crys-tals, then in increasingly abundant clots, until, finally, only granitic minerals are present, and only an occasional streakiness gives a hint of the former metamorphic foliation. Some gran-ites contain nebulous patterns that resemble stratification or other structures found in sedi-mentary rocks. Still other granites enclose frail

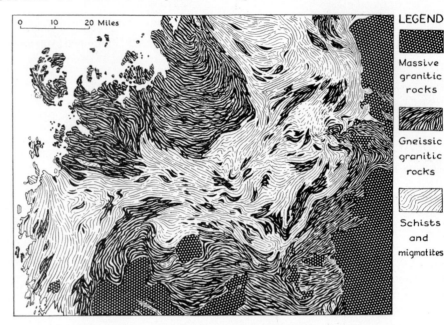

Figure 18-18.

Concordant batholiths and migmatites of southern Finland. The lined patterns indicate the strike of foliation in the gneissic granites, schists, and migmatites. (After Martti Saksela, 1935.)

unbroken layers of metamorphosed limestone and sandstone that could not have withstood forcible intrusion of magma without breaking up in the manner shown in Figure 3-6. Such structural features suggest that former sedimentary rocks have been transformed to granite by slow recrystallization and replacement in the solid state, and that limestone and sandstone beds were the least susceptible to replacement.

Thus some granites appear to be the products of metamorphic transformation; many are undoubtedly igneous. But how can we discriminate between the two modes of origin, either in the small granitic layers of migmatites or in the great, relatively uniform plutons? This question and the related one of how the huge granitic masses make room for themselves are among the most difficult problems in geology. Many geologists believe that all transitions exist—that recrystallized sedimentary and volcanic rocks can be partly melted deep within the earth, and that the magma thus formed may either solidify where

it was generated or be squeezed upward toward the surface, dragging the softened and partly melted wall rocks along with it, or slowly freeing itself from them as it rises into the colder rocks above.

Space and Time Relations.—The distribution of batholiths in space and time has significance to this problem. Granite has not been found on any of the isolated Pacific Islands, and it is probably not present in the crust beneath them, since fragments of granite have never been found in their volcanic ejecta. Further, the travel time of earthquake waves across the Pacific basin (Chap. 19) is such that there can be no significant amount of granite or granodiorite underneath this ocean. Quartz-bearing plutonic rocks thus appear to be confined almost entirely to the continents, although basalt occurs in both continental and oceanic areas. Large masses of granite apparently form mainly in the root zone of mountain belts (Chapters 9 and 20), and appear at the ground surface only in the cores of deeply eroded mountains, or in areas marking the site of former mountains that have been completely eroded away. It therefore appears likely that plutons are somehow related to mountain building, and that the growth of a mountain root may be the first step in the formation of these large igneous masses.

Physical Chemistry of Magmatic Crystallization

For well over a hundred years geologists have attempted to duplicate the processes that occur in crystallizing magmas by melting rocks and minerals in the laboratory and studying the products that separate from the melts on cooling. Because of the high temperatures necessary to melt rocks and because of the large number of solid-solution minerals with complicated chemical formulas that compose them, such experiments pose many difficulties.

The rapid development of physical chemistry in the last half century has given considerable impetus to such investigations. Most geological problems involve very complex chemical systems containing many components. The Norwegian geologist J. H. L. Vogt made a great step forward by applying the principles of physical chemistry to the crystallization of slags from blast furnaces. He also experimented with artificial rock melts. In 1904 the Geophysical Laboratory of the Carnegie Institution was founded in Washington, D. C., and its investigators began a serious long-range attack on the physical chemistry of artificial rock melts. The details of their work are beyond the scope of this book, as they require an advanced knowledge of both geology and physical chemistry. Their experiments, however, have sharpened, clarified, and, along some lines, completely revolutionized geological thinking about the origin of igneous rocks. In particular, the late N. L. Bowen of this laboratory has offered a comprehensive theory of the evolution of igneous rocks which is being tested and modified by field work and additional laboratory experiments.

Bowen's Theory

A greatly simplified statement of Bowen's theory is that *basalt magma is the parent of all the igneous rocks, and the many varieties have arisen through crystallization differentiation.* The great diversity of volcanic and plutonic rocks is explained by the separation of early-formed crystals from the parent basalt magma during its crystallization and segregation of these early minerals into a different part of the mass. Separation of crystals by gravity, the process suggested by the olivine-rich ledge of the Palisades sill, is considered very important. A second mechanism by which early-formed crystals are separated from the parent liquid is called "filter-pressing"—if a spongy mass of early-formed crystals is squeezed by crustal deformation while the spaces between the crystals are still filled with molten material, the liquid is forced out of the crystal mesh and the crystals are packed more tightly together. By careful laboratory experiments Bowen and his colleagues worked out the order of crystallization (i.e., the order in which the different minerals appear) during the freezing of basalt magma. This order is summarized in the following diagram, which is called the **Bowen Reaction Series.**

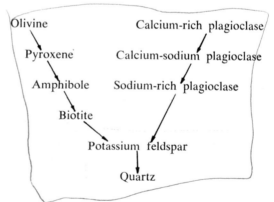

Olivine and calcium-rich plagioclase are the first minerals to crystallize in abundance from basaltic magma. Unless these early-formed crystals are removed from the melt by some such process as crystal settling or filter pressing, the olivine will react with the surrounding liquid as it cools to produce pyroxene, and the calcium plagioclase will react to produce a plagioclase richer in sodium. If no crystals are removed from the melt, thus allowing these reactions to go on unimpeded, the whole mass solidifies to a mixture of plagioclase and pyroxene with a small amount of olivine—the typical minerals of a basalt lava flow. If, however, the olivine or the calcium plagioclase, or both, are separated from the melt, perhaps by settling in large quantity to the floor of the magma chamber, such reactions between crystals and liquid cannot take place. Olivine contains a higher proportion of magnesium and a lower proportion of silica than the melt as a whole: calcium-rich plagioclase a higher proportion of calcium and a lower proportion of both sodium and silica than the melt. The liquid left behind will thus be relatively impoverished in magnesium and calcium and relatively enriched in silica, alkalis, and iron—it is thus no longer of basaltic composition but nearer andesitic. If no further crystals are separated, the liquid will crystallize to a rock of andesitic composition, but if the next crop of crystals (now pyroxene and calcium-sodium plagioclase) are removed as fast as they form, so that they are not available to react with the liquid, the ieft-over magma may continue to change in composition, ultimately reaching the composition of a siliceous, alkali-rich rhyolite. Only 10 per cent or less of the original basalt magma can be transformed to rhyolite; the rest has already accumulated as peridotites, olivine-rich gabbros, diorites, and similar rocks on the floor of the magma chamber.

By this simple mechanism Bowen explained the great diversity of the igneous rocks. The theory is powerfully supported by certain field occurrences: for example, the common presence of olivine-rich rocks along the floors of thick sills with quartz-bearing rocks in their tops, and the appearance of a small amount of rhyolite as late eruptions from great basaltic or andesitic volcanic cones. According to the theory, these small masses of siliceous rock represent the last liquids remaining after crystallization and gravitative separation had removed the earlier-formed crystals. Stratiform lopoliths may well have been formed by accumulation of the early crystallizing minerals into sheets and layers so closely packed that the remaining magma was squeezed out and could not react with the solid crystals.

Objections to Bowen's Theory

Although Bowen's theory has won wide acceptance as an explanation of differentiated sills, stratiform complexes, and some composite volcanoes, it has not been generally accepted as an explanation of the origin of the granite and granodiorite of plutons. It is difficult to believe that these huge igneous bodies represent only 5 to 10 per cent of the original magma from which they crystallized. The "room problem" of providing space within the crust for such huge bodies of molten granite as are needed to form great plutons such as those in British Columbia or California is staggering (Fig. 18-15). The relative rarity of intermediate rocks such as diorite also interposes an obstacle to those who would derive all granites by differentiation of basalt. Perhaps the most outstanding fact in igneous geology is the great dominance of basalt among volcanic rocks and of granite among the plutonics, in striking contrast is the paucity of rocks of intermediate composition. According to Bowen's theory, the intermediate rocks such as diorite should be far more abundant than granite.

The varied contacts of plutons also suggest processes other than crystal differentiation: it is evident that in places replacement, partial melting, and assimilation of wall rock fragments have all played important roles in developing large granite masses. The restriction of granite and granodiorite to continental areas, and the absence of granite in the Pacific Islands, also opposes the theory. Still more notable is the restriction of nearly all the batholithic masses in Cambrian and younger rocks to the root zones of mountain ranges, and their close association with zones of maximum metamorphic intensity within the mountain roots. There are also reasons to think that in Precambrian areas, too, these bodies occupy former mountain chains, now leveled by erosion. Basalt, on the other hand, is erupted in every kind of structural setting, and the greatest known floods of basalt, such as those in the Columbia River region or the Deccan Plateau in India, are in no way connected with mountain chains. Indeed, the fact that large plutons are virtually confined to the cores of present and former mountain chains strongly suggests a genetic connection between mountain building, metamorphism, and the development of plutons. Perhaps most granites are formed by partial melting of crustal rocks depressed deeply within the roots of growing mountain ranges.

Metamorphic Rocks

Metamorphic rocks commonly appear in the cores of mountain ranges, and are the chief components of the ancient shields. Deep drilling also shows that they underlie large parts of the continental plates, and as we saw in Chapter 17, it has been estimated that, together with the associated plutonic igneous rocks, they make up about 85 per cent of the earth's crust down to a depth of 10 miles.

As explained in Chapter 3, we know that slate and certain other metamorphic rocks grade locally into only slightly altered sedimentary rocks. Hence slate must have been formed by the recrystallization and growth of new minerals that replace those formerly present in shale. Moreover, relic structures such as stratification could have survived only if the growth of these new minerals had taken place in the solid state and was not due to melting of the rock. Actually, however, original textures and structures such as fossils and stratification, or the porphyritic texture characteristic of lavas, are generally obliterated during metamorphism. All too often in metamorphic terrains no relic features remain to record the original character of the rocks. Instead we face a bewildering assemblage of crystalline rocks that vary greatly in appearance and contain a large and diverse assemblage of minerals, many of them quite unfamiliar. How does one read the record of such puzzling rocks? No fossils remain to guide us, and the Law of Superposition is surely not reliable in rocks so strongly deformed. Indeed, even the Uniformitarian Principle can help us only indirectly; metamorphism goes on deep beneath the surface of the earth where we are unable to observe what is taking place. However, as mentioned in Chapter 3, recently invented machines can duplicate the pressures that prevail at depths of 20 miles or more in the crust, and the temperatures just below those at which rocks melt. This makes it possible to approach experimentally—even though crudely—some of the conditions that must prevail during metamorphism.

But the ultimate test of all geologic theories is in the field. What has field mapping brought out about the distribution and character of the metamorphic rocks, and what theories and criteria have geologists used in their attempts to unscramble the enigma of their origin?

The "Basement Complex"

Up to so recently as seventy-five years ago little progress had been made in unlocking the secrets of the metamorphic rocks. Geologists recognized their complexity, and that they had originated by transformation of other rocks, but their sequence in time, the secrets of their stratigraphic order, and even worthwhile clues as to the parental rocks from which many had been derived escaped even the most competent observers. On the geologic maps all metamorphic rocks, and most of the plutonic igneous rocks as well, were grouped together under one color in a vast wastebasket called the "Basement Complex," even though on the same map the unmetamorphosed sedimentary rocks might be subdivided into a great many small formations based on minor differences in lithology and fossil content. Since the metamorphic rocks generally lay at the base of the local fossiliferous section, and since their battered and recrystallized appearance (Fig. 18-19) gave an impression of great age, they were commonly assigned to the Precambrian —the early Scottish geologists called them the "Old Boy"—even though the fossiliferous rocks that rested upon them might be eons younger than the Cambrian.

Some geologists, however, were not willing to concede defeat by the "Old Boy." To them the wonderful diversity of the metamorphic rocks, the vast complexity of their textures and structures, and their unique mineral assemblages were a challenge. Successful discrimination between stratification and foliation in slate (Chap. 3), and the recognition that many coarse-grained foliated rocks rich in feldspar such as those shown in Figure 18-20 are not igneous granites, but are the recrystallization products of older sedimentary or igneous rocks, stimulated these observers to more careful field work, and to the search for unifying principles that would help unravel the history recorded in these enigmatic mineral assemblages and structures.

Mineral Zones and Isograds

One of the first breakthroughs in the understanding of metamorphism came from studies of the widespread and varied metamorphic rocks in the highlands of Scotland. George Barrow, a geologist with the Geological Survey of Scotland, noted that the metamorphic rocks bordering granite bodies in the Scottish highlands were generally coarse grained and rich in feldspar, whereas those farther from the plutonic centers were finer grained, more micaceous, and in some places preserved relic structures, such as stratification, that proved their derivation from sedimentary rocks. Looking more closely at the minerals in the metamorphic rocks, Barrow noted that the feldspar-rich gneisses and coarse schists near the central area of intrusions contained many needle-like crystals of sillimanite (Al_2SiO_5). A little farther away the schists contained blades of blue kyanite, a mineral with the same chemical composition as sillimanite but of different crystal form. Still farther from the focus of greatest plutonic and metamorphic intensity, cross-shaped twinned crystals of staurolite were prominent in the schists. Thus Barrow was able to recognize a crude **mineral zoning** from the centers of maximum metamorphic intensity outward. As this zoning did not parallel the changes in bulk composition, it could not be due to original compositional differences like those between sedimentary strata, but must be related instead to the intensity of the metamorphic processes. Careful petrographic work by the British geologist Alfred Harker showed that the mineral zoning could be extended farther. One of the garnets, almandine, characterized a zone of schistose rocks beyond the staurolite zone. Still farther out, in a broad belt of rocks that graded from mica schists into slates, a biotite zone and a chlorite zone could also be recognized. Decreasing tempera-

Contorted chlorite schist and phyllite. Note the complex folds and the broken and distorted layers. Mount Lydenia, Alaska. (Photo by J. C. Reed, U. S. Geological Survey.)

Figure 18-19.

Figure 18-20. Coarse-grained feldspathic gneisses alternating with thin layers of amphibolite. Note local contortion and faulting. (Photo by Sidney Paige, U. S. Geological Survey.)

ture outward from the center of maximum metamorphic intensity appeared to have controlled the kind of minerals that had developed during recrystallization of the shales. C. E. Tilley, another British geologist, proposed in 1925 that the *first appearance* in the rocks of one of these characteristic key minerals recorded a definite temperature of formation. By drawing a line on a map connecting all points where a specific key mineral first appeared he could delimit an **isograd, or line** of equal temperature in the earth's crust at the time the key mineral was formed by the metamorphism.

Physical Factors that Affect Metamorphism

Significant and important as these advances were, the mapping of metamorphic rocks during the past thirty years has demonstrated that Tilley's original concept was oversimplified. Many other factors besides temperature influence the formation of minerals during metamorphism. We still do not understand the relative importance of all these factors and the exact role that each plays in the genesis of specific minerals, yet certain broad relations are evident.

We know that pressure affects a system in chemical equilibrium, and must therefore affect the chemical reactions by which a new mineral forms. Chemists have shown that high pressure normally promotes growth of minerals of high density, but laboratory investigations of this effect on specific minerals are few.

Grain size is important. Field observations have repeatedly shown that a coarse-grained rock such as granite may endure almost intact a metamorphic environment that has brought about complete recrystallization of fine-grained rhyolites and tuffs which overlie the granite unconformably. There is, of course, no difference in composition between rhyolite and granite—rhyolite is the volcanic equivalent of granite, and they differ only in grain size. The smaller the grains the greater the surface of contact between minerals partaking in a metamorphic reaction. The difference in grain size also explains why shearing stress is important in metamorphism. If, through shearing and movement, a granite is intimately crushed and pulverized, the area of contact between minerals is greatly increased; hence recrystallization into new minerals may proceed as readily as in rhyolite. Moreover, the mechanical stirring accompanying shearing constantly brings new surfaces in contact and so promotes metamorphic reactions.

The chemical composition of the rock being metamorphosed greatly affects the kinds and abundance of the new minerals formed. Obviously no mineral can form unless the chemical elements composing it are available, even though temperature and pressure might be favorable to its formation. For example, the rocks that Barrow, Harker, and Tilley studied were all derived from the metamorphism of shale. Besides the six minerals characteristic of the different mineral zones, or isograds, these metamorphic rocks also contain much mica, quartz, and, near the center of greatest metamorphic activity, potassium feldspar. But a basalt lava interbedded with shales, and metamorphosed with them, forms an entirely different suite of minerals. The micas, quartz, and potassium feldspar characteristic of the metamorphosed shale are absent, or present only in small amounts. The minerals developed by metamorphism of basalt include epidote, amphiboles, and pyroxenes. Water is also an important variable, for many metamorphic minerals are hydrous, and apparently even some anhydrous minerals form only if water is present.

Metamorphic Facies

In 1921, P. Eskola, a Finnish geologist, sought to determine the relationship between chemical composition and grade of metamorphism a little more closely. He observed that several kinds of metamorphic rocks, which differ markedly in mineral composition and texture, all have the same chemical composition as basalt. Some of these rocks have been shown to be transitional to basalt, but in most, any relic structures that might relate them to basalt have been destroyed. Eskola reasoned that because of the identity in chemical com-

position the latter, too, must have been derived from basalt—or from its coarse-grained igneous equivalents, gabbro and dolerite—but under metamorphic conditions so intense that all traces of original structures had disappeared. Therefore the mineral assemblage of each must record the intensity of its metamorphism. Eskola suggested that metamorphic rocks of the same chemical composition could be separated into distinct **metamorphic facies,** each characterized by a unique assemblage of minerals. There are as many different metamorphic facies as there are different assemblages of metamorphic minerals, and *each metamorphic facies must represent a special metamorphic environment (within definite ranges of pressure and temperature) wherein this particular assemblage of minerals is stable.* If metamorphic intensity increased, some minerals formerly stable would recrystallize into a new assemblage adjusted to the new conditions.

Among the metamorphic equivalents of basalt Eskola recognized four very common metamorphic facies which, together with their characteristic minerals, are listed in Table 18-1.

Recent Laboratory Studies

Eskola's work focused attention on the **stability relations** of different minerals. If we knew the exact conditions of pressure, temperature, and the other metamorphic factors under which a given metamorphic mineral such as sillimanite, staurolite, or muscovite is formed we could use the presence of this mineral in the rocks as a guide in reconstructing the conditions of metamorphism. But metamorphic minerals are notably difficult to synthesize in the laboratory. Van't Hoff's classic experiments with the relatively easily synthesized Hartsalz from Stassfurt were mentioned in Chapter 3. V. M. Goldschmidt, a Norwegian geologist and chemist, also made significant laboratory studies of the much more difficult silicate minerals in the period from 1911 to 1940. But a great many metamorphic minerals are hydrous silicates and nearly all at-

Original Igneous Rock	*Mineral Composition*
(Basalt, gabbro, dolerite).	Pyroxene; Plagioclase
Metamorphic Facies	
Greenschist facies.	Chlorite; Epidote; Albite
Amphibolite facies.	Amphibole; Ca-Na Plagioclase
Pyroxene granulite facies.	Pyroxenes (augite and hypersthene); Ca-Plagioclase
Eclogite facies.	Na-Pyroxene; Pyrope variety of garnet

TABLE 18-1

The Metamorphic Facies Equivalent to Basalt in Bulk Composition (Eskola).

tempts to synthesize these failed until in the late 1940's when O. F. Tuttle, an American geologist, succeeded in constructing "hydrothermal bombs" in which water vapor could be held in contact with a mineral charge at high temperatures and pressures. Since then workers in a few laboratories have successfully synthesized most mineral groups found in metamorphic rocks, and have thrown a flood of light on the stability relations of various mineral assemblages.

Moreover, the recent discovery that we can determine the age in years of the abundant mica that is so common in metamorphic rocks by determining the ratio of radioactive potassium to argon contained within the mineral (Chapter 7) gives promise of being the golden key that will unlock the stratigraphy of metamorphic terrains. This discovery may bring the same rapid advances in the study of sequence in metamorphic terrains (and for

the same reason) that Smith's and Cuvier's studies of fossils brought in our understanding of sequence and correlation among the sedimentary rocks. However, this key can unlock only the secret of the time at which the metamorphism that crystallized the mica took place—we still have no measuring rod that will reveal the date when the original sediment was laid down, perhaps millions of years before its metamorphism.

Thus we stand today on the verge of another major breakthrough in the understanding of metamorphic rocks. The "Old Boy" still retains many of his secrets, but the bastions of his citadel are being rapidly undermined by concerted laboratory and field attacks. These recent discoveries are also bringing new understanding of two other complex and controversial subjects—the origin of earthquakes and of mountain ranges, subjects that are the themes of the next two chapters.

FACTS, CONCEPTS, TERMS

SHIELD VOLCANOES
  Fissure eruptions; radial dikes; cinder cones
  Calderas; ring dikes
  Lava pools; lava fountains
COMPOSITE VOLCANOES
  Small rhythmic explosions
    Incandescent bombs; lapilli
  Strong explosions
    Eruption clouds
    Ash flows
    Welded tuffs

  Volcanic mudflows
  Spines; domical protrusions
PLATEAU BASALTS
  Submarine eruptions; pillow lavas
SHALLOW INTRUSIVE BODIES
  Plugs; dike swarms; sill swarms; laccoliths
  Gravitative differentiation
DEEP INTRUSIVE BODIES
  Lopoliths
    Layering in lopoliths and stratiform complexes

QUESTIONS

1. Why are cinder cones more likely to develop along a dike after the dike has fed lava flows and is in process of congealing than when the dike first breaks through to the surface?

2. How can you distinguish a deposit of welded tuff from a flow or domical protrusion of flow-banded rhyolite?

3. Obsidian from a Japanese volcano has a specific gravity of 2.60, pumice lapilli from the same volcano floats two-thirds submerged in water. Approximately what volume of pumice would be required to account for the formation of a caldera 4 miles in diameter and with an average depth of 1,000 feet on the top of this volcano, assuming that the caldera was the result of piecemeal subsidence after strong explosions of pumice lapilli?

4. Draw cross-section diagrams of the following igneous bodies: (a) a spine, (b) a ring dike, (c) a differentiated sill, (d) a stratiform complex.

5. Draw a sketch or a geologic map showing a portion of the edge of a batholith. Show and label the following typical features: (a) a discordant contact, (b) inclusions, (c) a series

of dolerite sills that are older than the batholith, (d) a rhyolite dike that is younger than the batholith, (e) a series of sedimentary rocks that are older than the batholith, (f) a welded tuff that is younger than the batholith.

6. Explain the process of gravitative crystallization differentiation in igneous masses.

7. What is the evidence that some granites are of metamorphic origin?

8. How could you tell whether a granite body had been injected into cold rocks, or had formed in a zone of high metamorphic intensity where the recrystallizing wall rocks were nearly as hot as the granite?

9. Why is it more difficult to make synthetic metamorphic minerals in the laboratory than it is to make the minerals that occur in evaporites?

10. Many greenschists composed of chlorite, epidote, and albite show well-developed pillow structures. Would you expect these to be interlayered with chlorite-bearing mica schists typical of the chlorite zone of Barrow-Harker-Tilley, or with highly feldspathic sillimanite-bearing gneisses. Why?

SUGGESTED READINGS

Bowen, N. L. *The Evolution of the Igneous Rocks*. Princeton, N. J., Princeton University Press, 1928.

James, H. L. *Zones of Regional Metamorphism in the Precambrian of Northern Michigan*, Geological Society of America, Bull., Vol. 66 (1955), pp. 1455-1488.

Read, H. H., *The Granite Controversy*, London & New York, Interscience Publishers, 1957.

Tyrrell, G. W. *Volcanoes*. London, T. Butterworth, 1931. (Written in nontechnical language.)

19 EARTHQUAKES AND THE EARTH'S INTERIOR

Effects of Earthquakes

IN THE EARLY morning of November 1, 1755, All Saint's Day, the churches of Lisbon were thronged with worshippers. Suddenly the ground thundered forth a terrifying roar and began to heave and writhe in horrible, jarring shocks that seemed endless. The roofs and arches of the great stone churches crumbled, crushing hundreds beneath them. Most of the buildings in the city crashed in rubble. Within six minutes, when the awful quaking stopped, nearly a quarter of the population had perished, and thousands more lay trapped beneath the wreckage. The sea withdrew from the harbor, exposing the bar at its mouth, then rushed in as a wall of water fifty feet high, drowning hundreds who had taken refuge on the open wharves, and destroying ships, docks, and nearly everything in its path. At the same time came a shorter shock of great intensity. Slides of rock cascaded down the mountains behind the city, raising dust clouds so dense that many thought a volcanic eruption had begun. A third shock struck the desolate city two hours later. Fires completed the destruction: by nightfall 60,000 people of a population of 235,000 had perished, and thousands of the survivors were crippled, maimed, or mad from terror.

Probably no other earthquake in recorded history has been so widely felt. Rivers as far away as Lübeck, Germany (1,400 miles), rose or fell several feet. Loch Lomond, 1,200 miles away in Scotland, was thrown into waves two feet high. At Fez and Mequinez, Morocco, 400 miles from Lisbon, many thousands perished in wreckage nearly as complete as that in Lisbon; buildings were wrecked in scores of towns in Spain and North Africa. It has been estimated that the shock was felt over an area at least five times as large as that of the United States.

On December 16, 1811, at 2 A.M., the pioneers of the Mississippi Valley near New Madrid, Missouri, were thrown from their beds by a terrifying shock. In a few seconds, many of their log cabins had toppled, and over great areas sand, mud, and water gushed out of cracks in the earth, burying many of the fields. For miles, the alluvial banks of the Mississippi caved into the river; islands sank, others rose; river boats were swamped or hurled ashore. In the next fifteen months there were thousands of minor shocks and at least two earthquakes as severe as the first one. Large areas of land rose, draining former swamps. A huge tract nearly 150 miles long and 35 miles wide, mostly on the Mississippi floodplain, sank 3 to 10 feet and was flooded by the river to form new lakes and swamps. One of these, Reelfoot Lake, is several miles across. The shocks were strong enough to stop pendulum clocks and ring church bells as far away as Boston, and to crack plaster in Virginia. Had this earthquake come a century later, the loss of life would have been appalling, but in those pioneer days few were endangered.

On September 10, 1899, after a long series of minor shocks, a great earthquake wracked southeastern Alaska, centering in the region of Yakutat Bay. Though this shock was felt as far north as the Yukon, and from Sitka on the southeast to Cook Inlet on the west, little damage was done in this sparsely settled area. This earthquake, however, is distinguished for having accompanied the greatest vertical displacement of any yet studied: barnacles and boring clams marking the old sea level were lifted more than 47 feet above the sea in some places, while other areas nearby were depressed.

This earthquake affected the coastal glaciers (Fig. 13-6) in a most interesting way. Muir Glacier, more than a hundred miles to the east, was so severely shaken that it shed gigantic icebergs from its snout and soon wasted back at abnormal speed. The glaciers at Yakutat Bay, near the area of greatest shaking, reacted differently. Though many bergs also shook free from them, tremendous snowslides crashing down from the towering St. Elias Range at the head of the glaciers more than made up for the loss. The added load of new snow drove the glaciers vigorously forward—in places many hundreds of yards in less than ten months. Even stagnant parts of the Malaspina Glacier, so long inactive that a dense forest had grown on the debris-strewn ice, resumed motion, and its surface was tossed into a wild confusion of tilted and overturned trees, crevasses, hummocks, and pinnacles.

This account of major earthquakes could be greatly extended: the one that struck eastern Sicily and the Calabrian Coast across the Straits of Messina on December 28, 1908, destroying the cities of Messina and Reggio, killing about 100,000 people, and leaving the coast at Messina submerged more than 2 feet below its former level; the two great earthquakes of Kansu, in western China, one in December, 1920, the other in May, 1927—each of which is reported to have killed about 100,000 people, chiefly by causing the collapse of dwellings dug in loess; the great earthquake of Kutch, at the mouth of the Indus, in 1819, felt as far away as Calcutta, during which a great area of low land was flooded by the sea, while to the north a scarp—the "Allah Bund" or "Dam of Allah"—50 miles long, was raised as much as 20 feet; the great Assam earthquake, in the bend of the Brahmaputra in 1897, during which a scarp was raised 35 feet and buildings were destroyed in Calcutta, 200 miles away; the Hawkes Bay earthquake of 1931 and the Wellington earthquake of 1855 in New Zealand, both of which were accompanied by land tilting and uplift of 6 to 10 feet; and many more. Doubtless, the greatest catastrophe in history was a quake on the Hoang Ho plain of China in the sixteenth century, which killed more than 800,000 persons.

The San Francisco Earthquake

The San Francisco earthquake is of special interest, for from study of it have developed many of our present ideas about earthquakes. At a little after 5 A.M. on April 19, 1906, a great earthquake struck San Francisco. Many buildings were wrecked, especially those on marshy or filled ground, but many built on solid rock were little damaged. Hundreds of people were killed or injured, pavements were broken, and gas and water mains and electric power lines were torn apart. Fires sprang up in hundreds of places and raged out of control for days—the firemen helpless because of the broken water mains. The city was a shambles. Though the loss of life could only be estimated, it probably exceeded 700. Material losses exceeded $400,000,000, mostly from the fire. San Francisco suffered most, but Santa Rosa, Palo Alto, San Jose, and many other towns, some more than a hundred miles away, were severely damaged.

A great fault zone—the San Andreas rift—cuts obliquely across the California Coast Ranges for more than 600 miles. It stretches from the ocean at Point Arena on the north, past San Francisco, and thence far to the southeast, where it is finally lost in the alluvium of the Colorado Desert (Fig. 19-1). During the earthquake, the ground was rent open along this fault from Point Arena to San Juan, more than 270 miles. The movement was nearly everywhere horizontal, with the ground on the west side moving northward in relation to that on the east. The greatest displacement—21 feet as measured by the offset of a road—took place about 30 miles northwest of San Francisco. The displacement

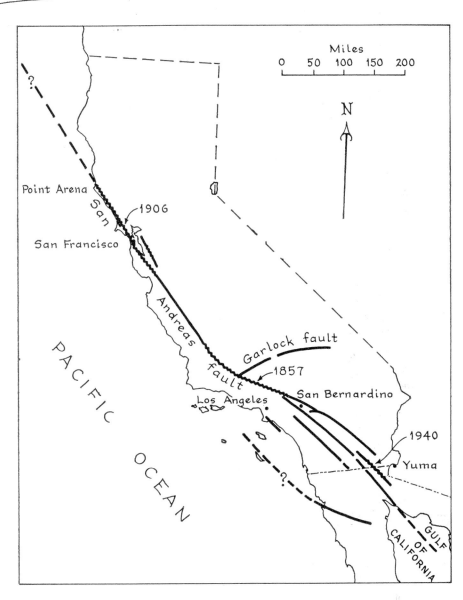

Figure 19-1.

The San Andreas and associated fault zones in California and northern Mexico. Zigzag lines show where the surface of the ground was broken during historic earthquakes. (After Clarence R. Allen, 1957.)

diminished both to north and south, though not regularly. Locally, especially toward the north, a slight vertical displacement took place, but nowhere more than 3 feet.

The San Andreas rift had been recognized as a fault zone for many years before the 1906 earthquake. Not only are geologic formations cut off and the rocks much sheared and crushed along it, but it is also conspicuous in the landscape. For much of its course, it is marked by large or small valleys and parallel ridges. Some streams bend abruptly when they reach it, and follow it for scores or hundreds of feet before swinging back to their original trends. Small ponds are strung out along it, some of them on steep slopes, strikingly anomalous features in arid southern California. In 1857 there was a strong earthquake shock along a segment of the San Andreas rift that crosses the Tehachapi Mountains, far south of the segment that broke open in 1906. It, too, was probably accompanied by movement of the west side of the fault northward relative to the east side. Though the San Andreas rift becomes difficult to trace, and is not identifiable as a continuous feature much to the southeast of San Bernardino, the fault zone continues southeast across the delta of the Colorado and into the Gulf of California. Several earthquakes along faults that form parts of this zone have also accompanied horizontal displacements in the same direction as the San Andreas farther north. Figure 19-2 shows an example of such an offset that occurred in

December, 1940, in an orange grove in the Imperial Valley about a mile north of the Mexican border.

Causes of Earthquakes

No one knows the ultimate cause of earthquakes. It seems certain that the immediate cause is the sudden movement of rock masses along faults, for such movements would be adequate to cause the shaking, and fault displacement has been observed during a large number of quakes. The great majority of earthquakes, however, are unattended by visible fault displacement, though such displacement may have occurred below the ground surface. Every fault is of finite length and beyond the last point of rupture it disappears: in 1906 no movement was measured on the San Andreas fault south of San Juan. Similar changes in amount of displacement of individual faults are known underground; many faults in mines can be observed to die out before they reach the surface. Furthermore, the close connection between fault displacement and intensity of shaking is clear. In 1906 buildings a few hundred yards from the San Andreas fault were not greatly damaged except where boggy ground rendered them particularly susceptible. Although, as we have seen in Chapter 8, faults like that at Buena Vista Hills may sever oil-well casings without producing earthquakes—presumably because of slow continuous movement rather than

Orange grove in Imperial Valley, California, displaced in December, 1940. At the Mexican border, about one mile south, the horizontal slip was almost 15 feet. (U. S. Army photo, courtesy Mr. E. Marliave.)

Figure 19-2.

GROUP	NUMBER OF STATIONS IN GROUP	AVERAGE DISTANCE FROM FAULT OF STATIONS IN GROUP (Miles)		DISPLACEMENT (Feet)	
		EAST	WEST	NORTHWARD	SOUTHWARD
A	1	4	. . .	. . .	1.9
B	3	2.6	. . .	. . .	2.8
C	10	.9	. . .	. . .	5.1
D	12	. . .	1.2	9.7	. . .
E	7	. . .	3.6	7.8	. . .
F	1	. . .	23	5.8	. . .

TABLE 19-1

Average Displacement of Points Between Surveys of 1874-1892 and 1906-1907, Relative to the Diablo-Mocho Line, Considered as Fixed in Position.

abrupt slipping—many oil wells in the Los Angeles basin have been cut off along faults during earthquakes, even though there was no surface sign of slipping. Because of such observations, all seismologists now agree that major earthquakes arise from movement on faults, even when no movement is discernable at the ground surface.

Elastic-rebound Theory

The fault motion accompanying the San Francisco earthquake was chiefly horizontal, and therefore could not be directly due to gravity. The region has no active volcanoes—and even if it had, no known volcanic eruption has shown energy remotely comparable to that released by the moving of thousands of cubic miles of rock for many feet along a break 270 miles long. What, then was the immediate source of this prodigious energy?

The American geologist H. F. Reid suggested an answer. Most crustal movements take place slowly. Though the fault displacement was sudden, the energy it released had probably been slowly accumulating in the rocks of the region. This energy had been built up as elastic strain in the crust as the rocks west of the fault slowly drifted northward in relation to those on the east. Slipping along the fault was long prevented by the cohesion of the rocks on the opposite sides. The strain continued to accumulate slowly, just as energy is stored elastically when we bend a bow. Ultimately, however, it reached a critical value, the friction along the fault plane was

overcome, and the rocks along the fault "snapped past each other," as a bow will snap and break if we bend it too far.

Reid showed that an analysis of the data from precise surveys of the San Francisco region supported this idea almost conclusively. Accurate triangulation surveys had been made by the U. S. Coast and Geodetic Survey in 1851-1865, 1874-1892, and also after the earthquake, in 1906-1907. Though the first survey was less accurate than the two later ones, its data are consistent with theirs. If the stations called Diablo and Mocho which are both 35 miles east of the rift, are considered not to have moved, then a comparison of their positions with the computed positions of points near the San Andreas rift and others west of it shows that large systematic movements have taken place with respect to Diablo and Mocho during the interval between the last two surveys. Reid grouped the data for these points according to the average distance of the several stations from the fault. His results are shown in Table 19-1.

The relations may be visualized from Figure 19-3. Let us assume a time when there was no elastic strain in the rocks of the region; the line AOC represents a line then crossing the fault at right angles. As the regional displacement began, the point A moved slowly north to A' and the point C south to C'. Because no slipping occurred along the fault during this time, the formerly straight line connecting the points through O became strongly bent. Just before the earthquake,

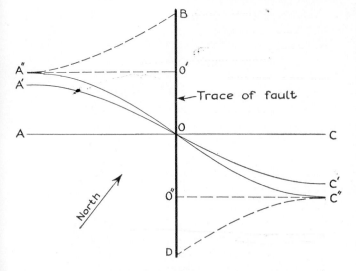

Figure 19-3. Diagrammatic map showing how the 1906 offset along the San Andreas fault is explained by the elastic-rebound theory. (After H. F. Reid, 1911.)

point A had advanced still farther, to A″, and point C to C″, these distances being such that the total A-A″ and C-C″ amounted, on the average, to 14.8 feet. (The greatest advance was 21 feet.) Then the stored force overcame the friction along the fault and the strain was relieved with explosive violence. A″O straightened out to A″O′ and C″O to C″O″. It is clear that the lines such as A″O′ and C″O′, which had been straight just before the movement, would be bent during movement into curves A″B and C″D, curves identical with A″O and C″O but bent in the opposite directions. When the fault broke, it may be assumed that the elastic strain (bending of the rocks without rupture) was almost completely released; the movement along the fault represents only the "elastic rebound" of the rocks from their condition of slowly accumulated strain before the fault. The data in Table 19-1 conform to the pattern of lines like A″B and C″D, lending strong support to the theory.

Since 1907 the Coast and Geodetic Survey has made further systematic resurveys of the same triangulation points; these confirm a continued northward displacement of stations west of the Diablo-Mocho line, which is assumed to be stationary. The movement seems to take place at a rate of about 2 inches a year. If we assume, though of course there is no sound basis for such an assumption, that when this displacement is again as great as it was in 1906 there will be another similar earthquake, about a century must still elapse. Such a prediction is wholly without value for we cannot be sure that the same displacement will be needed before faulting is renewed, nor that another nearly parallel fault, or even folding of the rocks, might not relieve the strain instead. But the existence of the movement is strong support for the "elastic-rebound" theory.

Seismic Sea Waves

The great wave that overwhelmed Lisbon harbor was doubtless caused by displacement of the sea floor just to the west, perhaps accompanied by submarine slides. The dramatic changes that the Tokyo and Grand Banks earthquakes made on the sea floor have already been mentioned in Chapters 8 and 5. These effects were chiefly due to slides and turbidity flows in the unconsolidated sediments. Few earthquakes on land are accompanied by very large topographic changes, and this is presumably true of submarine earthquakes also, for few of them are accompanied by such large waves as those that wrought havoc at Lisbon. Nevertheless, continuously recording tide gages do reveal many large waves, presumably set up by earthquakes, that would otherwise go unnoticed.

Waves caused by earthquakes are called **seismic sea waves** or **tsunamis** (Japanese). In many, as at Lisbon, the first movement is a withdrawal of water followed after an interval measured in minutes by a great inrush of the sea. Some seismic sea waves are truly gigantic: perhaps the greatest on record is one 210 feet high that broke on the south tip of Kamchatka in 1737; another, 93 feet high, struck the city of Miyako, Japan, in 1896; still another, in 1868, carried the U.S.S. *Watersee* far inland from its anchorage off the Chilean coast and left it high and dry. Waves from an earthquake off Peru were 8 feet high as they reached Japanese tide gages 10,300 miles from their source. These heights depend very largely on configuration of the shores; in the open ocean the waves are rarely noticed by ships. The speed of the waves depends only on the depth of water: it is often 400 or 450 miles an hour in the Pacific, but is much less in the shallower Atlantic. Damage and loss of life from tsunamis in Hawaii have been great enough that coastal warnings are now broadcast when the possibility of seismic sea waves is indicated by seismograph records of earthquakes.

Earthquake Waves and Their Transmission

If we break a bat while hitting a baseball, our hands are stung by the vibrations transmitted through the wood. In the same way, when two huge blocks of rock slip past each other along a fault, elastic vibrations are set up and transmitted through the earth in all directions.

The nature of these vibrations may be seen from Figure 19-4, *left.*

If we imagine that the point P in the figure is a particle within a uniform mass of perfectly elastic rock, and that it is pressed to the right, toward P', by some outside force, we can see that the material on its right is compressed, while that on its left expands. Since the rock is assumed to be perfectly elastic, these changes in volume mean that potential energy is stored up in it, and that the compressed material tends to expand to its original volume and the rarified material to contract. Let us now consider the movement of a line, APB, through P. If the point P is moved to P' by an external force the line must bend to some position such as A'P'B', thereby setting up a distortion, or shear, in the line. The nearer each point on the line APB is to P the farther it tends to slip, parallel to PP', from its original position, as the line becomes A'P'B'. This means that some energy is also stored up by distortion or shear.

Now let the outside force be removed. The point P' will not simply return to its original position P, but will have a momentum (like a

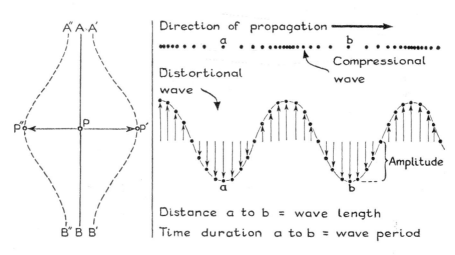

Figure 19-4.

Distance a to b = wave length

Time duration a to b = wave period

Left: *The distortion of line* AB *during the passage of compressional waves at right angles to* AB. Right: *The effect of compressional and distortional waves on the grouping of a series of equally spaced points. Note how the compressional wave affects their spacing in the direction of propagation, whereas the distortional wave offsets them as it passes from left to right. (After J. B. Macelwane,* When the Earth Quakes, *Bruce Publishing Co., 1947.)*

pendulum) that will carry it on past P to a point such as P″. The part of the rock to its left will now be compressed and that to the right rarified; the direction of the shearing tendency will also have been reversed. At P″, the kinetic energy that carried the point past the center will have been transformed again to potential energy; the point will again oscillate back through P to P′. The distance between P′ and P″ is the amplitude of the oscillation.

Of course, rocks are not perfectly elastic. In nature some of the energy is consumed as frictional heat, so that each oscillation is less than the preceding one. Still, the principle involved is not affected. If we consider the effects of the vibrations of a particle of rock at P on all other particles surrounding it, and of these, in turn, on their neighbors, we see that two types of waves, one compressional and the other a shear wave, must emanate from the point and spread through the surrounding rock in all directions.

In the compressional wave, the particles vibrate in the line of wave progress as alternate pulses of compression and rarefaction pass through the rock. It is thus like a sound wave in air. This wave is called the **P wave** (primary wave). The other wave, the shear wave, is a transverse wave; that is, the particles vibrate at right angles to the direction of wave progress (Figure 19-4, *right*). This is called the **S wave** (secondary). The particle motion in the S wave is like that set up in a loosely hanging rope when one end is given a sharp flip. Each particle of the rope moves essentially at right angles to the length of the rope, but the wave travels from end to end of the rope. These transverse vibrations are not the visible ground waves that can be seen at the surface in some strong earthquakes; their wave lengths are measured in tens of miles and their speeds in thousands of feet per second, far too fast for the human eye to see.

From the theory of elasticity we know that the compressional waves in an ideal elastic solid travel at speeds that vary directly as the resistance of the solid to compression and

shear and inversely as its density.* The speed of shear waves varies directly with resistance to shear and inversely with density. In rocks of the same density, the more rigid and incompressible the rock the faster both waves travel. In two equally rigid and incompressible rocks, on the other hand, the speed is greater in the less dense rock. As can be seen from the formulas, the compressional (P wave) travels faster than the shear wave (S wave).

The elastic properties of rocks—the incompressibility and rigidity—can be measured in the laboratory. Assuming that the wave theories are correct, they can also be computed from the measured speeds of waves in the earth made by exploding dynamite (artificial earthquakes). In a dynamite explosion, we know the exact point at which the "earthquake" occurred, and hence can accurately measure distance from the source. With sensitive chronometers, we can also time the explosion to less than 1/10,000 second. These measurements fail to agree exactly with those made on the same rocks in the laboratory, but the deviations are generally not great and are thought to come in part from imperfect sampling and errors in measurement, but mainly from inhomogeneity of the rocks in nature. When we think of all the faults, bedding surfaces, joints, gneissic structures, slaty cleavages, and other structures of rocks, this explanation of the discrepancies seems very reasonable. Rocks in the part of the earth accessible to us are certainly far from being ideal homogeneous solids.

The P and S waves travel in all directions from their origin through the elastic body of

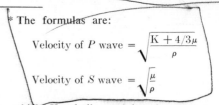

* The formulas are:

$$\text{Velocity of } P \text{ wave} = \sqrt{\frac{K + 4/3\mu}{\rho}}$$

$$\text{Velocity of } S \text{ wave} = \sqrt{\frac{\mu}{\rho}}$$

in which K = bulk modulus (a measure of incompressibility or resistance to change in volume); μ = modulus of rigidity (a measure of resistance to shear or change of shape); and ρ = density. It is assumed that the medium is isotropic and perfectly elastic.

the earth. In a homogeneous medium, waves travel in straight lines, but when they pass from one rock into another with differing elastic properties—say from limestone into shale—they are bent or refracted like water waves that encounter a pier or a float, or like light rays that pass through a lens. They may also be reflected at such a boundary, just as light is reflected from a mirror or sound echoes from a cliff. (The P wave is indeed a sound wave in rock.) Furthermore, when either a P or S wave strikes a sharp boundary —a **discontinuity** in the elastic properties of rocks along its path—it sets up new waves. The new waves generated at the discontinuity include new compressional and new shear waves set in motion by each of the original P and S waves, that is, two new S waves and two new P waves. Besides these, there are formed at least three kinds of "surface waves," so called because they travel along, or at least close to, the discontinuity. Such waves are set up, for example, at every geologic contact and at the surface of the earth, where the discontinuity consists of the contact between rock and atmosphere.

The surface waves set up at these discontinuities travel much more slowly than either the P or S waves and are far more complex: they are called long, or **L waves.** They travel on or near the earth's surface and do not penetrate deep within the crust.

From this brief discussion, it is obvious that earthquake waves are extremely complex. Because they are generally felt only near the source, delicate instruments are needed for recording them effectively. We will now turn to a brief discussion of these instruments, called seismographs, before passing to the deductions they enable us to make about the structure of the earth.

Seismographs

To record earthquake vibrations it is necessary to establish a point that can move as nearly independently of the earth as possible. We all know that we can knock the bottom book out of a pile laid on a table so quickly that the books above are hardly disturbed and so fall almost vertically, without tipping over. The inertia (tendency to resist acceleration) of the upper books prevents them from traveling along with the bottom book. The **seismograph** is an instrument designed to measure the displacement of the ground with respect to a mass that is, like the upper books, as independent as possible of the ground surface upon which it rests. A seismograph is so constructed that when the earth moves quickly under the impulse of an earthquake wave, as little motion as possible is transmitted to the main mass of the seismograph. If, then, we can measure the displacement between the ground and the seismograph mass, we thereby measure the ground motion during the earthquake.

This problem has been attacked in many ingenious ways: Masses have been supported by springs; long pendulums have been suspended from high structures (so that their time of swing would be great compared with that of earth vibrations); but for many years the most widely used mechanism has been the so-called **horizontal pendulum.** In this device (Fig. 19-5), a pendulum consisting of a heavy weight at the end of a boom is held by a wire fastened to a supporting pillar. The weight thus tends to remain in its position of rest as the support vibrates during an earthquake. Either by a delicate pen attached to the pendulum weight, or by a beam of light reflected from a mirror on the pendulum to a moving strip of photographic paper, the relative motion of the pendulum and the earth is recorded. Such a seismograph measures only the horizontal components of motion, at right angles to the length of the pendulum; to record all horizontal movements completely, two such pendulums are needed, one supported so that it hangs north–south, the other east–west. Still a third device, a mass suspended by a spring for measuring vertical movements, is necessary to give a full description of local earth motion. Time is marked automatically on the records, or seismograms,

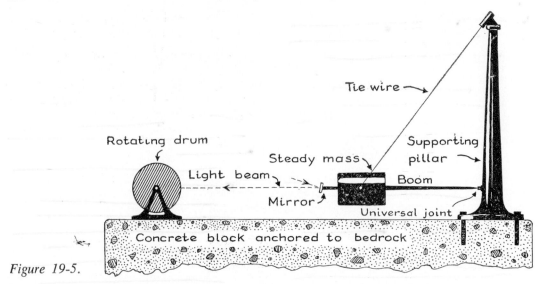

Figure 19-5.

Diagrammatic sketch of a horizontal pendulum seismograph.

usually by an electric clock suitably linked to the device that moves the photographic film or smoked paper on which the movement is recorded. In this way the time each vibration reached the seismograph can be determined very accurately—on some, to a small fraction of a second.

Inferences from Seismograph Records

By comparing seismograph records of the same earthquake at different stations, and of different earthquakes at the same station, seismologists are able to recognize the various kinds of waves that elastic theory predicts. In general, a seismogram shows several different kinds of waves, each of which can be related to a definite wave path through the earth. For example, in the seismograms shown in Figure 19-6, the points indicating the arrival of the P, S, and L waves, are labeled. The arrival of a reflected compressional wave, PP and of a reflected shear wave, SS, are also

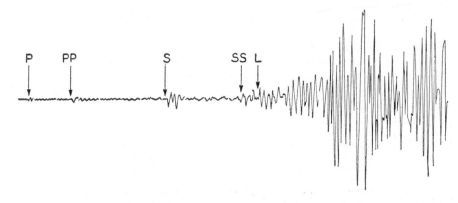

Figure 19-6.

Seismogram, with letters indicating the arrival of the various earthquake waves. (After L. D. Leet, Practical Seismology and Seismic Prospecting, *Appleton-Century-Crofts, 1938.)*

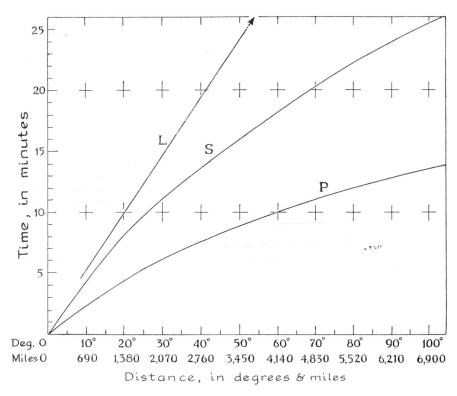

Figure 19-7.   Distance, in degrees & miles

Time-distance curves for the three principal earthquake waves. (Data from L. D. Leet, 1938.)

indicated (see also Fig. 19-9). Note that the onset of the surface waves (*L* waves) renders the seismogram much more complex than it is during earlier phases of the record.

REFRACTION AND REFLECTION AT DEPTH.   By tabulating the **travel times** of the waves from an earthquake of known source and by identifying the various wave groups on the seismograph records at many stations, **time-distance tables** have been made. When the distances from the source (in degrees of the earth's circumference), are plotted against travel time, we have a **time-distance curve** (Fig. 19-7). It is significant that the curves for the *P* and *S* waves are concave toward the axis of distance; that is, the greater the distance of travel, the faster the apparent speed of the waves. From this we infer that the waves travel faster as they

Figure 19-8.   The bending of rays of earthquake waves caused by the increase of wave velocity with depth. The rays must always progress in the direction at right angles to any small segment of the ray front. Only six of the infinite number of wave paths emanating from the source are shown in the figure.

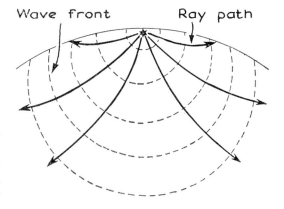

penetrate deeper within the earth, for the increase in speed is greater than would be expected if we considered only the difference between surface distance (arc) and straight-line distance (chord) to be the explanation. For the *L* wave, which travels along the surface, the time-distance curve is a straight line (Fig. 19-7); its travel time is directly proportional to its distance from the source.

Because of their increase in speed with distance, it is evident that the *P* and *S* waves do not travel along the surface, but through the body of the earth, and the deeper their paths the greater their speeds. From this it follows that their paths of travel are curved, just as light rays are curved by lenses (Fig. 19-8). This accounts for the fact that at points far from the source, the waves emerge at the surface at higher angles than they would if they followed straight lines. When they strike the surface, they are reflected back and proceed again in curved paths (Fig. 19-9). A whole train of reflected waves recorded on seismograms at distant stations, as shown in Figure 19-9, is thus explained.

We know from the earth's mass and dimensions that its average density is about 5.52, whereas the average density of the surface rocks is only about half as great. The material making up the earth's interior must therefore be far denser than that at the surface. As the formulas for wave speed show (footnote, page 392), if only the density of the rocks increased with depth and their other properties

Figure 19-9.   *Section through a part of the earth, showing the paths of a few of the many earth-quake waves and the records they leave on the seismograms at four stations. Note the reflected waves, PP, PPP, etc. The time scale of all the seismograms is the same. (After A. Sieberg,* Erdbebenkunde, *G. Fischer, 1923.)*

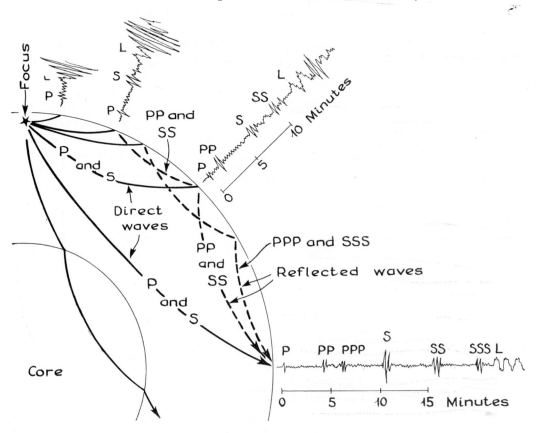

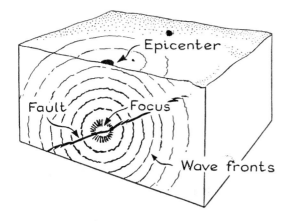

Figure 19-10. Diagram showing the positions of the focus and the epicenter of an earthquake caused by local deep-seated movement on an inclined fault.

remained unchanged, the waves should actually travel more slowly as they go deeper. Since they speed up, we see that the elastic properties—rigidity and incompressibility—must increase with depth even more than the density. We return to this important point later in this chapter, but before doing so let us see what other information the seismograms reveal.

EPICENTRAL DISTANCE.   The sharply pulselike records on seismograms suggest that most earthquakes begin in a very small area, even though many miles of fault may ultimately be active, as in the San Francisco earthquake. The point at which the first movements seem to occur is called the focus. The point on the surface directly above the focus is called the epicenter (Greek, "above the center"). See Figure 19-10.

The time lag between the *P* and *S* waves shown on a seismogram enables us to read the "epicentral distance" (the distance from the station to the epicenter) from the time-distance curves. This distance is measured in degrees of arc of the earth's curvature. If we draw a circle on a globe, using the seismograph station as the center and the epicentral distance as the radius, we know that the shock must have occurred somewhere on the

periphery of this circle. If we have adequate records from at least three stations, it is possible to find the location of the epicenter; it is the point at which the three circles drawn about the three stations intersect (Fig. 19-11). In fact, it is sometimes possible to make a close estimate of both direction and distance of an earthquake from a single station by observing the direction of first movement and the relative amplitudes of the waves recorded on the vertical and two horizontal records. The fact that time-distance curves for all stations more than a few degrees distant from the epicenter are essentially the same, regardless of the direction of approach of the seismic wave, shows clearly that the earth must everywhere be nearly homogeneous (or else similarly variable) at any particular depth greater than a few score miles. If it differed appreciably from place to place the differences would show up in the travel times of those waves that traversed the different kinds of material as, indeed, they do for nearby earthquakes which travel only in shallow zones of the crust.

ISOSEISMAL LINES.   We ordinarily have no quantitative way of measuring the force of tremors near the most intensely shaken area. We must rely on qualitative information such

Figure 19-11. Locating an epicenter in northwest Utah from seismograms recorded in Seattle, Berkeley, and Livingston, Montana.

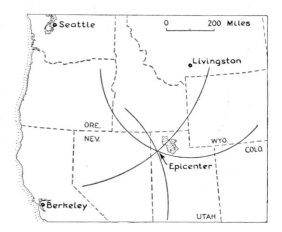

as the destruction caused or the perceptibility of the shock to persons. Many "scales of intensity" have been suggested by students of earthquakes, but most are highly influenced by the past experiences of persons interviewed, the methods used in questioning them, the density of population, the nature of the ground, and the quality of building construction in an area. Most scales now in use are modified from one proposed by the Italian seismologist Mercalli: the one most widely used in America is the "Modified Mercalli," or Wood-Neumann scale (1931).

Abridgea Wood-Neumann Scale of Earthquake Intensities

I. Not felt, except by very few, favorably situated.

II. Felt only on upper floors, by a few people at rest. Swinging of some suspended objects.

III. Quite noticeable indoors, especially on upper floors, but many people fail to recognize it as an earthquake; standing automobiles may sway; vibrations feel like those of a passing truck.

IV. Felt indoors by many during day, outdoors by few; if at night, awakens some; dishes, windows, and doors rattle, walls creak; standing cars may rock noticeably. Sensation like heavy truck striking a building.

V. Felt by nearly all, many wakened; some fragile objects broken, and unstable objects overturned; a little cracked plaster; trees and poles notably disturbed; pendulum clocks may stop.

VI. Felt by all; many run outdoors; slight damage; heavy furniture moved; some fallen plaster.

VII. Nearly everyone runs outdoors; slight damage to moderately well-built structures, negligible to substantially built, but considerable to poorly built; some chimneys broken; noticed by automobile drivers.

VIII. Damage slight in well-built structures; considerable in ordinary substantial buildings, with some collapse; great in poor structures. Panels thrown out of line in frame structures; chimneys, monuments, factory stacks thrown down; heavy furni-ture overturned; some sand and mud ejected, wells disturbed; automobile drivers disturbed.

IX. Damage considerable even in well-designed buildings; frame structures thrown out of plumb; substantial buildings greatly damaged, shifted off foundations; partial collapse; conspicuous ground cracks; buried pipes broken.

X. Some well-built wooden structures destroyed; most masonry and frame structures destroyed or knocked off their foundations; rails bent, ground cracked; landslides on steep slopes and river banks; water slopped over from tanks and rivers.

XI. Few if any masonry structures left standing; bridges destroyed; underground pipes completely out of service, rails bent greatly; broad cracks in ground and earth slumps and landslides in soft ground.

XII. Damage total; waves left in ground surface, and lines of sight disturbed; objects thrown upward into the air.

As we noted, local factors vary too much for such estimates of intensity to be either quantitatively accurate or directly comparable for different localities. Nevertheless, much information valuable to engineers, insurance underwriters, civic planners, and others can be derived from a systematic study of the way intensities are distributed. In the United States, immediately after a destructive earthquake, the Coast and Geodetic Survey sends post cards to persons living in the area affected. These cards contain lists of characteristic earthquake effects and the persons receiving them are asked to check those items that accord with their own experience during the shock. When the returned cards are tabulated by locality, a map showing the intensities according to the Wood-Neumann scale can be compiled.

Lines drawn on such a map through points of equal intensity are called **isoseismal lines** (Fig. 19-12). The isoseismals generally lie in rough ovals about a center which either coincides with the position of the epicenter as determined from seismograph records or is close to it. The fact that the instrumentally

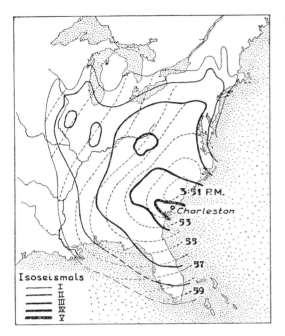

Figure 19-12. Isoseismals of the Charleston earthquake, 1886. The fine dashed lines (called coseismals) connect points where the earthquake struck at the same time; the heavy numerals indicate their actual arrival times. (After C. E. Dutton, U. S. Geological Survey.)

determined epicenter commonly does not quite coincide with the "field epicenter" may be accounted for by differences in surficial geology. Differences in the nature of the underlying rock not only influence the distribution of earthquake damage and therefore the isoseismals, but also control the speed of transmission of elastic waves to nearby seismographs and thus affect the instrumental records. A complex pattern of damage characterized the San Francisco earthquake because in the affected area hills of hard rock alternate abruptly with small basins filled with unconsolidated muds and silts.

EARTHQUAKE MAGNITUDE. The intensity scale gives only a crude idea of the effects as they are observed locally, and can not give a clear measure of the actual amount of energy released by the shock. How can we find some way of comparing the amounts

of energy released at the source in different earthquakes? To answer this question, we need a scale that does not depend on building construction, human reactions, or surficial geology.

Earthquake waves carry energy away from the source in all directions, and therefore it is clear that the amplitude of any wave must diminish with distance from the source. This enables us to build a scale by which to estimate the energy released at the source—but only to estimate, for the method is by no means accurate. No single seismograph can be sensitive to all the waves of different periods in which earthquake energy is carried, and no two seismographs will react identically, because of differences in the foundations on which they are placed, even though most seismographs are anchored to bedrock. Nor is it likely that the same proportion of the total energy of every quake is always carried in waves of a particular period. Nevertheless, even though the method is not precise, the tremendous range in the amount of energy released by earthquakes makes even a rough scale useful.

An American seismologist, C. F. Richter, has developed such a scale. It is based fundamentally on the amplitude of the largest horizontal trace made by a seismograph of standard mechanical properties 100 kilometers (60 miles) from the epicenter. Records from such standard instruments at several stations make it possible to compute what the amplitude should have been if one of them had been situated at the standard reference distance. The scale of magnitude is based on the logarithm of the amplitude rather than on the amplitude itself, hence each unit on the scale corresponds to an energy release about 60 times that of the preceding unit. Thus a shock with a magnitude of 8 releases as much energy as 200,000 shocks with a magnitude of 5.

On this scale, Nevada's Sonoma Range earthquake of 1915 (Chapter 8), although it caused only negligible damage because of the sparse population, had a magnitude of 7.75, just slightly less intense than that of the San

Francisco earthquake of 1906 (M = 8.25) or the Tokyo earthquake of 1923 (M = 8.1). The highest magnitudes yet determined by this method are those of an earthquake in Columbia in 1906 and one in Assam, India, in 1950, both approximately 8.6. A magnitude of 2 corresponds to a shallow shock barely perceptible near the epicenter; a magnitude of 7 is the lower limit of a major destructive earthquake.

DEPTH OF FOCUS. Since the L wave cannot start until the P wave hits the surface, the lag of the L wave gives us a clue to the depth of an earthquake's focus. So, too, does the time lag between P and S waves. From these data, the depth of focus can be computed.

Most earthquakes have focal depths between 5 and 20 miles. If the depth of focus is less than 5 miles, the earthquake is rarely felt for any great distance, though it may be strong

at the epicenter. Such shallow earthquakes are common near volcanoes, especially just before and during eruptions, and thus were formerly grouped as a separate class whose origin was supposedly different from that of "normal," or tectonic earthquakes. Their seismographic records, however, are similar to those of normal shocks; and hence they are now believed to originate in the same way, by movements of rocks along faults, even though the forces that bring about the faulting may result from the bursting of a magma chamber rather than from movements of the earth's crust.

Deep-focus Earthquakes.—About 4 per cent of the recorded earthquakes differ from normal ones in having few or no L waves recorded, and also in arriving at distant stations sooner than the normal time-distance curves would suggest. They seem to have taken a short-cut from their origin. Furthermore, when the isoseismals for some of these

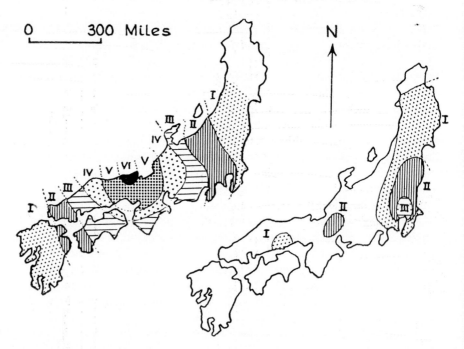

0   300 Miles

N

Figure 19-13.

Maps of Japan, showing the arrangement of isoseismals of the normal North Tazima earthquake (left), *and of the deep-focus earthquake of March 29, 1928* (right). *(After Wadati, redrawn from J. B. Macelwane,* When the Earth Quakes, *Bruce Publishing Company, 1947.)*

are drawn, they form very erratic patterns, in notable contrast with the fairly systematic arrangement of the isoseismals of most earthquakes (Fig. 19-13). This combination of features is taken to indicate that the focus of such a shock lies much deeper than that of most earthquakes. The focal depths determined for some shocks are as great as 700 kilometers. It has been suggested that these shocks are due to mysterious explosions within the earth, but this is not so. If they were, the first *P* motion at all stations should be a compressive one. That they are not is shown by seismographic records, which, except for the anomalies already mentioned, are identical with those of earthquakes known to be connected with faulting, as many beginning with a movement of rarification as of compression. We have, then, a further clue to conditions at great depth in the earth—the rocks to depths as great as one-eighth of the earth's radius are strong enough to accumulate elastic strain until they fault like those at shallow depths in the crust.

Practically all of these deep-focus earthquakes have their epicenters in the island arcs of the Pacific or in the Andean chain of South America. A single focus at a depth of 640 km (380 miles) under southeastern Spain shows that they are not restricted to the Pacific, however. None have been recorded beneath North America, although the Charleston earthquake, which took place before it was possible to determine depth, may have had a deep focus.

When the focal depths of the earthquakes along an island arc are plotted on a vertical section at right angles to the trend of the arc, some strikingly systematic associations are found. The deepest shocks invariably originate farther within the concave side of the arc, and the focuses are all close to a plane that intersects the sea floor at the boundary of arc and foredeep (Fig. 19-14). In South America, too, the focuses of the deeper shocks are farther from the Pacific than those of the shallow ones.

This pattern has suggested to some geolo-

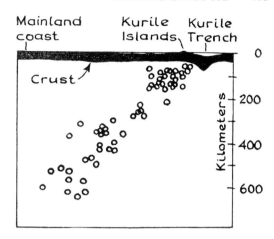

Figure 19-14.   Cross section of the outer earth, at right angles to the Kurile Island arc, showing the foci of deep earthquakes. There is no vertical exaggeration. (After H. H. Hess, 1948.)

gists that the shocks arise on thrust faults along which the island arcs and South America are overriding the floor of the Pacific. The systematic distribution of the focuses on planes dipping away from the Pacific Basin may be taken to support this idea, and the directions of the first motion recorded on seismograms at variously situated stations are also consistent with the theory.

DISTRIBUTION   OF   EARTHQUAKES. Seismologists estimate that every year more than a million earthquakes shake the earth strongly enough to be felt (M = 2), although only a very few are strong enough to be recorded at any distance from their sources. It has been estimated that about 220 great shocks (M = 7.75) and about 1,200 other strong earthquakes (M = 7.0 to 7.7) occur per century. Figure 19-15 shows the distribution of epicenters of recorded earthquakes. Small shallow shocks (M = 5 or less) apparently occur nearly everywhere over the earth, but the larger shocks do not. The crust of the earth seems to include several large blocks, notably the central part of the Pacific Basin (except the neighborhoods of the Hawaiian Islands and other island arcs)

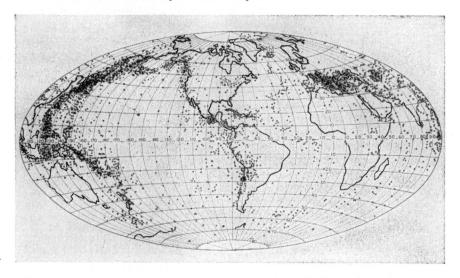

Figure 19-15.

Epicenters of most of the earthquakes recorded between 1899 and 1930. (Reproduced by permission from L. D. Leet, Practical Seismology and Seismic Prospecting, *Appleton-Century-Crofts, 1938.)*

and most of the shield areas of the continents, that have few large earthquakes. (It must not be forgotten, however, that the Charleston and Mississippi Valley earthquakes, both with focuses in the continental plates, must also have been powerful, though instruments were not available to measure them.) Between these relatively stable blocks are linear zones of major seismic activity. These include:

1. The *Circumpacific belt* of young mountains, including the branches through the Antilles and through the island arcs south of Japan. Here occur about 80 per cent of all shocks with focal depths of less than 60 kilometers.

2. The *Mediterranean* and *trans-Himalayan* zone, in which nearly all other large shallow shocks occur.

3. The *Mid-Atlantic* and *Mid-Indian ridges,* along which there are many shallow shocks.

4. The *Hawaiian Islands* and *African Rift Valleys,* where there is moderate activity.

The deep-focus shocks are still more closely localized: 90 per cent of those whose focuses lie between 60 and 300 kilometers, and all but one or two that have thus far been recognized from depths of more than 300 kilometers, are in the Circumpacific belt.

The Crust of the Earth

The Yugoslav seismologist Mohorovičić in 1909 found certain features in seismograms that indicate that the continental segments of the outer part of the earth have a layered structure. He saw that earthquakes occurring less than about 800 km (495 miles) from a recording station gave records of two compressional and two shear waves instead of one of each. By comparing travel times to more distant stations, the smaller pair could be identified as the normal *P* and *S* waves long known on records of distant shocks. The larger pair traveled more slowly but seemed to have started earlier. They were, therefore, received first at nearby stations (up to about 100 miles) but lagged farther and farther behind *P* and *S* as the distance from the source increased, finally becoming unrecognizable 450 to 600 miles from the source. Mohorovičić showed that this could be explained on the assumption that the earth has a layered structure, with an outer layer in which speeds are relatively slow that rests on the deeper body of the earth, where speeds are higher. A shock originating in the outer layer—the crust—will send waves directly to a nearby station. These waves will be powerful and will arrive before other waves that penetrate the deeper body—which is called the mantle— even though the travel speed in the mantle is higher. But at more distant stations the waves that penetrate below the crust into the mantle travel there at speeds high enough to more than make up for the time lost in traveling from the focus down to the high-speed medium, the mantle. Hence they will overtake the waves whose whole travel has been in the crust and arrive first at distant stations.

Although our knowledge of the nature of the rocks beneath the earth's crust is wholly indirect, there can be no doubt that this discontinuity between the crust and the deeper body of the earth is a fundamental feature of earth structure, and that there is a definite physical difference between the material above and that below it. It is called the **Mohorovičić discontinuity,** and *marks the base of the crust of the earth.*

The speed of the various waves in the continental crust vary somewhat from one place to another, but on the whole are surprisingly uniform (Table 19-2). It will be seen that the speed in the crust is considerably lower than that in the upper part of the mantle. The apparent delay in starting time of the waves in the outer part of the mantle just below the crust gives a way of measuring the thickness of the crust. Though this thickness varies from place to place (and in many places it includes a sedimentary blanket resting on crystalline

rocks, further complicating the interpretation) the crust generally ranges from 30 to 45 kilometers (18 to 27 miles) in thickness. In places, as beneath the Sierra Nevada and the Alps, the thickness of crust above the Mohorovičić discontinuity is nearly twice as great.

Seismographic records of the waves set up by large explosions have added to the information obtained from earthquake records, confirming and extending these inferences, especially during the years since World War II.

The Continental Crust

The crust beneath all the continents is surprisingly uniform in structure. From geologic mapping and from seismic and gravity studies, we of course know that in many parts of the earth there are deposits of sedimentary rocks, some as much as 15 kilometers (9 miles) thick. Compared to the whole body of the earth, however, this sedimentary layer is extremely thin, and it has been estimated that in North America it averages only 0.8 kilometers (about a half mile) for all Cambrian and younger rocks, and less than 2 kilometers (one and a quarter miles) for all sediments including the Precambrian. Beneath this thin film the upper part of the continental crust seems to transmit earthquake waves at speeds much more uniform than we might expect, considering the complexity of the basement rocks, which, where they are exposed to view, seem everywhere to be highly varied in both composition and structure, and to embrace granites, migmatites, and many kinds of schists and gneisses, in most complex structural arrangements.

Perhaps the nearly uniform earthquake

TYPE OF WAVE	CRUST, OR UPPER LAYER	UPPER PART OF MANTLE
Compressional (P wave)	5.5-6.0 at top; 6.5 to 7.0 at base	7.8 to 8.4
Shear (S wave)	3.3 to 3.7 at top; 3.8-3.9 at base	4.3 to 4.8

TABLE 19-2

Wave Speed in the Continental Crust and Outer Mantle (km per second).

speeds in the upper part of the continental crust represent averages of much more diverse speeds in differing rocks, but with the diversities so randomly distributed as to yield roughly comparable average distributions over large areas. The speeds, in any event, are nearly the same, whether measured in Europe, Japan, or North America. And further, the speeds in the upper part of the continental crust are quite similar to those that would be theoretically expected in granite, whose elastic properties have been determined in the laboratory. Granite is indeed the dominant rock in the exposed part of the continental basement. It also seems reasonable to infer that the average rock of the upper part of the continental crust, even though varied and not everywhere a true granite, has elastic properties like those of granite, for it consists mainly of minerals rich in silicon and aluminum. Following a suggestion of the Austrian geologist E. Suess, geologists call the material that constitutes this upper part of the crust by the coined name **sial** (Si for silicon, Al for aluminum).

Since earthquake speeds increase with depth even within the crust it is commonly thought that the material constituting the crust must change in average composition toward the base (see Table 19-2). Thus the crust consists of two more or less distinct layers (and where there are sedimentary rocks at the surface, of three). The lower part of the crust differs from the sial of the upper part. It was formerly thought that there was a rather sharp break between the sial and the lower crustal layer that intervenes between the sial and the Mohorovičić discontinuity. Recent studies seem to show that there is a transition rather than an abrupt boundary. The wave speeds in the lower part of the crust, though variable, are analogous to those to be expected if the rock were of roughly basaltic composition. As there is independent evidence that basalt is widespread in the earth's crust, the lower part of the crust has been referred to as the "basaltic layer." Suess suggested that, since magnesium is a prom-

inent constituent of basalt, the material should be referred to as **sima** (Si for silicon, Ma for magnesium.)

As we mentioned above, the rocks immediately below the Mohorovičić discontinuity constitute the "lower layer" or **mantle** of the seismologists. Within the mantle there seem to be no sharp discontinuities for great distances down into the earth. The elastic properties of the outer part of the mantle seem to vary somewhat from place to place (the speed of the P waves ranging from 7.8 to 8.4 kilometers per second). At depths of 60—or at most 100—kilometers (36 to 60 miles), so far as earthquake waves enable this to be determined, they apparently become uniform over the entire earth. The rock whose elastic properties seem most nearly comparable to those of this lower layer is peridotite, perhaps a variety especially rich in olivine. We must, however, maintain a lively skepticism about the exact composition of all rocks below the zone of observation, and refrain from taking a positive position about a peridotite layer. Perhaps the great pressures at this depth may so change the physical state of other rocks that their elastic properties come to resemble those of peridotite.

The Crust Beneath the Oceans

The crust beneath the oceans differs from that beneath the continents. The evidence is both from isostasy (see Chapter 10) and from seismology. The seismologic evidence is of three kinds, two from natural earthquakes and a third from the waves set up by explosion of submerged charges.

The earthquake evidence was the first to be interpreted. The higher the angle at which a wave strikes the surface, the greater the proportion of the wave energy reflected back into the earth; it is at a maximum for waves striking at right angles. The significant feature in crustal studies is that earthquake waves of equal epicentral distance, one of which has been reflected from a continental surface and the other from the bottom of the ocean,

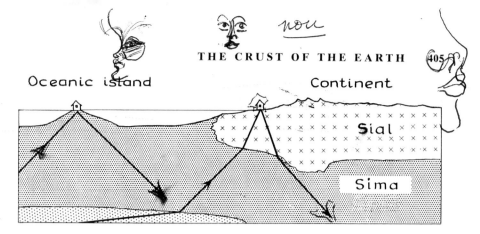

Oceanic island   Continent

Sial

Sima

Figure 19-16.

Angles of incidence of earthquake waves arriving beneath ocean basins and con-
tinents. (After B. Gutenburg, Internal Constitution of the Earth, *courtesy Dover*
Publications.)

differ greatly in intensity. If the crustal structure were the same, waves generated by shocks
of equal magnitude should have about equal
amplitudes; but the oceanic reflection is the
weaker. This difference suggests that the waves
make smaller angles with the surface beneath
the ocean than with the surface of the continents, a feature that would be explained if
the crust beneath the ocean lacked a sial
layer (Fig. 19-16). Because of their changes
in speed the waves curve as they pass through
the continental sial, and this causes them to
strike the surface at a higher angle than would
waves of the same epicentral distance in the
absence of such a layer. Thus the fact that
waves reflected from continental surfaces
carry more energy than those reflected from
the ocean floors suggests that sial is thin or
absent beneath the oceans.

The surface waves (*L* waves) tell a similar
story. The speeds of surface waves, unlike
those that pass through the body of the
earth, vary with their wave lengths. This
means that we can tell something about how
the elastic properties of the material beneath
the surface vary with depth, for a surface
wave of a given wave length travels at a speed
which depends on the elastic properties of a
layer about as thick as the wave is long. A
wave with a length of 3 kilometers travels at
a rate determined by the elastic properties
of the material within 3 kilometers of the surface; one with a wave length of 200 kilometers
travels at a rate determined by the elastic

properties of all the rocks from the surface
to a depth of about 200 kilometers.

Surface waves of short wave lengths travel
at different speeds in different parts of the
crust. Their speeds across segments of the
Pacific floor are higher than across other
areas, both oceanic and, especially, continen-

Figure 19-17.   Refraction and reflection paths
for oceanic seismic measurements. (After
Ewing and Press, Structure of the Earth's
Crust, Handbuch der Physik, *Springer, 1956.)*

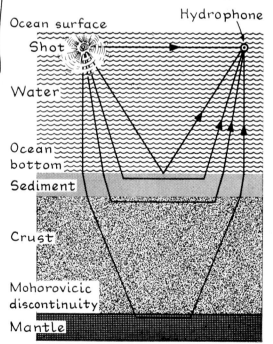

Ocean surface   Hydrophone

Shot

Water

Ocean
bottom

Sediment

Crust

Mohorovicic
discontinuity

Mantle

tal. But longer surface waves, whose speed is more dependent on the properties of deeper material, travel at nearly the same speed across both continents and ocean basins.

The American seismologist Beno Gutenberg has shown that these facts are consistent with the absence of a sialic layer beneath the floor of the Pacific. Rock like that deep within the crust—sima, or basaltic material—may floor the Pacific, but perhaps even this is lacking and the rocks that compose the mantle lie almost immediately beneath the deep-sea sediments. From similar evidence, it also seems likely that there is no sial, or that at most it is very thin and patchy, beneath the other oceans.

In the years since World War II, it has been found that shock waves emanating from an explosion under water can be transmitted from the water into the bottom, there to be refracted or reflected precisely like earthquake waves (Fig. 19-17). Sensitive pressure devices on shipboard enable the waves emerging from the bottom to be recorded, and the records can be analyzed like seismograms. The timing of the direct water wave from the explosion enables travel times of the reflected and refracted waves to be determined. In this way, it has been shown that both Atlantic and Pacific floors are underlain, immediately beneath the pelagic sediments, by material whose elastic properties are like those of the continental sima. It forms a layer only about 5 kilometers thick above the Mohorovičić discontinuity. The Mohorovičić discontinuity thus lies only 10 to 12 kilometers beneath the sea surface, in contrast to its depth of roughly 35 kilometers beneath the continents.

The Deep Interior

The fact that the speed of earthquake waves increases with depth within the mantle indicates that the rigidity and incompressibility of the deeper rocks increase more or less steadily downward. The increased speed cannot be due to lower density of the deeper rocks, for we know from measurements reviewed later in this chapter that the density of the earth as a whole (5.52) is far higher than that of surface rocks (2.2 to about 3.2). Furthermore, the approach of large surface blocks to isostatic balance implies that they are essentially floating on a substratum that must have a higher density.

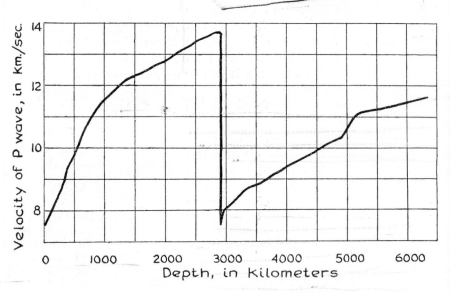

Figure 19-18.

Graph of velocity of the P wave in the interior of the earth, as related to the depth of its penetration. (After B. Gutenburg, Internal Constitution of the Earth, *courtesy Dover Publications.)*

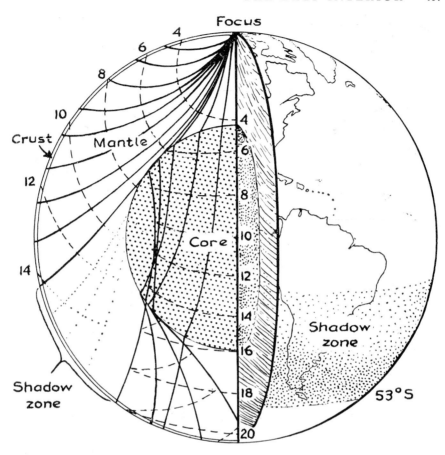

Figure 19-19.

The shadow zone of an earthquake originating near the North Pole. The cutout shows the effect of the core on the pattern of wave paths and wave fronts. (After B. Gutenburg, Internal Constitution of the Earth, 1928.)

Elasticity continues to increase with depth faster than density for a long way below the Mohorovičić discontinuity. It then changes abruptly. *P* waves emerging at about 102° to 104° epicentral distance have followed a curved path whose deepest part lies about 2,900 kilometers (1,740 miles) beneath the surface. Within a short distance beyond this, however, both *P* and *S* waves suddenly fade out. The *S* waves cannot be detected beyond this zone (except those that are reflected from discontinuities), and the *P* wave is found only by sensitive seismographs. But at epicentral distances of about 143°, a very powerful *P* wave reappears. The travel time for this *P* wave is much slower, however, than would be expected from the normal time-distance curves (Fig. 19-18).

If this deep-penetrating *P* wave had traveled through the center of the earth at the speed it had at a depth of 2,900 kilometers, it should arrive on the opposite side of the earth about 16 minutes after the earthquake. Instead, it arrives 20 minutes after—a delay of 4 minutes. This delay can only mean that the speed through the central core of the earth is far less than it is above the core. Moreover, if the speed is lower in the core than in the mantle above, we see a reason for the weak records between epicentral distances of 102° an 143°—the so-called **shadow zone.** A medium in which speed is low bends the wave paths toward its thickest part, just as a reading glass bends the light rays to a focus in line with its thickest part because the speed of light is less in glass than in air. Thus the central part of the earth acts like a huge converging lens. This is the basis for the interpretation indicated in Figure 19-19, which shows the earth with a central **core,** whose radius is about 3,400 kilometers (2,100 miles) surrounded by the *mantle* that extends from the core boundary to the Mohorovičić discontinuity at the base of the *crust.*

Figure 19-19 shows how the slower velocities in the core explain both the shadow zone and the extraordinary strength of the wave at 143°, for here are focused waves that impinge upon a considerable segment of the core. The abruptness of the core boundary is strikingly shown by Canadian records of a South Pacific earthquake. At Toronto (epicentral distance 141°) only a very faint record was made, but at Ottawa, only 2° farther from the epicenter, the *P* wave was very strong. (In Fig. 19-19, the shadow zone embraces the surface between 12°S and 53°S, that is, the belt between 102° and 143° from the North Pole, the assumed earthquake origin.)

Beyond an epicentral distance of 103°, the *S* waves, if present at all, are very faint. Although some seismologists believe that the waves may be present, but are so weak and obscured by reflected waves of various kinds that they cannot be identified, the consensus of experts is that *S* waves are not transmitted through the core. This means that the core has practically no rigidity (see footnote, page 392), and as an absence of rigidity is characteristic of all fluids, most seismologists commonly refer to the core as liquid. There is evidence to suggest, however, that the central part of the core, extending from a depth of about 5,000 kilometers to the earth's center at 6,350 kilometers has properties different from those of the outer core. This "inner core" appears to be highly rigid and thus to be solid rather than liquid, but the evidence is far from conclusive.

A Model of the Earth

Study of seismologic records has thus led to a postulated model of the earth that seems to fit nearly all the known data. This model has a central core, whose inner part seems to be a solid with a radius of about 1,300 kilometers; the outer part of the core is presumably liquid, though highly viscous, and extends to a radial distance of 3,400 kilometers. Here there is a sharp boundary between the core and the mantle. The mantle may contain some discontinuities, but, if so, none is considered important. It is bounded at its upper surface by the well-defined Mohorovičić discontinuity. This discontinuity marks the *base of the crust,* a fundamental feature of the earth's structure. The part of the crust beneath the continents consists of different materials than that beneath the oceans. The continental crust—about 30 to 40 kilometers (18 to 25 miles) thick on the average—grades upward from sima to sial, with perhaps the lower two-thirds sima. The sial is blanketed by sedimentary rocks to an average depth of about 2 kilometers (1.2 miles). In the oceanic crust the layer of sial is either entirely lacking or is thin and patchy. The sima is also thin, so that the Mohorovičić discontinuity lies at a depth of only 10 or 12 kilometers below the ocean's surface—approximately a third of its depth beneath the continents.

Other Clues to the Earth's Interior

What other information can we glean about the mysterious depths of the earth? The evidence from study of earthquake waves confirms our early inference that the continents stand high above the ocean basins because they are mainly composed of rocks less dense than those that underlie the oceans. The continents are huge rafts of granitic material underlain by basalt; the ocean floors presumably consist largely of basalt. Both these layers are "floating" on a thick layer of still denser material, the mantle, which lies beneath the Mohorovičić discontinuity. From the speeds of seismic waves, we can infer tentatively that the upper part of the mantle consists of rock much like peridotite. But of what are the lower part of the mantle, and the core, composed? Can we make reasonable deductions about them despite their inaccessibility?

The increase in earthquake speed downward throughout the mantle seems fairly regular. As we go deeper in the earth, the pressure increases tremendously; any reasonable estimates of density distribution indicate pressures of many millions of pounds per square inch at the boundary of the core. In the laboratory, tests of rocks and minerals at higher and higher confining pressures nearly always reveal that rigidity and incompressibility increase with pressure. Perhaps the entire mantle is composed of something near peridotite in its determinable properties, the greater elasticity at depth being due merely to the great confining pressure. But this does not account for the sharp discontinuity at the boundary between core and mantle. It seems clear for many reasons that the material of the core must be different from that above. What is it?

Of course, we do not know—such depths are inaccessible. From analogy with meteorites, which many astronomers suppose to represent fragments of other planets, the most likely material seems to be an alloy of metallic nickel and iron, perhaps in a molten state. Though the pressures involved at these depths are far beyond attainment in the laboratory, physicists have dealt with the question theoretically and concluded that a molten alloy of nickel and iron might be expected to give the measured speed of the P wave. It has been suggested, too, that the abundance of iron silicates in the mantle implies that the core consists of metallic iron, on which the mantle floats, as slag rich in silicates floats on molten iron in a crucible.

How do these deductions check with what we know of the distribution of density in the earth's interior?

Weighing the Earth

Strictly speaking, it is impossible to weigh the earth, because weight is defined as the gravitational pull of the earth on a mass. As was pointed out in Chapter 10, the weight of a given mass varies with its distance from the

Figure 19-20. *Von Jolly's method of "weighing the earth." (After J. H. Poynting,* The Earth, *G. P. Putnam's Sons, 1913.)*

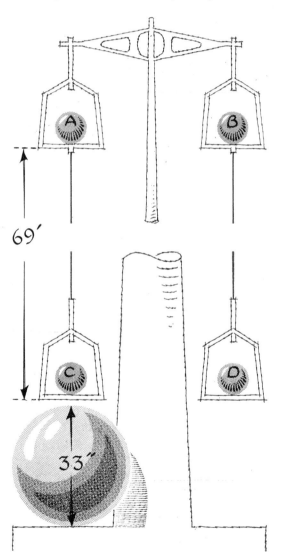

69′

33″

earth's center. When we speak of weighing the earth, then, we are really speaking of determining its total mass. This problem has been approached in several ways, but all depend upon comparing the attraction of the earth to that of a known mass. One of the most readily visualized experiments, though not the most accurate, was that performed by von Jolly, of Munich, in 1878.

Von Jolly mounted a balance on a support at the top of a high tower, with the usual scale pans under the beam (Fig. 19-20). Another pair of scale pans was suspended by wires from these, about 70 feet below. Four glass globes—A,B,C,D—of equal weight and volume were prepared and two of them, A and B, were each filled with 5,000 grams (11 pounds) of mercury, the other two being left empty. All four were sealed. A and B were put in the upper pair of pans, C and D in the lower, and a balance was made. Then A and C, which were on the same balance arm but at different levels, were interchanged, thus bringing the 11 pounds of mercury in A a measured distance closer to the earth. As no change other than this occurred, it was possible to measure the increased attraction of the earth on the mass of mercury by making a new balance. The gain in weight of the mercury was a little more than 31 milligrams (about 0.0007 pound) because of its approach to the earth's center.

Von Jolly now placed a lead sphere immediately beneath one of the lower pans. When he now repeated the two measurements as before, after interchanging A and C, he found that A gained 0.59 milligram (about .0000013 pound) more than it had before. This was the added attraction of the lead sphere. The distance between the centers of the lead sphere and the mercury was found to be 57 centimeters—about 2 feet. If then, the lead sphere at an effective distance of 57 centimeters exercised a pull of 0.59 milligrams on the mercury, and the earth at an effective distance equal to its radius—about 637,000,-000 centimeters—exercised a pull of 5 kilo-

grams or 5,000,000 milligrams, the mass of the earth could be easily calculated from the mass of the lead sphere. Von Jolly's result was about 6,100 billion billion metric tons—a figure so large as to be incomprehensible (a metric ton is about 10 per cent heavier than an avoirdupois ton). When von Jolly divided this figure by the known volume of the earth, his result indicated that the mean density of the earth is 5.69—in other words, the earth is 5.69 times as heavy as an equal volume of water. More accurate methods, too complex for discussion here, but embodying the same principle of comparing the attraction of known masses with that of the earth, give a figure of 5.516 as the best value to date. Now, the average density of the visible rocks is about 2.8, and only a few minerals have densities as high as the average for the earth as a whole. Obviously the density must be greater at depth; in fact, the deeper parts of the earth must be composed of material much denser than most known natural substances.

Since the earth shells appear to be concentric and smooth, as shown by the similarity of time-distance curves developed in many parts of the globe, any assumptions we make about the change in density with depth include assumptions as to the rotational inertia of the earth. Rotational inertia is a measure of the tendency of a rotating body to persist in its rotation against a braking action of any kind. Each particle of matter in a rotating body contributes to this tendency in proportion to its mass and its distance from the center of rotation. (When a spinning skater pulls in his arms, he speeds up; when he throws them out, he slows down, for the product of average speed and mass must be the same in the two postures.) When, therefore, we assume a particular density of material at a distance of, say, 3,000 kilometers from the center of the earth, we can compute the part of the earth's rotational inertia contributed by a shell of that density and radius. Estimates of the changes in density with depth

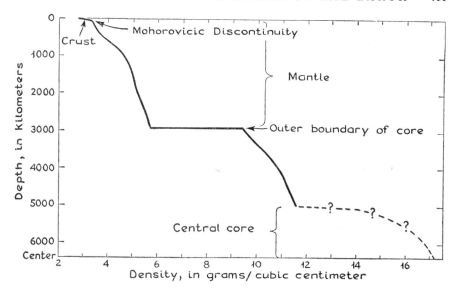

Figure 19-21.

Graph showing the variation of density with depth within the earth. (Data from K. E. Bullen, 1940 and 1942.)

in the earth can thus be checked against the astronomically measured value of the earth's rotational inertia.

The Australian geophysicist K. E. Bullen has made perhaps the most careful study of this, taking into account both seismic data and rotational inertia. His results are shown graphically in Figure 19-21. Here it can be seen that the density of the material at the center of the earth can hardly be less than 11.5 (which is higher than that of lead at the surface) and may be as high as 17.2 (nearly as dense as gold, 19.3). At the outer boundary of the core, the density can hardly be less than 9.4 or greater than 9.6, both higher than those of iron (7.9) or nickel (8.6) at the earth's surface.

Such a density distribution is consistent with that to be expected if the mantle were composed of peridotite with about the same composition as that of stony meteorites, and if the core were composed of molten iron and nickel in the proportions found in some metallic meteorites. The densities higher than those of corresponding surface materials could be due entirely to the very high pres-

sures that must prevail deep within the earth. Although the core boundary appears to be a fundamental discontinuity at which a marked change in composition must take place, it may be that some iron-nickel alloy is scattered within the lower part of the mantle, but in a solid rather than liquid state. If the amount of such metallic material diminishes gradually upward within the mantle, so that the upper part is near peridotite in composition, and if the peridotite then changes abruptly to basalt above the Mohorovičić discontinuity, we would have a reasonable accordance between the facts of geology relating to igneous rocks (Chapter 18) and the geophysical measurements.

Temperature within the Earth

Every well or mine shaft sunk into the rocks proves that the temperature of the earth increases downward. The rate of increase of temperature with depth is highly variable from place to place. In areas of hot springs and geysers, such as Yellowstone Park, temperatures of several hundred degrees Centigrade are found in drill holes only a few hundred feet deep. In the gold mines of the Transvaal, South Africa, on the other hand, the temperature increase is so slow that mining operations can be carried on at depths of more than 9,000 feet. The increase here is at the rate of about 1°C for 300 feet depth. But variable as it is, a rise in temperature with depth occurs everywhere. This proves that the earth is losing heat to outer space, for heat flows only from bodies of higher temperature to those of lower.

The actual rate of heat loss depends on two factors; the rate of temperature change with depth (the so-called **temperature gradient**), and the heat conductivity of the rocks. There have, unfortunately, been but few measurements of both these factors at the same localities. But the few that have been made indicate that, despite the wide range of the rate of temperature increase, the heat losses are everywhere nearly the same. (We shall note some exceptions in Chapter 20). The reason is that the conductivity varies with gradient, being high where the gradient is low and low where the gradient is high. The product of gradient and conductivity, which determines the actual amount of heat transferred, is thus nearly the same whether measured in England, Scotland, South Africa, or Colorado, though there are small but significant differences, particularly in places like Yellowstone where the heat is transferred mainly by steam and hot water instead of by conductivity of the rock. The actual heat loss is very small. As the sun supplies about 8,000 times as much per unit of area as is carried up from the depths, it has been computed that the surface temperature would fall only about 0.01°C if the internal heat were cut off entirely.

Since the discovery that certain atoms spontaneously disintegrate to yield others (radioactivity), and that this change is accompanied by the release of large amounts of heat, it has been necessary to reconsider the question of whether the earth is slowly growing colder as a result of this heat loss. The three radioactive elements whose disintegration contributes most to the earth's heat budget are uranium, thorium, and potassium. Sampling of the wide variety of rocks exposed at the earth's surface shows that these elements are far from uniformly distributed. All three of them are more abundant in granite and granodiorite than in gabbro or basalt, and more abundant in basalt than in peridotite. The olivine grains from peridotites contain even less than the peridotite as a whole. It has been computed that a layer of granite 13 kilometers (about 8 miles) thick, and having the average radioactivity found in granites exposed at the earth's surface, would supply all the heat the earth loses to outer space. The average basalt contains about one-third as much radioactive energy as the average granite, and the average olivine from peridotite about 1 per cent as much as granite.

If the radioactive content of the rocks within the crust is assumed to be the same as that of equivalent rocks at the earth's surface, an interesting conclusion is inescapable: the earth is not cooling at all, but is instead, gradually becoming hotter. For, as we have seen earlier in this chapter, there is an average thickness of perhaps 15 kilometers of granite and about 20 kilometers of basaltic material above the Mohorovičić discontinuity in the continental plates. The granite alone would supply more heat than is escaping at the surface, and the basalt would add another 40 per cent to this. Peridotite in the deeper mantle would contribute only 1 per cent as much per unit volume as granite, but the enormous volume of the peridotite in the mantle would also ensure a heating earth.

Inasmuch as no laboratory experiments have shown that high pressures have the slightest tendency to slow down radioactive disintegration, there seem to be only two possibilities: either the surface rocks are more radioactive than similar rocks at depth, or else the earth is actually becoming warmer. Any heating that may be going on has not been so great as to liquefy the mantle, at least in large volumes. The transmitted shear waves show that it is a solid, and is rigid under short term stresses, even though it does yield plastically under long-term loads, as shown by isostasy. Much more careful sampling and measurement of radioactivity is needed before this question can be conclusively settled, but at present it appears likely that the temperature within the earth does not melt much rock above the core boundary. What the temperature may be at the core boundary is pure conjecture, though it is probably less than 6,000°C (the temperature of the sun's surface), perhaps about 3,000°C.

Volcanoes, of course, attest to pockets of molten rock in the earth, either within or just below the crust. Perhaps the rock is melted by heat produced by localized radioactivity (which would explain the relatively high radioactive content of surficial lavas and of granites); or perhaps a release of pressure along faults lowers the melting point of the rocks and permits them to melt, for it is the confining pressure that keeps them solid at these depths. All rock minerals expand on melting, so that release of pressure operates to facilitate melting. Melting of this sort would, in turn, concentrate the radioactive elements within the magma, because radioactive minerals are much more closely associated with the low-melting than with the high-melting constituents. Thus we see that magma bodies which form and work upward in the crust may have brought to the surface rocks that contain more radioactive minerals than similar rocks at depth.

FACTS, CONCEPTS, TERMS

What are earthquakes?
Elastic-rebound theory
Elastic strain shown by triangulation
Seismic sea waves, or tsunamis
Earthquake waves: *P*, *S*, and *L*
Seismographs and seismograms
Time-distance curves
Epicentral distance
Isoseismal lines
Abridged Wood-Neumann scale
Earthquake magnitudes

Deep-focus earthquakes
Distribution of earthquakes
Mohorovičić discontinuity
The crust of the earth
Sial and sima
Mantle and core
Weighing the earth
Inferred composition of earth's interior
Temperature gradient
Possible causes of high temperature

QUESTIONS

1. During many Central American earthquakes well-built masonry buildings have been destroyed while bamboo huts nearby were undamaged. Can you suggest a reason?

2. The Bouguer anomalies for the Alps (see Chapter 10) suggest a greater thickness of light rocks beneath the mountains than beneath the lowlands to the north. What would this suggest regarding the heat flow to be expected in the two areas?

3. During the San Francisco earthquake the porch was sheared off a house and moved more than 10 feet by movement on the fault, without knocking over the brick chimney of the house, just a few feet from the fault. Well-built structures 4 miles from the rift were demolished. What factors can you suggest to account for this?

4. Why is the Mohorovičić discontinuity of greater importance than any discontinuity within the crust?

5. What does the elastic rebound theory

suggest concerning the distribution of changes in elevation near a fault line while strain is accumulating preparatory to a vertical displacement?

6. Assume that a mountain range with an average height of 10,000 feet is buoyed up isostatically by a "mountain root." The average density of the range and root is 2.7, that of the substratum 3.3. If this mountain range lost an average thickness of 1,500 feet by erosion, how high would it have to rise to restore isostatic equilibrium?

SUGGESTED READINGS

Daly, R. A. *Our Mobile Earth*. New York, Scribner's Sons, 1926.

Jeffreys, Harold. *Earthquakes and Mountains*. London, Methuen & Co., 1935.

20 MOUNTAINS

The Kinds of Mountains

ALMOST ANY tract of land that stands high above nearby areas is popularly called a mountain; geologists, though, distinguish among them. In the restricted geologic sense the main distinction is between mountains and plateaus. **Mountains** are elevated areas underlain by highly folded and faulted rocks or by lavas and tuffs erupted from central volcanoes. Land masses that may be higher or even more rugged in topography but are underlain by low-dipping sedimentary and volcanic rocks, are called **plateaus.** Thus the Colorado Plateau, even where it is intricately cut by stream canyons thousands of feet deep, is not considered a mountain range by geologists, although the canyon walls are in many places almost unscalable. The relief of this plateau is several times as great as that of the Appalachians or Urals and the terrain is far more rugged, but these lower ranges are nevertheless true mountains in the technical sense. Most of the rocks of the Colorado Plateau lie nearly flat whereas those of the Appalachians and Urals are highly distorted.

There are several kinds of mountains. Some, like the Alps, Appalachians, Urals, and Rockies, are linear belts of greatly distorted rocks. These are called **fold mountains,** and in much geologic writing about mountains are the only kind considered, as they are the most numerous and comprise the greatest ranges. Others, like the Cascades, are linear belts of old volcanoes that stand upon a basement which in some areas is an older fold-mountain, in others an actively folding range (Chapter 9), and in still other places is a gently tilted plateau. Still other mountains, like the so-called Basin Ranges of western North America, consist of huge blocks of rock separated by faults, along which there have been great differential vertical movements. The rocks making up these blocks may be either highly distorted, as in other mountains, or almost flat-lying, as in plateaus. But the relatively small size of the blocks and their close association shows that a large-scale disturbance has taken place in the part of the crust where they are found. The topography conditioned by this structural arrangement and the structure itself are thus called mountainous by geologists, even though some blocks would of themselves be called plateaus. Yet other elevated tracts are mountains in the geologic sense—for example, the Adirondacks and the highlands of Labrador. These are mountainous topographically, and, like fold mountains, are characterized by severely distorted rocks; the trends of the highlands, however, are nearly independent of the folded structures of the rocks composing them, whereas the trends of most fold ranges conform to the internal structures.

Most of the greatest ranges of the earth are fold mountains, and our study will begin with them.

Fold Mountains

Geosynclines

The great American geologist James Hall published some significant generalizations in 1859. He noted that the Appalachian Mountains form a linear belt of folded strata in which the rocks are much thicker than are strata of the same age in the Interior Lowland to the northwest. The early Paleozoic rocks of the Interior Lowland, for example, are everywhere only a few hundred or at most a few thousand feet thick, but rocks of this age in the Appalachians are many times as thick. Furthermore, the rocks of the Interior Lowland are largely limestone and dolomite, with subordinate clastics, whereas there are abundant clastic rocks in the Appalachians. But even the carbonate strata of the mountains are generally thicker than the correlative carbonate rocks of the Interior. In fact, the strata of nearly every System are both much thicker and more generally clastic in the mountain belt than in the continental plate to the northwest.

Comparable differences in both facies and thickness of strata of equivalent age between continental plates and nearby mountain chains are general over the earth. In the Alps, Himalayas, Urals, Andes, and the Cordilleran System of North America, strata as thick as 6 or even 9 miles have been measured, although the rocks of corresponding age over the adja-

cent continental plates do not average more than a few thousand feet.

The strata composing these great chains include sedimentary and volcanic rocks, and commonly, in the core of the range, their metamorphic derivatives. Fossils are nearly all of shallow-water organisms. Many rainprints, mudcracks, salt-crystal casts, and other indications that the sediments were deposited in shallow water are preserved, and some beds, such as the coals of Pennsylvania, are even land-laid. As Hall pointed out for the Appalachians, shallow-water deposits recur time after time through sections as thick as 40,000 feet. Though a few strata in the Alps, West Indies, and Timor have been thought by some geologists to be deep-sea oozes, their association with typical shallow-water deposits makes this doubtful, and in any case their volume is trivial. The great piles of strata on the mountain chains do not, therefore, represent the filling of an ocean deep, even though they are thick enough to fill any existing deep to overflowing. As Hall pointed out, only one conclusion seems possible; *the crust was slowly sinking at about the same rate that the sediment accumulated*—the surface of the sediments was never far above or below sea level during all the long time of their accumulation. A trough formed by downwarping and concurrently filled with sediments is called a **geosyncline,** and the pile of strata that fill it is a **geosynclinal prism,** (Fig. 20-1). Mountain belts differ from the rest of the continents in a fundamental way: their thicknesses of sedimentary rock are much greater.

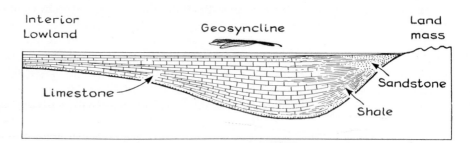

Figure 20-1.

The thickening of strata from the Interior Lowland into the Appalachian Geosyncline. (After A. W. Grabau, 1924.)

The thickening and coarsening of the Paleozoic strata southeastward from the continental interior into the Appalachians suggest that the sediments were mostly derived from a land southeast of the present mountains, possibly from the area of the present Piedmont and Coastal Plain, or, perhaps from an area now covered by the Atlantic. Similar relations have been found for other geosynclines; much of the Alpine sediment seems to have come from areas now covered by the Mediterranean.

The area that supplied the ancient sediments cannot, however, be located accurately. A modern example illustrates the difficulty. The Irrawaddy River of southeast Asia dumps its huge load almost at the end of a slender peninsula, down which it has flowed for nearly 500 miles. Examination of its delta alone would not tell us whether the source of the sediment was Thailand, directly east of this delta, or the eastern Himalayas, far to the northwest, which we know is the actual source. The Brahmaputra, whose delta is 450 miles—the distance from San Francisco to San Diego—from that of the Irrawaddy, also derives its sediment from the eastern Himalayas. Thus the huge Devonian delta which makes up the rocks of the Catskill Mountains may have been supplied by sediment directly from the east, but it also could have been supplied by sediment from either far north or south, along the trend of the Devonian seaway.

Three elements related to ancient geosynclines have commonly been recognized: (1) the geosyncline itself, with its thick geosynclinal prism of strata, (2) the foreland, the neighboring part of the continental plate whose sedimentary cover is relatively thin, and (3) on the opposite side of the geosyncline, the hinterland, from which most of the sediment filling the geosyncline was derived. Because the hinterland was being deeply eroded during the downwarping and filling of the geosyncline and thus left few fossiliferous rocks to record its history, we generally know little about it. Many old hinterlands must now be buried beneath younger rocks or drowned beneath the sea. The significance of these elements to the origin of mountains will be discussed later in this chapter; we pass now to another element of the geology of fold mountains—their structure.

Fold-mountain Structure

We mentioned that the rocks of most mountains are much more deformed than those of the main continental areas. Let us look at some of the structural details of a few of the more thoroughly investigated ranges.

THE APPALACHIANS. The folded and faulted rocks that characterize the Appalachians emerge from beneath the coastal plain of Alabama and extend northeastward in a sinuous belt 1,500 miles long to Nova Scotia and New Brunswick, where they disappear beneath the Atlantic. In general, individual faults and folds lie about parallel to the trend of the belt and persist for many miles, so that geologic cross sections spaced several miles apart generally resemble their neighbors closely. In the northwest part of the central Appalachians the folds are open, but to the southeast they become increasingly tight and have steeper limbs. The most northwesterly of the tighter anticlinal folds are merely asymmetrical, with the northwest limbs steeper than those on the southeast, but, farther southeast, the folds are overturned so that both limbs dip southeast (Fig. 20-2). In the southeast, too, thrust faults have repeated beds of Cambrian age as many as five times: Figure 20-2, *bottom,* shows three such faults. In the northwest, the rocks are unmetamorphosed, but as they are followed southeastward they become more metamorphosed, until, on the southeast side of the mountain belt, they are slates, schists, and gneisses, accompanied by both metamorphosed and unmetamorphosed granite plutons. Large exposures of plutonic rocks in areas characterized by intense folding are also common in other mountain ranges. They suggest deeper erosion in these areas of most intense deformation than in the less-disturbed forelands. Their rocks were once

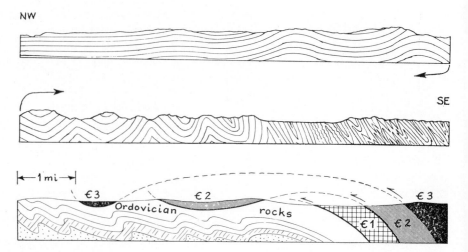

NW

SE

|←—1 mi—→|

€3   €2   €3

Ordovician   rocks   €1 €2

Figure 20-2.

The two upper sketches are the left and right halves of an idealized section across the Appalachians, showing the increase in deformation toward the southeast. (After W. B. Rogers, 1843.) The bottom sketch is an idealized section showing the repetition of Cambrian beds by thrust faults which have moved them over the younger Ordovician beds beneath. The rocks labeled C 1, C 2, and C 3 are all of essentially the same age. Their piling one on top of the other, and the outlying representatives of two of these sequences on top of the gently folded Ordovician rocks to the northwest, can only be explained by a shoving together of the rocks by lateral compression.

deeply buried but have been squeezed upward and deeply eroded.

In West Virginia and to the south, the main mass of the folded belt is in places thrust several miles northwestward over the rocks of the foreland. The existence of these great thrusts, some of which have themselves been folded, was first inferred from the pattern of their outcrops and the projection of their attitudes beneath the surface; that the inference was correct has been proved by oil wells drilled through rocks of the upper plate into younger strata beneath the fault. At the latitude of Knoxville as many as six large thrust faults and several small ones have been recognized (Fig. 20-3). Great thrust faults also mark the northwest border of the folded belt in the Hudson-Champlain Valley in northern New York and Vermont. Some of these faults have rocks of the same age both above and below them; but the rocks of the two plates are of wholly different facies—the lower plate consists largely of carbonate rocks

and the upper of metamorphosed clastics. This means that rocks of the same age, yet deposited so far apart that they were formed under wholly different conditions of sedimentation, have been brought into contact by thrusting. Ordinarily such a thrust must have a greater travel than one that merely piles up sheets of the same kinds of rocks, and it is inferred that here the thrusts have moved several miles.

Crustal shortening.—A series of symmetrical anticlines and synclines might be pictured as forming in either of two ways: by a force which pushes the edges of the strata horizontally so that they wrinkle and warp like a pile of blankets on a table when it is pushed from one side, or, possibly, by differential uplift and sinking of the basement on which the folded strata lie (rising beneath the anticlinal axes, sinking beneath the synclinal). But in the Appalachians, most of the folds are systematically asymmetric; they lean to the northwest, and the thrust faults consistently carry their upper plates northwestward in relation to their lower. Such features cannot be explained by vertical movement alone; the rocks must have been shoved together horizontally.

When the folds of the least deformed part of the Appalachians—in Pennsylvania—are straightened out in imagination, by measuring the length of beds along all the convolutions shown in geologic sections and then comparing this length with the width of the folded belt, it is found that points originally 81 miles apart have been brought nearer together by 15 miles. In other words, the upper part of the earth's crust has been shortened 18 per cent. This measurement takes no account of the shortening by thrust faults farther to the southeast. In the southern Appalachians, half a dozen thrust faults in a single cross section each demand several miles of overriding; there the shortening must have been far greater. Comparable or greater shortening has taken place in many other ranges. What forces could have brought about such tremendous deformation of the strong rocks of the earth? As an example of the magnitude of this

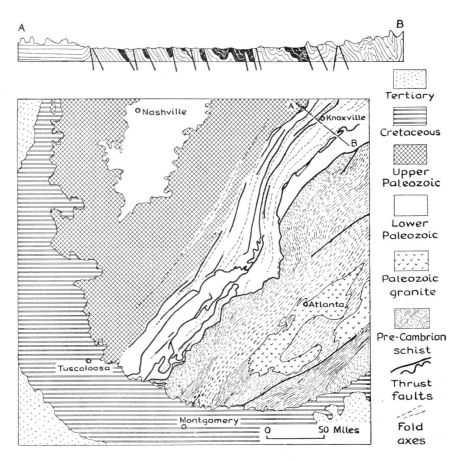

Figure 20-3.

Geologic map and section of the southern Appalachian region. The cross section (top) shows how the Ordovician rocks near Knoxville have been repeated eight times by thrust faults. The vertical scale of the section is tremendously exaggerated so that the faults appear to dip steeply; actually most have dips of less than 30°. (The map is after U. S. Geological Survey, Geologic Map of the United States, 1933. The section is based in part on other maps of the Knoxville region and is largely diagrammatic.)

problem, we cite the complex deformation of the Alps, a mountain range that has been more intensively studied by geologists than any other on earth.

THE ALPS. The Alps lie in a great arc looped northward from the Mediterranean and eastward through Switzerland to Vienna, where they plunge beneath the Hungarian plains. They are part of the great east-west mountain system that stretches across southern Europe and Asia from the Pyrenees, through the Himalayas to the island arcs of Indonesia.

Like the Appalachians, the Alps rise on the site of a great geosyncline, but the strata that filled this trough are chiefly Mesozoic and early Cenozoic rather than Paleozoic. The foreland lies to the north, where relatively thin Mesozoic rocks rest unconformably on Paleozoic and older rocks. Within the Alps the Mesozoic and Paleozoic rocks are quite different from those of the foreland and are far thicker.

Alpine structure is so complex and the facies changes are so great that, despite the marvelous cliff exposures, the arduous labor of hundreds of geologists for more than a century still leaves many problems unsolved. But the broader features are well established. A much simplified map of the Alps is shown in Figure 20-4. As our interest is in principles only, and not in the vastly complex details, we will consider only the western Alps of Switzerland and France, which are representa-

Figure 20-4.   *Generalized map of the Alps.* P, *Prealps;* M, *Mont Blanc and Aiguilles Rouges massifs;* A, *Aar massif;* LL, *Lake Leman (Geneva). (After R. Staub, redrawn from L. W. Collet,* Structure of the Alps, *Edward Arnold & Co., 1927.)*

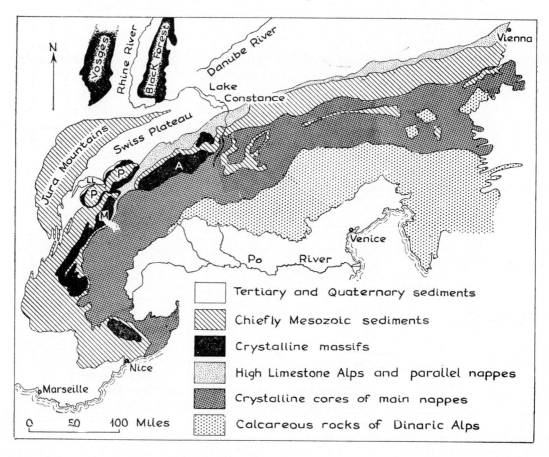

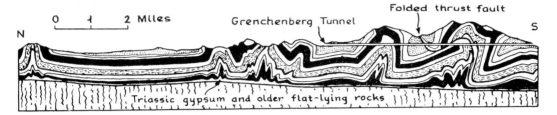

Figure 20-5.   *Cross section of the Swiss Jura, as interpreted by A. Buxtorf, 1908. Note the essentially undisturbed Triassic and older rocks, from which the overlying beds are considered to have been sheared off and then crumpled independently. (Redrawn from E. B. Bailey,* Tectonic Essays, *Clarendon Press, Oxford, 1935.)*

tive of much of the range. Their geology is outlined from north to south.

The Jura Mountains rise from a plateau north of the Alps. They consist of foreland rocks, chiefly Mesozoic, folded into anticlines separated by almost flat synclines. The more southeasterly anticlines are the larger, and some of those nearest the Swiss plateau are broken by small thrust faults (Fig. 20-5). Significantly, even the largest anticlines expose no rocks older than a series of anhydrite beds of Middle Triassic age. This fact, together with exposures in railroad tunnels and in areas north and west of the mountains, make it appear that the Jura folds were formed by the crumpling of a thin sheet of sedimentary rocks that had broken loose from the basement on which they were deposited and

glided northward. As shown in Figures 20-5 and 20-6, the folds cannot extend downward into the nearly flat Lower Triassic, Permian and older rocks that are known to underlie the mountains. Clearly the surficial rocks must have been sheared loose from the beds beneath, and crumpled much as we can crumple a tablecloth by sliding it over the table. As we shall see, this is only the most northerly and smallest of many examples of large-scale horizontal movement of the rocks, yet even here, if the explanation is correct, the surface rocks of the southern Jura have moved several miles northward from the site of their deposition.

When, in 1908, Buxtorf drew the section shown in Figure 20-5, the interpretation that the basement rocks were undeformed during

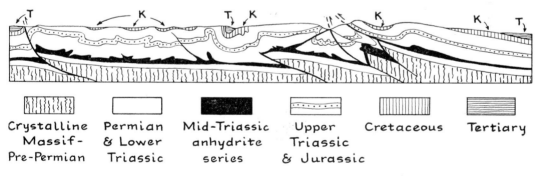

| Crystalline Massif– Pre-Permian | Permian & Lower Triassic | Mid-Triassic anhydrite series | Upper Triassic & Jurassic | Cretaceous | Tertiary |

Figure 20-6.   *Cross section of the Swiss Jura as interpreted by D. Aubert,* Geologische Rundschau, *1947. Note that although the bedded rocks are still largely "unglued" from the basement along the zone of the Mid-Triassic anhydrite, the disturbance is interpreted as largely a result of clean-cut thrusting within the basement rocks—the pre-Permian metamorphic rocks and their passively overlying cover of Permian and Lower Triassic beds.*

the movement of the upper strata was generally accepted. But there are several reasons for thinking this too simple. First, although most of the Jura folds are made up of Mesozoic rocks, they also involve Miocene beds and are therefore at least as young as Miocene. Yet the Miocene rocks of the Swiss Plateau to the southeast, although of the same age as those deformed in the Jura, are almost undisturbed for many miles between the Jura and the main Alpine mass. If the push that caused the crumpling came from the main Alps, as the structure section implies, why were not the weakly cemented Miocene rocks of the Swiss Plateau thrown into folds? How could they have been pushed passively over the underlying Mesozoic rocks without deformation? There are no gaps behind these Miocene rocks, either, as there should be if the rocks merely "came unglued" and slid downhill to make the Jura folds.

Wells drilled in some of the synclines of

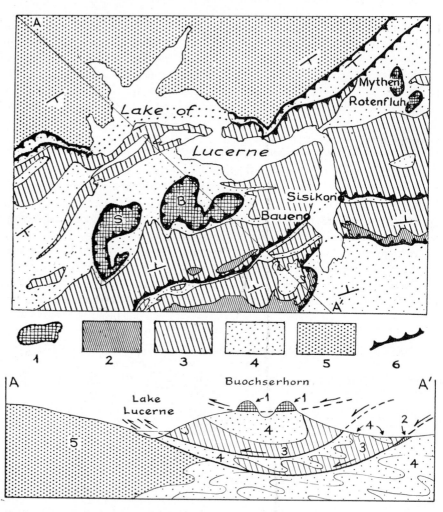

Figure 20-7.

Geologic map and section, showing remnants of the great thrust sheets of the Prealps. The symbols are: (1) klippes of far-traveled Mesozoic rocks; (2) Jurassic; (3) Cretaceous; (4) chiefly Eocene; (5) chiefly Miocene; (6) thrust faults. (Simplified after E. B. Bailey, Tectonic Essays, *Clarendon Press, Oxford, 1935. The section is schematic and not from Bailey.)*

Figure 20-8.

Sketch of the Mythen klippe. The steep peaks of white Mesozoic limestone rest on Eocene shale. (After L. W. Collet, Structure of the Alps, *Edward Arnold & Co., 1927.)*

the Jura gave a clue to the solution, a clue further supported by measurements of gravity that disclosed great local thickening of light rocks beneath some of the folds. Actually, the few thrust faults that had long been recognized in the folded Jura (and were considered to be merely minor breaks that had occurred during the crumpling) suggest that there are many others in the basement rocks beneath. Drilling proved that there are, and that some have not cut through the anhydrite beds to the surface, but have jammed the basement rocks against the plastic anhydrite, crumpled it, and locally squeezed and injected it upward. There is indeed a zone of structural "ungluing" along the anhydrite beds, as Buxtorf thought, but the basement rocks have also been heaved upward by thrust faults—a heaving that was concurrent with the folding of the overlying beds (Fig. 20-6). As these thrusts lie in the strong basement rocks deep beneath the Swiss Plateau, there is no reason for the Miocene deposits there to be disturbed even though all the structure is indeed part of the great Alpine mountain-making. Both basement and cover of the Jura moved together, though with a slip-plane between them. Their distortions, however, seem geometrically independent; that is, the deforma-

tion pattern of the basement rocks must differ greatly from that of the cover.

The Swiss Plateau.—Between the Jura and the Alps lies the Swiss Plateau with the beautiful lakes Geneva (Leman), Neuchatel, Zurich, and Constance. Most of the rocks are Tertiary, chiefly sandstones and coarse conglomerates derived from the Alps to the southeast. The source is shown both by their southward coarsening and by the pebbles, many of which can be matched with their parent formations, though, as we shall see, not always with their present neighbors. Though broadly synclinal and but little folded near the Jura Mountains, the rocks of the Plateau become more and more strongly disturbed toward the Alps, and along the Alpine border are overridden by great thrust sheets of older rocks.

The Prealps.—Between the Swiss Plateau and the main limestone Alps is a chain of lower but still impressive mountains that range from about 3,500 to 6,500 feet above sea level. These are the Prealps. In places they are separated from the main range to the south only by a line of saddles in their high projecting spurs. Their magnificent cliffs expose chiefly Mesozoic rocks that rest in thrust contact on the crumpled Tertiary strata of the Swiss Plateau. Thus they are thrust sheets whose rocks are completely foreign to the rock beneath them (Figs. 20-7 and 20-8). Erosion has cut through and removed much of a formerly continuous thrust sheet and left these huge remnants, completely surrounded by rocks of the crustal block beneath the thrust. Such masses, isolated by erosion from a formerly continuous thrust sheet, are called **klippes** (German; *klippen,* "cliffs"). They were first recognized in the Alps, but are

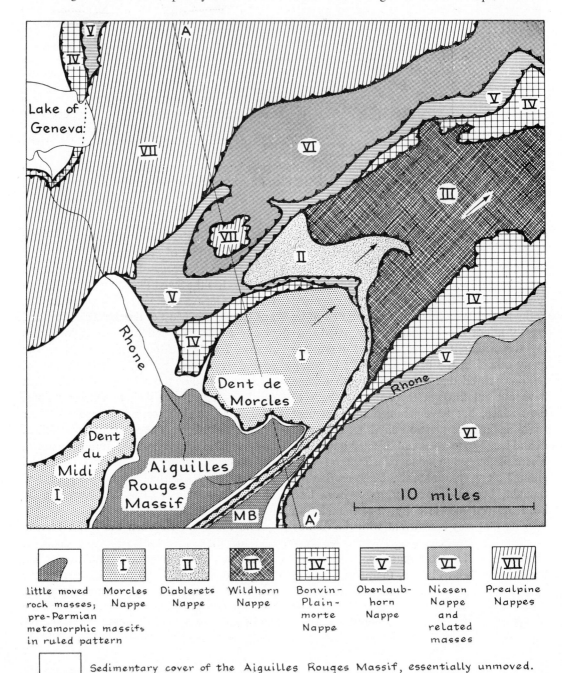

little moved rock masses; pre-Permian metamorphic massifs in ruled pattern

I Morcles Nappe

II Diablerets Nappe

III Wildhorn Nappe

IV Bonvin-Plain-morte Nappe

V Oberlaub-horn Nappe

VI Niesen Nappe and related masses

VII Prealpine Nappes

Sedimentary cover of the Aiguilles Rouges Massif, essentially unmoved.

common in many other mountain chains.

Figure 20-7 portrays the kind of evidence used in deciphering this complex geology. A study of this map shows that the Mythen and Rothenfluh, northeast of Lake Lucerne, and the Stanserhorn and Buochserhorn, on the southwest, are merely remnants of the highest of at least three thrust sheets piled one on top of the other. At the south end of Lake Lucerne the Eocene rocks (4 in Figure 20-7) dip beneath Jurassic rocks (2, in Figure 20-7), which are overlain in depositional succession by Cretaceous (3) and Eocene (4). These, in turn, at Sisikon and Bauen are overlain by a higher thrust sheet of Cretaceous (3), on which rests the highest thrust sheet of all, the Triassic rocks (1) of the Stanserhorn and Mythen.

The High Limestone Alps and the Crystalline Massifs.--It is beyond the scope of this book to detail the manifold complexities of Alpine geology. One feature, though, the analysis of a plunging structure that buries the crystalline basement of the Aiguilles Rouges beneath the thrust sheets of the High Limestone Alps, will be described as an example of a general method of structural interpretation.

The lower thrust sheets beneath the klippes of the Prealps continue southeastward into the High Limestone Alps. Their relations are diagrammatically shown in Figure 20-9. Here

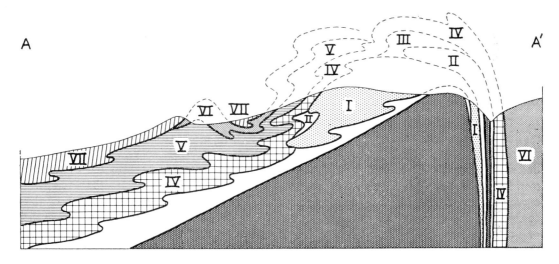

Figure 20-9.   *Map and schematic cross section at the northeast end of the Aiguilles Rouges massif, near the Rhone Valley, southeast of Lake Geneva. Unpatterned and lower dark pattern indicate the little-moved rock masses; pre-Permian metamorphic massifs are dark. (I) Dent de Morcles Nappe; (II) Diablerets Nappe, (III) Wildhorn Nappe; (IV) Bonvin-Plain Morte Nappe; (V) Oberlaubhorn Nappe; (VI) Niesen and related nappes; (VII) Prealpine nappes. MB is the extreme end of the Mont Blanc massif. Note how the Morcles Nappe begins in the tightly squeezed area between the Mont Blanc and Aiguilles Rouges massifs. The cross section is highly schematic and the topographic relief greatly exaggerated for clarity, but the relations of the several nappes are essentially correct as to age and superposition. (Greatly modified from E. B. Bailey,* Tectonic Essays, *Clarendon Press, 1935.)*

they are seen to lie one above another in great thrust sheets formed from dragged-out anticlinal folds that have been overturned so far as to lie nearly flat. Swiss geologists call such sheets **nappes** (French) or **decken** (German).

The crystalline rocks of the Aiguilles Rouges consist of granite, gneiss, schist, and other metamorphic rocks like those seen in the magnificent tower of Mont Blanc just to the south. A few highly distorted plant fossils have been found in anthracite coal associated with these metamorphic rocks; from them we know that at least part of the mass is of Carboniferous age. The overlying sedimentary rocks have yielded some Permian and Triassic fossils and contain pebbles of the underlying metamorphics. They were therefore either deposited not far from their present positions, or else the crystalline rocks and overlying sediments have been thrust forward together.

The clue to the geologic structure lies at the northeast end of the exposed mass of crystalline rocks. Here, in the valley of the Rhone, the sedimentary rocks on the south side of the crystalline mass can be followed northeast, north, and northwest as a strongly sheared-out fold—so compressed that its limbs are parallel—draped at a low angle over the much sheared sedimentary rocks that overlie the crystalline massif in normal succession. All the contacts dip east, northeast, or north at low angles. This isoclinal fold, shown on Figure 20-9 as the Morcles Nappe, lies at the Dent de Morcles on a mass that forms the Mesozoic cover of the Aiguilles Rouges massif. All the rocks, including the metamorphic core and sedimentary mantle of the isoclinally folded Morcles Nappe, are highly sheared, parallel to their contacts. The Morcles Nappe, which envelops the whole eastern end of the crystalline massif, has been squeezed against the south side of the massif, rolled over it into a tight fold, and pressed northward until it lies flat; on the north side it is even overturned above the sedimentary mantle covering the massif. The fold has been rolled and stretched northward for many miles

from the place where its rocks were deposited. When the folded mass is traced around the gently east-dipping northeast end of the Aiguilles Rouges massif, it is apparent that rocks composing the nappe are the same as those that mantle the crystalline core. They have been stripped completely off the south side and squeezed northward. The northeast-southwest trend of the folds is clear. Along this trend all the structural elements—massif, mantle, and overlying folds—tilt gently northeast. Such a tilt along a fold axis is called the plunge of the structure. If the gentle plunge of the massif is followed upward to the southwest it becomes clear that the folded mass of the Dent du Midi, across the Rhone Valley, is merely a continuation of the same structure. It is simply a part of the Morcles Nappe, once continuous with it. The two blocks have been separated by the erosion of the Rhone.

If we follow the plunge of the Morcles Nappe to the northeast, we find that two higher thrust sheets, the Diablerets and Wildhorn Nappes, overlie it in succession. Both these, and several still higher ones, plunge northeastward, overlying the end of the Morcles Nappe at gentle angles. When these nappes are followed to the northwest, they are seen to dip steeply beneath the even higher thrust sheets that constitute the Prealps.

The consistent northeast plunges of these folded thrust masses enable us to discern their structural arrangement and see which overlies which—a matter not always obvious locally because the beds and faults are overturned. We can see, for example, that the Morcles Nappe came from south of the Aiguilles Rouges massif and that the Diablerets and Wildhorn Nappes each came from still farther south. This is a general relationship in the Alps—each successively higher thrust sheet came from farther south than those below it.

Farther to the southwest the Aiguilles Rouges massif is separated from the Mont Blanc massif of similar crystalline rocks by a very narrow synclinal zone of highly sheared sedimentary rocks. It is from this synclinal zone that the Morcles Nappe was squeezed out and folded northward. Swiss geologists believe that the Mont Blanc and Aiguilles Rouges massifs moved only a few miles during the folding. In contrast, the great thrust sheet of the Morcles Nappe has been torn loose from its foundation and overfolded northward. The crumpled sheet can be followed foot by foot for more than ten miles to the northwest, where it disappears beneath still higher and farther-traveled thrust sheets, below the Prealps. Here is evidence enough of extensive horizontal movement in the outer crust of the earth. What, then, are we to think when, several miles still farther to the northwest, identical rocks reappear from beneath the Prealpine Nappes and rest in fault contact on the Tertiary of the Swiss Plateau! The only conclusion possible is that the displacement of these superficial rocks of the crust is measured in tens of miles.

If we go northeastward from the Wildhorn Nappe, east of the Rhone Valley, we find that the plunge of the folds reverses—instead of plunging gently eastward, the crests of the thrust masses plunge west. Thus the Diablerets Nappe rises again from beneath the Wildhorn,

then, in turn, the Morcles Nappe, and finally, metamorphics like those of the Aiguilles Rouges massif. This upfolded mass of crystalline rocks is called, from the river draining it, the Aar massif. What we have traversed from the Aiguilles Rouges massif to the Aar massif, is a sag in a northeast-trending ridge of crystalline rock and it is the plunge of the successive structural units toward the sag that enables us to work out their sequence. Figure 20-10, modified from a diagram of the Swiss geologist P. Arbenz, illustrates the principle involved.

Of course no single thrust sheet extends the whole length of the Alps, though several have been traced for many scores of miles. Nevertheless, the alternating depressions and elevations along the trends of the folded structures enable rather confident correlations of one structural unit with another for large parts of the Alps. It has thus been possible to make fairly confident projections of the architecture of this great range, even to surprising depths within the crust, and to reconstruct in our imagination the gigantic masses that must once have overlain the present surface but have been swept away by erosion.

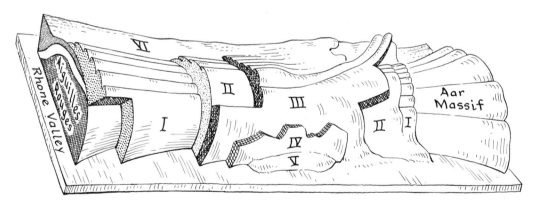

Figure 20-10. Block diagram, modified from P. Arbenz, showing how downwarped segments of the anticlinal structure represented by the Aiguilles Rouges–Aar crystalline massifs preserve a succession of thrust sheets (Nappes I, II, III, IV) that have been eroded away, both to the northeast and to the southwest. Such "axial depressions" are what enable the Alpine geologists to determine the mutual relations of the nappes, and to project the structures along the trend of the range. In this way the several nappes can be projected both under the surface and into the air, thereby reconstructing the rock masses as they were prior to erosion.

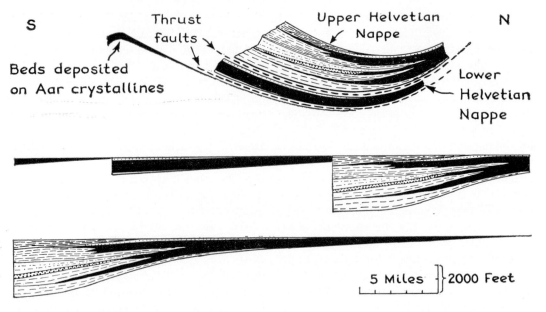

Figure 20-11. *Hypothetical reconstructions of the original sedimentary relations of the two thrust sheets and the unmoved sedimentary cover of the Aar Massif in eastern Switzerland.* Top: *The present relations.* Middle: *The relations that would have existed if the lower thrust sheet had always been north of the massif and if the higher thrust sheet were still farther north.* Bottom: *The inferred original sedimentary relations if both thrust sheets have been thrust over the massif from the south, the higher from farther south than the lower. Clearly this is the more probable reconstruction of the original relations. (After Arnold Heim.)*

One strongly overfolded crystalline core after another is found south of the Aiguilles Rouges and Aar massifs, all the way to the southern border of the range. Each is separated from the next by highly deformed schists. Some of these schists have yielded Mesozoic or early Tertiary fossils. The arrangement in space—the geometry—of the great thrust masses is such that there must have been tremendous shortening of the outer crust—a shortening that cannot, of course, be accurately measured, but which must amount to many scores of miles. A careful estimate by Albert Heim, and an independent one by J. Cadisch, both Swiss geologists, agree that a sedimentary region at least 400 miles wide has been piled together in a mountain range only about 100 miles across! Thus the superficial part of the crust beneath northern Italy must lie scores of miles—if not,

indeed, several hundred—closer to the Swiss Plateau than it did in Eocene time.

The evidence is not only geometric. The facies of the rocks composing the thrust masses also indicate great travel. For example, Arnold Heim mapped the Cretaceous rocks of the nappes of the High Limestone Alps in eastern Switzerland. Their pattern justified his drawing the cross section that is reproduced, very much simplified, at the top of Figure 20-11. The displacement suggested strongly that on both thrusts the overlying rocks moved northward in relation to those beneath. The facies of the Cretaceous rocks of the nappes can be explained only by this kind of movement. For example, if one believes that the upper thrust sheet, now exposed north of the lower, has always been north of it, and, similarly, that the Cretaceous covering the Aar massif has always been south of the lower nappe, as it now is, one must accept the unlikely original arrangement of sedimentary facies shown in the middle of Figure 20-11. If, however, we overrule our "common sense" reaction—that such great travel of the rocks is "unreasonable"—and accept the geometrical evidence of displacement at its face value, we can construct the more probably original arrangement of sedimentary facies shown at the bottom of Figure 20-11. This more logical arrangement of facies is not only consistent with the geometrical evidence, but it offers almost conclusive proof that both lower and upper nappes traveled northward relative to the basement and that the upper sheet has come from farther south than the lower.

Summary of Alpine Structure.—Although the few examples cited can only hint at the almost incredibly complex structures of the Alps, they suffice to show that prodigious horizontal forces must have operated here, just as they did in the Appalachians. The crust has been shoved together as though by the jaws of a great vise, and the material caught between the jaws has been squeezed out and shoved northward, relative to the underlying rocks, for distances measured in scores of miles (Fig. 20-12). In the process, the rocks have been dynamically metamorphosed—in a single rock mass all transitions between almost unaltered shale and highly metamorphosed schist can be found. Granitic rocks caught in the deformation have been granulated and partly or wholly recrystallized into gneiss, with all transitional stages apparent. These are significant observations, for, as we shall see, geometric patterns identi-cal with those in the towering Alps are repeated again and again in the metamorphic rocks of the great Precambrian shield areas of the earth.

The Alps and Appalachians are representative of many other ranges, which, though less well studied, are known also to contain long chains of folds, thrust faults, and cores of metamorphic rock that are so closely related to the folds and faults that it seems likely that the metamorphism was a part of the deformation. Such ranges are the fold mountains of geology. As we indicated in Chapter 18, it is common to find granitic intrusions in such ranges. The association of geosynclinal sediments, fold and thrust-fault mountains, granitic plutons with metamorphic aureoles, and deeply buried structures of other metamorphic rocks is so common that all must somehow be related in origin.

The Substructure of the Fold Mountains

The intense folding, thrusting, and crustal shortening revealed by the rocks of the mountains must, of course, have been accompanied by deformation in the deeper crust as well. In part the stratified rocks undoubtedly sheared off from the more massive rocks at depth, as is suggested by the difference between the deformation of the crystalline core of the Aiguilles Rouges and that of the overlying nappe. Nevertheless, we have clear evidence in the isostatic anomalies (Chapter 10, Fig. 10-13) and in the seismic data (Chapter 19) that fold mountains are underlain by unusually great thicknesses of sial. Seismic evidence indicates that the sial roots beneath

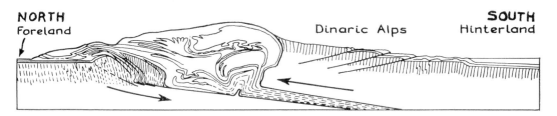

Figure 20-12.   Idealized reconstruction of the structure of the Alps, neglecting erosion. (After Emile Argand, 1916.)

both the Sierra Nevada and the Alps extend to a depth of at least forty miles—nearly twice the normal crustal thickness. Probably there is no sima beneath these roots, which extend clear to the Mohorovičić discontinuity; the sima elsewhere found beneath the sial has been pushed aside. Gravity measurements also indicate that, on any reasonable assumptions of rock density, the sial root beneath the Alps extends at least this deep. We have no direct knowledge of how this unusual thickening came about, but it is reasonable to suppose that the horizontal compression shown in the visible parts of the folded ranges was accompanied by similar compression of the crust throughout its thickness. Because a large mass of sial thickened in this way must sink isostatically, the thickness of the roots may be a measure of the amount of horizontal compression.

Volcanic Mountains

Volcanic ranges are less regular in trend than most fold mountains. Many are largely submarine, like the island arcs of the Pacific, and though some contain folded strata at depth (Chapter 8), their submergence makes it difficult to determine if all do. The Hawaiian Islands form an excellent example of a volcanic range, with each island being merely the highest portion of a volcanic cone or group of cones aligned along a gently curving line. None give any sign of a folded substructure, and it seems unlikely that one exists. Most geologists consider that this chain probably marks a deep rift in the crust that extends to great depths from which the magma of the volcanoes was derived.

Fewer volcanic ranges have been recognized on the continents than in the oceans. The only one of any consequence in the United States is the Cascade Range of Oregon and Washington. This range extends almost due north for about five hundred miles. It is crowned by several glacier-clad volcanic cones, among them Mount Rainier, Mount Hood, and Mount Shasta. Between these lie innumerable young, smaller cones and lava fields that rest on a platform of older, deeply eroded volcanic rocks, some of which were derived from older central volcanoes. In other parts of the range, as in the Mount Hood area, they rest on gently tilted to highly folded plateau lavas—the edge of the great Columbia Plateau flood basalt. Farther north in the Cascades, near Yakima, groups of younger volcanoes trend at a wide angle across older folded and currently folding, probably geosynclinal, rocks (Chapter 8). The inference is clear that the trend of this range is nearly independent of the previous history of the outer crust beneath it, and must be largely determined by some feature, either a fault or a magmatic alignment of some kind, that is deep-seated and unrelated to visible structures.

The Basin Ranges

Most of Nevada, western Utah, and large parts of Oregon, Idaho, Arizona, New Mexico, western Texas, eastern California, and northern Mexico constitute a geologic province characterized by isolated mountain ranges, separated by desert plains and basins. As Dutton said long ago: if we look at a relief map of North America, these ranges resemble an army of caterpillars crawling toward Mexico. Much of this desert area is occupied by the Great Basin, which does not drain to the sea. Hence the whole geologic province has become known as the Basin and Range Province, and the ranges are called the Basin Ranges.

The geology of this area is far less well known than that of the Appalachians or the Alps; only small segments have been mapped in detail. Yet our information shows that among themselves the Basin Ranges differ notably in structure. They clearly were formed from parts of the crust with widely differing histories, and did not rise from a relatively uniform geosyncline.

Some parts of the Basin and Range Province were indeed geosynclinal, but other parts have relatively thin sedimentary sections;

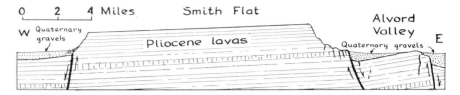

Figure 20-13.

Cross section of a relatively uneroded fault-block mountain range, Steens Mountain, Oregon. Note that right-hand fault is somewhat older than the middle one, and is overlapped by gravel which is unfaulted; the middle fault cuts the gravel, so is younger. All three faults, however, are relatively young, for their scarps have not been eroded back far from them. The marked bed indicates the interpretation of the actual displacement.

some parts contain only Paleozoic rocks, others contain thick sections of Cretaceous and Tertiary rocks. For example, the Sierra Nevada is composed largely of folded Mesozoic rocks and plutonics, with small patches of gently tilted Tertiary volcanics on its crest and western slope; Steens Mountain, Oregon (Fig. 20-13), consists entirely of flat to gently tilted Tertiary lavas and tuffs; the Wasatch Range of Utah includes Precambrian strata and thick geosynclinal Paleozoic and Mesozoic rocks that had been folded into a mountain range and cut by plutons in early Tertiary time; the Little Hatchet Mountains of southern New Mexico are made up chiefly of Lower Cretaceous sedimentary rocks, with a few Tertiary volcanics. Clearly these widely differing rocks and histories set the Basin Ranges apart from such ranges as the Alps and Appalachians, in which, for long distances along the trends of the ranges most of the components have had essentially similar histories.

What feature is common to all the Basin Ranges? Almost every one that has been adequately mapped is bordered on one or both sides by normal faults, along which the range has been uplifted and tilted (Fig. 20-13). The observed faults dip at angles that range between 40° and the vertical, averaging about 60°. Where the body of the range consists of folded rocks or of thrust masses, the normal faults cut across the older folds and thrust faults without regard to them. The intervening basins are downfaulted with respect to

the ranges and most of them are masked by alluvium. This relation is especially clear in Pleasant Valley, west of the Sonoma Range, as discussed in Chapter 8.

The Basin Ranges, then, unlike folded ranges, owe their existence directly to differential vertical movements of adjacent crustal blocks along normal faults, rather than to lateral compression of the outer crust followed by uplift and erosion. They are therefore often called **fault-block mountains.**

Upwarped Mountains

The mountains to be described under this heading illustrate the difficulty of classifying many natural phenomena. Some mountains are not readily classed as either fold mountains, volcanic mountains, or fault-block mountains. The Adirondacks are a good example. This mountain mass—and there are others, such as the Black Hills, the highlands of Labrador, and mountains in Africa, Asia, South America, and Europe—is composed of ancient metamorphic rocks that are folded and altered in much the same way as the deeper rocks of many fold-mountain chains. But the present mountain mass formed of these rocks is not elongated parallel to the fold structure of the metamorphic rocks, as it is in most folded ranges, but is almost independent of it. Though there are some faults bordering the Adirondacks, these seem all to be negligibly small and incapable of accounting for the relief of the range with respect to the surrounding rocks. These mountains seem to be parts of the Precambrian basement which long ago underwent deformation like that which produced the younger fold mountains. But, as shown by the even truncation of the folds beneath the overlapping Cambrian rocks, erosion later reduced them to an almost level surface—nearly all the mountainous relief had been erased before the incursion of the Cambrian sea. The uplift of the present mountains did not involve anything more than gentle warping of the overlying Cambrian and younger rocks, which must once have covered the whole mountain mass as a flat sedimentary blanket. In the Alps, the folding and thrusting immediately succeeded the filling of the geosyncline in mid-Tertiary time. In the Appalachians, also, the main folding followed the sedimentary filling in late Paleozoic time, but, as we shall see, the ridges and valleys that form the present Appalachian Mountains were caused by much later erosion acting upon the worn roots of the old Paleozoic range: as in the Adirondacks, the folding and metamorphism of the rocks long antedated the making of the present topographic relief. In fact, the strongly deformed rocks had been planed off and covered by a presumably normal—not geosynclinal—thickness of sedimentary rocks before they were warped up and eroded to form the present mountains. The mechanism of their formation must surely be very different from that of either the fold or the fault-block mountains.

Summary of Mountain Structure

Let us recapitulate the features in which mountains differ from other parts of the continental plates:

1. *The sial beneath the major mountain ranges is far thicker than that beneath the rest of the continents.* This generalization is supported by gravity measurements (Chapter 10) and by available seismic data. The difference in travel times for earthquake waves that pass beneath the Sierra Nevada, for example, can be satisfactorily accounted for only on the assumption that rocks like those of the outer crust—sial—extend below the Sierra to a depth nearly twice the average for the rest of the continent. The excessive heat flow (amount of heat escaping to the surface from the earth's interior) measured in the Colorado Rockies gives indirect evidence of such thickened sial there. As was noted in Chapter 19, the sialic rocks must contain higher proportions of the radioactive elements than deeper rocks. As radioactive decomposition is a heat-generating process, it is reasonable to attribute the high heat flow in the Colorado Rockies—far higher than the average for the continent—to an unusually thick prism of highly radioactive (hence sialic) rocks. The sima appears to be absent beneath the thickened sial; perhaps it was displaced sideways by the sinking root during the folding. Surveys are not adequate to permit us to say whether the sial thickens beneath such minor ranges as the smaller Basin Ranges, the Black Hills, or the Adirondacks.

2. *The rocks of the mountains are more deformed than those of the continental plates.* This generalization seems valid for nearly all ranges, though again we must note that it does not apply to many fault-block mountains. Many of these are undeformed internally, and the internal structure of others, though complex, long antedates and is independent of the bordering faults. These faults cut the older structure; movement on them accounts for the present relief. Nor are the rocks of the up-faulted masses notably more deformed than those of similar age in the nearby continental plates, which have not been upraised to form mountains. The uplift of many of the Basin Range mountains and of such upwarped masses as the Black Hills, the Adirondacks, and the present Appalachian Mountains took place whole eras later than their intense internal deformation. These older structures were not appreciably modified during the later uplift except at the borders of the mountain masses. Nevertheless, it is unquestionable that

the crust as a whole is much more disturbed in such areas as the Basin and Range Province than under the plains of Illinois or Iowa, so that our generalization of greater deformation in mountainous areas than elsewhere is still generally true.

3. *Granitic plutons are confined to mountains and to shield areas.* Although plutons constitute only small elements in the structure of either the Alps or the Appalachians, and are lacking in many smaller ranges, most fold ranges contain both large and small granitic masses. What is perhaps more significant, granitic masses are *not* found elsewhere in any considerable volume, except in the great shield areas of Precambrian rock. Here, too, granitic plutons are universally associated with strongly deformed and metamorphosed rocks —never with widespread flat-lying unde-formed strata. The generalization that all siza-ble granitic plutons are associated with folded and faulted rocks like those of the fold moun-tains seems valid.

4. *Sedimentary thicknesses are greater in mountain belts than in continental plates.* This generalization is well supported by data from many ranges, but it does not apply to the in-dividual ranges of the Basin and Range Prov-ince. It is also true that the sedimentary strata of some almost undeformed geosynclinal areas, such as the Gulf Coast region of the United States and the plains of Alberta, are as thick as those of many fold ranges.

5. *In many of the great mountain chains the rock structures are such as could have been produced only by great horizontal short-ening of the surficial crust,* as we have seen in the Jura and the Alps.

What is the meaning of those generaliza-tions in terms of mountain origin? We cannot identify any specific features, which, like the jaws of a vise, have squeezed wide segments of the crust into a narrow belt. How, then, has this come about? We will return to this enigma after we consider the subsequent his-tory of such a compressed belt, however it may have been formed.

The History of Folded Belts

Whatever the mechanism by which tightly folded belts are made, isostasy demands that the average level of the base of a sedimentary mass must sink after the mass has been folded (Figs. 10-9 and 10-10). Small masses may be sustained by the strength of the crust, but large loads of regional extent cannot be. The sial composing the outer crust has a density of about 2.7. We do not know the precise density of the underlying sima, but it is certainly greater. The material beneath the crust—the mantle—must be even denser or isostasy could not prevail. Estimates from seismic data range between 3.0 and 3.3 for the density just below the Mohorovičić discontinuity. Let us take the higher of these figures. If shortening of a belt of the outer crust thickens it by 5,000 feet, the bottom of the crust must sink into the mantle, just as a ship settles deeper in the water when a load is put aboard. The sink-ing would be enough to displace an equal mass of mantle, thus $2.7 \div 3.3 \times 5,000$ feet, or more than 4,000 feet. (Part of the adjustment might, of course, take place by flowage within the crust rather than beneath it, but the prin-ciple is the same, that the total mass above some "level of compensation" in the mantle must remain the same.)

Thus, if a thrust sheet 5,000 feet thick were pushed over a wide expanse of country, the surface of the land, after isostatic adjustment, would stand only 1,000 feet higher than it had originally. This statement cannot, of course, be taken literally, because the quantitative values are too uncertain; but the principle must be valid, for it agrees with, and in part explains, the long persistence of uplift along most folded and overthrust mountain masses.

Mountain Uplift

Although, for simplicity, we have neglected details of deposition during the geosynclinal history of both Alps and Appalachians, it is true that in both ranges deposition was inter-rupted by uplift at many different times. In other words, folds began to grow and project high enough to be eroded more than once during the geosynclinal phase of these ranges. This is quite common, and in some ranges has resulted in many angular unconformities. Other clues to uplift during the geosynclinal phase are the common occurrence of coarse clastic deposits in the outer, more gently folded parts of mountain chains, and the presence within these clastics of pebbles that could only have come from deeply buried rocks after these had been exposed nearby by deep erosion.

Folding, by thickening the sial, leads to high relief and subsequent erosion. In the Alps this is proved by the very coarse clastics of Miocene and Pliocene age which lie on the Swiss plain and lap against the complexly deformed older rocks that constitute the main range. In the Appalachians the coarseness of the Triassic sediments preserved in scattered fault blocks testifies to the existence of similar high relief after the late Paleozoic folding. In most folded ranges uplift does not all take place at one time, some is concurrent, or almost concurrent, with the deformation, and some takes place long after folding has ceased. The present relief of the Appalachians, and of most other ranges whose folding was pre-Tertiary, is due to vertical upbowing of the deformed rocks in late Tertiary time. Perhaps the most convincing evidence of this is given by the unconformities.

The Appalachians fall off in altitude and disappear as a topographic feature beneath the Cretaceous beds of the Gulf Coast, which lie on a nearly flat surface eroded across the folded Paleozoic strata. Figure 20-3 shows clearly that the original surface irregularities that must have formed during the folding of the southern Appalachians had been entirely erased by erosion—the surface reduced nearly to a plane—before the Cretaceous deposits were laid across the eroded edges of the folded rocks. This is shown by the fact that the basal contact of the Cretaceous beds passes in a smooth curve directly across the edges of the steeply dipping Paleozoic rocks. The ridges and valleys of the Appalachians, which reflect

the differing resistances of the folded rocks to erosion find no expression in the outcrop of the Cretaceous rocks. The pre-Cretaceous topography must have been reduced by erosion to a flat surface. All along the western edge of the coastal plain, as far northeast as New Jersey, the Cretaceous beds lie in strong unconformity upon the steeply dipping rocks of the Piedmont which are, of course, structurally a part of the Appalachians. It is clear that there can have been but little topographic relief in the present Appalachian country at the time of the Cretaceous deposition, and yet the present Appalachians attain a relief of nearly 6,700 feet, measured from the top of Mount Mitchell, their highest point, to the Coastal Plain. This relief must therefore be due to an upwarping long after the Cretaceous beds were deposited. The present mountains are but upbowed roots of the former fold range, etched into relief by late Tertiary erosion.

Less-convincing but still strong evidence of long-delayed uplift of many ranges is found in the smooth erosion surfaces carved across many of the summit uplands. Generally, the time at which such surfaces were formed is less readily determined than it is in the Appalachians because the unconformably overlying fossiliferous beds are lacking. Such a flat surface cut on diverse rocks demanded long erosion for its cutting. The profiles of most present streams have characteristically high gradients in their source areas. In some mountain ranges, however, the streams rise in relatively flat summit uplands, whose gently sloping surfaces cut smoothly across rocks that differ greatly in composition and structure, without reflecting these differences in hill and valley forms (Fig. 12-29). Such an area—like that in which the Cretaceous rests on the smoothly eroded upturned edges of the older strata of the southern Appalachians—must once have been a low plain on which the major streams had only low gradients at the time its fashioning was complete. Yet the flat-topped uplands are being cut into by a maze of deep canyons down which foaming torrents plunge. The contrast in gradient strongly suggests that the summit upland was formed when the major streams all had low gradients, such as could have existed only if the area was much nearer sea level than it is now. Such evidence strongly indicates that the entire mountain mass had been practically erased as a topographic feature before its latest uplift. And this erasure of relief was after the folding, for the old erosion surface transects the folds with little regard to the differences in resistance of the rocks beneath it.

To summarize, then: The recurrence of coarse clastics and unconformities in the geosynclinal sediments of most folded ranges testifies to repeated uplift and folding during the geosynclinal deposition. The growth of modern folds and the relief of geologically young ranges like the Alps, the Coast Ranges of California and Oregon, and the Cascades, testifies to mountain uplift concurrent with the major folding and crustal shortening. The history inferred from the Cretaceous unconformity and the present relief of the Appalachians is one of uplift and renewal of relief long after folding had ceased—in fact, after the relief resulting from it had been completely erased. Because these relations are repeated in range after range, all over the earth, they surely justify the generalization that fold mountains mark crustal zones along which, during the geosynclinal phase, uplift had taken place from time to time although depression dominated—perhaps for a whole era —whereas during and after the main folding phase, and continuing for geologically long times, uplift prevails.

Causes of Uplift

Both seismic and gravitational data show that the sial is thicker beneath folded mountains than elsewhere. This fact, considered in connection with the principle of isostasy, gives us a clue to the reason for the long persistence of uplift. The isostatic relations that exist during erosion of a mountain are the converse of those prevailing during crustal compression. The removal of rock from the top of the

Figure 20-14.   How summit level may increase owing to isostatic uplift, even though average level of the surface is being lowered by erosion. (A) Assumed summit and average level of mountain block at the close of folding. (B) Assumed topography after considerable erosion but with no isostatic uplift in response to the unloading of the volumes marked V from the block. A.L. is the average elevation of the block but we arbitrarily retain the same summit level as in A. (C) Relations after isostatic uplift of the block, dissected as shown in B. A.L. is higher than in B by (2.7/3.3) times the difference between A.L. and S.L. in B. (See text for assumptions underlying the choice of this fraction.) A.L. is average level of surface, S.L. the summit level, in all three diagrams.

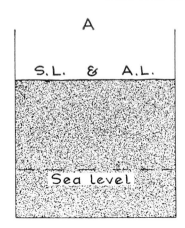
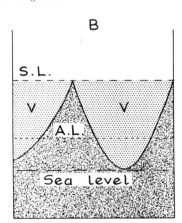
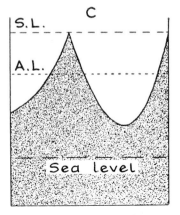

thickened prism of sial allows the whole mass to rise because of the lessened load. As we have already shown, a load of sial a mile thick would raise the surface only about 1,000 feet if isostasy prevails; similarly, erosion of a mile of material would reduce the average elevation only about 1,000 feet. Now, since most valley walls are concave upward, stream erosion normally removes more than half the mass between stream level and summit before the divides are greatly lowered. It is therefore entirely possible that the elevation of the mountain tops may increase because of isostatic uplift of the mountain block as a whole in response to the unloading by erosion, even though the average elevation of the mountain region is considerably lowered (Fig. 20-14). Isostatic uplift might thus account for many of the high flat-topped summits, but of course the fact that streams of low gradient had had time to cut a surface of low relief across the compressed belt after the folding but before the later uplift, implies that isostatic adjustment is very slow. Much remains to be learned before this paradox is fully understood.

The Mountain Root

So far we have considered the thickened sial beneath the mountains as though it had maintained all its properties unchanged when it thickened. But it certainly does not do so; all rocks whose structural relations show that they have been deeply buried and deformed are metamorphosed. Mere burial beneath other rocks will raise the temperature of the geosynclinal sediments by blanketing-in the earth's internal heat. The rocks contain radioactive elements whose disintegration also contributes heat. If a thick column of sialic rock is heated, it may expand enough to raise the surface notably, but because heating is slow it may be a long time before the surface of the column is raised because of such expansion: perhaps, then, thermal expansion accounts for part of the long delayed uplift of many ranges.

If a mass is buried several tens of miles deep in a mountain root, the downwarped sial may come into close contact with hot sima as well as being warmed by the blanketing-in of its own radioactive heat. Under these conditions it may gradually heat up and partially melt, forming a mass of granitic magma. The abundance of migmatites in deeply eroded mountain chains suggests such refusion, and so, too, does the fact that almost all granitic plutons are found in mountain chains. But a root softened in this way by partial melting can no longer maintain itself as a root, for it is lighter than the sima into which it projects and when it softens and loses rigidity it must gradually spread laterally and flatten out. In so doing, it thickens the sial alongside of the range, and this perhaps accounts for the high-standing plateaus and high plains of nearly flat-lying, little-distorted rocks that border many large ranges—for example, the Rocky Mountains and the Himalayas.

The Shield Areas

Each of the continents contains large areas of exposed Precambrian rocks. Among them are most of northern and eastern Canada, Finland and Sweden, northeastern Siberia, India, and much of Africa, western Australia, and eastern Brazil. These are the **Precambrian shields.** At their borders most of them are overlain by Cambrian or younger rocks that rest upon an unconformity of relatively low relief.

Most of the shield areas are only a few hundred feet above sea level, and the undeformed character of the surrounding younger sedimentary rocks suggests that they have been so through most of Paleozoic and later time. Not all of the shield areas are low, however; the Adirondacks of New York, which are a projection of the Canadian shield, the Black Hills, much of Labrador, the mountainous areas near Lake Baikal on the Siberian shield, are all parts of what we have called upwarped mountainous masses. So, too, large parts of the African and Brazilian shields now stand several thousand feet above the sea. They stand as high, for example, as most of the Urals and Appalachians (which were folded near the end of the Paleozoic), or the Scottish Highlands (where the folding was mid-Paleozoic). But these parts of the shields, even though large, are exceptional—most of the shield areas are low.

Owing to their lack of fossils, it is impossible to correlate Precambrian rocks over wide areas. In the shields, therefore, we cannot reconstruct the geologic history with anywhere near as much confidence as for such ranges as the Appalachians. Nevertheless, the structures in many shield areas can be deciphered well enough to permit us to recognize similarities to those of many present mountain chains; it seems highly probable that large parts of the shield areas consist of deeply eroded mountain chains.

The evidence lies in the structural patterns that are brought out by detailed mapping. Figure 18-18 shows the geology of part of the Baltic shield. When the attitudes and relations of the rocks are compared with those depicted in Figures 20-3 and 20-12, the similarity in complexity and general pattern is apparent. On the average, more granite and metamorphic rocks are exposed in the shield areas than in the younger ranges. Migmatites, also, which are rare or absent in the granitic borders of most younger ranges, are abundant in shields; they make up about a quarter of the exposed rocks in Finland—further evidence that the shield areas include many deeply eroded ancient mountains. In the cores of many Paleozoic and younger ranges, the rocks are more intensely deformed than on their borders, the extent of the metamorphic rocks is proportionately greater in older ranges than in mid-Tertiary ranges like the Alps, and most Late Tertiary and Quaternary ranges do not have metamorphic cores. The contorted and metamorphosed zones of the Precambrian shields thus consist of rocks such as we would expect to find at lower levels in a fold-mountain chain, as erosion progressed; their greater relative abundance in the shields is what might be expected from repeated uplifts and erosion during a much longer time.

The generally low relief and structural stability of the shield areas—for it must be remembered that the shields are continuous with the basement on which the largely flat-lying strata of the continental plates were deposited —may be due to long-continued erosion of their surfaces, combined with lateral spreading of the former mountain roots. In the long course of geologic time these processes have reduced the thickness of the sial until it is just thick enough to maintain the shields in isostatic balance near sea level. Further erosion is very slow. They may be further depressed by sedimentation, but for the most part they are stable. Why some relatively small parts of them may, after standing long in this low position, rise again to mountainous heights, as in the Adirondacks and Black Hills, is a problem for which no satisfactory answer has yet been found.

Ocean Deeps and the Belts of Negative Anomalies

In Chapter 16 we pointed out the close association of most of the great oceanic deeps with arcuate chains of islands. The many earthquakes that occur close to the deeps imply crustal unrest in these areas, as does the common, though not invariable, association of active volcanoes with the island arcs. Since the deeps are the maximum departures of the earth's surface from sea level, and many of them immediately adjoin large islands (Mindanao, Cuba, Puerto Rico, Sumatra, Java) or even the continent of South America (Atacama Deep, Leeward Trough), the deeps must be fairly young geologically or they would have been filled with sediment, as, indeed, some of them seem partly to be. We have noticed (Chapter 16) that the sediment dredged from the Philippine Deep east of Mindanao is obviously derived from that island, and if both deep and island had existed for a geologically long time, the deep would surely have been eliminated by filling. Yet it is one of the deepest in the world.

One of the most interesting geological discoveries of the past generation was that there are remarkable deviations from isostasy associated with some of the island arcs and ocean deeps. This discovery we owe to the distinguished Dutch geodesist F. A. Vening-Meinesz, who, between 1923 and 1932, determined the value of gravity at many points at sea from a submarine. His later work developed the information summarized in Figure 20-15.

As we noted in Chapter 10, if the earth's surface were level and the crust homogeneous, the attraction of gravity would be determined entirely by the latitude at which the observation is made. The anomalies shown in Figure 20-15 were determined by subtracting this theoretical value of gravity from the measured value, after certain corrections had been made. The corrections include allowances for the depth of the submarine beneath the surface, the topography of the land and sea floor for long distances around the station, the fact that sea water differs greatly in density from the rocks underlying land stations, and finally, an allowance for "regional compensation" (equivalent to assuming that a very large crustal block centering at the station is in isostatic balance with the rest of the crust).

The actual calculation of the compensation is laborious and far beyond the scope of this book, but the meaning is clear. The existence of a great belt of negative anomalies can mean only that in places the ocean floor is underlain by rocks whose density is far less than is usual at equivalent depths elsewhere—in other words, by light rocks. The anomalies are so great and the belt is so narrow—only 30 to 100 miles wide in the strongly anomalous part —that the deficiency in gravity demands that the light rocks must form a very deep septum (30 to 40 miles) to account for it. (The gravitational effect of course falls off with the square of the distance of the mass from the measuring station.)

The belt is about 3,000 miles long. For much of its course it lies close to the axis of a deep oceanic trough, though some sections lie

Figure 20-15.   Map of Indonesia, showing gravity anomalies. (After F. A. Vening-Meinesz, 1934.)

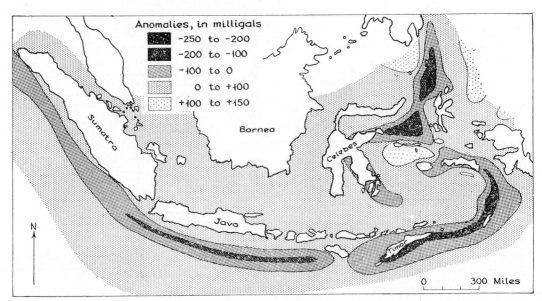

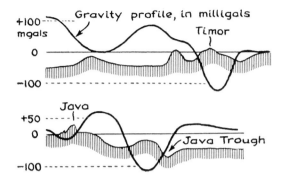

Figure 20-16. Cross sections of Indonesia, showing relations of gravity anomalies and topography. The upper section is NW–SE through the south end of Timor; the lower is N–S through the east end of Java. Note that both of the negative troughs in the curve showing values of anomalies overlie topographic ridges, though one ridge is submarine. (After F. A. Vening-Meinesz, 1934.)

on either side, and others overlie a submarine ridge that divides the trough lengthwise. In the islands of Timor, Tanimber, Kei, and Ceram this ridge comes to the surface, but the negative strip continues. On both sides of the negative strip, the gravity anomalies become positive over broad areas that are not obviously linear like the negative strip. The positive anomalies are thought to mean that the dense rocks of the crust are closer to the surface than they normally are, and hence exert greater than normal attraction (Fig. 20-16). To summarize: along the negative strip light crustal rocks are greatly thickened and extend to unusual depths, forming a long narrow wedge in the denser rocks on either side.

Such large deviations from isostatic equilibrium are not at all common. The uplift of Scandinavia after removal of the glacial ice indicates that even in the shield areas (which have been unaffected by intense crustal movements or igneous activity since before the Paleozoic, and which might, therefore, be considered unusually strong) the crust has responded to far smaller forces than those implied by these great gravity differences in Indonesia. Both the many earthquakes and

active volcanoes indicate that the crust is probably unusually weak along the Indonesian arc; much weaker, for example, than in the shield areas. Vening-Meinesz pointed out that these facts can only be reconciled by assuming that *the rocks of the negative strip are being held down so that they are prevented from floating at the level appropriate to their density.* In other words, some downward force of great magnitude is now operating here along a narrow zone; for, were this negative strip like that in the Alps, we would expect to find the sial standing at high elevations, floated upward on the denser material of the mantle. Clearly, such a force might be expected to produce folding and thrusting of the kind we associate with mountain chains. In conformity with this deduction, the islands along the belt are, indeed, composed of highly deformed rocks, and, as we saw in Chapter 8, some are capped by uplifted coral reefs. Do we have here a mountain chain in process of formation?

The analogy with old mountain chains is far from complete. We have already pointed out that most geosynclines are filled with deposits dominantly of shallow-water origin; the water depths in the Indonesian deeps are far greater than those at which most geosynclinal sediments are inferred to have been deposited. The location, bordering a truly oceanic segment of the crust, seems also to be anomalous; the forelands of most ancient geosynclines were not oceanic, but shelf-seas. Consequently, although there are practical proofs of strong lateral compression in the Indonesian area—compression like that which must have produced the folded ranges of the geologic past—the setting is so different that we cannot be sure whether we are here seeing a mountain range being born.

Speculations Regarding Mountain-Building

Although the student will by now have recognized that every statement of a scientific "law" or a geologic "fact" necessarily carries within it an element of inference, the facts enumerated in this chapter are generally regarded by geologists as well established. The objectives of science include, however, not merely the description of natural phenomena, but also the coordination of these raw data into broader generalizations, and the development from them of a comprehensive theory. And although most geologists agree on the facts we have stated and even on most of the generalizations we have discussed, hardly one of them would venture to say that any theory yet advanced satisfactorily explains the making of mountains. Nevertheless, hypotheses and speculations are valuable in the progress of science, for they provoke tests that may, when carried out, negate, modify, or confirm some of the ideas proposed. What are some of the reasonable speculations that have been made about the great enigma of mountain-making?

Theory of a Shrinking Earth

An old idea favored by many early geologists (and supported today by some) was that the earth is shrinking. As it shrinks the more rigid rocks of the crust must accommodate themselves to a smaller interior by crumpling, just as the skin of an apple crumples and wrinkles when the inner part dries. It was assumed that the deformation of rocks in mountain chains has been localized by the unusual thickness of relatively weak sediments in the geosynclines. An object contracts as it cools, and the earth is losing heat at the surface, as is proved by the downward increase of temperature measured in mines and oil wells. It seemed certain, therefore, before radioactivity was discovered, that the earth must be cooling, and hence contracting.

Although many geological objections have been made to this theory, perhaps the principal one is that shrinking would shorten every great circle equally. Thus, either the geosynclines would have to be symmetrically distributed (as the mountains clearly are not) or there would be many mountains without geosynclinal sediments. The distribution of folded mountains is far from what is to be expected

from this theory. A second argument against the theory that is less easily tested, but seems valid is based on the fact that there is only one great east-west chain on earth, namely the Alpine-Himalayan. Considering scale and strength, it seems unlikely that the crust is strong enough to transmit the great forces that would be produced by shrinking for distances as great as half-way around the earth so as to concentrate almost all of the north-south shortening into this single belt. The distances between fold belts of other trends also seem far too great for the rocks to carry the compressive stresses, considering the scale. The most serious objection, however, and one that most geologists regard as unanswerable, is that, from reasonable estimates of the distribution of radioactive materials in the earth, it seems probable that all the heat now escaping from the interior is of radioactive origin, so that the earth as a whole is probably not becoming appreciably cooler. It may even be heating up, for computations of heat transfer show that even in two billion years the earth cannot have lost any appreciable heat by conduction from a depth greater than about 400 miles—a tenth of its radius. Until these objections are overcome, this once popular theory seems unlikely to be valid.

Theory of Continental Drift

Probably every school boy who has studied a globe has independently discovered that, if the Americas were pushed eastward, they would almost fit the coast of Africa and Europe. This rough fit seems even more striking when we notice that the Mid-Atlantic Ridge swings sharply eastward at about the right place to fit the Guinea Coast of Africa. About a century ago, Antonio Snider published the speculation that the continents east and west of the Atlantic had formerly been joined and have since drifted apart. This idea seemed so fantastic to geologists of that time that it was lost sight of until about fifty years ago, when it was again independently suggested by the American geologist F. B. Taylor and the German, Alfred Wegener. If whole continents can move so far, the shortening of the outer crust by a few scores of miles becomes insignificant. Any force that could move the Americas westward two or three thousand miles could supply the Rockies, Coast Ranges, and Andes as minor by-products. Although a mechanism adequate for bodily displacing the continents is unknown, this theory has nevertheless won favor from some geologists.

Wegener assumed that the continents float isostatically on the denser substratum and that this is so weak that it yields almost like a fluid to very small forces. Two forces tend to move the continents. The first is centrifugal: the sial masses float higher than the sima and so are farther from the earth's axis; hence the centrifugal force acting on them is greater,

and they tend to drift toward the equator. The second is the tidal attraction of the sun and moon, which, as the earth rotates from west to east, tends always to drag the continents westward. (It must not be forgotten that the tidal forces act on the solid earth as well as on the oceans and atmosphere.) Wegener thought that the Alpine-Himalayan chain was formed when Eurasia collided with Africa and India in response to the first force, and that the Andes and Rockies were piled up by friction as the Americas were dragged westward through the viscous substratum by tidal forces.

Both these forces exist, but computations show that they are millions of times too small to have folded the rocks. If that is so, one may wonder why the theory is still seriously

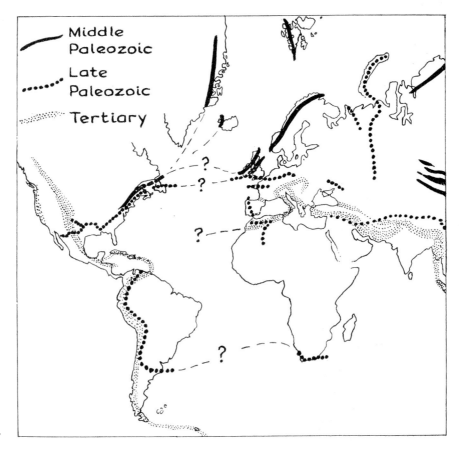

Figure 20-17.

Map showing trend lines of folded belts on both sides of the Atlantic. (Data chiefly from J. H. F. Umbgrove, 1947.)

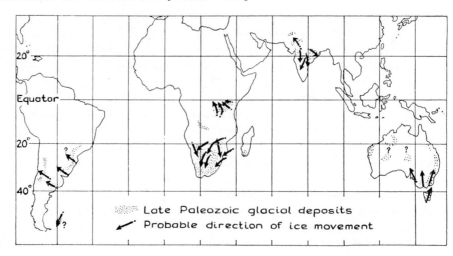

Figure 20-18.

Map showing areas of Late Paleozoic continental glaciation. See also Figure 20-19. (Data from A. L. DuToit, and D. N. Wadia.)

considered. The fact is that if geologists were convinced that the continents were formerly more closely grouped, they would accept the fact, even though no adequate mechanism for moving them has yet been suggested. Many geological phenomena are well-established— continental glaciation, for one—that have so far defied explanation. So let us critically examine the geological evidence that has been advanced in support of such a grouping.

Obviously, more than the apparent fit of the Atlantic shores is needed. This fit is far less exact at a depth of 10,000 feet than at sea level, and there were notable differences in the continental outlines in Cretaceous or even in mid-Tertiary time from those of today. The main supporting arguments advanced are the similarities in the trends of mountain belts, in strata, and in fossils of land-dwelling organisms on opposite sides of the Atlantic.

In the mountain belts of New England and Newfoundland, fold axes formed during the middle and late Paleozoic are cut off at the shore. Mountain structures of nearly, but not exactly, the same ages in the British Isles and western Europe also end at the Atlantic shore (Figure 20-17). Likewise, pre-Devonian fold axes in Brazil and Uruguay end at the Atlantic, as do some folds of about the same age in

South Africa. The apparent interruption of these fold lines by the ocean suggests, but does not prove, that they were formerly joined and have since drifted apart. The hazard in assuming that this occurred is shown by the fact that the Atlas and Pyrenees ranges also end at the shore, and that although some geologists have tried to identify their western continuation in the Greater Antilles, it is clear from the patterns of the gravity anomalies and island arcs that the Antilles structures never did extend eastward to join the European and African ranges, but curve southward through the nearly drowned arc of the Lesser Antilles to join the Venezuelan ranges.

More suggestive, though still open to question, are similarities in the strata of South America and Africa. In both regions the oldest fossil-bearing rocks are Upper Silurian or Devonian. The fossils in them resemble those of the Falkland Islands but differ from those of Europe, northern Asia, and North America. In both regions similar continental rocks overlie these marine beds, and both areas contain Late Paleozoic tillites. Tillite of about the same age is found also in South Australia, Madagascar, and, in the northern hemisphere, in India (Fig. 20-18). Many fossil plants are associated with this tillite and coal beds overlie it. In all these widely separated areas in the southern hemisphere, two genera of fernlike plants, *Gangamopteris* and *Glossopteris,* occur—genera found in the northern hemisphere only in Russia, northeastern Siberia, and India. The *Glossopteris* flora has been cited as "proving" a complete separation of the southern lands and India from the rest of the northern hemisphere, and the name "Gondwana Land," from a rock series in India that contains this flora, has been given the hypothetical continent that is supposed once to have included all the areas in which these plants have been found.

The presence of this flora in Russia and Siberia, on the opposite side of the Himalayan geosyncline, seems to show, though, that the plants may have migrated across a sea and not have been restricted to a single land mass. Comparable vagaries in plant distribution are not rare. Many Permian plants of Texas and Arizona are not known to occur in the more easterly parts of North America or in Europe, but are found in China. These are never cited as evidence of a former union between Asia and North America. The weakness of this floral argument does not, of course, disprove former closer associations of the supposed fragments of Gondwana Land.

Perhaps the strongest argument for a drastically different arrangement of continents in Late Paleozoic time lies in the glacial pattern. As Figure 20-18 shows, glaciers invaded South America from the east and the Falkland Islands from the north, apparently radiating from a point now in the South Atlantic. Glaciers entered Australia from the south, extending as far north as latitude 28°S. An ice cap centered near 15°S in Africa, leaving its northern moraines on the equator. The Indian glacier centered in the Aravalli Mountains, north of Bombay, in latitude 20°N: characteristic rocks from these mountains are found in the tillite hundreds of miles away, both to the southeast and northwest. How are we to account for continental ice sheets in the present tropics unless the continents have moved? One suggestion is that the earth's poles have shifted

in position; another suggestion, sometimes linked with it, is that the now-scattered parts of Gondwana Land were formerly parts of a single mass near the South Pole (Fig. 20-19).

Mere shifting of the earth's axis without moving the land masses would not avoid the seeming paradox of continental ice sheets in the tropics, for the tillites are so placed that no possible position of the poles would fail to leave one or another glaciated area within 20° of the equator. Wegener thought, therefore, that in the late Paleozoic the Gondwana fragments were gathered into a single mass, while the South Pole was near the common junction of Africa, Australia, Antarctica, India, and Madagascar. His sketch of assumed relations is shown in Figure 20-19. He thought the American and European coals (of about the same age as the Gondwana glaciation) represented tropical peat bogs, whereas the *Glossopteris* coals were formed in peat bogs of colder climates like those of Ireland or Alaska. Tillite near Boston, within a few miles of the Rhode Island coals, was interpreted by Wegener as that of a mountain glacier. But, even on this assumption, both the Russian and the Siberian *Glossopteris* localities must have been in the tropics, so climatic zoning of the plants is not an adequate explanation of their distribution.

Others besides Wegener have tried to explain the climates of the late Paleozoic by a different grouping of the continents. All require special explanations for nearly as many phenomena as they explain. The plants of the late Paleozoic are all extinct and few paleobotanists have much faith in climatic inferences from them, for there are many examples of adaptations of plants to environments that differ widely from those in which they arose.

The earth's angular momentum is great. Like a gyroscope, it strongly resists change in its axis of rotation, and astronomers do not believe that the polar axis has ever shifted more than a very small amount.

Another good reason to doubt that the drifting of continents causes mountain folding is that even if we grant it for the Tertiary mountain chains we are left with the necessity of accounting for the formation of the many far older ones. Though the theory is a brilliant *tour-de-force,* its support does not seem substantial. It has nevertheless focused attention on one of the most difficult problems of geology: if the continents are indeed light masses floating on a dense substratum, how it is possible for an area that was once continental later to become part of the ocean floor? And the glacial record of Australia, the Falkland Islands, and Argentina seems clearly to show that some land areas have indeed subsided to oceanic depths.

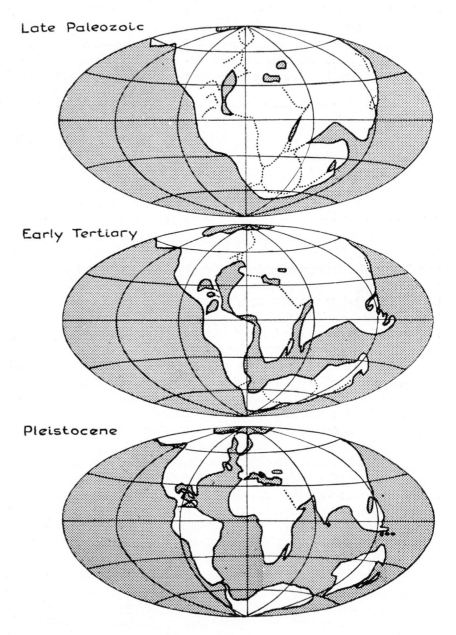

Figure 20-19.

Wegener's conception of the drifting of continents. (After A. Wegener, 1912.)

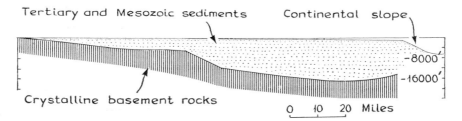

Figure 20-20.

The structure of the Atlantic Coastal shelf off Cape May, N. J. (Modified from W. M. Ewing, 1950.)

EVIDENCE FOR DEEP SUBMERGENCE OF CONTINENTAL MARGINS. Facies changes of many ancient formations have suggested that some land areas have been drowned to considerable depths, and the recent work of Maurice Ewing, an American geophysicist, has demonstrated almost conclusively that the Atlantic coastal shelf of the United States was once part of the continent itself. Using instruments that record seismic waves set up in the rocks by artificial explosions, Ewing was able to trace several strata with distinctive elastic properties from their exposures on land (and in deep wells) far out to sea—in fact, to the edge of the continental shelf (Fig. 20-20). In this way he determined that the rocks which lie unconformably upon the folded Appalachians form a huge embankment, in places more than three miles thick. The basement of this embankment has the same elastic properties as the metamorphosed rocks exposed in the Appalachian Piedmont; thus it is practically certain that the unconformity separating this from the younger rocks has been identified for about a hundred miles offshore. In other words, an eroded land surface beneath the Mesozoic sediments, which we find at many places in the Piedmont, has been traced almost to the edge of the continental shelf, where it is more than two miles below the sea.

Figure 20-20 is interesting for two reasons: first, in the present context, it shows that former continental areas may become submerged to the depth of the ocean floor near the continental border; second, it suggests the probability that the material of the continental shelf, above the crystalline floor, is in part a sedimentary deposit of Mesozoic and Tertiary rocks. The continental shelf is thus essentially a depositional surface, even though there is no doubt that marine erosion has modified and planed it. Although, in the light of the earth's general isostatic condition, features such as these pose difficult problems, they give strong reason to doubt that continental drift is necessary to explain the present wide separation of terrestrial plant and animal fossils, which was once thought to have required former land connections such as those assumed for Gondwana Land. Some of the extensions of the fragments of the postulated Gondwana Land may have somehow become submerged rather than having drifted laterally.

Another recent theory reconciles some of the apparently conflicting facts we have been seeking to explain. This is the theory that mountains are built by convection currents within the body of the earth.

The Convection Theory

Any fluid heated from below tends to lose heat in two ways: by conduction and convection. In large masses, conduction is ineffectively slow because the amount of heat transferred in a given time decreases as the square of the thickness of the mass through which it must be transmitted. The effectiveness of convection depends on the rate of convective overturn within a liquid (Fig. 20-21). Convection is most effective if the liquid is very fluid (has low viscosity) and also if it is of low conductivity and large volume. Low conductivity and large volume insure considerable density dif-

Figure 20-21. A familiar example of convection.

which the lighter crust is floating. The viscosity of the outer mantle, computed from the rate of uplift of the Scandinavian area in response to the unloading of glacial ice, is very high, but, since the temperature increases downward, it is possible that the viscosity is less near the core, despite the tremendous pressure there. If, then, the deeper parts of the mantle contain even as small a proportion of radioactive material as meteorites, enough heat may be generated there by radioactive disintegration to make the mantle unstable. A slow convective overturn may start.

This theory has been analyzed by the Israeli physicist Pekeris in the idealized scheme shown in Figure 20-22, which, for convenience in computation, assumes two polar continents and an equatorial ocean. Pekeris found that convective currents moving more than one inch a year may be present beneath such idealized continents, and that their drag on a rigid crust would be strong enough to crush crustal rocks even if they were three times as strong as tests indicate. Other theoretical work

Figure 20-22. A scheme of convection currents in an idealized earth with polar continents and an equatorial ocean. The rate of movement, in centimeters per year, is indicated by the length of the straight arrows, whose scale is shown at the lower right. (After C. L. Pekeris, redrawn from D. T. Griggs, 1939.)

ferences from bottom to top in the fluid mass because of thermal expansion of the lower portion. A low viscosity favors overturn, allowing the heat to be dissipated to the surface.

It may seem absurd to think of the mantle of the earth as a liquid capable of convective overturn, for the speed of transverse seismic waves shows that it behaves like a rigid solid as far down as the core boundary, 2,900 kilometers deep. Nevertheless, we know from the folded structures of sedimentary rocks in mountain ranges and from the contortion of many metamorphic rocks, that both, though not molten, have been plastic and have flowed. And isostasy shows that over broad regions the mantle acts much like a dense liquid on

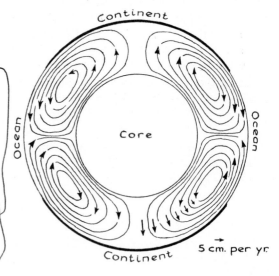

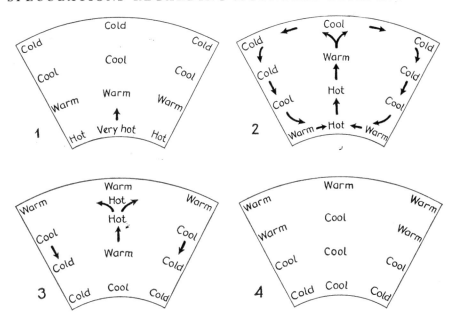

Figure 20-23.

Cross section through the mantle, illustrating four phases of Grigg's convection theory. (After D. T. Griggs, 1939.)

on the problem, assuming different convective depths, yield comparable results. These computations are all based on a constant rate of convective overturn, such as would take place in liquids with no shear strength but with high viscosities.

The American geophysicist Griggs, however, has pointed out that the mantle is not a true liquid but has some shear strength, even though this is small at the high temperatures existing deep within the earth. He assumed, therefore, that in any particular convection cell the rate of overturn is not constant, but that a certain threshold strength must be overcome before convection can begin. Furthermore, when the driving force drops below a certain amount, convection will cease rather abruptly, because the rock strength must always be exceeded if motion is to take place. Thereby he derived a cyclic scheme in which convection starts slowly, speeds up to a maximum, and then slows down and stops, until the material has again been heated by conduction from the core and by radioactive disintegration of material within itself (Fig.

20-23). If we accept certain assumptions that he thinks reasonable, the several phases would be about as follows:

First phase: Slowly accelerating currents
  (25 million years)
Second phase: Rapid currents
  (5 to 10 million years)
Third phase: Decelerating currents
  (25 million years)
Fourth phase: Quiescence
  (500 million years)

Because it seems likely that during the long quiescent period of any particular convection cell some other cell will become active it is impossible to put a definite time limit on the crustal drag exerted by currents at a given place.

Both Griggs and Kuenen of Holland have constructed models carefully scaled down in strength as well as size, so that they simulate earth conditions. These models suggest that, if convection does take place in the mantle, it could cause all the features found in the surface rocks—folding and shortening, overthrusting, and the crowding together of roots of light crustal material as they are dragged downward into the substratum (Fig. 20-24). In Griggs' model the subcrustal currents are produced by slowly rotating drums. The subcrustal material is simulated by glycerine, and the crust by cylinder oil mixed with fine saw-

dust. (Physical analysis (Chapter 10) indicates that these substances have about the right properties to act, in the model, as the rocks do in the natural situation.)

Properly to evaluate these experiments and the theoretical basis on which they rest demands more background in physics and

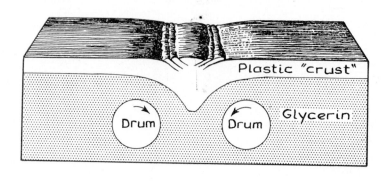

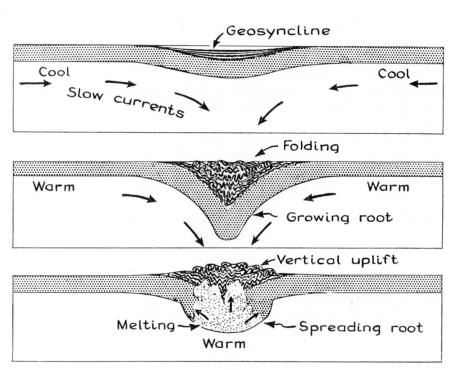

Figure 20-24.

Grigg's hypothesis of mountain development. Top: *Model showing how convective currents can drag a plastic crust together and form a "root" in the subcrustal layer.* Bottom: *Cross sections suggesting conditions during three stages of mountain building, according to the convection theory. (Modified from D. T. Griggs, 1939.)*

mathematics than can be given in this book. Nevertheless, we can see that a surprisingly large number of the phenomena connected with mountains are coordinated by this hypothesis.

Perhaps the weakest aspect of the convection theory is its explanation of the formation of the geosyncline: the period assigned to slowly accelerating currents whose downward drag develops the crustal sag that will later be filled with sediments is much too short for most geosynclines, which have been filled only in the course of many geologic periods. But further study and experimentation may overcome this weakness, and in the meantime the overthrusting and intense deformation of the passive sedimentary cover, the dragging down of the crust to form "negative belts," and the uplift of mountains after the convection current stops are all nicely accounted for. When the current stops, the mountain root is no longer held down and will rise isostatically: furthermore, when the root is dragged down it enters a region of higher temperature where the highly sheared and deformed crustal rocks of which it is composed recrystallize to metamorphic rocks and are injected with magmas. The magma may be produced simply by the heat at these deeper levels, or by liquefaction of deeply buried and hot crustal material that is already near the melting point and ready to "flash" into liquid in zones of fracture, where the pressure suddenly falls. Some of the root may melt only partly, and form migmatites, while some may melt completely and flow upward to congeal at higher levels in the mountain structure as granitic batholiths. It is reasonable to believe, moreover, that a softened and partly melted root may flow laterally as well as upward, thereby accounting for the common widespread vertical uplift that affects

the areas of unfolded rocks alongside a folded belt.

On such a hypothesis, the belts of negative anomaly in the East Indies and comparable belts in the West Indies and along some of the island arcs of the Pacific, such as the Marianas and the Japanese arc, would be interpreted as due to the dragging down of the crust by existing currents in the mantle. The fact that deep-focus earthquakes seem definitely aligned in planes that dip away from the ocean deeps supports the idea that such currents are actually dragging the oceanic crust landward and forcing it beneath the land masses alongside. The fault plane marked by the earthquake foci (Fig. 19-14) may be thought of as a shear zone dipping down between the passive crust and the descending convection currents.

It is obviously premature to accept the convection theory, at least in its present form, as a satisfactory explanation of all the complexities of mountain-making. Until we have further knowledge of conditions deep within the earth—and such knowledge is necessarily indirect and hard to evaluate—we cannot even be sure that the necessary driving force exists. The dearth of conclusive evidence for the other suggested theories constitutes no support for this one. Yet it is possible, since so many phenomena fit naturally into this scheme, that it holds the seeds of an ultimately satisfactory explanation of the fascinating enigma that confronts us; an earth at least two billion years old that, beneath its passive crust, is still endowed with energy literally to move mountains! Indeed, should evidence for continental drift ever become compelling, it may be that subcrustal convection currents will prove to be the driving mechanism that brings about the displacements.

FACTS, CONCEPTS, TERMS

MOUNTAINS; PLATEAUS

FOLD MOUNTAINS; FAULT-BLOCK MOUNTAINS; VOLCANIC MOUNTAINS

GEOSYNCLINE; FORELAND; HINTERLAND

MOUNTAIN STRUCTURES: FOLDS, ASYMMETRIC FOLDS, THRUST FAULTS

CRUSTAL SHORTENING; STRUCTURAL UNGLUING

KLIPPES; NAPPES; MASSIFS

USE OF FOLD PLUNGE IN DECIPHERING STRUCTURAL HISTORY AND GEOMETRY AT DEPTH

USE OF SEDIMENTARY FACIES IN DECIPHERING STRUCTURAL HISTORY

THICKENING OF SIAL BENEATH MOUNTAINS
    Evidence from gravity; from heat flow

Mountain roots

SUBSTRUCTURE OF FOLD-MOUNTAIN BELTS
    Metamorphism; migmatites; plutonic activity

UPWARPED MOUNTAINS: RENEWED UPLIFT LONG SUBSEQUENT TO FOLDING

BASIN RANGES: FAULT-BLOCK MOUNTAINS

DATING OF MOUNTAIN FOLDING; OF RENEWED MOUNTAIN UPLIFT

THE SHIELDS

BELTS OF NEGATIVE ANOMALIES

THEORY OF A SHRINKING EARTH

THEORY OF CONTINENTAL DRIFT

THEORY OF CONVECTION CURRENTS

QUESTIONS

1. In both the East and West Indies, volcanoes are arranged on an inner arc parallel to the arc of the ocean deeps and associated negative anomalies. The surface on which the deep-focus earthquakes occur slopes downward toward this inner arc (Fig. 19-14). What does this suggest as to the source of the magmas?

2. Many of the highest ridges of the Appalachians are synclinal in structure. In the light of Chapters 8, 9, and 12 can you offer a suggestion for the reasons?

3. What inferences can you make regarding the forces causing crustal deformation from such features as the San Andreas rift (Chap. 19)?

4. Many of the buildings of western England are roofed with slate, whereas those near London are chiefly tiled. Can you draw from this any inferences as to the regional geology of England?

5. Many deep wells drilled in the search for oil have shown the existence of a long, rather narrow mass of granite beneath the Carboniferous strata of eastern Kansas and southeastern Nebraska. What features of the rocks brought up by the drill would enable you to decide whether this mass is unconformably buried by the sedimentary rocks or whether it invaded the sediments after they were deposited?

6. The Triassic rocks of the Atlantic slope of North America are commonly thought to have been formed under both topographic and climatic conditions that were closely similar to those of the present Great Basin. What features would you expect them to have from which such an origin was inferred?

7. In western Nevada a fossil-rich Permian limestone lies nearly horizontally across upturned slates beneath. A few fossils identifiable as Ordovician in age have been found in the slate. What history is recorded by these relationships?

8. What features would enable you to distinguish a sill of granitic rock (whose lower contact only is exposed) from a block of granite thrust over flat-lying sedimentary rocks?

9. How would you distinguish a klippe (an erosional remnant of a thrust sheet) from the erosional remnant of a resistant bed in an undeformed sedimentary series? Assume in both cases that the remnant is of Carboniferous rocks resting upon flat-lying Devonian.

SUGGESTED READINGS

Bailey, E. B. *Tectonic Essays: Mainly Alpine.* Oxford, Clarendon Press, 1935.

Daly, R. A. *Architecture of the Earth.* New York, Appleton-Century, 1938.

Jeffreys, Harold. *Earthquakes and Mountains.* London, Methuen and Co., 1935.

Umbgrove, J. H. F. *The Pulse of the Earth.* The Hague, Martinus Nijhoff, 1947. (Especially Chapter 2, pp. 26-39.)

MINERAL RESOURCES

The Industrial Revolution

OUR WORLD differs more from that of the Founding Fathers than theirs did from the world of Alexander the Great. In 1800, nearly four-fifths of all persons in Great Britain and Italy lived on farms, as did more than nine-tenths of those in the rest of Europe. Land transport was by wagons on roads hardly better than those Caesar used in Gaul; and Napoleon's crossing of the Alps was little less of a feat than Hannibal's, two thousand years before. Today a Zulu miner travels third-class to his labor compound in the Rand gold field in greater comfort than Louis XIV did in his state coach between Versailles and Paris. By our standards, the Zulu's lot is hard and his pay pitiably small; yet he is better clothed and fed than most of the people of George the Third's England. He is fortunate, indeed, when compared to a slave in the mines of Laurium, whose life expectancy beneath the Athenian lash was only four years, but whose labors produced the silver that sustained the Golden Age of Greece.

Most of us now reject the slave-holding philosophy of Plato and Pericles, but it is not primarily ethical principles that account for the differences between the ancient and modern worlds. Material goods are perhaps as unevenly distributed today as under most of the cultures of the past, but the standard of living of the Western World, at least, is higher.

The change began with two events of the eighteenth century. Neither attracted as much notice at the time as the intrigues of Bonnie Prince Charlie or the campaigns of Frederick the Great. But about 1730 a Shropshire Quaker, Abraham Darby, discovered how to use coke for smelting iron; and in 1768 James Watt invented the steam engine. These men made possible cheap iron, steel, mechanized power—and the industrial age. Without machinery, population would long since have outstripped food supply the world over, as Malthus predicted in 1798, and as indeed it has in China and India, where the Industrial Revolution has only feeble roots.

Now, as always, agriculture is the basic industry. But a wholly agricultural economy imposes sharp limits on division of labor and the increased productivity that this allows. As transport improved, first with iron rails and then locomotives and steam-driven ships, a specialization formerly unknown made possible tremendous savings in labor. By 1830 a twelve-year-old girl operating a machine loom in a Lancashire mill could turn out 35 yards of calico daily—in a year, enough to clothe about 1,200 persons.

This little girl's existence was doubtless as dismal as any Norman serf's, and even today the "better life for all' is an ideal that is still far from realization. Yet this very ideal would be pathetically ludicrous if there had been no Industrial Revolution. Even now the food supply of much of the world is less than that required for subsistence; it would be pitifully smaller if we were to revert to the economy of 1800.

These facts are commonplace and generally accepted. But what is not so widely understood is that all these changes in living standards ultimately depend upon the world's diminishing and nonreplenishable assets—its mineral resources.

The Mineral Basis of Civilization

Throughout history mineral resources have played a greater role than is usually recognized. Today this role is second only to that of agriculture. The relationship between mineral wealth and national power even in ancient times, can be clearly traced, though most historians ignore it. The Greeks who turned back the Persian hosts at Marathon were armed with bronze swords and shields, while many of the enemy had only leathern shields and stone weapons; the Greek fleet at Salamis was built by the Athenian profits from the silver and lead mines of Laurium, discovered only a few years earlier. These profits also paid the mercenaries who fought Athens' battles in the Peloponnesian Wars, and with the exhaustion of the mines came the end of Athens as a military power. Philip burst from the wild Macedonian Mountains, and his son, Alexander the Great, swept over the world, financed by the flush production of gold—roughly a billion dollars in modern equivalent—from the new mines on Mount Pangaeus. When Scipio drove the Carthaginians from Spain and won for Rome the gold, iron, copper, silver, and mercury of that peninsula, he sealed the fate of Carthage.

These are but a few examples from pre-industrial days. Today, mineral resources and national power and well-being are even more closely linked. Gold and silver could hire mercenaries and influence military campaigns, but useful goods could not be created from them; they merely gave control of the few goods then available to one group rather than another. They still possess this conventional value, but living standards and national power depend only incidentally on them. The greater part of the useful goods of the world depend on the mineral fuels and the industrial metals—iron, copper, aluminum, lead, and others. It was no accident that Britain was able to maintain the *Pax Britannica* through the nineteenth century; her industrial and military supremacy came from the happy fortune that her "tight little island" held a greater known mineral wealth per acre than any similar area in the world, together with a population intelligent and aggressive enough to exploit it.

At one time or another in the nineteenth century, Great Britain was the world's largest producer of iron, coal, lead, copper, and tin. From these came her machines, her mills, and the great cities founded on them. Before 1875 she had built more miles of railroad than any of the much larger Continental countries. Her flourishing internal markets and manufactured products, carried to all the world by the British merchant marine, brought her the greatest wealth any country in history had ever enjoyed. True, the cheap foodstuffs she received in return eventually ruined the island's agricultural economy, but her favorable trade balance enabled British capital to control Malayan tin, Spanish iron, and many of the mines and oil fields of Mexico, Chile, Iran, Australia, Burma, and the United States. These holdings saw her through one world war and maintained her credit through a second. When her flag followed her mining investments into South Africa and the Boers were defeated, she gained control of more than half the world's production of new gold, and ultimately of great deposits of copper, chromite, diamonds, asbestos, and manganese.

Nowhere better than in the United States can be seen the close dependence of living standards and national power upon minerals.

Before 1840, manufacturing was inconsequential and only heavy subsidies and tariffs made it possible to compete with the advanced British industries. The small, scattered iron deposits along the eastern seaboard did, it is true, supply enough of the local demand to influence the British Parliament in 1750 to forbid their further exploitation; after independence there was slow growth, but as late as 1850 iron production was only about half a million tons annually. In 1855 the "Soo Canal" brought the rich Lake Superior iron deposits within economic reach of Pennsylvania coal; by 1860 iron production had trebled; by 1880 it had passed that of Great Britain.

It was the greater productivity of Northern industry, and the weight of armament, supplies, and equipment flowing over its superior railway net that were decisive in the Civil War. The Tredegar iron works at Richmond was the only one worth mentioning in the Confederacy, and it could not compete alone with the overwhelming output of the Pennsylvania furnaces.

Our huge internal market, our prodigious endowment in all the minerals basic to manufacturing and our favorable agricultural heritage have all contributed to make our country the most powerful in the world at present. During the Battle of the Bulge in World War II, our troops hurled more metal at the Germans than was available in all the world in Napoleon's time. Cannon and tanks, as well as plowshares and tractors, are made of metals, and all are transported by mineral fuels.

Salient Features of Mineral Resources

That mineral resources are concentrated in relatively small areas, and that they are exhaustible and irreplaceable, are facts—facts of great social and political implication that are often overlooked by those not familiar with the mineral industry. Their effect on society is so profound that no student of geology should fail to be aware of them and of the geological factors that determine them.

Sporadic Distribution

As we shall see in more detail later in this chapter, mineral deposits of all kinds are essentially "freaks of nature." An abnormal pituitary may make a man a giant, although his physiological processes are otherwise normal. Similarly, mineral deposits result from normal geological processes, but under exceptional conditions. Only a few geological environments favor the formation of mineral deposits.

These favored spots are by no means evenly distributed over the earth. Nearly nine-tenths of the world's nickel comes from less than a score of mines in the Sudbury district of Ontario. A single mine at Climax, Colorado, produces about as large a share of the world's molybdenum from an area of far less than one square mile. Nearly 30 per cent of the copper produced in the United States since 1880 has come from an area of less than four square miles at Butte, Montana. The Rand gold field of South Africa, which is much larger than most gold districts, produces half the new gold of the world from an area about 50 miles long and 20 wide.

Though the mineral fuels are far less localized, they underlie only a trivial part of the continents. Less than 25 per cent of Pennsylvania, a leading coal state, is underlain by coal. The East Texas oil field, the greatest thus far found in the United States, covers an area about 10 by 40 miles—a mere dot on the vast expanse of Texas—yet for several years it yielded about a quarter of the nation's oil. The most extensive oil field in the world is the El Nala anticline in Saudi Arabia. It is almost continuously productive for a length of 105 miles, but is only a few miles wide.

The economic implications of this unequal distribution of the mineral fuels are great. Modern chemistry may be able to make a rayon purse (perhaps even better than a silk one) out of a sow's ear, but only with the expenditure of energy. Today this means mineral fuels, or, less importantly, water power. The dreams of many countries of emulating the industrial development of the United States are foredoomed to failure because they lack adequate sources of cheap fuel. It is this fact that explains the tremendous interest of all nations in the prospect of the development of cheap atomic power. If such power could be obtained safely, the backward economies of many nations might come abreast of that of the United States. Some countries, such as the Scandinavian, have higher educational standards, or, like Argentina, a higher agricultural output per capita, than we. But none is now so fortunate as the United States in the combination of high average education (and hence a skilled population), great agricultural productivity, and a nearly balanced supply of mineral resources. These give us the greatest industrial development of any free-trade area in the world.

Exhaustibility

All mineral deposits are limited in extent; they represent unusual associations of geologic factors that have permitted their concentration. Once the valuable materials are extracted by mining, all that is left are holes in the ground. This is the fate of all mines, even of the greatest.

It is true that the mines of Almaden, Spain, have yielded mercury since the days of the Carthaginians and still hold the richest known reserves of this metal. But these deposits are almost unique. The mines of Cornwall—the "Cassiterides," or Tin Islands—supplied tin to the Phoenicians and provided varying amounts of this metal throughout the years until less than a generation ago: in the nineteenth century they led the world in production. But now the mines are worked out, and the Cornish miners have had to disperse throughout the world and spread their traditional mining lore far from Britain. The world's greatest single oil well, the Cerro Azul No. 4, in the Tampico Field, Mexico, yielded nearly sixty million barrels of petroleum in a few years, then suddenly gave forth only salt water. Neither the old Cornish tin mines nor the Cerro Azul will ever yield a new crop.

The still fertile Valley of the Nile has been the granary of the Mediterranean through most of recorded history, and huge areas in China and India have been farmed nearly or quite as long. The forests of Norway that built the Viking ships still produce lumber. But the mines of Freiberg, where Werner's Mining Academy flourished, and where even now a mining school survives, have long been abandoned. Belgium and Wales, with their cheap coal and metallurgical traditions, are still centers of smelting, but nearly all the metal mines on which their industries were founded have been exhausted for generations. Potosi, which supplied tons of silver to the viceroyalty of Peru, the fabulous Comstock Lode of Nevada, and the copper deposits of Michigan are not quite dead, but they are pale shadows of their former greatness. *There is no second crop of minerals!* And, lest the meaning of this statement—economically, politically, and socially—be overlooked, let it be noted: More metal has been mined since 1920 than in all preceding history.

It seems inevitable that a generation hence the world supply of readily available minerals will be so depleted that what remains can be won only by a greatly increased expenditure of energy. We are now in the period of the greatest exploitation of mineral resources in the long sweep of history. That we will be able to maintain our present standard of living is by no means a foregone conclusion; unless tremendous technological improvements can be made, the inevitable increase in the amount of energy required to win a pound of iron, a gallon of oil, or a ton of coal must be reflected in a lower standard of living. Such is the inevitable result of the localization of mineral resources in the earth's crust. Only technological improvements of a revolutionary nature (such as indeed may be developing now in the use of nuclear fuels) can postpone such a development for more than a very few decades.

What the exhaustibility of mineral resources means socially can be seen in the long roll of our own Western "ghost towns," in which a few families now live where thousands lived before. More dramatically, it is seen in the "distressed" coal-mining towns of England, where, although the mines are not, strictly speaking, exhausted, the increased cost of deeper mining, of pumping ground water from greater depths, and of longer hauls from coal face to portal, have weakened the competitive position of the mines in world trade. Unemployment, wage cuts, and lower living standards have followed. Only drastic technologic changes can keep costs down.

Although geological conditions make it inevitable that mineral procurement must in the future be more expensive *in terms of energy,* it does not necessarily follow that all industrial costs need rise. Many times in the past, technical improvements have made it feasible to rework a deposit that had been thoroughly exploited by an outmoded method. Alaskan gold dredges now operate at a profit on placer deposits that contain only a few cents' worth of gold per cubic yard—deposits that to the sourdough working with his sluice box were "exhausted." Similarly, most of the world's copper is taken today from deposits that were impossible to exploit by methods in use sixty years ago. But there are limits to the development of low-grade deposits, and it is important to realize that these technological limitations, as well as the sporadic distribution and exhaustibility of mineral resources, place upon the mineral industries restrictions that differ *in kind* from those affecting most other economic activities.

Cycles of Mineral Production

The mineral industry, like others, constantly fluctuates, but follows discernible long-term trends. Newly discovered deposits and new technologies may increase prosperity for a while, but eventually the higher costs of deep mining and exhaustion of the deposits bring harder times. An American economic geologist, D. F. Hewett, has analyzed the history of the mineral industry in many countries, and has found a surprisingly consistent sequence of stages. Briefly put, these are as follows:

1. *Period of mine development:* Exploration, new discoveries; boom towns; many small mines and a few large deposits recognized; rapid increase in output.

2. *Period of smelter development:* Few new deposits found; small mines being worked out; greater output from the larger mines; many smelters competing for ore.

3. *Period of industrial development:* Lower costs, higher living standards; rapid increase in internal and external markets and wealth; approaching height of commercial power.

4. *Period of rapid depletion of cheap domestic raw materials:* Higher costs of mining and of recovered metals; more power required; bitter commercial rivalry for sources of raw materials; trade balance unfavorable, with gradual loss of home trade to foreign competitors.

5. *Period of decreasing domestic and foreign trade:* Higher costs of manufacture because of necessity of using foreign raw materials; lower living standards and declining commercial power; stiff competition for cheap foreign materials, often leading to international friction and wars.

Hewett did not maintain, of course, that there have been no deviations from this pattern nor that all phases are inevitable, but the sequence has been well enough followed in the past to merit serious attention. Broadly speaking, stage 1 is represented at present by Rhodesia; stage 2 by Canada; early stage 3 by the USSR; late stage 3 and early stage 4 by the United States (note our heavy investments in petroleum in the Caribbean and Near East; in copper in Chile and Rhodesia; in iron in Brazil, Venezuela, and Cuba); stage 4 by Germany; and stage 5 by Great Britain, which passed through the first four stages during the eighteenth and nineteenth centuries. The stages in mine development alone (stages 1 and 4) without corollary industrial development, may be recognized even in countries like Bolivia or Malaya, where lack of fuel or other sources of power prevents any significant manufacturing activity.

The Economic Importance of Mineral Resources

Although mineral resources account directly for less than 2 per cent of the total national product in the United States, they play a crucial role in industry, for all heavy manufacturing depends on them. Our industrial might depends upon them absolutely. More than two-thirds—in some years nearly three-fourths—of the value of mineral production of the United States is supplied by the energy sources; the **mineral fuels**—petroleum, gas, and coal. We are doubtless witnessing the technologic evolution of still other mineral fuels, the so-called nuclear fuels based on the radioactive elements uranium and thorium and the artificial elements made from them. Mineral resources other than fuels include the **metalliferous deposits,** the source of our metals; and the **nonmetallic deposits,** such as building stone, cement rock, clay, sand, and gravel. From 1940 to 1954 the total annual value of mineral products in the United States has ranged between 6 and 14½ billion dollars.

The Mineral Fuels

The mineral fuels are the most important mineral resources. They are essential for heat and power and for metal refining, and are also the source of many useful chemicals and of nitrogen fertilizers. They are especially important to the geological profession, for the search for oil is the principal work of more than half of all geologists.

The Industrial Revolution was based on coal, and coal is still the basic fuel, though petroleum is displacing it in the field of transport, and natural gas is making huge inroads in power plants and in metallurgy. One of the most striking recent shifts in industry is the great increase in the use of natural gas. Since

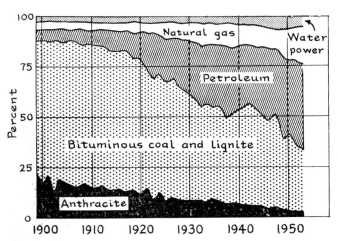

Figure 21-1. Percentages of total energy from fuels used in the United States. (After U. S. Bureau of Mines, Mineral Yearbooks.)

1940 its contribution to the national power output of the United States has practically doubled. Nevertheless, coal still supplies the world with more energy than oil and gas combined, despite the rapid increase in petroleum production and technology. In the United States, however, only about a third of the energy is still supplied by coal (Fig. 21-1); oil supplies about 40 per cent, and most of the rest comes from natural gas—water power is by far the smallest source.

World production of coal in 1953 was 1½ billion tons, mostly in Europe and the United States, with a value at the mines of about 7½ billion dollars. World production of petroleum in 1953 was 4¾ billion barrels (about 830 million tons), most coming from the United States, Venezuela, Russia, and the region of the Persian Gulf. Its value at United States prices was more than 12 billion dollars (Fig. 21-2), nearly three times that of coal, although its tonnage was little more than half as great. Oil and gas bring much higher prices per heat unit than coal because of their greater convenience, absence of ash, and ready transportation by pipeline and tanker.

COAL.   Coal is a brownish-black to black combustible rock (see Chapter 3). It forms

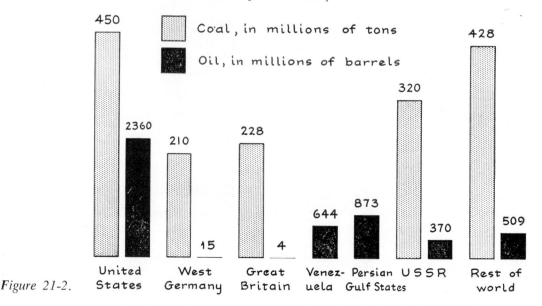

Figure 21-2.

World coal and oil production during 1953. (Data from U. S. Bureau of Mines and Bituminous Coal Institute.)

beds that range from a fraction of an inch to many feet in thickness, interstratified with shale, sandstone, and other sedimentary rocks (Fig. 21-3). A single sequence of strata may include several coal beds: in West Virginia 117 different beds have been named. They are distributed through several thousand feet of strata, which, taken together, are called the **coal measures.** Coal-bearing strata include many alternations of marine and nonmarine beds. The coal beds are in the nonmarine parts of the section and contain evidence that they themselves are of nonmarine origin. They are composed chiefly of flattened, compressed, and more-or-less altered remains of land-dwelling plants: wood, bark, roots (some in place), leaves, spores, and seeds.

Coal Rank.—Coals appear to have been formed chiefly from plant residues that accumulated in swamps. There is a continuous series from brown peat, obviously made up of slightly modified plant residues, to a hard, black, glistening type of coal that contains no recognizable plant remains. The principal members of this series are **peat, lignite, subbituminous coal, bituminous coal,** and **anthra-**

Coal beds on Lignite Creek, Yukon region, Alaska. (Photo by C. A. Hickcox, U. S. Geological Survey.)

Figure 21-3.

KIND OF COAL	PHYSICAL APPEARANCE	CHARACTERISTICS
Lignite	Brown to brownish black	Poorly to moderately consolidated; weathers rapidly; plant residues apparent.
Subbituminous coal	Black; dull or waxy luster	Weathers easily; plant residues faintly shown.
Bituminous coal	Black; dense; brittle	Does not weather easily; plant structures visible with microscope; burns with short blue flame.
Anthracite coal	Black; hard; usually with glassy luster	Very hard and brittle; burns with almost no smoke.

TABLE 21-1

Distinctive Features of Coal of Various Ranks.

cite coal. The more obvious features of all except peat, which is not considered a coal, are shown in Table 21-1.

When coal is heated in the absence of air, it gives off water vapor and hydrocarbon gases. These are called the volatile matter. The woody and other plant components in peat are complex compounds of carbon, oxygen, and hydrogen. In the air they oxidize and rot away, yielding chiefly carbon dioxide and water, but if air is excluded by geologic burial, they slowly alter into many solid products, as well as some gases. Among the solid products is finely divided black elemental carbon, a substance whose presence distinguishes coal from peat. The higher the proportion of elemental ("fixed") carbon and the lower that of volatile matter, the higher the rank of the coal in the series from peat to anthracite. Clay and sand that were washed into the swamp where the coal accumulated are left as ash when the coal is burned. This lessens the heating value and increases waste, and thus detracts from coal value.

Most bituminous and anthracite coals are of Carboniferous age. Such coals are abundant in Europe and eastern North America. Most high-rank coal in Europe lies in a belt extending from Britain across Belgium, Luxembourg, and Germany into southern Russia. This is the industrial heart of Europe.

Coal Reserves.—Coal is so abundant (Fig. 21-4) that generally only the thicker, more accessible, and higher-rank deposits are now

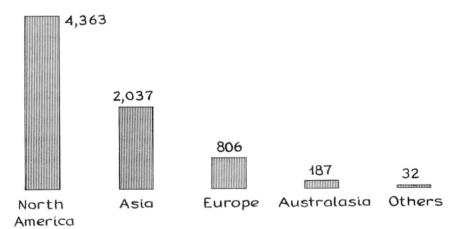

Figure 21-4.

The coal reserves of the world, in billions of tons. (Data from Bituminous Coal Institute, 1948.)

being mined. An estimate of coal reserves thus means little unless limits of thickness, depth, and quality (including both rank and percentage of ash) are stated in the estimate. Officials in different countries rarely use the same limits, so that estimates for different areas are rarely comparable. The older estimates for the United States and Canada included beds as thin as 14 inches, but coal cannot be mined profitably from beds this thin either by the mechanical methods now used for more than 90 per cent of United States' underground production, or by surface stripping, which in 1953 yielded more than a fifth of the country's coal. Accordingly, the older estimates are not economically significant. The U. S. Geological Survey is now (1959) completing an evaluation, which has been under way for more than a decade, that should give a realistic estimate of the nation's coal reserves. Such an appraisal involves much more than statistics. Especially in the western United States, low- and medium-rank reserves are large (Fig. 21-5), but there has been relatively little mining because of the distance to markets. In making the estimates much

field work is necessary to determine the amount of coal in the ground in such areas. Outcrops are traced and recorded on maps, thicknesses are measured, drill cores studied, folds and faults mapped out, and the overburden calculated (see Chapter 9). The coal tonnage in beds of various thicknesses and to various depths must then be calculated. Preliminary estimates indicate that the United States reserves are nearly 2 trillion tons (Fig. 21-6).

Using the old figures from a survey made in 1922 as the best currently available for North America, and a set of German estimates (1938) as best for the rest of the world, the total coal reserves of the world, including all ages and all ranks, reach the enormous total of more than 7 trillion tons. Of this, North America contains 58.8 per cent (Fig. 21-4). Coal fields cover about one-ninth of the United States (Fig. 21-5). The distribution of the chief ranks of coal by states is shown in Figure 21-6. Though Wyoming and North Dakota lead in tonnage, the former has little high-rank coal and the latter none. In 1953, by far the greatest output was of bi-

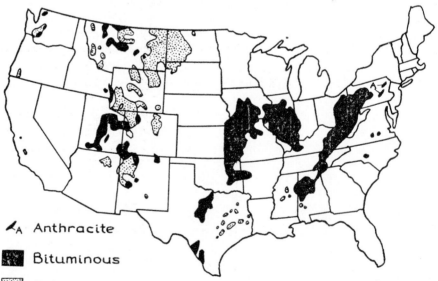

Figure 21-5.

⟋_A Anthracite

▓ Bituminous

░ Sub-bituminous and lignite

The coal fields of the United States. (After Bituminous Coal Institute, 1948.)

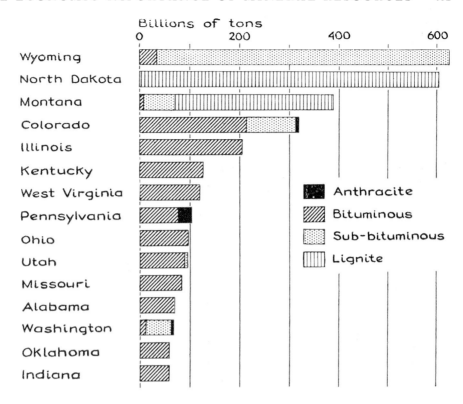

Figure 21-6.

The original coal resources of the United States. Other states than those shown had a total of about 200 million tons. (After Bituminous Coal Institute, 1948.)

tuminous and anthracite coal, from West Virginia, Pennsylvania, Kentucky, Illinois, and Ohio, in that order.

OIL AND GAS.   Earth oil (petroleum) and natural gas are found in similar environments and usually together. Commercial accumulations exist only in special geologic conditions and are almost entirely limited to sedimentary rocks. Producing areas are generally called "pools," although the oil and gas generally fill pore spaces in rocks, like ground water, rather than open caverns.

There seem to be four requisites for the formation of a commercial oil pool: (1) a source rock, (2) a permeable reservoir rock which will yield the oil rapidly enough to make drilling worthwhile, (3) an impermeable cap rock, and (4) a favorable structure, which allows the cap rock to retain the oil below ground. We will defer the discussion of

the source rock until we have dealt briefly with each of the other requisites.

The essential feature of a **reservoir rock** is the presence of connected pores or cavities through which a liquid can move. Permeability (Chapter 14) is thus its prime characteristic, though the percentage of pore space, and hence the storage capacity of a given volume of the rock, is also obviously significant. Most reservoir rocks are sandstones, though some are limestones or dolomites, either granular, with interstitial pore spaces, or jointed and cavernous. Shattered brittle rocks like chert and basalt, and very rarely even granite and schist, are productive reservoir rocks in a few fields. Extremely fine-grained sandstones, from many of which it was formerly impossible to obtain oil in commercial quantities because their pore spaces, though abundant, were too fine for ready transmission of fluids, have in recent years been transformed into highly productive reservoirs: methods have been developed to shatter them underground by fluid pressure and to fill the newly formed crevices with coarse sand through which the oil can drain to the wells.

A **cap rock** must be practically impermeable to oil or gas. Most are shale, but nonporous limestone seals some reservoirs; others are sealed by the asphalt left near the surface where oil has escaped and evaporated—such spots are called oil **seeps,** or, in Spanish countries, **breas.** Drilling beneath them has frequently led to the development of commercial oil accumulations.

Oil and gas fill pores in rocks much more rarely than water, and their accumulation in commercial quantities requires **favorable structure.** Because water fills most spaces below the water table, and because oil is lighter than water and hence floats on it, the favorable structures are generally high in the reservoir rock, directly beneath a cap rock seal. Since gas is lighter than oil it ordinarily rises to the top, although, when it is greatly compressed, much dissolves in the oil and is released only when the pressure is decreased. Some favorable structures are diagrammed in Figure 21-7.

Most oil fields extend along the crests of elongate anticlinal folds, which are often called domes (Fig. 21-7, A). The Salt Creek Dome, Wyoming; the Kettleman Hills North

Figure 21-7.   *Structures favorable to the commercial accumulation of oil and gas.* (A) *Anticlinal fold, with reservoir sand underlain by shale (possible source rock) and overlain by shale (cap rock). Note the reservoir sand capped by asphalt at the outcrop, making a second trap for oil.* (B) *Salt dome, with oil at crest and on flanks.* (C) *Trap in sandstone, formed where unconformity is overlain by shale.* (D) *Porous limestone reef reservoir, in impermeable limestone and shale.* (E) *Fractured schist reservoir, beneath domed shale.*

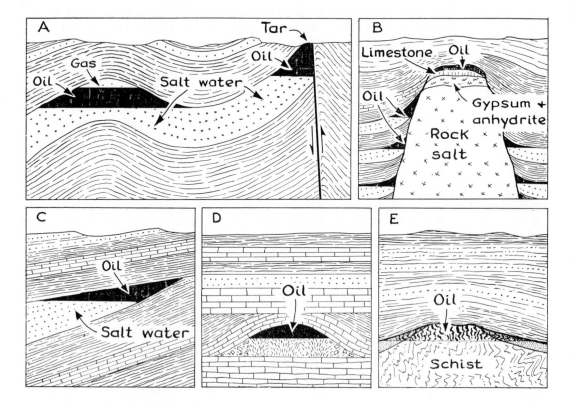

Dome, California; the tremendous anticline called En Nala in Saudi Arabia, apparently the longest continuous oil field in the world; and the prolific field of Bahrein Island in the Persian Gulf are typical. Less common are the "salt dome" fields, which lie above or beside plugs of massive salt that have been injected from beneath, tilting the strata (Fig. 21-7, B). There are many of these along the Gulf of Mexico in Texas and Louisiana; the famous Spindletop Field, one of the earliest, is representative. Similar accumulations have been found along the Caucasus and in the Carpathian foothills of Rumania. Finally, there are the stratigraphic traps (Fig. 21-7, C), with the reservoir capped, generally unconformably, by an overlying blanket of impermeable sediment. The greatest of all American oil fields, East Texas, is a stratigraphic trap on a gently dipping sandstone bed whose former outcrop is covered by younger strata. The great Leduc oil field of Alberta lies in the porous organic layers of a fossil coral reef, buried beneath impermeable strata (Fig. 21-7, D). The small but interesting Edison Field, California, has as its reservoir rock a fractured mass of schist, into which the oil must have seeped from sedimentary rocks that buried the old hill of schist (Fig. 21-7, E).

Some traps, like the immense Hugoton gas field of Kansas and Oklahoma, contain gas, but no oil.

Source Rocks of Petroleum.—The conclusions about reservoir rock, cap rock, and favorable structure are well-established geological generalizations inductively based on repeated observations. Oil is found in permeable rocks confined by nonpermeable, and in structural positions determined by hydraulic laws. But the sources of earth oil are matters of less certain inference. Some very important conclusions seem well established, but much more needs to be known.

Practically all geologists believe that petroleum originates exclusively in sediments. Nearly all oil pools are in sedimentary rocks. The rare exceptions, typified by the Edison Field just mentioned, could have received their oil by migration from adjoining oil-bearing sandstones. Most pools are separated from the nearest igneous or metamorphic rock by thousands of feet of barren sedimentary rocks which contain no traces of oil.

Many oil fields, too, are in or near thick accumulations of marine or deltaic sediments that include large accumulations, measured in cubic miles, of shales that generally contain several per cent—exceptionally as much as 80 per cent—of organic matter, chiefly compounds of carbon originating from the bodies of former plants or animals. These organic shales were probably derived from marine ooze, for similar compounds have been extracted from marine ooze on the present sea floor. The original synthesis of carbon dioxide and water to form the organic compounds must have been by plants, perhaps in large part by the very abundant diatoms. The organic compounds of carbon, hydrogen, and oxygen thus produced may then have been repeatedly worked over in the digestive tracts of many kinds of animals in the sea or on its floor, before final burial beneath accumulating ooze. The bodies of dead animals also contribute. Even after burial, the animal and plant residues in the ooze are further altered by bacteria, with partial elimination of oxygen. Some oozes probably accumulated in stagnant basins where the sea water did not contain enough oxygen to permit the transformation of the hydrogen-carbon residues into water and carbon dioxide again. Many geologists believe that most oil is thus formed, mainly because so many oil fields seem to be associated with strata whose character suggests such an environment. But the transformation of organic matter into liquid oil is hidden in mystery. In many places, it seems clear that this transformation must have occurred only after a cover of younger strata had accumulated, and that the pressure and rise of temperature resulting from burial were essential factors.

The tentative prehistory of petroleum just outlined is based on much geological and chemical research. Three additional generalizations seem justified, though not all are universally accepted. First, little free oil has been found in areas containing only fresh-water sedimentary rocks, despite the vast quantities of "oil shale" (which contains no free oil, but from which liquid oil can be distilled) in the Eocene lake beds of Utah, Colorado, and Wyoming. Second, oil and coal are not the liquid and solid products, respectively, of the alteration of peat, even though both oil and coal are found in the same sedimentary sequences (but at different levels) in the midcontinent region of the United States. Third, the oil-forming process seems to be very slow, as no oil has been found in modern sediments, though similar compounds have been extracted from them. The hope, expressed by some chemists, that earth oil may now be forming at approximately the present rate of consumption seems quite unjustified geologically.

Oil Map of the World.—Because of the economic importance of oil, a knowledge of petroleum geology is essential for the formulation of intelligent domestic and foreign poli-

cies. Where is oil now being produced? What reserves are still in the ground? Where may additional supplies be found in the future?

First, we may mark off on a map the areas where only igneous and metamorphic rocks crop out, calling these impossible or wholly unimportant because of the absence of marine organic sedimentary rocks. We can add to them, as unfavorable, the areas where only thin or nonmarine sedimentary rocks overlie the crystallines (Fig. 21-8). Then we may outline as favorable the areas where oil is being produced, and add those areas where thick marine strata have yielded evidences of oil, such as seeps. Finally, we may distinguish an intermediate, or possible, group of areas, which contain thick marine strata but no positive indications of petroleum.

Although such a map is valuable it leaves many questions unanswered. Which areas have produced the most oil? Which have the most left? Up to 1948 the United States had produced more than half of the world's oil, but by 1957 it was producing less than 47 per cent. And what about proved reserves? The

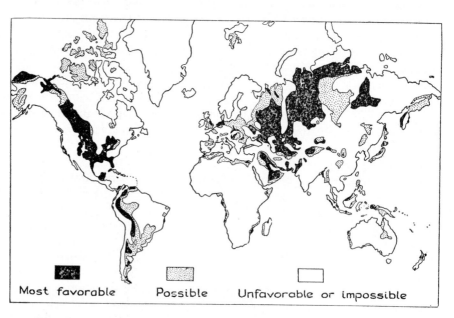

Figure 21-8.   Most favorable   Possible   Unfavorable or impossible

Oil map of the world based on the probability of finding oil in any one region. (After Arabian-American Oil Company, Middle East Oil Developments, 1948.)

United States still has much oil—proved reserves at the end of 1957 were at least 30 billion barrels and probable reserves were eight or ten times that figure. But the proved reserves of the Middle East—Iraq, Kuwait, Bahrein, and Saudi Arabia—were more than five times as great. Those of Venezuela and other nearby parts of South America were more than half as large, and it seems reasonable, in view of the later development of the oil industries in these areas, to assume that their ultimate reserves are far greater than those of North America. There seem clearly to be two great petroliferous provinces on the earth: the region around the Persian Gulf and the region around the border of the Caribbean —Venezuela, eastern Mexico, and the Gulf Coast of the United States. The fields of Iran, Arabia, and Kuwait are intrinsically so rich, and are being managed so much more efficiently than were those of the United States in the early days of wasteful competition, that their value is almost unimaginably great. Never in human history have there been such prizes of concentrated wealth. Even in 1957, early in their development, more than 3½ million barrels flowed daily from a few hundred wells. Compare this with America's hundreds of thousands of wells, with an average production of less than 10 barrels a day, and consider the vast wealth that has come from them. Clearly, a crucial spot in the history of the next generation will be the Middle East and its vast treasures of oil.

No inventory of potential oil provinces would be complete without mention of the continental shelves. These submerged extensions of the continents are repositories of huge volumes of sedimentary rocks, most of them undoubtedly marine. Though the technological difficulties of both exploration and exploitation of these underwater reserves are tremendous, there can be little doubt that they contain vast amounts of petroleum. Whether their exploitation is economically feasible, in the face of the high costs of offshore work and the probable competition from synthetic oil

derived from coal or oil shale, is an important problem now being tested.

OIL FINDING.   The first earth oil put to human use oozed from oil seeps. Noah's Ark, like the present native boats of the Near East, may have been calked with asphalt from a Mesopotamian seepage. The first successful oil well (in Pennsylvania, 1859), was drilled beside a seepage, and so were many later wells that discovered oil. Most of the wells beside seepages have been small producers, but Cerro Azul No. 4, the greatest single producer in history, was an exception. This well, near Tampico, Mexico, "blew in" on February 10, 1916, for 260,000 barrels a day, the column of oil rising 598 feet into the air. The well produced almost 60 million barrels of oil before suddenly yielding only salt water. It was drilled in limestone and apparently penetrated a real pool of oil and gas floating on salt water in interconnected caverns.

Seepages are obvious clues to oil, but their absence does not deter exploration. By 1883, random drilling in Pennsylvania and West Virginia had shown that many of the productive wel's were grouped along anticlinal crests. Noting this, I. C. White announced the **anticlinal theory** of accumulation and outlined the physical reasons for such concentration. This theory came to be generally accepted as a guide to exploration. Between 1900 and 1918 most oil companies built up geological staffs and gradually came to rely, in their exploratory programs, not on random drilling, but on systematic search, guided by surface geology, for anticlines and similar favorable structures. By 1928 the drill had tested most anticlines recognizable from surface geology in the sedimentary rocks of the United States, and hundreds of fields had been discovered.

But many large areas are covered by surface beds known to rest unconformably upon older ones. Structures in the surficial rocks do not necessarily reveal anticlines below the unconformity, and can, of course, give little clue to stratigraphic traps, which, until the early

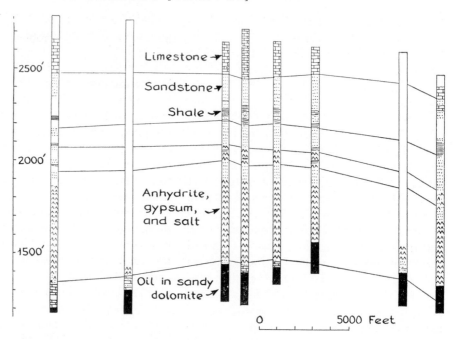

Figure 21-9.

SW–NE section across the Yates oil field, western Texas, showing rock correlations from well to well. (After G. C. Gester and H. J. Hawley, Structure of Typical American Oil Fields, *American Association of Petroleum Geologists, 1929.)*

1930's had been generally overlooked as potential sources of oil. Systematic exploration demanded some means of determining geologic structure at depth.

Geophysical Methods.—The first geophysical method applied was the **gravity survey.** A few domes along the Texas coast had yielded much oil from the flanks or crests of huge salt plugs (Fig. 21-7, B). As salt is lighter than most other rocks, it was reasoned that measurements of the relative value of gravity over the flat coastal country should reveal similar buried salt plugs by the smaller gravitational attraction such lighter masses would exert. Systematic surveys during the 1920's did, in fact, reveal many such anomalously low values of gravity, and by 1930 the coast of Texas and Louisiana was dotted with salt-dome oil fields located by drilling these "gravity lows." The application of gravity methods, however, is greatly handicapped in other regions because of lesser contrasts in rock densities and the difficulties introduced by rough local topography. Accordingly, gravity surveys have been mainly useful in flat terrain and in the search for salt domes.

Seismic methods of geophysical exploration, first applied about 1924, have proved more widely useful than gravity methods. Of the several methods used, "reflection shooting" has been the most successful. Small charges of dynamite are exploded in shallow holes, thereby producing artificial earthquakes of small intensity. The travel times of the elastic waves are recorded on small field seismographs with an accuracy of tenths of a second. Though the interpretation of such records is a highly technical problem and not always free from ambiguity, it is possible to identify reflections from various strata of differing elastic properties, and, by comparing travel times to different points on the surface, to deduce the structure of buried strata.

By this method many oil fields have been found in structures not apparent on the surface. For example, the Louden field, in Illinois, was so accurately located by seismic work that the oil company was able to lease in advance of drilling nearly all of the 20,000 acres that have since been proved productive. This is a major field with an ultimate recovery estimated at about 200 million barrels. Similarly many fields in Texas and some hidden by the alluvium of the Central Valley of California have been discovered by use of the seismograph.

Subsurface Methods.—By the late twenties, so many wells had been drilled in and near oil fields that the geology of the surrounding area at depth could often be determined almost independently of the surface rocks. This is obviously extremely important where uncon-

formities, lensing of beds, or facies changes are present. The major problem is that of correlating beds between wells. If this can be done, favorable structures may be further explored and unfavorable ones avoided.

Three principal methods, lithologic, paleontologic, and electrical, are employed in correlation. **Lithologic correlations** are based on study of well cuttings or cores from the drill holes. An illustration showing such correlation in the Yates Field in Texas is given in Figure 21-9.

Where the rocks are not so readily distinguished as the anhydrite and red shale of the Yates Field, **paleontologic methods** are sometimes applicable. As any of the larger fossils

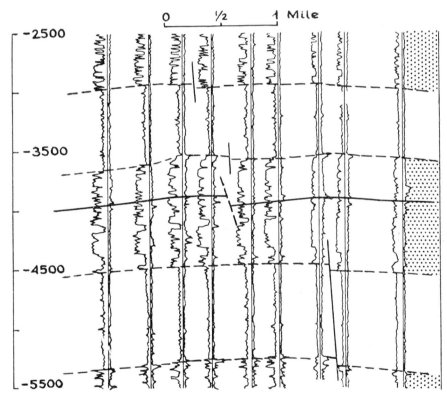

Figure 21-10.

SW–NE sections across Odem dome, southern Texas, showing correlations (dashed lines) from electric logs. The irregular lines to the right of the well-location lines record the resistance of the rocks to an electric current; the lines to the left measure the amount of natural current produced by the rocks themselves. Note that the latter lines effectively mark the position of the three sandstone strata shown by the dotted pattern at the right. (After Society of Exploration Geophysicists, Geophysical Case Histories, 1949.)

that may be present are generally ground to bits in drilling, the principal paleontological materials are microfossils, chiefly Foraminifera (Fig. 17-8). These tiny fossils are extremely abundant in many strata and are small enough to escape being ground up. Some fossil zones—strata characterized by particular species of fossils—only 10 or 20 feet thick can be distinguished by their microfossils and readily traced from one oil field to another nearby, even though they may change from sand to shale in this distance. Hundreds of micropaleontologists are now working in the oil industry to make correlations by means of these fossils.

Many methods of correlation by physical properties have been tried. Of these the most widely used is the **electric log**. Electrodes lowered into an uncased well measure differences in electrical characteristics of the beds penetrated. These characteristics vary markedly because of differences in the composition of the rocks, in their porosity, and in the kind of fluid—oil, salt water, or fresh water—that occupies the pores. Figure 21-10 illustrates the structure of a flat anticline in Texas as worked out from electric logs. The results confirmed the structure as inferred from an earlier seismic survey.

Summary of Methods of Oil Exploration. —This brief review of some of the many technical and scientific approaches to oil exploration shows that, although the presence of oil in a particular place at a particular depth cannot be foretold in advance of drilling, the search is not a blind one. Oil is localized, in response to definite physical laws, in structures and stratigraphic traps that are geologically determined. The problem of finding it is a geological one, and the solution depends on the application of many principles of geophysics, physics, petrography, paleontology, and chemistry. Systematic and economical exploitation of fields already found, and the cutting down of waste involved in random drilling, have resulted from such efforts; hence all the large oil companies find it profitable to maintain elaborate geological departments.

Ore Deposits

Ore deposits are rock masses from which metals are obtained commercially. Every ore body has been formed by the selective concentration of one or more elements in which the rock is greatly enriched as compared with the average of the earth's crust. How great this enrichment must be can be realized from the fact that more than 99 per cent of the earth's crust is made up of only ten elements (Chapter 2, Table 2-1, and Appendix IV, Table IV-3). Of these ten, aluminum, iron, and magnesium are industrial metals, and yet only a tiny fraction of the total volume of each of these three is concentrated in deposits

ELEMENT	WEIGHT PERCENTAGE	ELEMENT	WEIGHT PERCENTAGE
Aluminum	8.13	Cobalt	0.0023
Iron	5.0	Lead	0.0016
Magnesium	2.09	Tungsten	0.0015
Titanium	0.44	Uranium	0.0004
Manganese	0.1	Antimony	0.0001
Chromium	0.02	Mercury	0.00001
Vanadium	0.015	Silver	0.00001
Nickel	0.008	Gold	0.0000005
Copper	0.007	Platinum	0.0000005
Zinc	0.005	Radium	0.0000000013
Tin	0.004		

TABLE 21-2

Abundance of the Industrial Metals in the Average Igneous Rock.

METAL	MINERAL	ELEMENTS CONTAINED	PERCENTAGE OF METAL IN ORE MINERAL	CHEMICAL COMPOSITION
Gold	Native gold	Gold	50 to 100 (alloyed with silver)	Au and Ag
Silver	Native silver	Silver	100	Ag
	Argentite	Silver, sulfur	87.1	Ag_2S
Copper	Native copper	Copper	100	Cu
	Chalcopyrite	Copper, iron, sulfur	34.6	$CuFeS_2$
	Chalcocite	Copper, sulfur	79.8	Cu_2S
	Enargite	Copper, arsenic, sulfur	48.3	$3Cu_2S \cdot As_2S_5$
Lead	Galena	Lead, sulfur	86.6	PbS
Zinc	Sphalerite	Zinc, sulfur	67	ZnS
	Franklinite	Zinc, iron, oxygen, manganese	About 12	$(Fe,Mn,Zn)O \cdot (Fe,Mn)_2O_3$
Iron	Hematite	Iron, oxygen	70	Fe_2O_3
	Magnetite	Iron, oxygen	72.4	$FeO \cdot Fe_2O_3$
Aluminum	Bauxite (actually a mixture of several minerals)	Aluminum, oxygen, hydrogen	35 to 40	$Al_2O_3, 2H_2O$ (varies)

TABLE 21-3

The Common Ore Minerals.

rich enough to constitute a mineable deposit. Most other industrial metals—copper, zinc, lead, tin, and others—are found in only minute amounts in the earth's crust (Table 21-2).

Even an aluminum ore near the lowest usable grade (about 25 per cent metal) contains three times as much of the metal per pound as the average igneous rock; an iron ore with 50 per cent iron has ten times as much as the average; a copper ore with 1 per cent copper more than a hundred times the average. Most gold mines operate on less than one-third of an ounce of gold per ton of ore, but even this is 20,000 times the content of the average igneous rock. Since the "average rock" may be thought of as having been formed under "average" geologic conditions, these concentrations must reflect either very unusual conditions or the carrying of ordinary geologic processes to unusual perfection. As we shall see, examples of both deviations from "normal" are found.

Few ore deposits contain metals as such. Most are rock bodies containing one or more minerals in which the metallic element is combined with other elements (Table 21-3). If this combination is such that the useful metal may be economically recovered, the deposit is called an **ore.** The valuable minerals that contain the metallic element are **ore minerals.** The separation of the ore minerals from the associated useless minerals—the **gangue minerals**—and the extraction of the valuable metals from the ore mineral itself is called **metallurgy.**

The definition of ore is purely economic: it is a rock mass that can be worked commercially for the extraction of a useful metal. There is no stipulation as to the exact per-

TYPE	MANNER OF FORMATION	REPRESENTATIVE DEPOSIT
Magmatic segregation	By settling of early-formed minerals to the floor of a magma chamber during consolidation.	Layers of magnetite and chromite in the Bushveld lopolith, South Africa.
	By settling of late-crystallizing but dense metalliferous parts of the magma, which either crystallize in the interstices of older silicate minerals, or are injected along faults and fissures of the wall rocks.	Copper-nickel deposits of Norway and parts of those of the Sudbury district, Canada.
		Injected bodies of magnetite in Sweden (greatest in Europe) and in New York.
	By direct magmatic crystallization.	Diamond deposits of South Africa.
Contact-metamorphic	By replacement of the wall rocks of an intrusive by minerals whose components were derived from the magma.	Magnetite deposits of Iron Springs, Utah.
Hydrothermal deposits (deposits from hot, watery solutions)	By filling fissures in and replacing both wall rocks and the consolidated outer part of a pluton by minerals whose components were derived from a cooling magma. These differ from contact-metamorphic deposits in having fewer silicate minerals and more obvious fissure control.	Copper deposits of Butte, Montana, and Bingham, Utah; lead deposits of Idaho; zinc deposits of Missouri, Oklahoma, and Kansas; silver deposits of the Comstock Lode; gold of the Mother Lode, California, and Cripple Creek, Colorado.
Sedimentary beds	Sedimentary deposits under conditions which lead to deposition of relatively pure minerals.	Salt and potash deposits of Stassfurt, Germany, and of New Mexico.
	Deposition of rocks unusually rich in particular elements.	Iron deposits of Lorraine, France.
	Deposition of rocks in which the detrital grains of valuable minerals are concentrated because of superior hardness or density.	Placer gold deposits of Australia, California, and probably of the Rand gold field, South Africa; or the beach placers of Nome, Alaska, and Travancore, India.
Residual deposits	By weathering, which causes leaching out of valueless minerals, thereby concentrating valuable materials originally of too low grade into workable deposits.	Iron ores of Minnesota, Cuba, and Bilbao, Spain. Barite deposits of Missouri.
	By such concentration together with further leaching and enrichment of the valuable mineral itself.	Bauxite (aluminum) ores of Arkansas, France, Hungary, and British Guiana.

TABLE 21-4

Types of Mineral Deposits.

centage of the metal in the ore—only that it be enough to extract at a profit. A particular rock may pass from subore to ore with increased metal prices (as happened to many mercury deposits during both world wars), with improved metallurgical techniques (like many deposits of copper, zinc, and lead when the "flotation process" of separating ore minerals from gangue and from each other was developed), or with subsidies (as did the very low-grade Rhineland iron deposits under the Nazi "self-sufficiency" program). Conversely, a price decline or higher mining and metallurgical costs may change a valuable ore into worthless rock.

Among the many factors that determine whether a particular material is ore are:

1. The size, shape, and depth of the deposit. (All these greatly affect the cost of mining.)

2. The amenability of the ore to metallurgical treatment. (Fine-grained mineral aggregates may need to be ground very fine for clean separation from the gangue minerals; this grinding is more costly than direct smelting of the ore.)

3. The distance to metallurgical centers or to market. (The exploitation of Brazilian iron ores, though they are richer than the Lake Superior ores, has lagged because of distance from fields of coking coal.)

There are many dramatic examples of the influence of these factors on mining. The great copper mine at Bingham Canyon, Utah, can today mine ore containing as little as 0.85 per cent (17 pounds of copper to the ton), yet forty years ago masses of pure copper weighing several tons were occasionally found in the Michigan mines but were not ore because they could not be effectively blasted and it cost too much to chisel them out. A generation ago rock containing 50 per cent iron could not be mined on the Minnesota "Iron Ranges" because blast furnaces were designed to use only higher-grade ores; but with the exhaustion of the high-grade ores, furnace practices were changed so that these lower-grade materials can be used. At Birmingham,

Alabama, the happy combination of abundant local coal and limestone flux for use in the metallurgy permits the mining of ores with as little as 35 per cent iron. Such material would be useless rock, not ore, in Montana, California, or even in Minnesota, our greatest producer of iron ore.

ORE FORMATION. *Processes of Concentration.*—The processes that concentrate minerals into economic deposits are both mechanical and chemical, acting alone or in combination. These processes are those we have already noted: weathering, solution, transportation, and sedimentation at the surface; volcanism and flow of solutions below the surface. Ore bodies are rocks, and at one place or another nearly every rock-forming process has produced a valuable mineral deposit. This is indicated in Table 21-4, a brief tabulation of a few geologic types of mineral deposits, to which many others could be added. These few are selected because they are economically important and illustrate different ways in which particular elements have been selectively concentrated to many times their normal proportions.

Magmatic Segregations.—As we noted in Chapter 18, many of the larger floored intrusive bodies show a density stratification—a more-or-less regular banding with the dense, early crystallizing minerals near the base. In the Palisade sill the mineral so concentrated by sinking was olivine, of no economic value. But in some places, economic minerals have accumulated in similar ways to form ore deposits. Among these are the chromite ores of the Bushveld, South Africa, and of the Stillwater region, Montana. A representative specimen of such segregated chromite, in Alaska, is illustrated in Figure 21-11.

Floored intrusions of a variety of gabbro called norite, with concentrations of nickel sulfides and copper sulfides near their bases, are found in localities as widely scattered as Norway, Canada, and South Africa. The great Norwegian geologist J. H. L. Vogt pointed out in 1893 that the bulk composition of these

Figure 21-11.

Banded chromite, Seldovia district, Alaska. (*Photo by P. W. Guild, U. S. Geological Survey.*)

intrusives resembles that of smelter charges of sulfide ores—that is, a small percentage of sulfide and a large preponderance of silicates of aluminum, magnesium, iron, and calcium. When such a sulfide ore is smelted, the molten sulfides (the matte) sink to the bottom of the crucible, while the slag of silicates rises to the top. Vogt suggested that the same mechanism might have operated in nature to produce the observed concentrations.

Among such deposits are the greatest nickel deposits of the world, those of Sudbury, Ontario, which occur along the base of the lopolith shown in Figure 18-14. Here nickel sulfides are commonly molded against the silicate minerals, which possess their own crystal forms. This suggests strongly that the sulfides remained molten after the silicates had crystallized and that they accommodated themselves to the intergrain spaces between the silicate minerals. Certain details of the Sudbury deposits suggest that the final distribution of some of the sulfides may have been affected not only by gravity but by other factors as well —perhaps some have been dissolved and remobilized by solutions from a younger granitic intrusion. But the settling process is generally considered an important step in the formation of the ore.

Contact-Metamorphic Deposits.—In Chap-

ters 3 and 18, it was pointed out that the wall rocks of some intrusives contain quite different minerals than the same rocks do at a distance. In many places features such as bedding and even fossils are still identifiable in beds of limestone right up to an intrusive contact, although the limestone near the contact may have been completely transformed to garnet, pyroxene, amphibole, and epidote. Such mineral changes in an already existing rock at contacts with an intrusive prove that material has been transferred from magma to wall rock during the cooling of the intrusive. If the new minerals were merely concentrated from the limestone itself by solution and removal of other constituents, there would have been a shrinkage in volume. Although such shrinkage has occurred in some places, no volume change has taken place in most contact zones, as is proved by the preservation of details of the bedding and of delicate fossil structures. Clearly new material from the magma must have been added to the wall rock, and carbon dioxide and other substances removed, in order to change its carbonates to silicates. Supporting this interpretation is the observation that gases escaping through fissures at Vesuvius and Katmai have deposited iron-rich minerals such as magnetite and hematite on the fissure walls.

Only atoms or gases and relatively dilute solutions of low viscosity could so intimately permeate the wall rocks as to bring about their transformation without disturbing the finer textural features of the rock, and it is equally evident that part of the material of which the rock was formerly composed must have been removed in the same solutions. The replacement of calcite by garnet or pyroxene must have taken place volume by volume, the unused atoms from the disintegrating calcite being removed at the same moment that the garnet crystals were being built in the space formerly occupied by the calcite. This volume-for-volume replacement is one of the most widespread phenomena of geology. It takes place not only at intrusive contacts, but in many other environments where circulating ground water or other fluids can transfer material. The contact-metamorphic deposits are distinctive, however, because of the high-temperature minerals they contain.

There are innumerable examples of contact-metamorphic deposits that yield many useful products: garnet, for sandpaper; corundum (Al_2O_3), for emery wheels and, as rubies and sapphires, for gem use; copper; zinc; iron; and lead. The iron deposits of Iron Springs, Utah, are representative (Fig. 21-12). These deposits are pod-shaped, having replaced a limestone, in places to its full thickness, but elsewhere only in part. The ore is a mixture of magnetite and hematite, with a little apatite and smaller amounts of garnet, pyroxene, and quartz. Of these minerals, only quartz is found in the unaltered limestone. The rest have been introduced from the magma, concurrently with the removal of calcium and carbon dioxide from the limestone.

Hydrothermal Deposits.—Most ores of copper, lead, zinc, mercury, silver, and many of those of gold and tungsten are classed geologically as hydrothermal deposits; that is, they were formed by deposition from hot water solutions, as proved by the following facts.

1. Closely similar deposits have been seen to form in hot springs and fumaroles.

2. Many deposits are localized along faults and fissures that cut pre-existing rocks and therefore must have crystallized from fluids that penetrated cracks in the hot rock.

3. The minerals of many of these ores are identical, though the deposit can be traced from one kind of wall rock into another. The ores must have formed in an environment independent of, and consequently later than, the diverse environments that prevailed during the formation of the different wall rocks.

4. Although the adjacent wall rocks often show drastic mineral changes, delicate structures inherited from the time of their own origin are preserved in them; hence the alterations must have been brought about by solutions so fluid that their passage did not mechanically disturb the rocks.

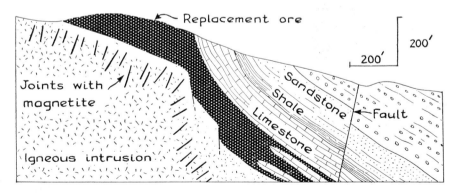

Figure 21-12.

Contact-metamorphic deposit at Iron Springs, Utah. (After J. H. Mackin, Utah Geological Survey, 1947.)

5. The well-developed crystal faces found on many of the minerals imply growth from solution, for such faces can readily be produced in this way in the laboratory and can be seen to form from solutions in nature.

That the solutions inferred from these features were of magmatic origin cannot always be proved, but is strongly implied by:

1. The close association of most of the deposits with intrusive masses.

2. The clustering of deposits about particular intrusives.

3. The especial abundance of these deposits near the upper parts of plutons.

4. The identity of the minerals in some of these deposits and their wall rocks with those that have been seen to form in volcanic areas; and also the identity of some of the minerals with minerals found in contact-metamorphic deposits. As there is between these extremes an essentially unbroken chain of deposits of intermediate characteristics, it seems probable that they, like the extreme varieties, are of magmatic origin.

Among the minerals that have been seen to form within fumaroles, geysers, and hot springs are magnetite, galena, sphalerite, and cinnabar (HgS, the principal source of mercury). In a few places, such as the sulfur mines of Sicily and the mercury deposit at Sulphur Bank, California, economic mineral deposits are directly associated with hot springs, and their valuable minerals were obviously deposited by the ascending hot waters. The similarities of both ore minerals and wall-rock alteration of these deposits to those of other deposits where hot springs are not now active are so close that most geologists agree that the latter—the so-called hydrothermal deposits—have been formed from magmatic solutions. Along the walls of these metallic deposits, just as along the walls of modern hot springs, the rocks have been altered to clay minerals, chlorite, and other hydrous minerals, doubtless by the action of the long-vanished hot solutions.

Paradoxically, one of the strongest evidences that hydrothermal deposits are of magmatic origin, and not formed from circulating ground water merely set in motion by magmatic heat, lies in the fact that many igneous bodies are *not* accompanied by such deposits, though other igneous masses that cut identical wall rocks nearby have great suites of them. A characteristic of ore deposits is their habit of being grouped into clusters around certain igneous bodies.

The argument runs as follows: We know that ground water fills the pores of all rocks to great depths. Any intrusive must stimulate the groundwater circulation by heating the wall rocks. It would therefore be possible to maintain, as was done by some geologists for many years, that the metals of ore deposits were leached from the rocks of the surrounding area and reconcentrated by heated ground water. Even if the original metal content of the rock were very low, one might expect ore deposits to form if the solutions gathered from large volumes of rock were constrained to flow through a restricted channel. If they formed in this way, however, there should be no more ore deposits near one kind of intrusive rock than near another, since the presence or absence of an ore deposit near a particular pluton would not depend on the magma's composition. But in many areas this is obviously not the case. For example, nearly all the great copper deposits of Arizona and Utah are associated with or lie within intrusives that are very similar in composition, although other intrusive bodies in the same region that are comparable in size, surrounding rocks, and structural setting have no associated copper ores. This strongly supports the idea that the parental magma of some intrusives was somehow richer in copper than that of others. Just as we are unable to explain the association of nickel and copper with many norites, we are completely at a loss to explain this pristine enrichment of a particular magma in a few other elements. But the association is so well established as to leave little doubt that the greater part of the metals was derived from the magma and not from the wall rocks.

Hydrothermal deposits are not associated with all parts of intrusive bodies. Where erosion has been deep enough to disclose the form of the pluton, the ore deposits appear to be grouped about the higher parts—the apexes or "cupolas." A few deposits lie in deep sags of the roof or along its steeper walls. Further, in plutons so deeply eroded as to destroy all remnants of the roof, ore bodies are rare. These relations suggest that the ore-depositing solutions were hot-water residues from crystallization of the magma, and that they were concentrated in the higher parts by the upward convergence of the walls as they escaped toward the surface during magmatic crystallization (Fig. 21-13).

Form and Relations of Hydrothermal Ore Bodies.—The commonest form of hydrothermal ore body is the **vein.** Unlike the cylindrical veins of animals and plants, mineral veins are generally tabular—hundreds or even thousands of times as long and wide as they are thick. They may lie at any angle from vertical to horizontal; they pinch and swell, branch and swerve. Many occupy faults, as shown by offsets of geologic contacts across them. Some follow dikes or bedding planes and still others occupy joints. The so-called "true fissure veins" are veins that differ sharply in mineral content and structure from their wall rocks and generally break away from them cleanly. These are so common in some districts that many of the mining laws of the United States are based on the fallacious assumption that all ore deposits are "true fissure veins."

Many veins, particularly in volcanic rocks, where the geologic relations indicate that the veins formed at depths of only a few hundred feet, are filled with quartz, calcite, and other carbonate minerals, plus a little feldspar, sulfides, and perhaps native gold. These minerals are arranged in bands (Fig. 21-14), in definite sequence from the walls toward the center of the vein. Unfilled cavities, lined with well-formed crystals, testify to the fact—already clear from the crustlike arrangement of the minerals—that the vein partly fills a formerly open channel, and that its minerals were deposited as crusts on the walls by the passing solutions. These are called crustified veins.

Other veins are not sharply separable from their walls; their vein matter blends into the walls. Microscopic study shows that the vein matter has replaced the wall rock without disturbing it, just as in the contact-metamorphic deposits. These are replacement veins. Parts of a vein may show evidence of replacement, while other parts have features pointing to mineral growth in open spaces.

Lodes are unusually thick veins or groups of veins. Some lodes are scores or even hundreds of feet thick. Clearly the walls of an

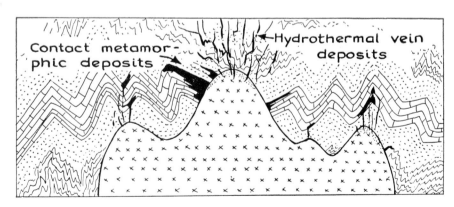

Figure 21-13.

Concentration of ore deposits in and near the apexes of a large intrusion. (After B. S. Butler and G. F. Loughlin, 1913.)

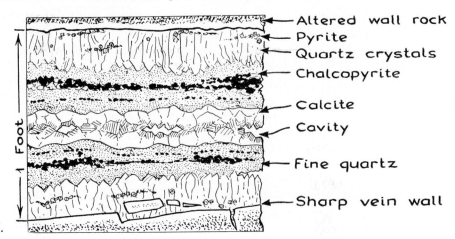

Figure 21-14.

A section across a banded vein.

opening wide enough to provide space for such a lode would have collapsed from the weight of the overlying rock. Yet such features as chunks of wall rock lying along the lower side of a dipping vein and the crustified arrangement of well-formed crystals in the vein (Fig. 21-15) prove that open spaces existed. Careful study of many large veins and lodes shows that the quartz deposited early from the hydrothermal solutions has been broken and recemented with later quartz,

often in several generations. This evidence of repeated rupture suggests that the fault occupied by the vein or lode was recurrently active for a long time, and repeatedly formed an avenue of escape for the hot solutions. Movement along an irregular fault would necessarily bring bends into contact and leave openings between (Fig. 21-16). Renewed faulting after such spaces were filled would produce new openings to be filled in their turn, and so on—in this way a lode could

Figure 21-15.

Part of a crustified quartz vein from Grass Valley, California. (Photo by W. D. Johnston, U. S. Geological Survey.)

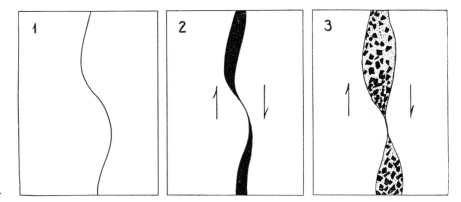

Figure 21-16.

Vein deposits along an irregular fault. (1) Fracture, before movement. (2) Ore filling cavities, after movement. (3) Renewed movement and fracturing of old ore and emplacement of new.

be made far thicker than would have been possible in any cavity filled by a single generation of vein-stuff.

Disseminated Deposits.—Other hydrothermal deposits are very irregularly shaped. Notable among these are the great so-called "porphyry copper" deposits, such as those of Bingham, Utah; Ely, Nevada; Morenci, Arizona; and Chuquicamata, Chile, which is the largest of the world's copper deposits. Most of the ore in these districts is disseminated along small fissures in porphyritic intrusive rocks, which it impregnates and replaces with copper and iron sulfides. The rock surrounding and within the ore body is generally highly altered to clay and fine-grained mica, with a little epidote and chlorite, and is so intimately veined with sulfides and quartz that it is hard to find an unveined piece as big as a tennis ball in a mass comprising many thousand cubic yards. What shattered these great rock masses in such an intimate way as to permit this thorough impregnation is a mystery. Because many of these deposits occupy the higher parts of plutons, the shattering has been attributed to the streaming of volatiles to the top of the intrusive mass as it slowly congealed, but this is only conjecture.

A different kind of disseminated deposit is exemplified by the lead ores of south-eastern Missouri and the zinc-lead deposits of the "Tri-State District" (Oklahoma, Missouri, and Kansas). These lie along irregular and indefinite "runs" in limestone (Fig. 21-17). The ores are sulfides that replace the car-

Figure 21-17. Map (top) and section (bottom) showing the irregular distribution of ore and silicification of limestone in a Missouri zinc mine.

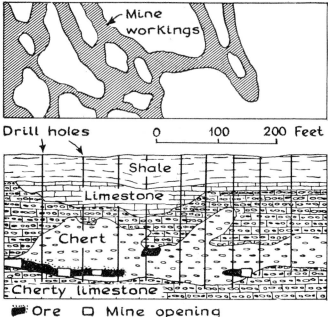

bonate wall rocks, and although the pattern of the ore bodies shows some control by faults and other fractures, there are no well-marked veins. The sulfides are accompanied by dolomite and calcite, often well crystallized. These minerals were apparently introduced in solutions that permeated the entire rock but deposited their ores selectively in certain beds and along certain trends or channels called runs—perhaps because of some obscure variations in permeability or chemical composition.

SUMMARY. The hydrothermal deposits consist of rocks that are, on the one hand, almost indistinguishable from contact-meta-morphic deposits, and, on the other, almost identical with deposits in fumarole vents and hot springs. Observations at fumaroles and hot springs show that the minerals so formed change with the temperature—as temperature falls, the earlier-formed minerals become unstable and are dissolved, and new minerals form. Although we have nowhere found within a single district a complete series of ore deposits filling the range from hot-spring to contact-metamorphic rocks, parts and gradations of such a series are apparent in many parts of the world. Study of many such partial series has made possible the tentative arrangement of ore deposits in a reasonably systematic sequence. Probably this sequence reflects the changes in composition, temperature, and pressure of magmatic solutions as they pass through and react with the minerals of different rocks, and as they cool on approaching the surface. Where conditions favorable to the deposition of one or more ore minerals have been fairly constant, and the volume of solution has been large, ore bodies have resulted. Where conditions changed too rapidly, or the volume of solution was too small, no ore was formed, though small quantities of minerals identical with those of ore bodies were deposited. "Gold is where you find it"—but it has been proved many times that there are often identifiable geologic factors that have controlled its deposition; factors that enable

us to locate new ore bodies or hidden extensions of those already known.

Of paramount importance is the structural setting that guided the flow of ore-forming solutions. Channels for these solutions, whether faults, fissures, schistose partings, or bedding planes, have all been geologically determined. By detailed mapping it has often been possible to recognize them and then to point to probable new ore bodies where similar structural settings exist. Second to structure as a localizing factor is the existence of particular strata readily susceptible to replacement by ore minerals. If the ore deposits in a particular bed are unusually abundant or rich, it is obvious that places where a channel-way for solutions intersects this bed are good prospecting ground. The many ways in which mining is facilitated by geologic mapping and research constitute, in the aggregate, one of the most important contributions of geology to society. With the depletion of our richest and most readily found ore deposits, it is inevitable that still more intensive geologic studies will be needed to supply the ever-expanding industrial needs of the world.

Sedimentary Deposits

Many economic deposits have been concentrated by sedimentation. Among those already discussed are the clay used in ceramics and cement; limestone for building stone, mortar, or cement; dolomite; rock salt; gypsum; and potassium salts. The total value of these deposits is very large; the value of each depends primarily on the kind and amount of impurities in the sedimentary rock, on the cost of mining or quarrying, and on the distance to market.

Some sedimentary strata, many of wide extent, consist of metallic ores. Among these are the iron ores of Alabama, Newfoundland, and northeastern France, and some of those of England. The ore beds in the Birmingham district of Alabama are of Silurian age, as shown by the associated fossils. Similar deposits of the same age are widespread in the Appalachians from New York southward, but the only large mines in them are near Birmingham, where the iron-rich beds are thickest—in some places as much as 20 feet. The ore beds are generally sharply separated from the adjoining beds of sandstone and shale, but in places they grade into sandstone. In these ores, hematite cements the rock and also coats and replaces some of the fossils. Some sand grains and pebbles, also, have rounded coatings of hematite. These show, by the abrasion of the hematite-covered surfaces, that the iron mineral was formed before the agitation of the grains was stopped by their burial. Many of the hematite granules are flattened in such a way as to suggest that they were soft and were squeezed during the consolidation of the rock. Fossils composed of calcite found with them are undeformed. These facts convince most students of these deposits that the present hematite granules were formerly soft jellylike aggregates of iron rust on the sea floor. The iron oxide was deposited in the sea on nuclei of clastic grains. It was presumably a hydrous oxide, from which the water was driven by heat and pressure after the rock was buried. These deposits are relatively low in iron, and are workable only because (1) they are slightly calcareous, and the calcite acts as a flux in the blast furnace, and (2) they are close to large sources of coking coal.

The present seas apparently contain no such concentrations of iron-rich sediments as must presumably have been present during the deposition of the Birmingham ores, although some iron is now being precipitated on the sea floor. We know from analyses of river waters that iron is leached from the rocks in great quantities; it is less abundant in the sea than in river water. The Silurian deposit is thought to have formed under exceptional conditions during which iron was carried to the sea in great abundance. In other words, it resulted from an unusual concentration in time and place, but from a normal geologic process.

PLACER DEPOSITS.   We saw in Chapter 4 that during normal weathering the feldspars and other silicate minerals tend to decompose to clays that are so fine grained and so weakly coherent as to break up with the slightest transportation. Quartz, however, is normally quite stable, and hence is concentrated in the stream beds of a granitic region, where it makes up most of the sand, even though it constitutes only 10 or 20 per cent of the bedrock. Minerals such as magnetite, chromite, diamond, gold, and cassiterite (SnO_2), the chief source of tin, are also chemically stable in most climatic environments, and since they are heavier than quartz, tend to fall to the bottom of a stream or to accumulate on the riffles of a sluice while quartz of the same grain size is carried on. Where streams from regions that supply such minerals reach the sea, the heavy minerals are concentrated by the waves. This is the origin of the "black sands" of the Oregon Coast (chromite), of the raised beaches of Nome, Alaska (gold), of the monazite (thorium) sands of the Malabar Coast of India, of the ilmenite (titanium) sands of Florida, and of the diamond beaches of Southwest Africa. In all these localities, minerals that form only very minor parts of the inland rocks have been concentrated because of their density and their resistance to weathering.

FACTS, CONCEPTS, TERMS

DEPENDENCE OF INDUSTRY ON MINERALS
SPORADIC DISTRIBUTION OF MINERAL RESOURCES
EXHAUSTIBILITY OF MINERAL RESOURCES

MINERAL FUELS
THE SEQUENCE OF COAL ALTERATION
    Peat to anthracite

QUESTIONS

1. Why did Holland and Denmark, which suffered greatly during World War II, oppose the suggestion to abolish the commercial production of coal from the Ruhr area in Germany despite their fear of renewed German aggression?

2. Why, in view of the great mineral endowment of the United States, did Congress authorize "stock-piling" of certain minerals as a defense measure?

3. From the description of placer deposits, explain how they can be used as guides to ore in bedrock. Why does a prospector carry a "pan"?

4. In view of the nonreplenishable nature of mineral deposits, what are the advantages and disadvantages of a tariff on minerals?

5. Although a "fault trap" was not described in the text, draw a cross section of an oil field which is a fault trap in a gently dipping sequence of sediments.

6. Why do the oil fields of the Persian Gulf region have fewer wells per square mile than those of East Texas? Does this reflect geologic or other conditions?

7. Determination of the depth of relatively recent unconsolidated river-deposited sediments in the estuary of the Congo River is important for the solution of the problem of submarine canyons (Chap. 15). What methods now routine in oil finding might be used to determine this depth at enough points to give the form of the bedrock surface? Which method would be quickest?

8. Sandstones used for making glass must consist of almost pure quartz. How is such purity attained by natural processes?

9. Why are placer deposits usually the first to be discovered in a gold mining region?

10. Pyrite is common in many deposits of copper, lead, zinc, and gold. Why is a conspicuously brown-stained outcrop often a guide to a buried ore deposit?

SUGGESTED READING

American Geographical Society. *World Atlas to Petroleum*. New York, 1950.

Bituminous Coal Institute. *Bituminous Coal Facts and Figures*. Washington, D. C., 1948.

Lalicker, Cecil G. *Principles of Petroleum Geology*. New York, Appleton-Century-Crofts, 1949.

Lovering, T. S. *Minerals in World Affairs*. New York, Prentice-Hall, 1943.

The Mineral Resources of the United States, by the staffs of the U. S. Geological Survey and Bureau of Mines. Washington, D. C., Public Affairs Press, 1948.

Rickard, T. A. *Man and Metals*. New York, McGraw-Hill, 1932.

Maps and Mapping

MAPS are the shorthand summary used by the student of the earth in presenting his data and observations. The earth's crust is complex. The intricate patterns of land and water, the forms of hills and valleys, the labyrinths that men have dug in mining are all so complicated in form that a true picture of them cannot be given by words alone. A map, however, condenses in intelligible form the findings regarding them.

Map Scales

A blueprint of a machine part or a dress pattern may be thought of as a map. Most of these are **full-scale** maps. An inch on such a map represents an inch on the object it portrays.

Few geographic and geologic maps, however, are full size. Most of them are scale drawings. In such **reduced-scale** maps, an inch on the map may correspond to 10 inches, 1,000 inches, 1,000,000 inches, or whatever unit of reduction the map maker deems desirable to show the features he wishes to portray. If he decides to reduce the length of objects on the map to 1/10 of their true length on the ground, he plots on a "1/10 scale." The fraction is the ratio of reduction and simply means that 1 inch on the map equals 10 inches on the ground. Many of the newer maps of the *Topographic Atlas of the United States* prepared by the United States Geological Survey are drawn on a scale of 1/24,000—1 inch on the map corresponds with 24,000 inches, or 2,000 feet, on the ground.

Limitations of Maps

On a full-scale drawing, it is possible to show, for example, the head of a nail 1/10 inch across in full size. If the nail were to be correctly represented on a 1/200 scale, however, it would have to be drawn as only 1/200 of 1/10, or 1/2,000, of an inch across. Such a point is too small to be visible. Thus, if such nails were to be shown at all on the 1/200 scale, they would have to be shown diagrammatically. Their positions might be indicated, but their size would have to be greatly exaggerated if they were to be seen. This limitation of reduced-scale maps must be constantly kept in mind by the map user.

All maps are generalizations, drawn to perform a particular service or function. All, therefore, represent selections of data chosen to serve the particular purpose and these data are commonly exaggerated in relation to other features. A navigator's chart emphasizes the features useful to navigation—for example, shoals and shallow rocks are emphasized more than deep-water features of similar size; a good road map stresses highway junctions and, in doing so, may distort the distances between them.

The maps of Seattle Harbor shown in Figure I-1 illustrate one effect of map scale. Details such as the docks in Elliott Bay can be shown only on the larger scale map.

Whatever the scale, limitations in drawing and printing make it almost impossible for maps to be accurate to more than 1/100 inch in the location of points. It is difficult to make

481

a legible pencil mark less than 1/100 inch across. The scale of a map of the United States that could be printed on this page would be about 1/25,000,000; on it, separate points less than 8 miles apart could not be shown without distortion. A thin line representing the Mississippi River on such a map would scale at least 4 miles in width.

Maps of the earth—the summaries of geographical knowledge—have still another limitation: they must depict, on a flat surface, the curved surface of the earth. It is impossible to

do this without distorting the distances between points or the angles between intersecting lines. Most maps are compromises between these evils. Some of the distortions that result from various methods of plotting are shown in Figure I-2.

Topographic Maps

The maps described thus far may be called **planimetric maps;** they show the relative positions of points but do not indicate their eleva-

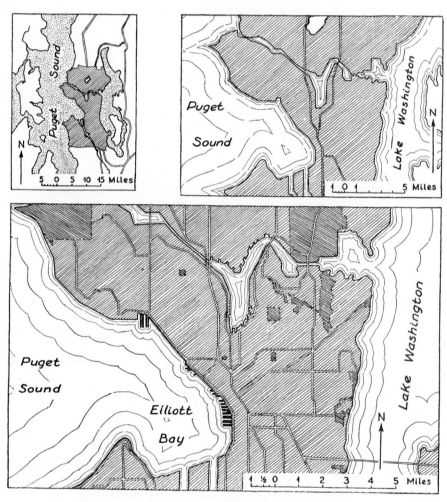

Figure I-1.

Maps of Seattle harbor on different scales. Note that the smaller-scale maps show much less detail, though all contain about the same number of lines per square inch. (After maps of the U. S. Geological Survey and of the Chamber of Commerce of Seattle.)

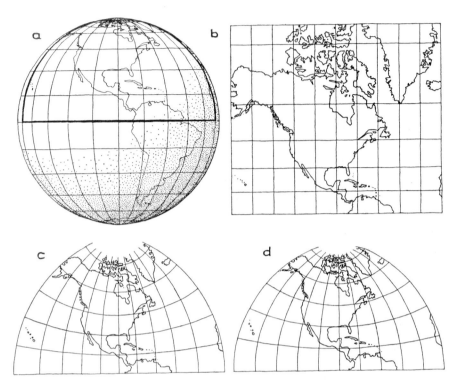

Figure 1-2.

The part of the world outlined in a *is reproduced in three common map projections:* b, *the Mercator;* c, *the stereographic; and* d, *the polyconic. By comparing the size and shape of the longitude and latitude grid, it can be seen that each kind of projection distorts the earth's surface to a varying degree. This distortion is an unavoidable result of transferring a curved surface to a flat one.*

tions above or below sea level. The **relief** of an area is the difference in altitude between the highest and lowest points within it. Although, by means of skillful shading, a so-called **relief map** can give an impression of the relative steepness of the slopes in an area, such a map cannot be used to determine accurately the actual differences in elevation between any two points. It is impossible to read height accurately from such a map.

To meet this difficulty, geodesists have devised **topographic maps,** which are designed to show the elevations as well as the positions of points. They portray the three-dimensional form of the land surface—its **topography.**

A topographic map depicts a three-dimensional surface—one having length, breadth,

and varying height above a reference plane or **datum** (usually mean sea level)—on a two-dimensional piece of paper. On such a map, lines called **contours** are drawn to portray the intersections of the ground surface with a series of horizontal planes at definite intervals above (or below) the datum plane (Fig. 1-3).

There are many different methods of making topographic maps and their actual making is a quite complex process. To illustrate the principles, we have chosen the "Plane Table Method," a method still widely used in making geologic maps even though most topographic maps are now made from airplane photographs.

The first step in the preparation of a

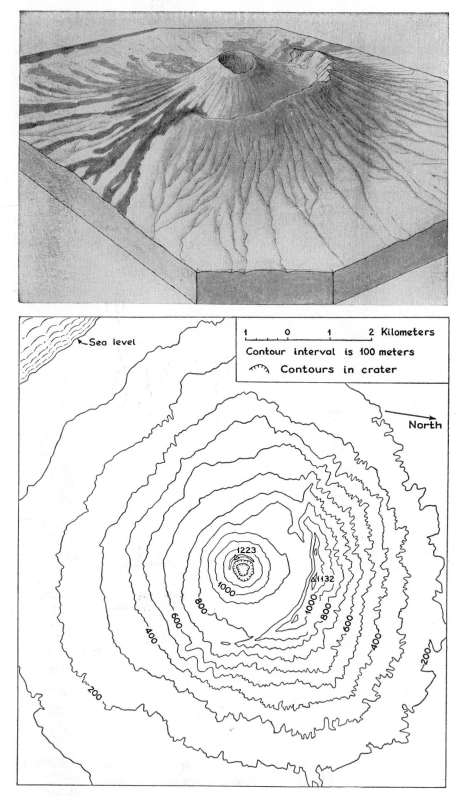

Figure I-3. *Relief model and topographic (contour) map of the volcano Vesuvius.*
(After Il Vesuvio sheet, Instituto Geografico Militaire.)

topographic map by any method is to acquire both **horizontal** and **vertical control** for the measurements. To attain this double control, we must first establish the position of a point on the earth's surface (*a*) by its latitude and longitude and (*b*) by its altitude with respect to sea level. The more points thus determined, the better our control. If we knew the elevation, latitude, and longitude of every point on the surface, we could quickly construct the map; the decision of how many we must determine for a given area is based on the scale and contour interval of the map, and the relief of the area.

Once the horizontal and vertical control (position and elevation) of one point, and the direction of the north-south line through it have been established, we can quickly determine many other points by a process called **triangulation.**

The first step in triangulation is the selection and measurement of a **base line.** The base line is a straight line from the point for which we have established control to another point. Each end of the base line is marked by a stake holding a flag (Fig. I-4), or by some other suitable marker, and the distance between them is measured carefully with a steel tape.

The accuracy of the whole map depends on the base line; therefore, as a check, the measurement is generally repeated. After the

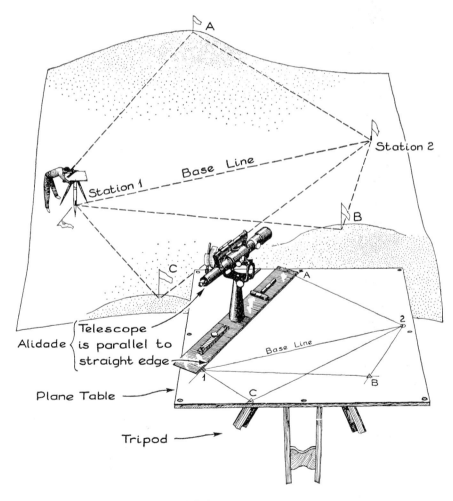

Figure I-4.

Mapping with plane table and alidade.

base line has been measured, it must also be carefully plotted on the plane table sheet (paper on which the map is to be constructed) in accordance with the reduced scale chosen for the map. Actually, the plotted length of the base line determines the scale, for if there are errors either in its measurement or in its plotting, they will be carried throughout the map.

Once the base line has been plotted, a **plane table** (essentially a drawing board mounted on a tripod) is set up over one end of the base line. Then the edge of an **alidade** (a telescope with a ruler as its base) is placed along the line drawn on the plane table sheet to represent the base line (Fig. I-4). The plane table, carrying the alidade, is rotated until the telescope points directly at the flag on the other end of the base line, and then clamped firmly in position. It is now correctly oriented, since the base line on the ground and the plotted base line on the plane table sheet have exactly the same trend (azimuth) in relation to true north.

With the table still clamped in this position, the telescope is pointed successively toward each of several other flags, such as A, B, C in Figure I-4, or other marked points that are visible, and lines are drawn along the edge of the alidade to indicate the directions of these lines of sight. The plane table is then taken to the other end of the base line, oriented in the same manner by sighting back to the first flag, and the process of sighting upon and drawing lines toward each point visible from this location is repeated. The point of intersection of the two lines of sight toward an object, one line of sight having been drawn from the first end of the base line and the other from the second end, marks the true position of that object on the reduced-scale map (Fig. I-4). This point and the two ends of the base line form the apexes of a triangle. The new point can then be used, just as if it were one end of the base line, to determine the position of additional points, extending the system of triangles (triangulation net)

within a given area. The more points thus determined, the better the control.

A surveyor's transit or theodolite can be used in triangulation instead of a plane table and alidade. With a transit, the horizontal angle from the base line to the point to be determined is carefully measured at each end of the base line. Knowing the two angles, and having measured one side (the base line) of the triangle, we can compute the position of the apex of the triangle by trigonometry and plot it on the map.

Vertical control is established in the same way, and can be done at the same time as the horizontal triangulation. We establish the elevation of one end of our base line from some point of known elevation. Then, with the elevation of one point in our triangulation system established, we can readily compute the elevation of a second station. We have already determined the distance between the two stations by triangulation. The only other measurement we need for the computation is the vertical angle between the horizon and the line of sight to the station. The alidade is equipped with a vertical arc (Fig. I-4) for making this measurement. Thus, the vertical control is extended throughout the triangulation net, and the elevations of many points are determined.

By these and other auxiliary techniques (not described here) for obtaining horizontal and vertical control, we locate enough additional points to allow the topographer to sketch the contours in their proper relation to the ground surface as determined by the positions and elevations of the many points thus located and plotted. The map that results from this procedure is, we repeat, a generalization. Many factors other than the already mentioned base-line determinations affect its accuracy—for example, the number and spacing of the control points, trees that obscure the ground forms, the skill of the topographer, and the amount of time he has at his disposal for study of the shape of the land surface. Topographical engineers rate a map as excellent if, on testing it, they find not more than 10 per cent of the elevations in error by more than one-half the vertical distance between two successive contours.

Recently, great strides have been made in preparing topographic maps from photographs taken from airplanes. This saves much time formerly spent in surveying on the ground. The basic principles are, nonetheless, the same as those employed in making maps on the ground and, for the basic horizontal and vertical control, a preliminary ground survey is still necessary.

Good topographic maps are available for relatively few parts of the land surface of the earth. Less than half the area of the United States has been mapped on a scale that permits drawing contours with intervals as small as one hundred feet. Poland and several of the "backward Balkans" have much better map coverage. For large parts of the earth's surface, we have only crude maps.

Hydrographic Maps

Hydrographic maps do for sea areas what topographic maps do for land areas. They not only depict the outlines of the water bodies but, by soundings (measurements of depth made by vessels at sea), they also show something of the topography of the bottom.

In the construction of maps of the sea floor, soundings were formerly made by measuring the length of a rope or wire paid out until it reached bottom. As a measurement in the deep part of the ocean would require several hours, it is not surprising that relatively few such soundings were made, except at shallow depth near the coasts.

In recent years, a new method, **sonic sounding,** has superseded measurement of depth by wire or rope. In sonic sounding the time required for a sound signal to travel from a ship to the sea bottom and rebound is measured, and the depth is then calculated from the speed of sound in sea water. By sonic sounding it is now an easy matter for a ship to chart a continuous record of the depths traversed while it is under way. The position of the ship is determined to within a distance of a few hundred feet by radio signals from shore stations.

Although sonic sounding has greatly increased our knowledge of the ocean floor (see Fig. 5-9), the vastness of the sea, the lack of interest of many navigators in obtaining detailed information of this kind from little-traveled sea lanes, and the cost of operating a vessel for surveying purposes alone, still conspire to prevent more than a mere sampling of the form of the ocean floor.

The hydrographer, compared with the topographer, is severely handicapped, for he is unable to see the sea bottom and therefore cannot choose the most suitable points to use for control in mapping. A series of points of equal depth can be connected by a contour line in several ways, but obviously only one such contour line represents the actual form of the sea floor. On land the topographer can see the topographic forms and sketch between his points accordingly; the hydrographer must get additional control or else make an interpretation which will probably be inaccurate in minor details, and may be seriously inaccurate.

APPENDIX II | # Identification of Minerals

THE laboratory techniques in most common use today for the identification of minerals are noted here.

Petrographic Analysis

Petrographic analysis is the most frequently used method for the precise identification of both minerals and rocks. A small piece of the substance to be identified is ground with abrasives on a revolving plate until it is 0.03 millimeters (about 0.001 inch) thick—much thinner than a sheet of paper. It is then mounted between thin glass slides. This **thin section** can then be examined under the petrographic microscope. In a thin section most minerals are transparent, or nearly so, and the optical properties which distinguish different minerals can be readily measured.

An alternative petrographic method is to crush the mineral to powder, place the powder in a drop of liquid of known optical properties on a glass slide, cover with a thin glass plate, and examine the fragments immersed in the liquid under the petrographic microscope.

X-Ray Analysis

As explained in Chapter 2, it is possible by means of X-rays to work out the internal structure of a mineral—the geometric arrangement of the ions or atoms within it. Since the internal structure is the most distinctive characteristic of a mineral, X-ray analysis is one of the most fundamental methods of mineral identification.

Chemical Analysis

A chemical analysis, or even a qualitative chemical test for some particular element, will generally help to identify an unknown mineral, although even a complete chemical analysis may fail to establish the identity of some. Some distinct minerals, diamond and graphite for example, have identical chemical compositions and so cannot be distinguished chemically. Furthermore, most minerals are highly insoluble silicates, difficult to treat by standard chemical procedures which require dissolving the substance to be analyzed. Most minerals are also "solid solutions" whose compositions vary widely. For these reasons standard chemical procedures are little used in ordinary mineral identification, though they may be employed in special kinds of research on minerals.

As supplements to petrographic and other methods, however, a few special chemical techniques have proved useful in mineral identification. Many minerals that are too opaque to be readily identified by ordinary petrographic methods, can be identified by simple chemical tests made on the surface of the thin section or on a polished piece of the mineral while it is being examined under the microscope.

The spectroscope is widely used to detect elements that may be present in small amounts in a mineral. Its use requires that the mineral be heated in an arc until it vaporizes.

Determination by Physical Properties

The common rock-forming minerals, and also many of the rarer minerals of economic value, can usually be identified without special instruments by a careful study of their physical properties. This method suffices for recognition of the minerals listed at the end of this appendix. The more important physical properties are given here.

CLEAVAGE. Many minerals **cleave** (break) along smooth planes controlled by the internal structure of the crystal (Figs. II-1 and 2-7). Some minerals—mica, for example—have only one cleavage and can be split into countless thin flakes, all of which are parallel to one another; many minerals have two cleavages; others have three or more. Broken fragments of these minerals have characteristic shapes, which aid in identifying the mineral, because the number of cleavages and the angles between them are characteristic for a particular mineral.

FRACTURE. Many minerals fracture irregularly instead of cleaving along smooth planes. Such rough fragments are less readily identified than cleavage fragments, but some minerals, of which quartz is an example, usually break with characteristic curved surfaces **(conchoidal fracture).** Others have a splintery or **fibrous fracture** that helps to distinguish them.

FORM. As mentioned previously, minerals tend to crystallize into definite, characteristically shaped crystals, bounded by smooth planes called **crystal faces.** When crystal faces are present, their shapes and interfacial angles are diagnostic (Figs. 2-2 and II-2), but many minerals occur in shapeless, granular forms, or in crystals so small that the crystal faces are not visible. In some minerals, crystal faces are parallel to cleavage surfaces; in others, they are not. For this reason, they should, of course, be carefully distinguished from cleavage surfaces. The distinction is not difficult if one remembers that crystal faces appear only on the outside of the crystal, whereas cleavage surfaces appear only on the broken or cracked fragments of a crystal.

COLOR. All specimens of some minerals, such as magnetite and galena, have a constant or uniform color; but others, such as quartz and calcite, are variable in color because of pigments that may be present as impurities. Even in minerals with constant intrinsic color, alteration of the surface through exposure to air and moisture may change the surface color. Nevertheless, the color of a freshly broken surface may be diagnostic, and even the color of the altered surface film aids in identifying some minerals.

STREAK. The color of the powdered mineral—which is called the **streak** because it is

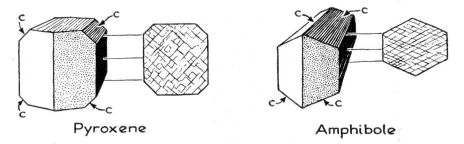

Figure II-1.   **Pyroxene**   **Amphibole**

The relation between crystal form and cleavage in pyroxene and amphibole. The cleavages parallel the crystal faces, c, and are shown in a sectional cut to the right of each crystal.

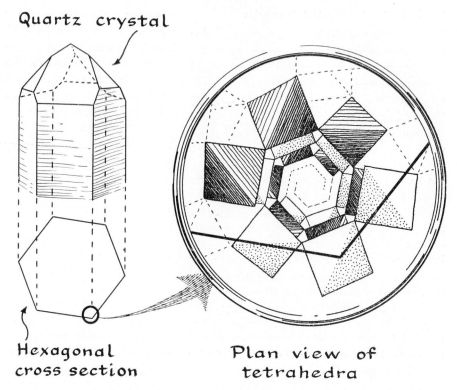

Quartz crystal

Hexagonal cross section

Plan view of tetrahedra

Figure II-2.

The crystal form of quartz and its internal structure. The internal structure consists of silica tetrahedra closely linked together because each oxygen atom serves as the corner for two tetrahedra. The linked tetrahedra lie in spirals around screw axes, producing a hexagonal basal pattern of the tetrahedra which is also reflected in the external shape of the crystal. In the enlarged plan view shown at the right the linked tetrahedra are indicated for one screw axis. (Adapted from models by L. Pauling and by P. Niggli.)

easily obtained as a "chalk mark" by rubbing the mineral against a piece of unglazed porcelain—is more constant and, for some minerals, more helpful in identification than the color of the mineral in a larger mass. The streak of a mineral may be similar to, or it may be entirely different from, the color of the mineral itself: si'very-gray galena gives a silvery-gray streak; but both the black and red varieties of hematite show a characteristic brownish-red streak that is very helpful in identifying the mineral.

LUSTER.   The **luster** of a mineral refers to the way ordinary light is reflected from its surfaces. Metallic luster is like that of polished metals; vitreous luster is like that of glass; adamantine like that of diamond. Other self-explanatory terms used to describe luster are resinous, silky, pearly, and dull or earthy.

HARDNESS.   The relative hardness of two different minerals can be determined by pushing a pointed corner of one firmly across the flat surface of the other.   If the mineral with the point is harder, it will scratch or cut the other. Laboratory tests of the hardness of minerals are usually recorded in terms of a **scale of hardness** ranging from 1 to 10. Each number refers to the hardness of a specific mineral, ten of which, arranged in order of increasing hardness, constitute the scale.

1. talc
2. gypsum
3. calcite
4. fluorite
5. apatite

6. orthoclase
7. quartz
8. topaz
9. corundum
10. diamond

When specimens to make up this series are not available, it is convenient to know that the steel of a pocketknife is about 5½ in this scale, a copper penny 3½, and the thumbnail about 2½.

SPECIFIC GRAVITY. The **specific gravity,** or density, of a mineral is given by the formula:

$$\text{Sp. Gr.} = \frac{\text{(wt. mineral in air)}}{\text{(wt. mineral in air)} - \text{(wt. mineral in water)}}$$

Specific gravity, therefore, is stated as a number indicating the ratio of the weight of the substance to that of an equal volume of water. Specific gravity can be determined by several different instruments, ranging from an ordinary spring scale for large specimens to sensitive microbalances for smaller ones. The specific gravity of different minerals varies greatly.

With a little practice, fairly small differences in specific gravity can be detected from the "heft" of a moderate-sized specimen held in the hand. Quartz, with a specific gravity of 2.65, may be used as the standard of comparison. Gypsum (2.2 to 2.4) would then be called light; olivine (3.2 to 3.6) heavy; magnetite (5.0 to 5.2) very heavy.

OTHER PROPERTIES. Many other physical properties are useful in identifying minerals. Some minerals are attracted by a magnet, others are not; some conduct electricity better than others; some "fluoresce," or glow in various colors when ultraviolet light is played on them; some are characterized by fine striations, or "twinning lines," on certain cleavage surfaces; others have different striations—"growth striations"—on certain crystal faces. Minerals also differ in fusibility, in solubility, in their reactions to simple chemicals —such as bubbling when dilute hydrochloric acid is applied to them; and in many other ways, but the major physical properties listed above will suffice to identify the more common kinds.

List of Minerals

The grouping of the minerals in the list that follows is not alphabetical but is based on similarities in chemical composition, physical properties, associations, or uses. The first group includes *common carbonates, sulfates, chlorides, and oxides.* These minerals are found mainly in the sedimentary rocks, though some of them (quartz and magnetite, for example) are abundant in many igneous and metamorphic rocks as well. The second group, *common rock-forming silicates,* includes chiefly minerals that crystallized in igneous and metamorphic rocks, but which may also be found as clastic particles in sedimentary rocks. Kaolinite, included in this group as a representative of the abundant clay minerals, is chiefly a weathering product. The third group, important *ore minerals,* are much less common, but are listed because of their importance as sources of valuable metals or other commercial materials.

In the tables those properties most useful in sight identification are italicized. Some minerals have more than one name; the less common names are given in parentheses. The chemical name and chemical formula follow the mineral name.

Common Carbonates, Sulfates, Chlorides, and Oxides

MINERAL	FORM	CLEAVAGE	HARD-NESS	SP. GR.	OTHER PROPERTIES
CALCITE. Calcium carbonate, $CaCO_3$.	"Dog-tooth" or flat crystals showing excellent cleavages; granular, showing cleavages; also masses too fine grained to show cleavages distinctly.	*Three highly perfect cleavages at oblique angles,* yielding rhomb-shaped fragments (Fig. 2-3).	3	2.72	Commonly colorless, white, or yellow but may be any color owing to impurities. Transparent to opaque, transparent varieties showing *strong, double refraction* (e.g., 1 dot seen through calcite appears as 2). Vitreous to dull luster. *Effervesces readily in cold dilute hydrochloric acid.*
DOLOMITE. Calcium magnesium carbonate, $CaMg(CO_3)_2$.	*Rhomb-faced crystals showing good cleavage;* also in fine-grained masses.	*Three perfect cleavages at oblique angles, as in calcite.*	3.5-4	2.9	Variable in color, but commonly white. Transparent to translucent. Vitreous to pearly luster. *Powder will effervesce slowly in cold dilute hydrochloric acid, but coarse crystals will not.*
GYPSUM. Hydrous calcium sulfate, $CaSO_4 \cdot 2H_2O$.	Tabular crystals, and cleavable, granular, fibrous, or earthy masses.	*One perfect cleavage, yielding thin, flexible folia;* 2 other much less perfect cleavages.	2	2.2-2.4	Colorless or white, but may be other colors when impure. Transparent to opaque. Luster vitreous to pearly or silky. Cleavage flakes flexible but *not elastic* like those of mica.
HALITE. (Rock salt.) Sodium chloride, NaCl.	Cubic crystals (Fig. 2-6), in granular masses.	Excellent cubic cleavage (3 cleavages mutually at right angles).	2-2.5	2.1	*Colorless to white,* but of other colors when impure. The color may be unevenly distributed through the crystal. Transparent to translucent. Vitreous luster. *Salty taste.*
OPAL. Hydrous silica, with 3% to 12% water, $SiO_2 nH_2O$. Does not have a definite geometric internal structure, hence is a mineraloid, not a true mineral.	Amorphous. Commonly in veins or irregular masses showing a banded structure. May be earthy.	None; *conchoidal fracture.*	5.0-6.5	2.1-2.3	*Color highly variable, often in wavy or banded patterns.* Translucent or opaque. *Somewhat waxy luster.*
CHALCEDONY. (Crypto-crystalline quartz.) Silicon dioxide, SiO_2.	Crystals too fine to be visible; sometimes conspicuously banded, or in masses.	None; *conchoidal fracture.*	6-6.5	2.6	Color commonly white or light gray, but may be any color owing to impurities. Distinguished from opal by *dull or clouded luster.*
QUARTZ. (Rock crystal.) Silicon dioxide, SiO_2.	*Six-sided prismatic crystals,* terminated by 6-sided triangular faces; also massive (Fig. II-2).	None or very poor; *conchoidal fracture.*	7	2.65	Commonly *colorless* or white, but may be yellow, pink, amethyst, smoky-translucent brown, or even black. *Transparent* to opaque. *Vitreous to greasy luster.*

MINERAL	FORM	CLEAVAGE	HARDNESS	SP. GR.	OTHER PROPERTIES
MAGNETITE. A combination of ferric and ferrous oxides, Fe_3O_4.	Well-formed, 8-faced crystals, more commonly in compact aggregates, disseminated grains or loose grains in sand.	None; conchoidal or uneven fractures; may show a rough parting resembling cleavage.	5.5-6.5	5.0-5.2	*Black.* Opaque. Metallic to submetallic luster. *Black streak. Strongly attracted by a magnet.* Magnetite is an important iron ore.
HEMATITE. Ferric iron oxide, Fe_2O_3.	Highly varied, compact, granular, fibrous, or earthy, micaceous; rarely in well-formed crystals.	None, but fibrous or micaceous specimens may show parting resembling cleavage; splintery to uneven fracture.	5-6.5	4.9-5.3	Steel-gray, reddish-brown, red, or iron-black in color. Metallic to earthy luster. *Characteristic brownish-red streak.* Hematite is the most important iron ore.
"LIMONITE." Microscopic study shows that the material called limonite is not a single mineral. Most "limonite" is a very finely crystalline variety of the mineral **GOETHITE** containing absorbed water. Hydrous ferric oxide with minor amounts of other elements, roughly $Fe_2O_3 \cdot H_2O$.	Compact or earthy masses; may show radially fibrous structure.	None; conchoidal or earthy fracture.	1-5.5	3.4-4.0	*Yellow,* brown, or black in color. Dull earthy luster, which distinguishes it from hematite. *Characteristic yellow-brown streak.* A common iron ore.
ICE. Hydrogen oxide, H_2O.	Irregular grains; lacelike flakes with hexagonal symmetry; massive.	None; conchoidal fracture.	1.5	0.9	Colorless, white or blue. Vitreous luster. *Melts at $0°C$,* so is liquid at room temperature. *Low specific gravity.*

Common Rock-Forming Silicates

MINERAL	FORM	CLEAVAGE	HARDNESS	SP. GR.	OTHER PROPERTIES
POTASSIUM FELDSPAR. (Orthoclase, microcline, and sanidine.) Potassium aluminum silicate, $KAlSi_3O_8$.	Boxlike crystals (Fig. 2-2,b); massive, with excellent cleavage.	One perfect and 1 good cleavage, making an angle of $90°$.	6	2.5-2.6	Commonly *white, gray, pink,* or pale yellow; rarely colorless. Commonly opaque but may be transparent in volcanic rocks. Vitreous. Pearly luster on better cleavage. *Distinguished from plagioclase by absence of striations.*

Common Rock-Forming Silicates – Continued

MINERAL	FORM	CLEAVAGE	HARD-NESS	SP. GR.	OTHER PROPERTIES
PLAGIOCLASE FELDSPAR. (Soda-lime feldspars.) A solid solution group of sodium calcium aluminum silicates, $NaAlSi_3O_8$ to $CaAl_2Si_2O_8$.	In well-formed crystals and in cleavable or granular masses.	*Two good cleavages nearly at right angles* (86°). May be poor in some volcanic rocks.	6-6.5	2.6-2.7	Commonly *white or gray*, but may be other colors. Some gray varieties show a play of colors called *opalescence*. Transparent in some volcanic rocks. Vitreous to pearly luster. Distinguished from orthoclase by the presence on the *better cleavage surface of fine parallel lines or striations.*
MUSCOVITE. (White mica; isinglass.) A complex potassium aluminum silicate, $KAl_3Si_3O_{10}(OH)_2$ approximately, but varying.	Thin, scalelike crystals and scaly, foliated aggregates.	*Perfect in one direction, yielding very thin, transparent, flexible scales.*	2-3	2.8-3.1	*Colorless*, but may be gray, green, or light brown in thick pieces. *Transparent to translucent.* Pearly to vitreous luster.
BIOTITE. (Black mica.) A complex silicate of potassium, iron, aluminum, and magnesium, variable in composition but approximately $K(Mg,Fe)_3\,AlSi_3O_{10}(OH)_2$.	Thin, scalelike crystals, commonly 6 sided, and in scaly, foliated masses.	*Perfect in one direction, yielding thin, flexible scales.*	2.5-3	2.7-3.2	Black to dark brown. Translucent to opaque. Pearly to vitreous luster. White to greenish streak.
PYROXENE. A solid-solution group of silicates. Chiefly silicates of calcium, magnesium, and iron, with varying amounts of other elements. The commonest varieties are *augite* and *hypersthene.*	Commonly in short, 8-sided, prismatic crystals; *the angle between alternate faces nearly 90°.* Also as compact masses and disseminated grains.	*Two cleavages at nearly 90°* (Fig. II-1). Cleavage not always well developed; in some specimens, conchoidal or uneven fracture.	5-6	3.2-3.6	Commonly greenish to black in color. Vitreous to dull luster. Gray-green streak. Distinguished from amphibole by the *right-angle cleavage, 8-sided crystals,* and by the fact that most crystals are short and stout, rather than long, thin prisms, as in amphibole (Fig. II-1).
AMPHIBOLE. A group of complex, solid-solution silicates, chiefly of calcium, magnesium, iron, and aluminum. Similar to pyroxene in composition, but containing a little hydroxyl (OH^-) ion. The commonest of the many varieties of amphibole is *hornblende.*	*Long, prismatic, 6-sided crystals;* also in fibrous or irregular masses of interlocking crystals and in disseminated grains.	*Two good cleavages meeting at angles of 56° and 124°* (Fig. II-1).	5-6	2.9-3.2	Color black to light green; or even colorless. Opaque. *Highly vitreous luster on cleavage surfaces.* Distinguished from pyroxene by the *difference in cleavage angle* and in crystal form. Amphibole also has much better cleavage and higher luster than pyroxene.

Mineral	Form	Cleavage	H	G	Remarks
OLIVINE. Magnesium iron silicate, $(Fe,Mg)_2SiO_4$.	Commonly in small, *glassy* grains and granular aggregates.	So poor that it is rarely seen; *conchoidal fracture.*	6.5-7	3.2-3.6	*Various shades of green*, also yellowish; opalescent and brownish when slightly altered. *Transparent to translucent. Vitreous luster.* Resembles quartz in small fragments but has *characteristic greenish color*, unless altered.
GARNET. A group of solid solution silicates having a general formula with variable proportions of different metallic elements. The most common variety contains calcium, iron, and aluminum, but garnets may contain many other elements.	Commonly in well-formed *equidimensional crystals* (Fig. 2-2,c) but also massive and granular.	None; *conchoidal or uneven fracture.*	6.5-7.5	3.4-4.3	Commonly *red, brown, or yellow*, but may be other colors. Translucent to opaque. *Resinous to vitreous luster.*
SILLIMANITE. (Fibrolite.) Aluminum silicate, Al_2SiO_5.	*In long slender crystals, or fibrous.*	Parallel to length, but rarely noticeable.	6-7	3.2	Gray, white, greenish-gray, or colorless. *Slender prismatic crystals or in a felted mass of fibers.* Streak white or colorless.
KYANITE. (Disthene.) Aluminum silicate, Al_2SiO_5.	Long, *bladelike crystals.*	One perfect, and one poor cleavage, both parallel to length of crystals; and a crude parting across the crystals.	4-7	3.5-3.7	Colorless, white, or a *distinctive pale blue color.* Can be scratched by knife parallel to cleavage, but is harder than steel across cleavage.
STAUROLITE. Iron-aluminum silicate, $Fe(OH)_2(Al_2SiO_5)_2$.	*Stubby prismatic crystals,* and in cross-shaped twins.	Poor and inconspicuous.	7-7.5	3.7	Red-brown or yellowish-brown to brownish black. Generally in well-shaped crystals larger than the minerals of the matrix enclosing them.
EPIDOTE. A complex group of calcium, iron, aluminum silicates, $Ca_2(Al,Fe)_3(SiO)_3(OH)$.	*Short, 6-sided crystals* or radiate crystal groups (Fig. 2-2,a) and in granular or compact masses.	One good cleavage; in some specimens, a second and poorer cleavage at an angle of 115° with the first.	6-7	3.4	Characteristic *yellowish-green (pistachio green)* color. Vitreous luster.
CHLORITE. A complex group of hydrous magnesium aluminum silicates containing iron and other elements in small amounts.	Commonly in *foliated or scaly masses;* may occur in tabular, 6-sided crystals resembling mica.	*One perfect cleavage,* yielding thin, flexible, but inelastic, scales.	1-2.5	2.6-3.0	Grass-green to blackish-green color. Translucent to opaque. Greenish streak. Vitreous luster. *Very easily disintegrated.*

Common Rock-Forming Silicates – Continued

MINERAL	FORM	CLEAVAGE	HARD-NESS	SP. GR.	OTHER PROPERTIES
SERPENTINE. A complex group of hydrous magnesium silicates, roughly $H_4Mg_3Si_2O_9$.	Foliated or fibrous, usually massive.	Commonly only one cleavage, but may be in prisms. Fracture usually conchoidal or splintery.	2.5-4	2.5-2.65	*Feels smooth, sometimes greasy.* Color *leek-green* to *blackish-green* but varying to brownish-red, yellow, etc. *Luster resinous* to *greasy.* Translucent to opaque. Streak white.
TALC. Hydrous magnesium silicate, $Mg_3(OH)_2Si_4O_{10}$.	In tiny *foliated scales* and soft compact masses.	*One perfect cleavage,* forming thin scales and shreds.	1	2.8	White or silvery white to apple green. *Very soft,* with a *greasy feel.* Pearly luster on cleavage surfaces.
KAOLINITE. Hydrous aluminum silicate, $H_4Al_2Si_2O_9$. Representative of the 3 or 4 similar minerals common in clays.	Commonly in soft, compact, *earthy masses.*	Crystals always so small that cleavage is invisible without microscope.	1-2	2.2-2.6	White color, but may be stained by impurities. *Greasy feel. Adheres to the tongue,* and *becomes plastic when moistened.* "*Clay-like*" odor when breathed upon.

Important Ore Minerals (See also the iron ores listed on p. 493)

MINERAL	FORM	CLEAVAGE	HARD-NESS	SP. GR.	OTHER PROPERTIES
GALENA. Lead sulfide, PbS.	Cubic crystals common, but mostly in coarse to fine granular masses.	*Perfect cubic cleavage* (three cleavages mutually at right angles).	2.5	7.3-7.6	*Silvery-gray color.* Metallic luster. Silvery-gray to grayish-black streak. Chief ore of lead.
SPHALERITE. Zinc sulfide (nearly always containing a little iron), ZnS.	Crystals common, but chiefly in fine to coarse-granular masses.	*Six highly perfect cleavages at 60° to one another.*	3.5-4	3.9-4.2	Color ranges from white to black but is commonly *yellowish-brown. Translucent* to opaque. *Resinous* to *adamantine luster.* Streak white, pale yellow or brown. Most important ore or zinc.
PYRITE. ("Fool's gold.") Iron sulfide, FeS_2.	*Well-formed crystals,* commonly cubic, with striated faces (Fig. 2-2,*d*); also granular masses.	None; uneven fracture.	6-6.5	4.9-5.2	Pale *brassy-yellow color;* may tarnish brown. Opaque. Metallic luster. Greenish-black or brownish-black streak. Brittle. Not a source of iron, but used in the manufacture of sulfuric acid. Commonly associated with ores of several different metals.

Mineral	Form	Cleavage	Hardness	Specific gravity	Remarks
CHALCOPYRITE. Copper iron sulfide, CuFeS$_2$.	Compact or disseminated masses, rarely in wedge-shaped crystals.	None; uneven fracture.	3.5-4	4.1-4.3	Brassy to *golden-yellow. Tarnishes* to blue, purple, and reddish iridescent films. Greenish-black streak. Distinguished from pyrite by deeper yellow color and softness. A common copper ore.
CHALCOCITE. (Copper glance.) Cuprous sulfide, Cu$_2$S.	Massive, rarely in crystals of roughly hexagonal shape. May be tarnished and stained to blue and green.	Indistinct, rarely observed.	2.5-3	5.5-5.8	Blackish-gray to steel gray, commonly *tarnished to green or blue.* Dark gray streak. *Very heavy.* Metallic luster. An important ore of copper.
COPPER. (Native copper.) An element, Cu.	Twisted and distorted leaves and wirelike forms; flattened or rounded grains.	None.	2.5-3	8.8-8.9	*Characteristic copper color,* but commonly stained green. *Highly ductile* and malleable. Excellent conductor of heat and electricity. *Very heavy.*
GOLD. An element, Au.	Massive or in thin plates; also in flattened grains or scales; distinct crystals very rare.	None.	2.5-3	15.6-19.3	*Characteristic gold-yellow color and streak.* Rarely in crystals. *Extremely heavy.* Very malleable and ductile.
SILVER. An element, Ag.	In flattened grains and scales; rarely in wirelike forms, or in irregular needle-like crystals.	None.	2.5-3	10-11	*Color and streak are silvery-white,* but may be tarnished gray or black. *Highly ductile and malleable. Very heavy.* Mirrorlike metallic luster on untarnished surfaces.
CASSITERITE. Tin dioxide, SnO$_2$.	Well-formed, 4-sided prismatic crystals terminated by pyramids; 2 crystals may be intergrown to form knee-shaped twins; also as rounded pebbles in stream gravels.	None; curved to irregular fracture.	6-7	7	*Brown to black.* Adamantine luster. White to pale-yellow streak. Chief ore of tin.
URANINITE. (Pitchblende.) Uranium oxide, UO$_2$ to U$_3$O$_8$.	Regular 8-sided or cubic crystals; massive.	None; fracture uneven to conchoidal.	5-6	6.5-10	Color black to brownish-black. Luster submetallic, pitchlike, or dull. Chief mineral source of uranium, radium, etc.
CARNOTITE. Potassium uranyl vanadate, K$_2$(UO$_2$)$_2$(VO$_4$)$_2$ · 8H$_2$O.	Earthy powder.	Not apparent.	Very soft	4.1 approx.	*Brilliant canary-yellow color.* An ore of vanadium and uranium.

APPENDIX III | Identification of Rocks

THE classification of rocks given in this Appendix is a field classification based on features that can be seen without the aid of the petrographic microscope or X-ray spectrometer. Much more elaborate classifications have been built with the aid of these instruments and other suitable laboratory techniques. Nearly all such classifications, however, have been made by expanding and adding varietal subdivisions to the major rock classes listed in the tables below. Therefore the field classification represents a broad framework into which more elaborate subdivisions can be fitted.

The field classification is based primarily upon the texture of the rock, and upon its mineral composition. Remember that rocks grade into one another, and hence some of the properties of an individual specimen you may be examining are likely to fall between the properties listed as typical of two major rock classes. To use the tables and lists below as guides in identifying an unknown rock specimen the student must be thoroughly familiar with the common rock-forming minerals listed in the Mineral Table of Appendix II. He must also have clearly in mind the basic distinctions between sedimentary, igneous, and metamorphic rocks and the general range of textures found in them. This fundamental information is given in Chapter 3. The common rock textures are here summarized in glossary form for easy reference.

Common Textures of Sedimentary Rocks

Differences in *the nature of the constituent particles,* and in *how they are bound together* determine the texture of a sedimentary rock.

CLASTIC (Greek, "broken"). Composed of broken and worn fragments of pre-existing minerals, rock particles, or shells that have been cemented together. Further distinctions can be made on the *size* of the particles, and on the amount of *rounding* by wear of the individual fragments.

ORGANIC. Composed of accumulations of organic debris (shells, plant remains, bones, etc.) in which the individual organic particles are so well preserved (not notably broken and worn) that organic features dominate the texture of the rock.

CRYSTALLINE. Composed of crystals precipitated from solution and therefore tightly interlocked by mutual interpenetration during growth. The rock owes its coherence to this interlocking of crystals, instead of to the presence of a cement as in the clastic and organic textures.

Common Textures of Igneous Rocks

Differences in the *degree of crystallinity,* and in the *size of the crystals* determine the texture of an igneous rock. Both of these factors are controlled primarily by *rate of cooling,* though the chemical composition of the magma and its content of volatile materials play roles.

Basic Textures

PYROCLASTIC (Greek, "broken by fire"). Composed of slivers of volcanic glass, bits of frothy pumice, phenocrysts, and broken fragments of volcanic rock cemented together. The glass slivers and pumice may be largely altered to clay. Pyroclastic rocks are the products of volcanic explosions or of ash flows.

GLASSY. Composed almost entirely of massive or streaky volcanic glass. Small phenocrysts of feldspar or other minerals may be scattered through the glass. The glass may be frothy, filled with minute bubbles, forming a *pumiceous glassy* texture.

APHANITIC (Greek, "invisible"). Composed chiefly of tiny crystals (less than 0.5 mm. in diameter), with or without a glassy residue between the crystals. The crystals are mere specks, large enough to be seen but too small to identify without the aid of the microscope. Their presence gives the rock a stony or dull luster in contrast to the glassy (vitreous) luster of rocks with glassy texture. Most lava flows have aphanitic texture; in some, flow has aligned the tiny mineral grains, giving a streaky or flow-banded appearance.

GRANULAR (Latin, "a grain"). Composed of crystals that are large enough to be seen and identified without the aid of lens or microscope. In different rocks the average size may vary from about 0.5 mm. to more than 1 cm. in diameter, but the common granular rocks such as granite have grains averaging from 3 mm. to 5 mm. in size.

Modifying Texture

PORPHYRITIC. Composed of two widely different sizes of minerals, giving a spotted appearance. Because porphyritic texture is most common in small intrusive bodies or in lavas, it has been attributed to a *change in the rate of cooling while the magma was crystallizing.* The inferred process is explained as follows: A large body of magma underground may cool to the temperature at which one or more minerals begin to crystallize. Because cooling is slow, the crystals of these minerals grow to considerable size. If, when the magma is perhaps half crystallized, a fissure opens in the roof of the chamber, some of the magma with its suspended crystals may escape to form a lava flow at the surface. The still-liquid portion of the magma quickly freezes at the surface of the ground and surrounds the large crystals, called *phenocrysts,* with a *groundmass* of aphanitic crystals. The phenocrysts were formed underground, the aphanitic groundmass at the surface. Such a lava has a *porphyritic aphanitic* texture. The adjective porphyritic is used

to modify the prevailing texture of the groundmass. Rocks with *porphyritic granular* texture —large crystals in a granular groundmass of finer grain—are common in intrusive bodies. *Porphyritic glassy* texture appears in some lava flows, and in the pumice fragments of pyroclastic rocks. Rarely, conditions other than a change in the rate of cooling may produce porphyritic rocks.

Common Textures of Metamorphic Rock

Differences in the *orientation,* or alignment, of the crystals and in the *size* of the crystals determine the texture of a metamorphic rock. There are two general textural groups: *Foliated textures* (Latin, "leafy"), in which platy or leaflike minerals such as mica or chlorite are nearly all aligned parallel to one another so that the rock splits readily along the well-oriented, nearly parallel cleavages of its constituent mineral particles, and *Nonfoliated,* composed either of equidimensional minerals or of randomly oriented platy minerals, so that the rock breaks into angular particles.

Basic Textures

GNEISSOSE (from Greek, "banded rock"). Coarsely foliated; individual folia are 1 mm. or more, even several centimeters, thick. The folia may be straight, pancake-like, or wavy and crenulated. They commonly differ in composition; feldspars, for example, may alternate with dark minerals. Mineral grains are coarse, easily identified.

SCHISTOSE (Greek, "easily cleaved"). Finely foliated, forming thin parallel bands along which the rock splits readily. Individual minerals are distinctly visible. The minerals are mainly platy or rodlike—chiefly mica, chlorite, and amphibole. Equidimensional minerals like feldspar, garnet, and pyroxene may be present but are not abundant.

SLATY (from Old High German, "to split"). Very fine foliation, producing almost rigidly parallel planes of easy splitting due to the nearly perfect parallelism of microscopic and ultramicroscopic crystals of platy minerals, chiefly mica.

GRANOBLASTIC (Greek, "sprouting grains"). Unfoliated or only faintly foliated. Composed of mutually interpenetrating mineral grains that have crystallized simultaneously. Minerals are large enough to be easily identified without the microscope, and are chiefly equidimensional kinds such as feldspar, quartz, garnet, and pyroxene. Corresponds roughly to the granular texture of igneous rocks.

HORNFELSIC (German, "hornlike rock"). Unfoliated. Mineral grains commonly microscopic or ultramicroscopic, though a few may be visible. Breaks into sharply angular pieces with curved fracture surfaces.

How to Use the Rock Tables and Lists

After carefully examining a specimen of rock, but before referring to the tables and lists in this Appendix, the student should ask himself the following three basic questions, and if in doubt about the answers, should refer back to the material in Chapter 3, Appendix II, and the glossary of textures given above:

1. What is the texture of the rock? (Glossary above)
2. Of what minerals is it composed? (Appendix II)
3. Is it an igneous, sedimentary, or metamorphic rock? (Chapter 3)

Once this basic information is worked out, turn to the appropriate rock table (Sedimentary, p. 501; Igneous, p. 504; Metamorphic, p. 508) and find the rock's name, then check against the description of the rock in the appropriate rock list.

Common Sedimentary Rocks

Conglomerate. Conglomerate is cemented gravel. Gravel is an unconsolidated deposit composed chiefly of rounded pebbles. The pebbles may be of any kind of rock or mineral and of all sizes. Most conglomerates, especially those deposited by streams, have much sand and other fine material filling the spaces between the pebbles. Some cleanly washed beach conglomerates contain little sand.

Breccia. Sedimentary breccias resemble conglomerate except that most of their fragments are angular instead of rounded. They commonly grade into conglomerates. Since their constituent fragments have been little worn,

however, it is apparent that the components of breccia underwent relatively less transportation and wear before they were deposited. There are many kinds of breccias other than sedimentary breccias. Volcanic breccias, as well as sedimentary breccias, are described in this appendix; glacial breccias in Chapter 13; and fault breccias in Chapter 9.

Sandstone. Sandstone is cemented sand. Sand, by definition, consists of particles from 2 mm. to 1/16 mm. in diameter. Sandstones commonly grade into either shale or conglomerate. Three general varieties of sandstone are recognized:

Quartz sandstone is composed mainly of the mineral quartz. Most sand is chiefly quartz but contains small amounts of many other minerals and even small particles of rock.

Arkose is a feldspar-rich sandstone. It may contain nearly as many particles of partly weathered feldspar as of quartz, or even more. Most arkoses have been formed by the rapid erosion of coarse feldspar-rich rocks such as granites and gneisses, and the rapid deposition of this eroded debris before the feldspar has had time to weather completely into clay.

Graywacke is a cemented "dirty sand" containing large amounts of clay and rock fragments in addition to quartz and feldspar. Many graywackes contain much pyroclastic debris in various stages of weathering and decomposition; others are crowded with bits of slate, greenstone, or other metamorphic rocks; and still others are rich in ferromagnesian minerals. All contain appreciable amounts of clay. Graywackes are commonly dark gray, dark green, or even black. Like arkose, they indicate rapid erosion and deposition without much chemical weathering.

Sand, the original material that is cemented into sandstone, accumulates in many different environments. Some sand is deposited by streams; some is heaped up in dunes by the wind; some is spread out by waves and currents along beaches or in the shallow water of the continental shelves; some is washed by turbidity currents down steep submarine slopes onto the deep sea floor.

TABLE III-1. *Sedimentary Rocks*

CLASTIC SEDIMENTARY ROCKS			
CONSOLIDATED ROCK	CHIEF MINERAL OR ROCK COMPONENTS	ORIGINAL UNCONSOLIDATED DEBRIS	DIAMETER OF FRAGMENTS
Conglomerate	Quartz, and rock fragments	Gravel (rounded pebbles)	More than 2 mm.
Breccia	Rock fragments	Rubble (angular fragments)	
Sandstone	. . .	Sand	2 to $\frac{1}{16}$ mm.
Quartz Sandstone	Quartz	Quartz-rich sand	
Arkose	Quartz and feldspar	Feldspar-rich sand	
Graywacke	Quartz, feldspar, clay, rock fragments, volcanic debris	"Dirty sand," with clay and rock fragments	
Shale	Clay minerals, quartz	Mud, clay and silt	Less than $\frac{1}{16}$ mm.
Clastic Limestone	Calcite	Broken and rounded shells and calcite grains	Variable
ORGANIC AND CHEMICAL SEDIMENTARY ROCKS			
CONSOLIDATED ROCK	CHIEF MINERAL OR ROCK COMPONENTS	ORIGINAL NATURE OF MATERIAL	CHEMICAL COMPOSITION OF DOMINANT MATERIAL
Limestone	Calcite	Shells; chemical and organic precipitates	$CaCO_3$
Dolomite	Dolomite	Limestone, or unconsolidated calcareous ooze, altered by solutions	$CaMg(CO_3)_2$
Peat and Coal	Organic materials	Plant fragments	C, plus compounds of C, H, O
Chert	Opal, chalcedony	Siliceous shells and chemical precipitates	SiO_2 and SiO_2nH_2O
Evaporites, or Salt Deposits	Halite, gypsum, anhydrite	Evaporation residues from the ocean or saline lakes	Varied, chiefly NaCl and $CaSO_4 2H_2O$

Shale. Shale is hardened mud. Mud is a complex mixture of very small mineral particles less than 1/256 mm. in diameter (chiefly clay), and coarser grains, called silt, from 1/256 to 1/16 mm. in diameter. Shale frequently contains small bits of organic matter.

The predominant minerals in shale are the hydrous aluminum silicates called clay minerals, but most shales also contain appreciable amounts of mica, quartz, and other minerals. Shale splits readily along closely spaced planes, parallel or nearly parallel to the stratification. Some rocks of similar grain size and composition show little layering and break into small angular blocks: these are more correctly called *mudstone*.

Shales accumulate in many different environments. As the main load brought down to the sea by great rivers is mud and fine sand, it is not surprising that shale is the most abundant marine sedimentary rock. Mud deposited in deltas, on lake bottoms, and on plains along sluggish rivers may also harden into shale.

Many shales are black, some because they contain large amounts of carbon-rich organic matter in various stages of decomposition, some because of the precipitation of black iron sulfide (FeS_x) by sulfur bacteria. The iron sulfide may later crystallize into pyrite (FeS_2), forming small brass-colored crystals sprinkled through the rock. Many blue-green, dark gray, gray-green, or purplish-red mudstones owe their color to decomposed volcanic material.

Limestone.   Limestone is composed almost entirely of calcium carbonate ($CaCO_3$), chiefly as the mineral calcite, though aragonite (which is also $CaCO_3$ but with a different crystalline form) may be plentiful.

Organic limestones are common rocks, and occur in great variety because of the many kinds of shells from which they are formed. Among the most common are: *coral limestone,* which contains a framework of coralline deposits but also includes the shells of many other animals, especially foraminifers, molluscs, and gastropods; *algal limestone,* made largely of deposits of calcite precipitated by algae and bacteria; *foraminiferal limestone,* composed chiefly of the tiny shells of foraminifera; *coquina,* composed mostly of the coarse shells of molluscs and gastropods; and *chalk,* which consists largely of almost ultramicroscopic blades and spines of calcite that are called coccoliths.

Clastic limestones are composed of broken and worn fragments of shells or of crystals of calcite. The white sands of the Florida Keys are made up largely of calcite grains worn from shells and organic limestones.

Chemically precipitated limestone is also forming today in shallow warm seas, in hot springs, and in saline lakes. The role of inorganic precipitation is, however, difficult to separate from that of biochemical and organic agents. Very fine-grained, flourlike, white *calcareous ooze* (calcareous means calcite-rich) is abundant in parts of the southwest Pacific and on the shallow Bahama Banks of the Atlantic. Some of this ooze consists of microscopic shells, but much of that in the Bahamas consists of tiny spines and crystals of aragonite and calcite, perhaps in part precipitated inorganically, or else precipitated from sea water as a result of the life processes of such microorganisms as algae and bacteria.

Limestone deposited from hot springs is coarsely crystalline, and commonly is full of small irregular holes stained yellow or red by iron oxides. Such limestone is called *travertine.*

Limestones differ greatly in texture and color depending on the size of the shells or crystals composing them and the impurities they contain. Some black limestones are rich in hydrocarbons from the partially decayed bodies of organisms, as is shown by the strong, fetid odor they give off when freshly broken. Most limestomes, however, are light colored and contain many fossils.

Dolomite.   Dolomite rock is composed chiefly of dolomite, the mineral of the same name. Dolomite resembles limestone, and also grades into it, by changes in the amount of calcite in the rock. Chemical and microscopic tests are generally necessary to determine the relative amounts of the minerals calcite and dolomite in the rock.

Most dolomite appears to result from alteration of limestone or its parental calcareous ooze by magnesia-bearing solutions. The alteration that formed most dolomite is thought to have taken place during slow deposition, by the action of the magnesium ions in sea water on calcareous ooze or other calcareous deposits. Some limestone, however, changed to dolomite long after it was deposited and consolidated.

Dolomite has rarely, and perhaps never, been deposited directly as a precipitated sediment.

Fine-grained Siliceous Rocks.   Rocks composed almost entirely of fine-grained silica are common, but they rarely form large masses. Many different kinds of siliceous (siliceous means silica-rich) sedimentary rocks have been described and named, but the most common is *chert,* a hard rock with grains so fine that a broken surface appears uniform and lustrous.

Chert nodules, many of them resembling a knobby potato in shape and size, are common in limestone and dolomite. Dark-colored chert nodules are often called *flint.* Chert also appears as distinct beds and as thin, wedgelike, discontinuous layers. Beds of chert are commonly associated with volcanic deposits.

The microscope shows that some cherts are made up largely of spines or lacelike shells of silica (opal) secreted by microscopic animals and plants. In other cherts, siliceous fossils are rare or absent, but siliceous shells may have been partly dissolved and reprecipitated as structureless silica during cementation. Abundant undissolved siliceous shells usually make the rock porous and light in weight. An example is *diatomite,* a white rock composed almost entirely of the siliceous shells of microscopic plants called diatoms.

Not all fine-grained siliceous rocks are of organic origin. Some are believed to have precipitated around silica-bearing submarine hot springs. Many have been formed by the replacement of wood, limestone, shale, or other materials by silica-bearing solutions. *Petrified wood* is a familiar example.

Peat and Coal.   Peat and coal are not common sedimentary rocks but their economic importance justifies their mention here.

Peat is an aggregate of slightly decomposed plant remains. It can be seen in process of accumulation in swamps and shallow lakes in temperate climates and even on steep hillsides in wet semi-arctic regions. Coal is the result of compression and more thorough decomposition of the plant material in ancient peat bogs which were buried under later sediments. Coals grade from *lignite,* which differs little from peat, through *bituminous* to *anthracite,* which may contain 90 per cent or more of

carbon. From evidence obtained in mines and by geologic mapping, we infer that the grade of the coal depends largely on the depth to which it has been buried (i.e., the pressure and heat to which it has been subjected).

Evaporites, or Salt Deposits.   Evaporites vary greatly in mineral composition and texture. They are now being formed by the evaporation of land-locked masses of sea water, as at the Rann of Kutch in northwest India, and in saline lakes like Great Salt Lake. When sea water evaporates completely many different salts are precipitated from it, but *rock salt* (halite, NaCl) is the most abundant. In nature, however, calcium sulfate, which occurs both as a hydrated form, *rock gypsum* ($CaSO_4 2H_2O$), and as the anhydrous mineral called *anhydrite* ($CaSO_4$), is much more common than rock salt. Gypsum separates out early in the process of evaporation and will, therefore, accumulate in quantity from water bodies that are not saline enough to precipitate halite. Rock gypsum, accompanied by little or no rock salt, is abundant in the Paris Basin of France, in the Dakotas, and elsewhere. Thick beds of rock salt, accompanied by gypsum and anhydrite, are found in Texas, New Mexico, Germany, Iran, India and many other areas.

In a few places where relatively complete evaporation of sea water has occurred, deposits of potassium salts and other valuable, late-crystallizing minerals are found. Many rare and useful mineral products such as potash, salsoda, borax, nitrates, sodium sulfate, and epsom salts are recovered from salt deposits formed by the evaporation of ancient desert lakes.

Common Igneous Rocks

Volcanic Tuff.   Volcanic tuff is a fine-grained pyroclastic deposit composed of fragments less than 4 mm. in diameter. Most of the fragments are volcanic glass, either microscopic slivers called *shards* or frothy bits of *pumice.* Other common constituents are broken phenocrysts and fragments of solidified lava. Pieces

TABLE III-2. *Igneous Rocks*

TEXTURES	PREDOMINANT MINERALS			
	FELDSPAR AND QUARTZ	FELDSPAR PREDOMINATES (no quartz)	FERROMAGNESIAN MINERALS AND FELDSPAR (no quartz)	FERROMAGNESIAN MINERALS (no quartz or feldspar)
PYROCLASTIC	**Volcanic tuff** (fragments up to 4 mm. in diameter) **Volcanic Breccia** (fragments more than 4 mm. in diameter)			Rocks of the texture and composition represented by this part of the table are rare or unknown.
GLASSY	**Obsidian** (if massive glass) **Pumice** (if a glass froth)		**Basalt Glass**	
APHANITIC (generally porphyritic-aphanitic)	**Rhyolite** and **Dacite**	**Andesite**	**Basalt**	
GRANULAR	**Granite** (potassium feldspar predominates) and **Granodiorite** (plagioclase feldspar predominates)	**Diorite**	**Gabbro** **Dolerite** or **Diabase** (if fine grained)	**Peridotite** (with both olivine and pyroxene) **Pyroxenite** (with pyroxene only) **Serpentine** (with altered olivine and pyroxene)

INCREASING GRAIN SIZE →

⇛——————— DECREASING SILICA CONTENT ———————→

Notes: In this table textures are listed at the left; the major differences in mineral composition along the top. Names of major rock groups are in bold-face type. Thus, the texture of any rock group appears to the *left* of its name, and the predominant minerals it contains *above* it. Except for the pyroclastics, fine-grained rocks are at the top of the table; grain size increases downward. Rocks high in silica are found to the left of the table, and the silica content decreases gradually to the right. This difference is reflected in the color of the rocks. Rocks high in silica (at the left of the table) are ordinarily light colored because of the abundance of high-silica minerals such as quartz and feldspar. Those at the right of the table are dark colored because they are rich in ferromagnesian minerals. Glassy and pyroclastic rocks contain few, if any, recognizable minerals and the columns showing predominant mineral composition do not strictly apply to them. Here, as with the aphanitic rocks, we depend, in field classification, on the minerals represented among the phenocrysts. If no phenocrysts are present, the rock can only be classified after microscopic work or chemical analysis. For example, **rhyolite** contains predominantly potassium feldspar, **dacite** plagioclase feldspar, but without the microscope the two rocks can be distinguished only if the feldspars occur as phenocrysts. **Porphyry**, omitted from the table, is described in the list which follows.

of the basement rock on which the volcano rests may also be present.

Pumice and other kinds of glass fragments have been seen to form by the explosive disruption of sticky lava highly charged with gases. Evidently the gas pressure increases until it exceeds the containing pressure on the magma; then the pent-up gases separate into bubbles, causing the lava to expand tremendously and to froth. Upon breaking out to the surface, the froth disrupts further into a cloud of glass fragments and pumice which may be blown high into the air in a great volcanic explosion, or may froth forth more quietly and roll down the slope of the volcano as an *ash flow,* or "glowing avalanche."

The fragments from a volcanic explosion may be cemented together in the same way as the fragments of a sedimentary rock, forming an ordinary volcanic tuff. The component particles deposited by many ash flows, however, when viewed under the microscope, show flattening and collapse of the bits of frothy pumice and glass shards upon one another as if the rock had been welded—stuck together under its own weight while sticky and partly melted. Such *welded tuffs* are common products of rhyolitic and dacitic volcanoes. Many appear to have frothed out in fissure eruptions. Before C. N. Fenner, an American geologist, recognized their true mode of origin by observation of the products of the 1912 eruptions from Mount Katmai in Alaska, welded tuffs were thought to be lava flows. Even today they are often confused with rhyolite and dacite lavas because of the close similarity of the welded fragmental matrix to the flow-banded aphanitic texture of lava flows.

Volcanic Breccia.   Volcanic breccia is composed dominantly of fragments more than 4 mm. in diameter. In general, fragments of lava are more abundant than in tuff; glass slivers and pumice may be scarce. *Scoria* (see p. 28) is abundant in some breccias. The scoria may form large angular blocks, streamlined bombs 1 to 6 inches long shaped into cigarlike or teardrop forms by flying through the air while still molten, or small bits of frothy lava less than an inch in diameter, called *lapilli.*

Some volcanic breccias are formed like the tuffs, but many are products of volcanic mudflows. Heavy rains falling on the steep slopes of a volcanic cone have been seen to set great avalanche-like slides of unconsolidated pyroclastic debris in motion. Other mudflows are formed by eruption clouds falling into rivers, or onto snowfields and glaciers, or by explosive eruptions through crater lakes. The water-soaked volcanic debris may travel for many miles down stream valleys.

Obsidian.   Obsidian is natural glass, formed chiefly from magmas of rhyolitic, dacitic, or andesitic composition. It is lustrous and breaks with a curved fracture. Most obsidians are black because of sparsely disseminated grains of magnetite and ferromagnesian minerals, but they may be red or brown from the oxidation of iron by hot magmatic gases. Thin pieces of obsidian are almost transparent.

Obsidian forms lava flows and rounded domes above volcanic vents. It also is found as thin selvages along the edges of intrusions, and, rarely, makes small intrusive masses. Most intrusive obsidians have a dull, pitchlike luster, and are called *pitchstone.*

Pumice.   Pumice is obsidian froth, characteristically light-gray to white and crowded with tiny bubbles. The bubbles are so numerous that pumice will float on water. Pumice is abundant as fragments in tuffs and breccias. It also may form distinct flows, or more commonly, it caps flows of obsidian or rhyolite, and grades downward into the unfrothed lava beneath.

Basalt Glass.   Basalt glass is a jet-black natural glass formed by chilling of basaltic magma. Unlike obsidian, it is not noticeably transparent on thin edges. Basalt glass has never been found in large flows like those of obsidian; on this fact is based the inference that basalt magma crystallizes much more readily than rhyolite. Basalt glass forms thin crusts on the surfaces of lava flows, small fragments in volcanic breccia, and thin contact selvages in volcanic necks and dikes. Breccias of basalt glass form in abundance when basalt magma is extruded into water and quickly quenched. These may quickly alter to a yellow mineraloid called palagonite.

Rhyolite.   Rhyolite has an aphanitic groundmass generally peppered with phenocrysts of quartz and potassium feldspar. The color of rhyolite ranges widely, but generally is white or light yellow, brown, or red. Most rhyolites are flow banded; that is, they show streaky irregular layers that were formed by the flowing of the sticky, almost congealed magma.

Dacite is like rhyolite except that plagioclase predominates instead of potassium feldspar. It bears the same relation to rhyolite that granodiorite does to granite (see below).

Rhyolite and dacite are found in lava flows and as small intrusions.

Andesite. Andesite is an aphanitic rock, generally porphyritic, that resembles dacite but contains no quartz. Plagioclase feldspar is the most common phenocryst, but pyroxene, amphibole, or biotite may appear. Most andesites are flow banded, though not so conspicuously as rhyolites. Andesites range from white to black, but most are dark gray or greenish gray.

Andesite is abundant as lava flows and as fragments in volcanic breccia, particularly in volcano-capped mountain ranges such as the Andes (from which it is named), the Cascades, and the Carpathians. Andesite also forms small intrusive masses.

Basalt. Basalt is a black to medium-gray aphanitic rock. Most basalts are nonporphyritic, but some contain phenocrysts of plagioclase and olivine.

Basalt is the world's most abundant lava and is very widespread, forming great lava plateaus that cover thousands of square miles in the northwestern United States, India, and elsewhere. It is the chief constituent of the isolated oceanic islands. Although it typically forms lava flows, basalt is also common in small intrusive masses.

Granite. Granite, characterized by a granular texture, has feldspar and quartz as its two most abundant minerals, and in consequence most granite is light colored. Biotite or hornblend, or both, are also present in most granite.

Technically, the term *granite* is reserved for those granular quartz-bearing igneous rocks that have potassium feldspar as the chief mineral. Those in which plagioclase predominates are called *granodiorite*. (Compare rhyolite and dacite above.) Granodiorite can usually be distinguished from granite by the fine striations that characterize one cleavage surface of plagioclase.

Geologic mapping shows that great quantities of granite and granodiorite are present in the earth's crust. They form large intrusive masses along the cores of many mountain ranges and in other areas where deep erosion has occurred, such as northeastern Canada, the Scandinavian region, and eastern Brazil. They are typical continental rocks and have never been found on isolated oceanic islands far from continental masses.

Some granites are of metamorphic instead of igneous origin. (Chapters 3 and 18).

Diorite. Diorite is a granular rock composed of plagioclase and lesser amounts of ferromagnesian minerals. The most common ferromagnesian minerals are hornblende, biotite, and pyroxene. In general, diorite masses are much smaller than those of granite or granodiorite.

Gabbro. Gabbro is a granular rock composed chiefly of plagioclase and pyroxene commonly with small amounts of other ferromagnesian minerals, especially olivine. If ferromagnesian minerals predominate over the plagioclase so that the rock is dark-colored, it is generally correct to call it gabbro, though the microscopic distinction from diorite rests on the composition of the plagioclase, a character not determinable with the unaided eye.

Gabbro is widely distributed in both large and small masses. Dikes and thin sills of fine-grained gabbro are especially common. In most of these small intrusions, the mineral grains are so small that they are barely recognizable without the aid of the microscope. Such gabbros, intermediate in grain size between basalt and normal gabbro, are called *dolerite*. (Some geologists prefer the name *diabase* instead of dolerite.)

Peridotite, Pyroxenite, and Serpentine. Granular rocks composed almost entirely of ferromagnesian minerals and without feldspar are common in some areas. If the rock contains olivine as a conspicuous constituent, it is called *peridotite;* if it is made up almost wholly of pyroxenes, it is called *pyroxenite*.

Olivine is a very unstable mineral, easily altered to a mixture of greenish hydrous minerals. Some varieties of pyroxene also alter easily. These alterations probably occur soon after consolidation of the magma and are caused by the hot gases and solutions that escape from the crystallizing peridotite or perhaps from nearby granite or gabbro masses. Such altered peridotites and pyroxenites are called *serpentine*. Because serpentine is composed almost entirely of secondary minerals which did not solidify directly out of the magma, it is often classed as a metamorphic rock instead of an igneous rock. Nearly all plutonic igneous rocks, however, show some features that suggest alteration and "working over" by hot gases during the last stages of crystallization, although most are not modified as much as serpentine.

Serpentine forms sills, dikes, and other small intrusive masses.

Porphyry. The ancient term porphyry is used rather indefinitely. It is commonly applied to porphyritic-textured, fine-grained intrusive igneous rocks in which phenocrysts constitute 25 per cent or more of the volume. The groundmass may be either coarse-grained aphanitic, or fine-grained granular. The name of the rock whose composition and texture fit the groundmass part of the rock is usually prefixed to the word porphyry. Thus *diorite* porphyry has a fine-grained granular groundmass and contains abundant phenocrysts of plagioclase and perhaps some ferromagnesian mineral. Andesite porphyry is similar except that the groundmass is aphanitic.

The noun "porphyry," as distinguished from the adjective "porphyritic," should not be applied to porphyritic rocks with a coarse granular groundmass or to porphyritic lava flows containing a few scattered phenocrysts. The former should be called porphyritic diorite and the latter porphyritic andesite if they have the same composition as diorite and andesite.

Granite porphyry, granodiorite porphyry, and diorite porphyry form many dikes near granite and granodorite masses. Rhyolite porphyry, dacite porphyry, and andesite porphyry are common in volcanic plugs and other small intrusive masses.

Metamorphic Rocks

Hornfels. Hard, unfoliated, very fine-grained rock which breaks into sharp angular pieces. In many hornfels traces of original structures such as stratification, flow banding, or slaty cleavage can be seen, but the rock will not break along them. The mineral composition is highly variable, and grains are, in general, too small to be recognizable without a microscope.

Hornfels is formed by the partial or complete recrystallization, near an igneous intrusion, of such fine-grained rocks as shale, shaly limestone, slate, chlorite schist, tuff, and lavas.

Quartzite. Very hard, sugary-textured granoblastic rock, composed predominantly of interlocking quartz grains. Unlike most sandstones, quartzite breaks across the grains, not around them. Colors range from white through pale buff to pink, red, brown, and black, but most quartzite is light colored.

Quartzite is formed by the metamorphism of quartz sandstone. It is a widely distributed metamorphic rock.

Sandstone with a cement of silica (sedimentary "quartzite") is difficult to tell from metamorphic quartzite since both break across the grains. Distinction by use of the petrographic microscope is usually not difficult for the cement can be readily distinguished from the original sand grains. Metamorphic quartzite can also be distinguished from silica-cemented sandstone by the rocks associated with it in the field, for true quartzite is associated with other metamorphic rocks, and sandstone with other sedimentary rocks.

Marble. Granoblastic, fine to coarse-grained rock composed chiefly of calcite or dolomite or both. Many marbles show a streaky alteration of light and dark patches; others show brecciated structures healed by veinlets of calcite.

Marble is formed by the metamorphism of limestone and dolomite; if from dolomite, it commonly contains magnesium-bearing silicates such as pyroxene, amphibole, and serpentine.

Tactite. Granoblastic, but variable in texture,

TABLE III-3. *Metamorphic Rocks*

NAME	TEXTURE	COMMONLY DERIVED FROM	CHIEF MINERALS
UNFOLIATED OR FAINTLY FOLIATED			
Hornfels	Hornfelsic	Any fine-grained rock	Highly variable
Quartzite	Granoblastic, fine grained	Sandstone	Quartz
Marble	Granoblastic	Limestone, dolomite	Calcite, magnesium and calcium silicates
Tactite	Granoblastic, but coarse and variable	Limestone or dolomite plus magmatic emanations	Varied; chiefly silicates of iron, calcium, and magnesium, such as garnet, epidote, pyroxene, amphibole
Amphibolite	Granoblastic	Basalt, gabbro, tuff	Hornblende and plagioclase, minor garnet and quartz
Granulite	Granoblastic	Shale, graywacke, or igneous rocks	Feldspar, pyroxene, garnet, kyanite, and other silicates
FOLIATED			
Slate (and **Phyllite**)	Slaty	Shale, tuff	Mica, quartz
Chlorite schist	Schistose to slaty	Basalt, andesite, tuff	Chlorite, plagioclase, epidote
Mica schist	Schistose	Shale, tuff, rhyolite	Muscovite, quartz, biotite
Amphibole schist	Schistose	Basalt, andesite, gabbro, tuff	Amphibole, plagioclase
Gneiss	Gneissose	Granite, shale, diorite, mica schist, rhyolite, etc.	Feldspar, quartz, mica, amphibole, garnet, etc.
Migmatite	Coarsely banded, highly variable	Mixtures of igneous and metamorphic rocks	Feldspar, amphibole, quartz, biotite

grain size, and mineral composition. Tactite is rich in silicates of calcium, iron, and magnesium—amphibole, pyroxene, garnet, and epidote. It occurs in many areas where limestone or dolomite has been invaded by granite or granodiorite. From this it is inferred that fluids escaping from the congealing magma have carried into the limestone large quantities of silica, iron, and other substances that combined with the calcite and dolomite to form new minerals. Ores of iron, copper, tungsten, and other minerals may be associated with these rocks.

Amphibolite. Granoblastic, commonly coarse-grained rock consisting chiefly of amphibole and plagioclase. Garnet, quartz, and epidote may be present in small quantities. Amphibolites have been formed by the metamorphism of basalt, gabbro, and rocks of similar composition; some are derived from impure dolomite.

Granulite. Granoblastic-textured, medium-to coarse-grained rock consisting chiefly of feldspars, pyroxenes, and garnet, but commonly containing small amounts of many other minerals such as quartz, kyanite, and staurolite. May show an indefinite streakiness or a faint foliation. The grains of feldspar it contains may show a fine mottling when viewed under a lens or microscope. Granulites are formed by the high-grade metamorphism of shale, graywacke, and many kinds of igneous rock.

Slate and Phyllite. Very fine-grained, exceptionally well-foliated rocks. Because of their excellent foliation, they split into thin sheets. Mineral grains are too small to be identified without the microscope or X-rays. Slate is dull on cleavage surfaces; phyllite is shiny and coarser grained, containing some mineral grains large enough to be identified by the eye. Slate and, to a lesser extent, phyllite, commonly show remnants of sedimentary features such as stratification, pebbles, and fossils.

Slate and phyllite are abundant. Most were formed by the metamorphism of shale, but others are derived from tuffs or other fine-grained rocks.

Chlorite Schist or **Greenschist.** Green, very fine-grained, schistose to slaty rock. It is generally a soft, greasy, and easily pulverized rock composed of chlorite, plagioclase, and epidote, but all except chlorite may be in grains too small to identify. Remnants of original volcanic structures such as phenocrysts and scoria may be present.

Chlorite schists are common. They are often called *greenschist* or, if poorly foliated, *greenstone,* from the color of the chlorite. Most have been formed by the metamorphism of basalt or andesite and their corresponding tuffs, but some have been derived from dolo-

mitic shale, gabbro, and other ferromagnesian rocks.

Mica Schist. Schistose rock composed chiefly of muscovite, quartz, and biotite in varying proportions; any one of these minerals may predominate. The most common varieties are rich in muscovite.

Mica schist is one of the most abundant metamorphic rocks. Like slate, most has been formed from shales and tuffs, although some derives from arkose, shaly sandstone, rhyolite, or other rocks. It represents more intense metamorphism than slate.

Amphibole Schist. Schistose rock, composed chiefly of amphibole and plagioclase, with varying amounts of garnet, quartz, or biotite. It is a common metamorphic derivative of basalt, gabbro, chlorite schist, and related rocks.

Gneiss. Coarse-grained gneissose rock with distinct layers or lenses of different minerals. Mineral composition variable, but feldspar especially abundant. Other minerals common in gneiss are quartz, amphibole, garnet, and mica.

Gneisses are among the most plentiful metamorphic rocks. They may be derived from many different rocks—granite, granodiorite, shale, rhyolite, diorite, slate, and schist, among others.

Migmatite. Migmatites are highly complex rocks (see Chapter 18 and Fig. 18-17). In general, they are intimate small-scale mixtures of igneous and metamorphic rocks, characterized by a roughly banded or veined appearance. They are widespread, especially near large granite masses. Their mineral composition is complex and highly variable, but most contain abundant feldspar and quartz, and smaller amounts of biotite, and amphibole.

| # Chemical Data

TABLE 1. *The Atomic Numbers, Symbols, and Names of the Elements*

ATOMIC NUMBER	SYMBOL	ELEMENT	ATOMIC NUMBER	SYMBOL	ELEMENT
1	H	Hydrogen	33	As	Arsenic
2	He	Helium	34	Se	Selenium
3	Li	Lithium	35	Br	Bromine
4	Be	Beryllium	36	Kr	Krypton
5	B	Boron	37	Rb	Rubidium
6	C	Carbon	38	Sr	Strontium
7	N	Nitrogen	39	Y	Yttrium
8	O	Oxygen	40	Zr	Zirconium
9	F	Fluorine	41	Nb	Niobium
10	Ne	Neon	42	Mo	Molybdenum
11	Na	Sodium	43	Tc	Technetium
12	Mg	Magnesium	44	Ru	Ruthenium
13	Al	Aluminum	45	Rh	Rhodium
14	Si	Silicon	46	Pd	Palladium
15	P	Phosphorus	47	Ag	Silver
16	S	Sulfur	48	Cd	Cadmium
17	Cl	Chlorine	49	In	Indium
18	A	Argon	50	Sn	Tin
19	K	Potassium	51	Sb	Antimony
20	Ca	Calcium	52	Te	Tellurium
21	Sc	Scandium	53	I	Iodine
22	Ti	Titanium	54	Xe	Xenon
23	V	Vanadium	55	Cs	Cesium
24	Cr	Chromium	56	Ba	Barium
25	Mn	Manganese	57	La	Lanthanum
26	Fe	Iron	58	Ce	Cerium
27	Co	Cobalt	59	Pr	Praseodymium
28	Ni	Nickel	60	Nd	Neodymium
29	Cu	Copper	61	Pm	Promethium
30	Zn	Zinc	62	Sm	Samarium
31	Ga	Gallium	63	Eu	Europium
32	Ge	Germanium	64	Gd	Gadolinium

TABLE 1—*Continued.*

ATOMIC NUMBER	SYMBOL	ELEMENT	ATOMIC NUMBER	SYMBOL	ELEMENT
65	Tb	Terbium	84	Po	Polonium
66	Dy	Dysprosium	85	At	Astatine
67	Ho	Holmium	86	Rn	Radon
68	Er	Erbium	87	Fr	Francium
69	Tm	Thulium	88	Ra	Radium
70	Yb	Ytterbium	89	Ac	Actinium
71	Lu	Lutetium	90	Th	Thorium
72	Hf	Hafnium	91	Pa	Protactinium
73	Ta	Tantalum	92	U	Uranium
74	W	Tungsten	93	Np	Neptunium
75	Re	Rhenium	94	Pu	Plutonium
76	Os	Osmium	95	Am	Americium
77	Ir	Iridium	96	Cm	Curium
78	Pt	Platinum	97	Bk	Berkelium
79	Au	Gold	98	Cf	Californium
80	Hg	Mercury	99	E	Einsteinium
81	Tl	Thallium	100	Fm	Fermium
82	Pb	Lead	101	My	Mendellium
83	Bi	Bismuth	102	No	Nobelium

TABLE 2. *Chemical Composition of the Earth's Crust, Ocean, and Atmosphere*

ELEMENT	ROCKY CRUST	OCEAN	ATMOSPHERE (Dry air to height of 25 kilometers)
O	46.6%	85.79%	21.0%
Si	27.7	...	...
Al	8.1	...	...
Fe	5.0	...	...
Ca	3.6	...	...
Na	2.8	1.14	...
2.6	2.6	...	...
Mg	2.1	0.14	...
Ti	0.4	...	...
H	0.14	10.67	...
Cl	...	2.07	...
N	...	...	78.1
A	...	...	0.9
CO_2	...	...	0 3 (variable)

TABLE 3. *Averaged Chemical Compositions of Igneous Rocks and Sedimentary Rocks*

CONSTITUENT	IGNEOUS ROCKS	SEDIMENTARY ROCKS
SiO_2	59.14%	57.95%
TiO_2	1.05	0.57
Al_2O_3	15.34	13.39
Fe_2O_3	3.08	3.47
FeO	3.80	2.08
MgO	3.49	2.65
CaO	5.08	5.89
Na_2O	3.84	1.13
K_2O	3.13	2.86
H_2O	1.15	3.23
P_2O_5	0.30	0.13
CO_2	0.10	5.38
SO_3	. . .	0.54
BaO	0.06	. . .
C	. . .	0.66
Total	99.56	99.93

NOTE: The compositions in the table above are based on 5,159 analyses of igneous rocks compiled by F. W. Clarke, and on selected analyses of sedimentary rocks compiled by C. K. Leith and W. F. Mead. The sedimentary rocks have been weighted in the proportions of 82 per cent shale, 12 per cent sandstone and 6 per cent limestone. The compositions are reported as *oxides*, which is the conventional system for reporting data on the composition of rocks and minerals.

TABLE 4. *Chemical Composition of Dissolved Solids in River Water and in the Sea.* (After F. W. Clarke)

ION	RIVER WATER (Weighted average)	SEA WATER
CO_3^{--}	35.15%	0.41 (HCO_3^-)%
SO_4^{--}	12.14	7.68
Cl^-	5.68	55.04
NO_3^-	0.90	. . .
Ca^{++}	20.39	1 15
Mg^{++}	3.41	3.69
Na^+	5.79	30.62
K^+	2.12	1.10
$(Fe,Al)_2O_3$	2.75	. . .
SiO_2	11.67	. . .
Sr^{++}, H_3BO_3, Br^-	. . .	0.31
Total	100.00	100.00

INDEX

(Page references to important concepts and technical terms are indicated in **boldface** type.)

513